# fluid mechanics

# fluid mechanics

Victor L. Streeter
professor of hydraulics
university of michigan

fifth edition

**mcgraw-hill book company**

new york   st. louis   san francisco
düsseldorf   london   mexico   panama
rio de janeiro   singapore   sydney   toronto

**fluid mechanics**

*Library of Congress Catalog Card Number* 77-125110

ISBN  07-062191-8

567890  K P K P  79876543

# preface

In this revision the main changes have been made in the chapter on fluid-flow concepts and basic equations. A generalized approach to the derivation of the control-volume equations has been utilized; this presents a unified approach to continuity, energy, and momentum.

More emphasis has been placed on use of the digital computer; the programs are in FORTRAN IV (G level). Three short programs on solution of simple pipe problems are introduced in Chapter 5. They can easily be extended to more complex systems. Additional information on shock waves is introduced in Chapter 6, while some of the descriptive material on high-speed flight has been removed.

The first five chapters plus portions of Chapters 6 and 7, with selected topics from Part 2, is adequate for a first course. Part 2 contains enough material for a second course, including laboratory.

The author wishes to acknowledge the invaluable advice received from reviewers.

**Victor L. Streeter**

# contents

# fluid mechanics

# part one

# fundamentals of fluid mechanics

In the first three chapters of Part 1, the properties of
fluids, fluid statics, and the underlying framework of
concepts, definitions, and basic equations for fluid
dynamics are discussed.   Dimensionless parameters
are next introduced, including dimensional analysis and
dynamic similitude.   Chapter 5 deals with real fluids
and the introduction of experimental data into fluid-
flow calculations.   Compressible flow of both real and
frictionless fluids is then treated.   The final chapter on
fundamentals deals with two- and three-dimensional
ideal fluid flow.   The theory has been illustrated with
elementary applications throughout Part 1.

# 1

# fluid properties and definitions

Fluid mechanics is one of the engineering sciences that form the basis for all engineering. The subject branches out into various specialties such as aerodynamics, hydraulic engineering, marine engineering, gas dynamics, and rate processes. It deals with the statics, kinematics, and dynamics of fluids, since the motion of a fluid is caused by unbalanced forces exerted upon it. Available methods of analysis stem from the application of the following principles, concepts, and laws: Newton's laws of motion, the first and second laws of thermodynamics, the principle of conservation of mass, equations of state relating fluid properties, Newton's law of viscosity, mixing-length concepts, and restrictions caused by the presence of boundaries.

In fluid-flow calculations, viscosity and density are the fluid properties most generally encountered; they play the principal roles in open- and closed-channel flow and in flow around immersed bodies. Suface-tension effects are of importance in the formation of droplets, in flow of small jets, and in situations where liquid-gas-solid or liquid-liquid-solid interfaces occur, as well as in the formation of capillary waves. The property of vapor pressure, accounting for changes of phase from liquid to gas, becomes important when reduced pressures are encountered.

A liquid-fuel-injection system is an example of an engineering problem in which the performance of the product is significantly affected by the properties of the fluid being handled. Fuel is pumped from a storage tank through a series of fuel lines and spray nozzles. The process is intermittent and occurs at high speed. It appears reasonable to expect that less force, and less power, is needed to pump a light-grade, or "thin," oil than a heavy-grade, or "thick," oil.   The terms "light" and "heavy" are qualitative terms which describe how easily the fuel flows.   There is a quantitative way of specifying this fluidity property, and it will be described later in this chapter.   Indeed it will be necessary to define a fluid in a rigorous manner and to see how our fuel fits this definition.

The manner in which the fuel sprays from the nozzle will be affected by the way surface tension determines the drop formation.   The actual design of the nozzle passages will be influenced by other properties of the liquid.

The fluid flow in the lines is intermittent because fuel is supplied to the spray nozzles only at specific times during the operating cycle of an engine. The duration of fuel delivery is carefully regulated.   Consequently there are pulsations of pressure in the system.   These pressures can be very high and, surprisingly, also very low.   It is possible that when the pressure gets low enough, the fuel may momentarily vaporize and interfere with the expected performance of the system.   The pressure pulses are transmitted along the column of liquid in the fuel lines similarly to sound waves in air.   These pressure waves may be in such a phase relationship with one another that the waves result in momentary pressure peaks, which are many times the expected system pressures.   The speed of the pressure waves depends on a property called the bulk modulus.

The sections which follow point up the importance of the physical properties of a liquid or gas.   A number of definitions are also included so that one can be specific about the property, quantity, or assumption which is being considered.

## 1.1   definition of a fluid

A fluid is a substance that deforms continuously when subjected to a shear stress, no matter how small that shear stress may be.   A shear force is the force component tangent to a surface, and this force divided by the area of the surface is the average shear stress over the area.   Shear stress at a point is the limiting value of shear force to area as the area is reduced to the point.

In Fig. 1.1 a substance is placed between two closely spaced parallel plates, so large that conditions at their edges may be neglected.   The lower plate is fixed, and a force $F$ is applied to the upper plate, which exerts a shear stress $F/A$ on any substance between the plates.   $A$ is the area of the upper plate.   When the force $F$ causes the upper plate to move with a steady (nonzero) velocity, no matter how small the magnitude of $F$, one may conclude that the substance between the two plates is a fluid.

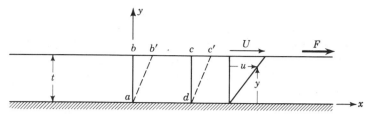

**Fig. 1.1** Deformation resulting from application of constant shear force.

The fluid in immediate contact with a solid boundary has the same velocity as the boundary; i.e., there is no slip at the boundary.[1] This is an experimental fact which has been verified in countless tests with various kinds of fluids and boundary materials. The fluid in the area $abcd$ flows to the new position $ab'c'd$ with each fluid particle moving parallel to the plate and the velocity $u$ varying uniformly from zero at the stationary plate to $U$ at the upper plate. Experiments show that other quantities being held constant, $F$ is directly proportional to $A$ and to $U$ and is inversely proportional to $t$. In equation form

$$F = \mu \frac{AU}{t}$$

in which $\mu$ is the proportionality factor and includes the effect of the particular fluid. If $\tau = F/A$ for the shear stress,

$$\tau = \mu \frac{U}{t}$$

The ratio $U/t$ is the angular velocity of line $ab$, or it is the *rate of angular deformation* of the fluid, i.e., the rate of decrease of angle $bad$. The angular velocity may also be written $du/dy$, as both $U/t$ and $du/dy$ express the velocity change divided by the distance over which the change occurs. However, $du/dy$ is more general as it holds for situations in which the angular velocity and shear stress change with $y$. The velocity gradient $du/dy$ may also be visualized as the rate at which one layer moves relative to an adjacent layer. In differential form,

$$\tau = \mu \frac{du}{dy} \tag{1.1.1}$$

is the relation between shear stress and rate of angular deformation for

---

[1] S. Goldstein, "Modern Developments in Fluid Dynamics," vol. II, pp. 676–680, Oxford University Press, London, 1938.

one-dimensional flow of a fluid.    The proportionality factor $\mu$ is called the *viscosity* of the fluid, and Eq. (1.1.1) is *Newton's law of viscosity*.    In the second book of his "Principia," Newton considered the circular motion of fluids as part of his studies of the planets and wrote

*hypothesis*

The resistance arising from the want of lubricity in the parts of a fluid, is, other things being equal, proportional to the velocity with which the parts of a fluid are separated from one another.

A plastic substance cannot fulfill the definition of a fluid because it has an initial yield shear stress that must be exceeded to cause a continuous deformation.    An elastic substance placed between the two plates would deform a certain *amount* proportional to the force, but not continuously at a definite rate.    A complete vacuum between the plates would not result in a constant final rate, but in an ever-increasing rate.    If sand were placed between the two plates, dry friction would require a *finite* force to cause a continuous motion.    Thus sand will not satisfy the definition of a fluid.

Fluids may be classified as Newtonian or non-Newtonian.    In Newtonian fluid there is a linear relation between the magnitude of applied shear stress and the resulting rate of deformation [$\mu$ constant in Eq. (1.1.1)], as shown in Fig. 1.2.    In non-Newtonian fluid there is a nonlinear relation between the magnitude of applied shear stress and the rate of angular

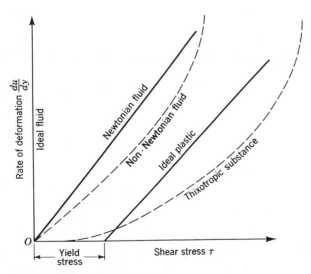

**Fig. 1.2** Rheological diagram.

deformation.  An *ideal plastic* has a definite yield stress and a constant linear relation of $\tau$ to $du/dy$.  A *thixotropic* substance, such as printer's ink, has a viscosity that is dependent upon the immediately prior angular deformation of the substance and has a tendency to take a set when at rest.  Gases and thin liquids tend to be Newtonian fluids, while thick, long-chained hydrocarbons may be non-Newtonian.

For purposes of analysis, the assumption is frequently made that a fluid is nonviscous.  With zero viscosity the shear stress is always zero, regardless of the motion of the fluid.  If the fluid is also considered to be incompressible it is then called an *ideal* fluid, and plots as the ordinate in Fig. 1.2.

## 1.2  force and mass units

The unit of force adopted in this text is the pound (lb).  Two units of mass are employed, the slug and the pound mass ($lb_m$).  Since thermodynamic properties are generally tabulated on a pound-mass basis, they are listed accordingly, but the example problems are solved in slug units.

The pound of force is defined in terms of the pull of gravity, at a specified (standard) location, on a given mass of platinum.  At standard gravitation, $g = 32.174$ ft/sec$^2$, the body having a pull of gravity of one pound has a mass of one pound mass.  By writing Newton's second law of motion in the form

$$\mathbf{F} = \frac{m}{g_0}\,\mathbf{a} \tag{1.2.1}$$

and applying it to this object falling freely in a vacuum at standard conditions

$$1\ lb = 1\ \frac{lb_m}{g_0}\ 32.174\ ft/sec^2$$

it is clear that

$$g_0 \equiv 32.174\ lb_m\text{-ft/lb-sec}^2 \tag{1.2.2}$$

Whenever the pound mass is used in this text, it is labeled $lb_m$.  The pound force is written lb.  The number $g_0$ is a constant, independent of location of application of Newton's law and dependent only on the units pound, pound mass, foot, and second.  At any other location than standard gravity, the mass of a body remains constant but the weight (force or pull of gravity) varies:

$$W = M \text{ (lb}_m) \frac{g}{g_0} \tag{1.2.3}$$

For example, where $g = 31.0 \text{ ft/sec}^2$,

$$10 \text{ lb}_m \text{ weighs } 31.0 \times \frac{10}{32.174} = 9.635 \text{ lb}$$

The slug is a derived unit of mass, defined as the amount of mass that is accelerated one foot per second per second by a force of one pound. For these units the constant $g_0$ is unity, i.e., 1 slug-ft/lb-sec$^2$. Since fluid mechanics is so closely tied to Newton's second law, the slug may be defined as

$$1 \text{ slug} \equiv 1 \text{ lb-sec}^2/\text{ft} \tag{1.2.4}$$

and the consistent set of units slug, pound, foot, second may be used without a dimensional constant $g_0$.

In the development of equations in this treatment, consistent units are assumed and the equations appear without the constant $g_0$. If the pound mass is to be used in dynamical equations, then $g_0$ must be introduced.

## 1.3 viscosity

Of all the fluid properties, viscosity requires the greatest consideration in the study of fluid flow. The nature and characteristics of viscosity are discussed in this section as well as dimensions and conversion factors for both absolute and kinematic viscosity. Viscosity is that property of a fluid by virtue of which it offers resistance to shear. Newton's law of viscosity [Eq. (1.1.1)] states that for a given rate of angular deformation of fluid the shear stress is directly proportional to the viscosity. Molasses and tar are examples of highly viscous liquids; water and air have very small viscosities.

The viscosity of a gas increases with temperature, but the viscosity of a liquid decreases with temperature. The variation in temperature trends may be explained upon examination of the causes of viscosity. The resistance of a fluid to shear depends upon its cohesion and upon its rate of transfer of molecular momentum. A liquid, with molecules much more closely spaced than a gas, has cohesive forces much larger than a gas. Cohesion appears to be the predominant cause of viscosity in a liquid, and since cohesion decreases with temperature, the viscosity does likewise. A gas, on the other hand, has very small cohesive forces. Most of its resistance to shear stress is the result of the transfer of molecular momentum.

**Fig. 1.3** Model for illustrating transfer of momentum.

As a rough model of the way in which momentum transfer gives rise to an apparent shear stress, consider two idealized railroad cars loaded with sponges and on parallel tracks, as in Fig. 1.3.   Assume each car has a water tank and pump, arranged so that the water is directed by nozzles at right angles to the track.   First, consider $A$ stationary and $B$ moving to the right, with the water from its nozzles striking $A$ and being absorbed by the sponges.   Car $A$ will be set in motion owing to the component of the momentum of the jets which is parallel to the tracks, giving rise to an apparent shear stress between $A$ and $B$.   Now if $A$ is pumping water back into $B$ at the same rate, its action tends to slow down $B$, and equal and opposite apparent shear forces result.   When $A$ and $B$ are both stationary or have the same velocity, the pumping does not exert an apparent shear stress on either car.

Within fluid there is always a transfer of molecules back and forth across any fictitious surface drawn in it.   When one layer moves relative to an adjacent layer, the molecular transfer of momentum brings momentum from one side to the other so that an apparent shear stress is set up that resists the relative motion and tends to equalize the velocities of adjacent layers in a manner analogous to that of Fig. 1.3.   The measure of the motion of one layer relative to an adjacent layer is $du/dy$.

Molecular activity gives rise to an apparent shear stress in gases which is more important than the cohesive forces, and since molecular activity increases with temperature, the viscosity of a gas also increases with temperature.

For ordinary pressures viscosity is independent of pressure and depends upon temperature only.   For very great pressures, gases and most liquids have shown erratic variations of viscosity with pressure.

A fluid at rest, or in motion so that no layer moves relative to an adjacent layer, will not have apparent shear forces set up, regardless of the viscosity, because $du/dy$ is zero throughout the fluid.   Hence, in the study of *fluid statics*, no shear forces can be considered because they do not occur in a static fluid, and the only stresses remaining are normal stresses, or pressures.   This greatly simplifies the study of fluid statics, since any free body of fluid can have only gravity forces and normal surface forces acting on it.

The dimensions of viscosity are determined from Newton's law of viscosity [Eq. (1.1.1)]. Solving for the viscosity $\mu$,

$$\mu = \frac{\tau}{du/dy}$$

Inserting dimensions $F$, $L$, $T$ for force, length, and time,

$\tau$: $FL^{-2}$    $u$: $LT^{-1}$    $y$: $L$

$\mu$ is seen to have the dimensions $FL^{-2}T$. With the force dimension expressed in terms of mass by use of Newton's second law of motion, $F = MLT^{-2}$, the dimensions of viscosity may be expressed as $ML^{-1}T^{-1}$.

The English unit of viscosity (which has no special name) is 1 lb-sec/ft² or 1 slug/ft-sec (these are identical). The cgs unit of viscosity,[1] called the *poise*, is 1 dyne-sec/cm² or 1 gm/cm-sec. The *centipoise* is one one-hundredth of a poise. Water at 68°F has a viscosity of 1.002 centipoises.

*kinematic viscosity*

The viscosity $\mu$ is frequently referred to as the *absolute* viscosity or the *dynamic* viscosity to avoid confusing it with the *kinematic* viscosity $\nu$, which is the ratio of viscosity to mass density,

$$\nu = \frac{\mu}{\rho} \tag{1.3.1}$$

The kinematic viscosity occurs in many applications, e.g., the Reynolds number, which is $VD/\nu$. The dimensions of $\nu$ are $L^2T^{-1}$. The English unit, 1 ft²/sec, has no special name; the cgs unit, called the *stoke*, is 1 cm²/sec.†

---

[1] The relation of the English unit to the poise may be established by converting from one system of units to the other. Consider a fluid that has a viscosity of 1 lb-sec/ft². After pounds are converted to dynes and feet to centimeters,

$$1 \text{ lb-sec/ft}^2 = \frac{454 \times 980}{(30.48)^2} \times 1 \text{ dyne-sec/cm}^2 = 479 \text{ poises}$$

The English unit is much larger. Hence, to convert from the poise to the English unit, divide by 479; to convert from the English unit to the poise, multiply by 479.

† The conversion from English unit to cgs is

$$1 \text{ ft}^2/\text{sec} = (30.48)^2 \times 1 \text{ cm}^2/\text{sec} = (30.48)^2 \text{ stokes}$$

The English unit is again much larger than the cgs unit; therefore, to convert from the stoke to the English unit, divide by $(30.48)^2$; to convert from the English unit to the stoke, multiply by $(30.48)^2$.

To convert to the English unit of viscosity from the English unit of kinematic viscosity, it is necessary to multiply by the mass density in slugs per cubic foot.   To change to the poise from the stoke, it is necessary to multiply by the mass density in grams per cubic centimeter, which is numerically equal to the specific gravity.

**example 1.1**   A liquid has a viscosity of 0.05 poise and a specific gravity of 0.85.   Calculate $(a)$ the viscosity in English units; $(b)$ the kinematic viscosity in stokes; and $(c)$ the kinematic viscosity in English units.

$(a)$   $\mu = \dfrac{0.05}{479} = 0.000105$ slug/ft-sec

$(b)$   $\nu = \dfrac{0.05}{0.85} = 0.0589$ stoke

$(c)$   $\nu = \dfrac{0.000105}{1.935 \times 0.85} = 0.0000638$ ft²/sec

Viscosity is practically independent of pressure and depends upon temperature only.   The kinematic viscosity of liquids, and of gases at a given pressure, is substantially a function of temperature.   Charts for the determination of absolute viscosity and kinematic viscosity are given in Appendix C, Figs. C.1 and C.2, respectively.

## 1.4   continuum

In dealing with fluid-flow relationships on a mathematical or analytical basis, it is necessary to consider that the actual molecular structure is replaced by a hypothetical continuous medium, called the *continuum*.   For example, velocity at a point in space is indefinite in a molecular medium, as it would be zero at all times except when a molecule occupied this exact point, and then it would be the velocity of the molecule and not the mean mass velocity of the particles in the neighborhood.   This dilemma is avoided if one considers velocity at a point to be the average or mass velocity of all molecules surrounding the point, say, within a small sphere with radius large compared with the *mean distance between molecules*.   With $n$ molecules per cubic centimeter, the mean distance between molecules is of the order $n^{-1/3}$ cm.   Molecular theory, however, must be used to calculate fluid properties (e.g., viscosity) which are associated with molecular motions, but continuum equations can be employed with the results of molecular calculations.

In rarefied gases, such as the atmosphere at 50 miles above sea level, the ratio of the mean free path[1] of the gas to a characteristic length for a body or conduit is used to distinguish the type of flow. The flow regime is called *gas dynamics* for very small values of the ratio, the next regime is called *slip flow*, and for large values of the ratio it is *free molecule flow*. In this text only the gas dynamics regime is studied.

The quantities density, specific volume, pressure, velocity, and acceleration are assumed to vary continuously throughout a fluid (or be constant).

### 1.5  density, specific volume, specific weight, specific gravity, pressure

The *density* $\rho$ of a fluid is defined as its mass per unit volume. To define density at a point the mass $\Delta m$ of fluid in a small volume $\Delta \mathcal{V}$ surrounding the point is divided by $\Delta \mathcal{V}$ and the limit is taken as $\Delta \mathcal{V}$ becomes a value $\epsilon^3$ in which $\epsilon$ is still large compared with the mean distance between molecules,

$$\rho = \lim_{\Delta \mathcal{V} \to \epsilon^3} \frac{\Delta m}{\Delta \mathcal{V}} \tag{1.5.1}$$

When mass is expressed in slugs, $\rho$ is in slugs per cubic foot; when mass is expressed in pounds mass, then $\rho$ is in pounds mass per cubic foot. These units are related by

$$\rho_{\text{slugs}} = \frac{\rho_{\text{lb}_m}}{32.174} \tag{1.5.2}$$

For water at standard pressure (14.7 lb/in.²) and 75°F,

$\rho = 1.935 \text{ slugs/ft}^3 \text{ or } 62.4 \text{ lb}_m/\text{ft}^3$

The *specific volume* $v_s$ is the reciprocal of the density $\rho$; i.e., it is the volume occupied by unit mass of fluid. Hence

$$v_s = \frac{1}{\rho} \tag{1.5.3}$$

The *specific weight* $\gamma$ of a substance is its weight per unit volume. It changes with location,

$$\gamma = \rho_{\text{slugs}} g = \frac{\rho_{\text{lb}_m}}{32.174} g \text{ lb/ft}^3 \tag{1.5.4}$$

depending upon gravity. It is a convenient property when dealing with fluid statics or with liquids with a free surface.

The *specific gravity* $S$ of a substance is the ratio of its weight to the

---

[1] The mean free path is the average distance a molecule travels between collisions.

weight of an equal volume of water at standard conditions.[1]  It may also be expressed as a ratio of its density or specific weight to that of water.

The normal force pushing against a plane area, divided by the area, is the average *pressure*.  The pressure at a point is the ratio of normal force to area as the area approaches a small value enclosing the point.  If a fluid exerts a pressure against the walls of a container, then the container will exert a reaction on the fluid which will be compressive.  Liquids can sustain very high compressive pressures, but unless they are extremely pure, they are very weak in tension.  It is for this reason that the absolute pressures used in this book are never negative, since this would imply that fluid is sustaining a tensile stress.  Pressure has the units force per area and may be pounds per square inch or pounds per square foot.  Pressure may also be expressed in terms of an equivalent length of a fluid column, as shown in Sec. 2.3.

## 1.6  perfect gas

In this treatment, thermodynamic relationships and compressible-fluid-flow cases have been limited generally to perfect gases.  The perfect gas is defined in this section, and its various interrelationships with specific heats are treated in Sec. 6.1.

The perfect gas, as used herein, is defined as a substance that satisfies the *perfect-gas law*

$$pv_s = RT \tag{1.6.1}$$

and that has constant specific heats.  $p$ is the absolute pressure, $v_s$ the specific volume, $R$ the gas constant, and $T$ the absolute temperature. The perfect gas must be carefully distinguished from the ideal fluid.  An ideal fluid is frictionless and incompressible.  The perfect gas has viscosity and can therefore develop shear stresses, and it is compressible according to Eq. (1.6.1).

Equation (1.6.1) is the equation of state for a perfect gas.  It may be written

$$p = \rho RT \tag{1.6.2}$$

The units of $R$ may be determined from the equation when the other units are known.  For $p$ in pounds per square foot, $\rho$ in slugs per cubic foot, and $T$ (°F + 459.6) in degrees Rankine (°R),

$R$: (lb/ft²)(ft³/slug °R) = ft-lb/slug °R

---

[1] These conditions are normally 4°C.  In this text standard conditions are considered to be a temperature of 68°F and a pressure of 30 in. mercury absolute, unless specified otherwise.

For $\rho$ in pounds mass per cubic foot,

$R$: $(\mathrm{lb/ft^2})(\mathrm{ft^3/lb}_m\ {}^\circ\mathrm{R}) = \mathrm{ft\text{-}lb/lb}_m\ {}^\circ\mathrm{R}$

The magnitude of $R$ in slug units is 32.174 times greater than in pound mass units. Values of $R$ for several common gases are given in Table C.2.

Real gases at low pressure tend to obey the perfect-gas law. As the pressure increases, the discrepancy increases and becomes serious near the critical point. The perfect-gas law encompasses both Charles' law and Boyle's law. Charles' law states that for constant pressure the volume of a given mass of gas varies as its absolute temperature. Boyle's law (isothermal law) states that for constant temperature the density varies directly as the absolute pressure. The volume $\mathcal{U}$ of $m$ mass units of gas is $mv_s$; hence

$$p\mathcal{U} = mRT \tag{1.6.3}$$

Certain simplifications result from writing the perfect-gas law on a mole basis. A pound-mole of gas is the number of pounds mass of gas equal to its molecular weight; e.g., a pound-mole of oxygen $O_2$ is 32 $\mathrm{lb}_m$. With $\bar{v}_s$ being the volume per mole, the perfect-gas law becomes

$$p\bar{v}_s = MRT \tag{1.6.4}$$

if $M$ is the molecular weight. In general, if $n$ is the number of moles of the gas in volume $\mathcal{U}$,

$$p\mathcal{U} = nMRT \tag{1.6.5}$$

since $nM = m$. Now, from Avogadro's law, equal volumes of gases at the same absolute temperature and pressure have the same number of molecules; hence their masses are proportional to the molecular weights. From Eq. (1.6.5) it is seen that $MR$ must be constant, since $p\mathcal{U}/nT$ is the same for any perfect gas. The product $MR$ is called the universal gas constant and has a value depending only upon the units employed. It is

$$MR = 1545 \text{ ft-lb/lb}_m\text{-mole } {}^\circ\mathrm{R} \tag{1.6.6}$$

The gas constant $R$ can then be determined from

$$R = \frac{1545}{M} \text{ ft-lb/lb}_m\ {}^\circ\mathrm{R} \tag{1.6.7}$$

or in slug units,

$$R = \frac{1545 \times 32.174}{M} \text{ ft-lb/slug } {}^\circ\mathrm{R} \tag{1.6.8}$$

so that knowledge of molecular weight leads to the value of $R$.   In Table C.2 of Appendix C molecular weights of some common gases are listed.

Additional relationships and definitions used in perfect-gas flow are introduced in Chaps. 3 and 6.

**example 1.2**   A gas with molecular weight of 44 is at a pressure of 13.0 psia (pounds per square inch absolute) and a temperature of 60°F.   Determine its density in slugs per cubic foot.

From Eq. (1.6.8)

$$R = \frac{1545 \times 32.174}{44} = 1129 \text{ ft-lb/slug } °R$$

Then from Eq. (1.6.2)

$$\rho = \frac{p}{RT} = \frac{13.0 \times 144}{1129(460 + 60)} = 0.00319 \text{ slug/ft}^3$$

## 1.7  bulk modulus of elasticity

In the preceding section the compressibility of a perfect gas is described by the perfect-gas law.   For most purposes a liquid may be considered as incompressible, but for situations involving either sudden or great changes in pressure, its compressibility becomes important.   Liquid compressibility (and gas also) becomes important also when temperature changes are involved (e.g., free convection).   The compressibility of a liquid is expressed by its *bulk modulus of elasticity*.   If the pressure of a unit volume of liquid is increased by $dp$, it will cause a volume decrease $-d\upsilon$; the ratio $-dp/d\upsilon$ is the bulk modulus of elasticity $K$.   For any volume $\upsilon$ of liquid,

$$K = -\frac{dp}{d\upsilon/\upsilon} \tag{1.7.1}$$

Since $d\upsilon/\upsilon$ is dimensionless, $K$ is expressed in the units of $p$.   For water at ordinary temperatures and pressures, $K = 300,000$ psi.

To gain some idea about the compressibility of water, consider the application of 100 psi pressure to 1 ft$^3$ of water.   When Eq. (1.7.1) is solved for $-d\upsilon$,

$$-d\upsilon = \frac{\upsilon \, dp}{K} = \frac{1.0 \times 100}{300,000} = \frac{1}{3000} \text{ ft}^3$$

Hence, the application of 100 psi to water under ordinary conditions causes its volume to decrease by only 1 part in 3000.   As a liquid is compressed, the resistance to further compression increases; therefore $K$ increases with pressure.    At 45,000 psi the value of $K$ for water has doubled.

For a gas the equation of state can be written as

$$p = p(v_s, T) \tag{1.7.2}$$

One notes that Eq. (1.6.1) is a specific example of this general form.    The method of differentiating a function of two variables (reviewed in Appendix B) can be used on Eq. (1.7.2), so that

$$dp = \left(\frac{\partial p}{\partial v_s}\right)_T dv_s + \left(\frac{\partial p}{\partial T}\right)_{v_s} dT$$

At constant temperature, $dT = 0$; and the isothermal bulk modulus is, by virtue of its definition in Eq. (1.7.1),

$$K = -\frac{dp}{dv_s} = -\left(\frac{\partial p}{\partial v_s}\right)_{T=\text{const}}$$

**example 1.3**    A liquid compressed in a cylinder has a volume of 0.400 ft³ at 1000 psi and a volume of 0.396 ft³ at 2000 psi.    What is its bulk modulus of elasticity?

$$K = -\frac{\Delta p}{\Delta \text{v}/\text{v}} = -\frac{2000 - 1000}{(0.396 - 0.400)/0.400} = 100,000 \text{ psi}$$

## 1.8   vapor pressure

Liquids evaporate because of molecules escaping from the liquid surface. The vapor molecules exert a partial pressure in the space, known as *vapor pressure*.    If the space above the liquid is confined, after a sufficient time the number of vapor molecules striking the liquid surface and condensing are just equal to the number escaping in any interval of time, and equilibrium exists.    Since this phenomenon depends upon molecular activity, which is a function of temperature, the vapor pressure of a given fluid depends upon temperature and increases with it.    When the pressure above a liquid equals the vapor pressure of the liquid, boiling occurs.    Boiling of water, for example, may occur at room temperature if the pressure is reduced sufficiently.    At 68°F water has a vapor pressure of 0.339 psi, and mercury has a vapor pressure of 0.0000251 psi.

In many situations involving the flow of liquids it is possible that very low pressures are produced at certain locations in the system.    Under such circumstances the pressures may be equal to or less than the vapor pressure.    When this occurs, the liquid flashes into vapor.    This is the phenomenon of cavitation.   A rapidly expanding vapor pocket, or cavity, forms, which is usually swept away from its point of origin and enters regions of the flow where the pressure is greater than vapor pressure.   The cavity collapses.   This growth and decay of the vapor bubbles affects the operating performance of hydraulic pumps and turbines and can result in erosion of the metal parts in the region of cavitation.

## 1.9   surface tension

*capillarity*

At the interface between a liquid and a gas, or two immiscible liquids, a film or special layer seems to form on the liquid, apparently owing to attraction of liquid molecules below the surface.   It is a simple experiment to place a small needle on a quiet water surface and observe that it is supported there by the film.

The formation of this film may be visualized on the basis of *surface energy* or work per unit area required to bring the molecules to the surface. The surface tension is then the stretching force required to form the film, obtained by dividing the surface-energy term by unit length of the film in equilibrium.   The surface tension of water varies from about 0.005 lb/ft at 68°F to 0.004 lb/ft at 212°F.   Surface tensions of other liquids are given in Table 1.1.

**Table 1.1   Surface tension of common liquids in contact with air at 68°F**

| Liquid | Surface tension $\sigma$, lb/ft |
|---|---|
| Alcohol, ethyl | 0.00153 |
| Benzene | 0.00198 |
| Carbon tetrachloride | 0.00183 |
| Kerosene | 0.0016–0.0022 |
| Water | 0.00498 |
| Mercury: | |
|   In air | 0.0352 |
|   In water | 0.0269 |
|   In vacuum | 0.0333 |
| Oil: | |
|   Lubricating | 0.0024–0.0026 |
|   Crude | 0.0016–0.0026 |

The action of surface tension is to increase the pressure within a droplet of liquid or within a small liquid jet. For a small spherical droplet of radius $r$ the internal pressure $p$ necessary to balance the tensile force due to the surface tension $\sigma$ is calculated in terms of the forces which act on a hemispherical free body (see Sec. 2.6),

$$p\pi r^2 = 2\pi r\sigma$$

or

$$p = \frac{2\sigma}{r}$$

For the cylindrical liquid jet of radius $r$, the pipe-tension equation applies,

$$p = \frac{\sigma}{r}$$

Both equations show that the pressure becomes large for a very small radius of droplet or cylinder.

Capillary attraction is caused by surface tension and by the relative value of adhesion between liquid and solid to cohesion of the liquid. A liquid that *wets* the solid has a greater adhesion than cohesion. The action of surface tension in this case is to cause the liquid to rise within a small vertical tube that is partially immersed in it. For liquids that do not wet the solid, surface tension tends to depress the meniscus in a small vertical tube. When the contact angle between liquid and solid is known, the capillary rise may be computed for an assumed shape of the meniscus. Figure 1.4 shows the capillary rise for water and mercury in circular glass tubes in air.

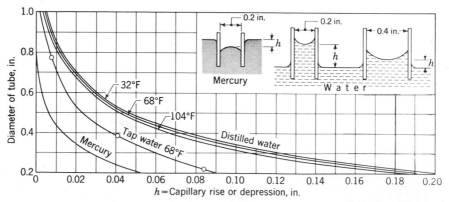

**Fig. 1.4** Capillarity in circular glass tubes. (*By permission, from "Hydraulics," by R. L. Daugherty, copyright 1944, McGraw-Hill Book Company.*)

## problems

**1.1**  Classify the substance that has the following rates of deformation and corresponding shear stresses:

| $du/dy$, rad/sec | 0 | 1 | 3 | 5 |
|---|---|---|---|---|
| $\tau$, lb/ft$^2$ | 10 | 20 | 30 | 40 |

**1.2**  Classify the following substances (maintained at constant temperature):

($a$)

| $du/dy$, rad/sec | 0 | 3 | 4 | 6 | 5 | 4 |
|---|---|---|---|---|---|---|
| $\tau$, lb/ft$^2$ | 2 | 4 | 6 | 8 | 6 | 4 |

($b$)

| $du/dy$, rad/sec | 0 | 0.5 | 1.1 | 1.8 |
|---|---|---|---|---|
| $\tau$, lb/ft$^2$ | 0 | 2 | 4 | 6 |

($c$)

| $du/dy$, rad/sec | 0 | 0.3 | 0.6 | 0.9 | 1.2 |
|---|---|---|---|---|---|
| $\tau$, lb/ft$^2$ | 0 | 2 | 4 | 6 | 8 |

**1.3**  A Newtonian liquid flows down an inclined plane in a thin sheet of thickness $t$ (cf. Fig. 1.5). The upper surface is in contact with air, which offers almost no resistance to the flow. Using Newton's law of viscosity, decide what the value of $du/dy$, $y$ measured normal to the inclined plane, must be at the upper surface. Would a linear variation of $u$ with $y$ be expected?

**1.4**  What kind of rheological materials would paint and grease be?

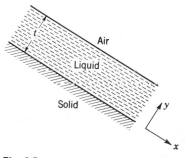

**Fig. 1.5**

**1.5**   A Newtonian fluid is in the clearance between a shaft and a concentric sleeve.   When a force of 100 lb is applied to the sleeve parallel to the shaft, the sleeve attains a speed of 2 ft/sec.    If 300-lb force is applied, what speed will the sleeve attain?   The temperature of the sleeve remains constant.

**1.6**   Determine the weight in pounds of 3 slugs mass at a location where $g = 31.7$ ft/sec$^2$.

**1.7**   When standard scale weights and a balance are used, a body is found to be equivalent in pull of gravity to two of the 1-lb scale weights at a location where $g = 31.5$ ft/sec$^2$.   What would the body weigh on a correctly calibrated spring balance (for sea level) at this location?

**1.8**   Determine the value of proportionality constant $g_0$ needed for the following set of units: kip (1000 lb), slug, foot, second.

**1.9**   On another planet where standard gravity is 8 ft/sec$^2$, what would be the value of the proportionality constant $g_0$ in terms of the pound, pound mass, foot, and second?

**1.10**   A correctly calibrated spring scale records the weight of a 51-lb$_m$ body as 17.0 lb at a location away from the earth.   What is the value of $g$ at this location?

**1.11**   Does the weight of a 5-lb bag of flour denote a force or the mass of the flour?   What is the mass of the flour in slugs?   What are the mass and weight of the flour at a location where the gravitational acceleration is one-seventh that of the earth's standard?

**1.12**   Explain each of the numerical substitutions made in the calculations in the first footnote on page 10.

**1.13**   A shear stress of 4 dynes/cm$^2$ causes a Newtonian fluid to have an angular deformation of 1 rad/sec.   What is its viscosity in centipoises?

**1.14**   A plate, 0.020 in. distant from a fixed plate, moves at 1 ft/sec and requires a force of 0.04 lb/ft$^2$ to maintain this speed.   Determine the fluid viscosity of the substance between the plates, in English units.

**1.15**   A 3.0-in.-diameter shaft slides at 0.4 ft/sec through an 8-in.-long sleeve with radial clearance of 0.003 in. (Fig. 1.6) when a 20.0-lb force is applied.   Determine the viscosity of fluid between shaft and sleeve.

**Fig. 1.6**

**1.16**   A flywheel weighing 100 lb has a radius of gyration of 1 ft.   When it is rotating 600 rpm, its speed reduces 1 rpm/sec owing to fluid viscosity between sleeve and shaft.   The sleeve length is 2.0 in., shaft diameter 1.0 in., and radial clearance 0.002 in.   Determine the fluid viscosity.

**1.17**   A steel cylinder is 12 in. long and 1 in. in diameter.   It falls, because of its own weight, at a uniform rate of 0.5 ft/sec inside a tube of slightly larger diameter.   A castor-oil film of constant thickness is between the cylinder and the tube.   Determine the clearance between the tube and the cylinder.   The temperature is 100°F.

**1.18**   A six-cylinder automobile engine has pistons with a diameter of 3.000 in. and cylinders with a diameter of 3.005 in.   Determine the percentage decrease in force necessary to move the pistons when the lubricant warms up from 30 to 250°F.   Use crude-oil viscosity from Fig. C.1, Appendix C.

**1.19**   How much greater is the viscosity of water at 32°F than at 212°F? How much greater is its kinematic viscosity for the same temperature range?

**1.20**   A fluid has a viscosity of 4 centipoises and a density of 50 $lb_m/ft^3$. Determine its kinematic viscosity in English units and in stokes.

**1.21**   A fluid has a specific gravity of 0.83 and a kinematic viscosity of 3 stokes.   What is its viscosity in English units and in poises?

**1.22**   A body weighing 90 lb with a flat surface area of 2 ft² slides down a lubricated inclined plane making a 30° angle with the horizontal.   For viscosity of 1 poise and body speed of 3 ft/sec, determine the lubricant film thickness.

**1.23**   What is the viscosity of gasoline at 100°F in poises?

**1.24**   Determine the kinematic viscosity of benzene at 60°F in stokes.

**1.25**   How many molecules are contained within a cube of gas which has a side of 0.01 mm?   Do you consider this number sufficient to determine the average values of the fluid properties at the location occupied by this cube?

**1.26**   What is the specific volume in cubic feet per pound mass and cubic feet per slug of a substance of specific gravity 0.75?

**1.27**   What is the relation between specific volume and specific weight?

**1.28**   The density of a substance is 2.94 gm/cm³.   What is its ($a$) specific gravity, ($b$) specific volume, and ($c$) specific weight?

**1.29**   A force, expressed by $\mathbf{F} = 4\mathbf{i} + 3\mathbf{j} + 9\mathbf{k}$, acts upon a square area, 2 by 2 in., in the $xy$ plane.   Resolve this force into a normal-force and a shear-force component.   What are the pressure and the shear stress? Repeat the calculations for $\mathbf{F} = -4\mathbf{i} + 3\mathbf{j} - 9\mathbf{k}$.

**1.30**   A gas at 60°F and 30 psia has a volume of 4.0 ft³ and a gas constant

$R = 48$ ft-lb/lb$_m$ °R.   Determine the density and number of slugs of gas.

**1.31**   What is the specific weight of air at 60 psia and 90°F?

**1.32**   What is the density of water vapor at 6 psia and 48°F, in slugs per cubic foot?

**1.33**   A gas with molecular weight 44 has a volume of 4.0 ft$^3$ and a pressure and temperature of 2000 psfa and 600°R, respectively.   What are its specific volume and specific weight?

**1.34**   1.5 lb$_m$ of hydrogen is confined in a volume of 1 ft$^3$ at $-40$°F.   What is the pressure?

**1.35**   Express the bulk modulus of elasticity in terms of density change rather than volume change.

**1.36**   For constant bulk modulus of elasticity, how does the density of a liquid vary with the pressure?

**1.37**   What is the bulk modulus of a liquid that has a density increase of 0.02 per cent for a pressure increase of 1000 lb/ft$^2$?

**1.38**   For $K = 300,000$ psi for bulk modulus of elasticity of water what pressure is required to reduce its volume by 0.5 per cent?

**1.39**   A steel container expands in volume 1 per cent when the pressure within it is increased by 10,000 psi.   At standard pressure, 14.7 psia, it holds 1000 lb$_m$ water $\rho = 62.4$ lb$_m$/ft$^3$.   For $K = 300,000$ psi, when it is filled, how many pounds mass water need be added to increase the pressure to 10,000 psi?

**1.40**   What is the isothermal bulk modulus for air at 70 psia?

**1.41**   At what pressure can cavitation be expected at the inlet of a pump that is handling water at 100°F?

**1.42**   What is the pressure within a droplet of water 0.002 in. in diameter at 68°F if the pressure outside the droplet is standard atmospheric pressure of 14.7 psi?

**1.43**   A small circular jet of mercury 0.005 in. in diameter issues from an opening.   What is the pressure difference between the inside and outside of the jet when at 68°F?

**1.44**   Determine the capillary rise for distilled water at 104°F in a circular glass tube $\frac{1}{4}$ in. in diameter.

**1.45**   What diameter of glass tube would be required so that the level of the water within it would not be affected by capillary effects to an extent of more than 0.02 in.?

**1.46**   Using the data given in Fig. 1.4, estimate the capillary rise of tap water between two parallel glass plates 0.20 in. apart.

**1.47**   A method of determining the surface tension of a liquid is to find the

**Fig. 1.7**

force needed to pull a platinum wire ring from the surface (cf. Fig. 1.7). Estimate the force necessary to remove a 1-in.-diameter ring from the surface of water at 68°F.   Why is platinum used as the material for the ring?

**1.48**    A fluid is a substance that

(*a*)  always expands until it fills any container
(*b*)  is practically incompressible
(*c*)  cannot be subjected to shear forces
(*d*)  cannot remain at rest under action of any shear force
(*e*)  has the same shear stress at a point regardless of its motion

**1.49**    A 2.0-lb$_m$ object weighs 1.90 lb on a spring balance.   The value of $g$ at this location is, in feet per second per second,

(*a*)  30.56      (*b*)  32.07      (*c*)  32.17      (*d*)  33.87      (*e*)  none of these
　　answers

**1.50**    At a location where $g = 30.00$ ft/sec², 2.0 slugs is equivalent to how many pounds mass?

(*a*)  60.0      (*b*)  62.4      (*c*)  64.35      (*d*)  not equivalent units
(*e*)  none of these answers

**1.51**    The weight, in pounds, of 3 slugs on a planet where $g - 10.00$ ft/sec² is

(*a*)  0.30      (*b*)  0.932      (*c*)  30.00      (*d*)  96.53      (*e*)  none of these
　　answers

**1.52**    Newton's law of viscosity relates

(*a*)  pressure, velocity, and viscosity
(*b*)  shear stress and rate of angular deformation in a fluid
(*c*)  shear stress, temperature, viscosity, and velocity
(*d*)  pressure, viscosity, and rate of angular deformation
(*e*)  yield shear stress, rate of angular deformation, and viscosity

**1.53**  Viscosity has the dimensions

(a) $FL^{-2}T$    (b) $FL^{-1}T^{-1}$    (c) $FLT^{-2}$    (d) $FL^2T$    (e) $FLT^2$

**1.54**  Select the *incorrect* completion.  Apparent shear forces

(a) can never occur when the fluid is at rest
(b) may occur owing to cohesion when the liquid is at rest
(c) depend upon molecular interchange of momentum
(d) depend upon cohesive forces
(e) can never occur in a frictionless fluid, regardless of its motion

**1.55**  Correct units for dynamic viscosity are

(a) dyne-sec$^2$/cm    (b) gm/cm-sec$^2$    (c) gm-sec/cm
(d) dyne-cm/sec$^2$    (e) dyne-sec/cm$^2$

**1.56**  Viscosity, expressed in poises, is converted to the English unit of viscosity by multiplication by

(a) $\frac{1}{479}$    (b) 479    (c) $\rho$    (d) $1/\rho$    (e) none of these answers

**1.57**  The dimensions for kinematic viscosity are

(a) $FL^{-2}T$    (b) $ML^{-1}T^{-1}$    (c) $L^2T^2$    (d) $L^2T^{-1}$    (e) $L^2T^{-2}$

**1.58**  In converting from the English unit of kinematic viscosity to the stoke, one multiplies by

(a) $\frac{1}{479}$    (b) $1/(30.48)^2$    (c) 479    (d) $(30.48)^2$    (e) none of these answers

**1.59**  The kinematic viscosity of kerosene at 90°F is, in square feet per second,

(a) $2 \times 10^{-5}$    (b) $3.2 \times 10^{-5}$    (c) $2 \times 10^{-4}$    (d) $3.2 \times 10^{-4}$
(e) none of these answers

**1.60**  The kinematic viscosity of dry air at 25°F and 29.4 psia is, in square feet per second,

(a) $6.89 \times 10^{-5}$    (b) $1.4 \times 10^{-4}$    (c) $6.89 \times 10^{-4}$    (d) $1.4 \times 10^{-3}$
(e) none of these answers

**1.61**  For $\mu = 0.60$ poise, sp gr $= 0.60$, $\nu$, in stokes, is

(a) 2.78    (b) 1.0    (c) 0.60    (d) 0.36    (e) none of these answers

**1.62**  For $\mu = 2.0 \times 10^{-4}$ slug/ft-sec, the value of $\mu$ in pound-seconds per square foot is

(a) $1.03 \times 10^{-4}$    (b) $2.0 \times 10^{-4}$    (c) $6.21 \times 10^{-4}$
(d) $6.44 \times 10^{-3}$    (e) none of these answers

**1.63**  For $\nu = 3 \times 10^{-4}$ stoke and $\rho = 0.8$ gm/cm$^3$, $\mu$, in slugs per foot-second, is

(a) $5.02 \times 10^{-7}$    (b) $6.28 \times 10^{-7}$    (c) $7.85 \times 10^{-7}$
(d) $1.62 \times 10^{-6}$    (e) none of these answers

**1.64**  A perfect gas

(a) has zero viscosity    (b) has constant viscosity    (c) is incompressible    (d) satisfies $p\rho = RT$    (e) fits none of these statements

**1.65**  The molecular weight of a gas is 28.  The value of $R$ in foot-pounds per slug degree Rankine is

(a) 53.3    (b) 55.2    (c) 1545    (d) 1775    (e) none of these answers

**1.66**  The density of air at 40°F and 100 psia in slugs per cubic foot is

(a) 0.00017    (b) 0.0168    (c) 0.21    (d) 0.54    (e) none of these answers

**1.67**  How many pounds mass of carbon monoxide gas at 20°F and 30 psia is contained in a volume of 4.0 ft$^3$?

(a) 0.00453    (b) 0.0203    (c) 0.652    (d) 2.175    (e) none of these answers

**1.68**  A container holds 2.0 lb$_m$ air at 120°F and 120 psia.  If 3.0 lb$_m$ air is added and the final temperature is 240°F, the final pressure, in pounds per square inch absolute, is

(a) 300    (b) 362.2    (c) 600    (d) indeterminable    (e) none of these answers

**1.69**  The bulk modulus of elasticity $K$ for a gas at constant temperature $T_0$ is given by

(a) $p/\rho$    (b) $RT_0$    (c) $\rho p$    (d) $\rho RT_0$    (e) none of these answers

**1.70**  The bulk modulus of elasticity

(a) is independent of temperature
(b) increases with the pressure
(c) has the dimensions of $1/p$
(d) is larger when the fluid is more compressible
(e) is independent of pressure and viscosity

**1.71**  For 1000-psi increase in pressure the density of water has increased, in per cent, by about

(a) $\frac{1}{300}$    (b) $\frac{1}{30}$    (c) $\frac{1}{3}$    (d) $\frac{1}{2}$    (e) none of these answers

**1.72**  A pressure of 150 psi applied to 10 ft³ liquid causes a volume reduction of 0.02 ft³.  The bulk modulus of elasticity, in pounds per square inch, is

(a)  −750      (b)  750      (c)  7500      (d)  75,000      (e)  none of these answers

**1.73**  Surface tension has the dimensions

(a)  $F$      (b)  $FL^{-1}$      (c)  $FL^{-2}$      (d)  $FL^{-3}$      (e)  none of these answers

# 2

# fluid statics

The science of fluid statics will be treated in two parts: the study of pressure and its variation throughout a fluid and the study of pressure forces on finite surfaces. Special cases of fluids moving as solids are included in the treatment of statics because of the similarity of forces involved. Since there is no motion of a fluid layer relative to an adjacent layer, there are no shear stresses in the fluid. Hence, all free bodies in fluid statics have only normal pressure forces acting on them.

## 2.1 pressure at a point

The average pressure is calculated by dividing the normal force pushing against a plane area by the area. The pressure at a point is the limit of the ratio of normal force to area as the area approaches zero size at the point. At a point a fluid at rest has the same pressure in all directions. This means that an element $\delta A$ of a very small area, free to rotate about its center when submerged in a fluid at rest, will have a force of constant magnitude acting on either side of it, regardless of its orientation.

To demonstrate this, a small wedge-shaped free body of unit length is taken at the point $(x,y)$ in a fluid at rest (Fig. 2.1). Since there can be no shear forces, the only forces are the normal surface forces and gravity. So, the equations of equilibrium in the $x$- and $y$-directions are, respectively,

$$\Sigma F_x = p_x \, \delta y - p_s \, \delta s \sin \theta = \frac{dx \, dy}{2} \rho a_x = 0$$

$$\Sigma F_y = p_y \, \delta x - p_s \, \delta s \cos \theta - \gamma \frac{\delta x \, \delta y}{2} = \frac{dx \, dy}{2} \rho a_y = 0$$

**Fig. 2.1** Free-body diagram of wedge-shaped particle.

in which $p_x$, $p_y$, $p_s$ are the average pressures on the three faces, $\gamma$ is the specific weight of the fluid, and $\rho$ is its density. Taking the limit as the free body is reduced to zero size, by allowing the inclined face to approach $(x,y)$ while maintaining the same angle $\theta$, and using the geometric relations

$$\delta s \sin \theta = \delta y \qquad \delta s \cos \theta = \delta x$$

the equations simplify to

$$p_x \, \delta y - p_s \, \delta y = 0 \qquad p_y \, \delta x - p_s \, \delta x - \gamma \frac{\delta x \, \delta y}{2} = 0$$

The last term of the second equation is an infinitesimal of higher order of smallness and may be neglected. When divided by $\delta y$ and $\delta x$, respectively, the equations may be combined,

$$p_s = p_x = p_y \qquad\qquad\qquad (2.1.1)$$

Since $\theta$ is any arbitrary angle, this equation proves that the pressure is the same in all directions at a point in a static fluid. Although the proof was carried out for a two-dimensional case, it may be demonstrated for the three-dimensional case with the equilibrium equations for a small tetrahedron of fluid with three faces in the coordinate planes and the fourth face inclined arbitrarily.

If the fluid is in motion so that one layer moves relative to an adjacent layer, shear stresses occur and the normal stresses are, in general, no longer the same in all directions at a point. The pressure is then defined as the average of any three mutually perpendicular normal compressive stresses at a point,

$$p = \frac{p_x + p_y + p_z}{3}$$

In a fictitious fluid of zero viscosity, i.e., a frictionless fluid, no shear stresses can occur for any motion of the fluid, and so at a point the pressure is the same in all directions.

## 2.2  basic equation of fluid statics

*pressure variation in a static fluid*

The forces acting on an element of fluid at rest, Fig. 2.2, consist of surface forces and body forces.  With gravity the only body force acting, and by taking the $y$-axis vertically upward, it is $-\gamma\,\delta x\,\delta y\,\delta z$ in the $y$-direction. With pressure $p$ at its center $(x,y,z)$, the approximate force exerted on the side normal to the $y$-axis closest to the origin is approximately

$$\left(p - \frac{\partial p}{\partial y}\frac{\delta y}{2}\right)\delta x\,\delta z$$

and the force exerted on the opposite side is

$$\left(p + \frac{\partial p}{\partial y}\frac{\delta y}{2}\right)\delta x\,\delta z$$

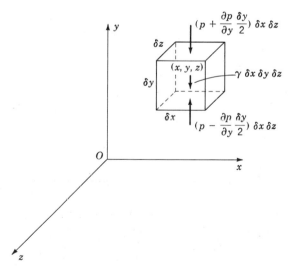

**Fig. 2.2**  Rectangular parallelepiped element of fluid at rest.

By summing the forces acting on the element in the $y$-direction,

$$\delta F_y = -\frac{\partial p}{\partial y}\,\delta x\,\delta y\,\delta z - \gamma\,\delta x\,\delta y\,\delta z$$

For the $x$- and $z$-directions, since no body forces act,

$$\delta F_x = -\frac{\partial p}{\partial x}\,\delta x\,\delta y\,\delta z \qquad \delta F_z = -\frac{\partial p}{\partial z}\,\delta x\,\delta y\,\delta z$$

The elemental force vector $\delta\mathbf{F}$ is given by

$$\delta\mathbf{F} = \mathbf{i}\,\delta F_x + \mathbf{j}\,\delta F_y + \mathbf{k}\,\delta F_z = -\left(\mathbf{i}\,\frac{\partial p}{\partial x} + \mathbf{j}\,\frac{\partial p}{\partial y} + \mathbf{k}\,\frac{\partial p}{\partial z}\right)\delta x\,\delta y\,\delta z$$

$$-\,\mathbf{j}\,\gamma\,\delta x\,\delta y\,\delta z$$

If the element is reduced to zero size, after dividing through by $\delta x\,\delta y\,\delta z = \delta\mathcal{V}$, the expression becomes exact.

$$\frac{\delta\mathbf{F}}{\delta\mathcal{V}} = -\left(\mathbf{i}\,\frac{\partial}{\partial x} + \mathbf{j}\,\frac{\partial}{\partial y} + \mathbf{k}\,\frac{\partial}{\partial z}\right)p - \mathbf{j}\gamma \qquad \lim \delta\mathcal{V} \to 0 \qquad (2.2.1)$$

This is the resultant force per unit volume at a point, which must be equated to zero for a fluid at rest. The quantity in parentheses is the *gradient*, called $\nabla$ (del),

$$\nabla = \mathbf{i}\,\frac{\partial}{\partial x} + \mathbf{j}\,\frac{\partial}{\partial y} + \mathbf{k}\,\frac{\partial}{\partial z} \qquad (2.2.2)$$

and the negative gradient of $p$, $-\nabla p$, is the vector field $\mathbf{f}$ of the surface pressure force per unit volume,

$$\mathbf{f} = -\nabla p \qquad (2.2.3)$$

The fluid static law of variation of pressure is then

$$\mathbf{f} - \mathbf{j}\gamma = 0 \qquad (2.2.4)$$

In component form,

$$\frac{\partial p}{\partial x} = 0 \qquad \frac{\partial p}{\partial y} = -\gamma \qquad \frac{\partial p}{\partial z} = 0 \qquad (2.2.5)$$

The partials, for variation in horizontal directions, are one form of Pascal's law, stating that two points at the same elevation in the same continuous mass of fluid at rest have the same pressure.

Since $p$ is a function of $y$ only,

$$dp = -\gamma\,dy \qquad (2.2.6)$$

This simple differential equation relates the change of pressure to specific weight and change of elevation, and holds for both compressible and incompressible fluids.

For fluids that may be considered homogeneous and incompressible, $\gamma$ is constant, and Eq. (2.2.6), when integrated, becomes

$$p = -\gamma y + c$$

in which $c$ is the constant of integration.   The hydrostatic law of variation of pressure is frequently written in the form

$$p = \gamma h \tag{2.2.7}$$

in which $h$ is measured vertically downward ($h = -y$) from a free liquid surface and $p$ is the increase in pressure from that at the free surface. Equation (2.2.7) may be derived by taking as fluid free body a vertical column of liquid of finite height $h$ with its upper surface in the free surface. This is left as an exercise for the student.

**example 2.1**   An open tank contains 2 ft of water covered with 1 ft of oil, sp gr 0.83.   Find the pressure at the interface and at the bottom of the tank.

At the interface, $h = 1$, $\gamma = 0.83 \times 62.4 = 51.7$ lb/ft³, and

$$p = \gamma h = 51.7 \text{ lb/ft}^2$$

At the bottom of the tank the pressure is that at the interface plus $\gamma h$ for the water, or

$$p = 51.7 + 2 \times 62.4 = 176.5 \text{ lb/ft}^2$$

*pressure variation in a compressible fluid*

When the fluid is a perfect gas at rest at constant temperature, from Eq. (1.6.2)

$$\frac{p}{\rho} = \frac{p_0}{\rho_0} \tag{2.2.8}$$

When the value of $\gamma$ in Eq. (2.2.6) is replaced by $\rho g$ and $\rho$ is eliminated between Eqs. (2.2.6) and (2.2.8),

$$dy = \frac{-p_0}{g\rho_0} \frac{dp}{p} \tag{2.2.9}$$

It must be remembered that if $\rho$ is in pounds mass per cubic foot, then $\gamma = g\rho/g_0$ with $g_0 = 32.174$ lb$_m$-ft/lb-sec². If $p = p_0$ when $\rho = \rho_0$, integration between limits

$$\int_{y_0}^{y} dy = - \frac{p_0}{g\rho_0} \int_{p_0}^{p} \frac{dp}{p}$$

yields

$$y - y_0 = - \frac{p_0}{g\rho_0} \ln \frac{p}{p_0} \tag{2.2.10}$$

in which ln is the natural logarithm.   Then

$$p = p_0 \exp\left(- \frac{y - y_0}{p_0/g\rho_0}\right) \tag{2.2.11}$$

which is the equation for variation of pressure with elevation in an iso-thermal gas.

The atmosphere frequently is assumed to have a constant temperature gradient, expressed by

$$T = T_0 + \beta y \tag{2.2.12}$$

For the standard atmosphere, $\beta = -0.00357°F/ft$ up to the stratosphere. The density may be expressed in terms of pressure and elevation from the perfect-gas law:

$$\rho = \frac{p}{RT} = \frac{p}{R(T_0 + \beta y)} \tag{2.2.13}$$

Substitution into $dp = -\rho g\, dy$ [Eq. (2.2.6)] permits the variables to be separated and $p$ to be found in terms of $y$ by integration.

**example 2.2**   Assuming isothermal conditions to prevail in the atmosphere, compute the pressure and density at 5000 ft elevation if $p = 14.7$ psia, $\rho = 0.00238$ slug/ft³ at sea level.

From Eq. (2.2.11)

$$p = 14.7 \exp\left(- \frac{5000}{14.7 \times 144/(32.2 \times 0.00238)}\right) = 12.27 \text{ psia}$$

Then, from Eq. (2.2.8)

$$\rho = \frac{\rho_0}{p_0} p = \frac{0.00238}{14.7} 12.27 = 0.00199 \text{ slug/ft}^3$$

When compressibility of a liquid in static equilibrium is taken into account, Eqs. (2.2.6) and (1.7.1) are utilized.

## 2.3  units and scales of pressure measurement

Pressure may be expressed with reference to any arbitrary datum.  The usual ones are *absolute zero* and *local atmospheric pressure*.  When a pressure is expressed as a difference between its value and a complete vacuum, it is called an *absolute pressure*.  When it is expressed as a difference between its value and the local atmospheric pressure, it is called a *gage pressure*.

The *bourdon* gage (Fig. 2.3) is typical of the devices used for measuring

**Fig.**  **2.3** Bourdon  gage.  (*Crosby Steam Gage and Valve Co.*)

**Fig. 2.4**   Units and scales for pressure measurement.

gage pressures.   The pressure element is a hollow, curved, flat, metallic tube, closed at one end, with the other end connected to the pressure to be measured.   When the internal pressure is increased, the tube tends to straighten, pulling on a linkage to which is attached a pointer and causing the pointer to move.   The dial reads zero when the inside and outside of the tube are at the same pressure, regardless of its particular value.   The dial may be graduated to any convenient units, common ones being pounds per square inch, pounds per square foot, inches of mercury, and feet of water.   Owing to the inherent construction of the gage, it measures pressure relative to the pressure of the medium surrounding the tube, which is the local atmosphere.

Figure 2.4 illustrates the data and the relationships of the common units of pressure measurement.   Standard atmospheric pressure is the mean pressure at sea level, 29.92 in. mercury (rounded to 30 in. for slide-rule work).   A pressure expressed in terms of a column of liquid refers to the force per unit area at the base of the column.   The relation for variation of pressure with altitude in a liquid [Eq. (2.2.7)],

$$p = \gamma h \tag{2.3.1}$$

shows the relation between head $h$, in length of a fluid column of specific weight $\gamma$, and the pressure $p$.   In consistent units, $p$ is in pounds per square foot, $\gamma$ in pounds per cubic foot, and $h$ in feet.   For water $\gamma$ may be taken as 62.4 lb/ft³.   With the specific weight of any liquid expressed as its specific gravity $S$ times the specific weight of water, Eq. (2.3.1) becomes

$$p = 62.4Sh$$

When the pressure is desired in pounds per square inch, both sides of the

equation are divided by 144,

$$p_{\text{psi}} = \frac{62.4}{144} Sh = 0.433Sh \qquad (2.3.2)$$

in which $h$ remains in feet.[1]

Local atmospheric pressure is measured by a mercury barometer (Fig. 2.5) or by an *aneroid* barometer which measures the difference in pressure between the atmosphere and an evacuated box or tube, in a manner analogous to the bourdon gage except that the tube is evacuated and sealed.

A mercury barometer consists of a glass tube sealed at one end, filled with mercury, and inverted so that the open end is submerged in mercury. It has a scale arranged so that the height of column $R$ (Fig. 2.5) can be determined. The space above the mercury contains mercury vapor. If

---

[1] In Eq. (2.3.1) the standard atmospheric pressure may be expressed in pounds per square inch,

$$p_{\text{psi}} = \frac{62.4}{144} \times 13.6 \times \frac{30}{12} = 14.7$$

when $S = 13.6$ for mercury. When 14.7 is multiplied by 144, the standard atmosphere becomes 2116 lb/ft². Then 2116 divided by 62.4 yields 34 ft water. Any of these designations is for the standard atmosphere and may be called *one atmosphere*, if it is always understood that it is a standard atmosphere and is measured from absolute zero. These various designations of a standard atmosphere (Fig. 2.4) are equivalent and provide a convenient means of converting from one set of units to another. For example, to express 100 ft of water in pounds per square inch,

$$\tfrac{100}{34} 14.7 = 43.3 \text{ psi}$$

since $\tfrac{100}{34}$ is the number of standard atmospheres and each standard atmosphere is 14.7 psi.

**Fig.  2.5** Mercury barometer.

the pressure of the mercury vapor $h_v$ is given in inches of mercury, the pressure at $A$ may be expressed as

$$h_v + R'' = h_A \qquad \text{in. mercury}$$

Although $h_v$ is a function of temperature, it is very small at usual atmospheric temperatures. The barometric pressure varies with location, i.e., elevation, and with weather conditions.

In Fig. 2.4 a pressure may be located vertically on the chart, which indicates its relation to absolute zero and to local atmospheric pressure. If the point is below the local-atmospheric-pressure line and is referred to gage datum, it is called *negative*, *suction*, or *vacuum*. For example, the pressure 18 in. mercury abs, as at 1, with barometer reading 29 in., may be expressed as $-11$ in. mercury, 11 in. mercury suction, or 11 in. mercury vacuum. It should be noted that

$$p_{\text{abs}} = p_{\text{bar}} + p_{\text{gage}}$$

To avoid any confusion, the convention is adopted throughout this text that a *pressure is gage unless specifically marked absolute*, with the exception of the *atmosphere*, which is an absolute pressure unit.

**example 2.3**   Express 4 psi eight other customary ways.   Barometer reading 28.5 in. mercury.

At point 2 in Fig. 2.4, other customary gage units are

(a)    4 lb/in.$^2$ $\times$ 144 in.$^2$/ft$^2$ = 576 lb/ft$^2$

(b)    $\dfrac{4 \text{ psi}}{14.7 \text{ psi/atm}}$ $\times$ 30 in. mercury/atm = 8.16 in. mercury

(c)    $\dfrac{4 \text{ psi}}{14.7 \text{ psi/atm}}$ $\times$ 34 ft water/atm = 9.25 ft water

With absolute units,

(d)    From (b), 8.16 in. mercury (gage) + 28.5 in. mercury (bar) = 36.66 in. mercury abs

(e)    From (a) $\dfrac{36.66 \text{ in. mercury abs}}{30 \text{ in. mercury/atm}}$ = 1.222 atm

(f)    From (e) 1.222 atm $\times$ 14.7 psi/atm = 18.0 psia
(g)    From (e) 1.222 atm $\times$ 2116 (lb/ft$^2$)/atm = 2583.16 lb/ft$^2$ abs
(h)    From (e) 1.222 atm $\times$ 34 ft water/atm = 41.6 ft water abs

The pressure conversion chart in Fig. 2.4 is most useful in working with pressure units and should be carefully studied.

## 2.4   manometers

Manometers are devices that employ liquid columns for determining differences in pressure.   The most elementary manometer, usually called a *piezometer*, is illustrated in Fig. 2.6*a*; it measures the pressure in a liquid when it is above zero gage.   A glass tube is mounted vertically so that it is connected to the space within the container.   Liquid rises in the tube until equilibrium is reached.   The pressure is then given by the vertical distance $h$ from the meniscus (liquid surface) to the point where the pressure is to be measured, expressed in feet of the liquid in the container. It is obvious that the piezometer would not work for negative gage pressures, because air would flow into the container through the tube.   It is also impractical for measuring large pressures at $A$, since the vertical tube would need to be very long.   If the specific gravity of the liquid is $S$, the pressure at $A$ is $hS$ ft of water.

For measurement of small negative or positive gage pressures in a liquid the tube may take the form shown in Fig. 2.6*b*.   With this arrangement the meniscus may come to rest below $A$, as shown.   Since the pressure at the meniscus is zero gage and since pressure *decreases* with elevation,

$$h_A = -hS \quad \text{ft water}$$

For greater negative or positive gage pressures a second liquid of greater specific gravity is employed (Fig. 2.6*c*).   It must be immiscible in the first fluid, which may now be a gas.   If the specific gravity of the fluid at $A$ is $S_1$ (based on water) and the specific gravity of the manometer liquid is $S_2$, the equation for pressure at $A$ may be written, starting at either $A$ or the upper meniscus and proceeding through the manometer, thus

$$h_A + h_2 S_1 - h_1 S_2 = 0$$

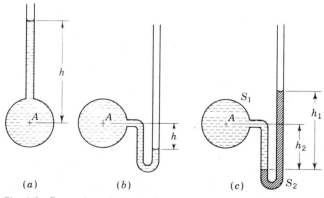

**Fig. 2.6**   Examples of simple manometers.

in which $h_A$ is the unknown pressure, expressed in feet of water, and $h_1$, $h_2$ are in feet.   If $A$ contains a gas, $S_1$ is generally so small that $h_2S_1$ may be neglected.

A general procedure may be followed in working all manometer problems:

1.   Start at one end (or any meniscus if the circuit is continuous), and write the pressure there in an appropriate unit (say, pounds per square foot) or in an appropriate symbol if it is unknown.
2.   Add to this the change in pressure, in the same unit, from one meniscus to the next (plus if the next meniscus is lower, minus if higher).   (For pounds per square foot this is the product of the difference in elevation in feet and the specific weight of the fluid.)
3.   Continue until the other end of the gage (or the starting meniscus) is reached and equate the expression to the pressure at that point, known or unknown.

The expression will contain one unknown for a simple manometer or will give a difference in pressures for the differential manometer.   In equation form,

$$p_0 - (y_1 - y_0)\gamma_0 - (y_2 - y_1)\gamma_1 - (y_3 - y_2)\gamma_2$$
$$- (y_4 - y_3)\gamma_3 - \cdot\cdot\cdot - (y_n - y_{n-1})\gamma_{n-1} = p_n$$

in which $y_0, y_1, \ldots, y_n$ are elevations of each meniscus in feet and $\gamma_0, \gamma_1, \gamma_2, \ldots, \gamma_{n-1}$ are specific weights of the fluid columns.   The above expression yields the answer in pounds per square foot and may be converted to other units by use of the conversions in Fig. 2.4.

A differential manometer (Fig. 2.7) determines the difference in pressures at two points $A$ and $B$, when the actual pressure at any point in the system cannot be determined.   Application of the procedure outlined

**Fig. 2.7**  Differential manometers.

above to Fig. 2.7$a$ produces

$$p_A - h_1\gamma_1 - h_2\gamma_2 + h_3\gamma_3 = p_B$$

or

$$p_A - p_B = h_1\gamma_1 + h_2\gamma_2 - h_3\gamma_3$$

Similarly, for Fig. 2.7$b$,

$$p_A + h_1\gamma_1 - h_2\gamma_2 - h_3\gamma_3 = p_B$$

or

$$p_A - p_B = -h_1\gamma_1 + h_2\gamma_2 + h_3\gamma_3$$

No formulas for particular manometers should be memorized.   It is much more satisfactory to work them out from the general procedure for each case as needed.

If the pressures at $A$ and $B$ are expressed in feet of water, the above results can be written, for Fig. 2.7$a$,

$$h_A - h_B = h_1S_1 + h_2S_2 - h_3S_3 \qquad \text{ft water}$$

Similarly, for Fig. 2.7$b$,

$$h_A - h_B = -h_1S_1 + h_2S_2 + h_3S_3$$

in which $S_1$, $S_2$, and $S_3$ are the applicable specific gravities of the liquids in the system.

**example 2.4**   In Fig. 2.7$a$ the liquids at $A$ and $B$ are water and the manometer liquid is oil, sp gr 0.80.   $h_1 = 1.0$ ft, $h_2 = 0.50$ ft, $h_3 = 2.0$ ft.   (a) Determine $p_A - p_B$ in pounds per square inch.   (b) If $p_B = 10$ psia and the barometer reading is 29.5 in. mercury, find the gage pressure at $A$ in pounds per square foot.

(a)   $h_A - 1 \times 1 - 0.5 \times 0.8 + 2 \times 1 = h_B$
      $h_A - h_B = 1 + 0.4 - 2 = -0.6$ ft water

and

(b)   $p_A - p_B = -0.6 \times 0.433 = -0.26$ psi
      $p_A = p_B - 0.26 = 10 - 0.26 = 9.74$ psia

Local atmospheric pressure $= \dfrac{29.5}{30} \times 14.7 = 14.47$ psi.

In Fig. 2.4,

$$p_A = 9.74 - 14.47 = -4.73 \text{ psi}$$

and

$$p_A = -4.73 \times 144 = 681 \text{ lb/ft}^2 \text{ vacuum}$$

*micromanometers*

Several types of manometers are on the market for the determining of very small differences in pressure or precise determining of large pressure differences.   One type very accurately measures the differences in elevation of two menisci of a manometer.   By means of small telescopes with horizontal cross hairs mounted along the tubes on a rack which is raised and lowered by a pinion and slow-motion screw so that the cross hairs may be set accurately, the difference in elevation of menisci (the gage difference) may be read with verniers.

With two gage liquids, immiscible in each other and in the fluid to be measured, a large gage difference $R$ (Fig. 2.8) may be produced for a small pressure difference.   The heavier gage liquid fills the lower U-tube up to 0-0; then the lighter gage liquid is added to both sides, filling the larger reservoirs up to 1-1.   The gas or liquid in the system fills the space above

**Fig.   2.8** Micromanometer using two gage liquids.

1-1.  When the pressure at $C$ is slightly greater than at $D$, the menisci move as indicated in Fig. 2.8.  The volume of liquid displaced in each reservoir equals the displacement in the U-tube; thus

$$\Delta y \, A = \frac{R}{2} a$$

in which $A$ and $a$ are the cross-sectional areas of reservoir and U-tube, respectively.  The manometer equation may be written, starting at $C$, in pounds per square foot,

$$p_C + (k_1 + \Delta y)\gamma_1 + \left(k_2 - \Delta y + \frac{R}{2}\right)\gamma_2 - R\gamma_3$$

$$- \left(k_2 - \frac{R}{2} + \Delta y\right)\gamma_2 - (k_1 - \Delta y)\gamma_1 = p_D$$

in which $\gamma_1$, $\gamma_2$, and $\gamma_3$ are the specific weights as indicated in Fig. 2.8˙
After simplifying and substituting for $\Delta y$,

$$p_C - p_D = R\left[\gamma_3 - \gamma_2\left(1 - \frac{a}{A}\right) - \gamma_1\frac{a}{A}\right] \tag{2.4.1}$$

The quantity in brackets is a constant for specified gage and fluids; hence, the pressure difference is directly proportional to $R$.

**example 2.5**  In the micromanometer of Fig. 2.8 the pressure difference $p_C - p_D$ is wanted in pounds per square inch when air is in the system. $S_2 = 1.0$, $S_3 = 1.05$, $a/A = 0.01$, $R = 0.10$ in.

For air at standard conditions, 68°F, 30 in. mercury abs, $\gamma_1 = 0.0765$; then $\gamma_1\,(a/A) = 0.000765$,  $\gamma_3 - \gamma_2\,(1 - a/A) = 62.4\,(1.05 - 0.99) = 3.74$. The term $\gamma_1\,(a/A)$ may be neglected.  Substituting into Eq. (2.4.1) produces

$$p_C - p_D = \frac{0.10}{12}\frac{3.74}{144} = 0.00022 \text{ psi}$$

$$h_C - h_D = 0.00022 \times \frac{30}{1.47} = 0.00044 \text{ in. Hg}$$

The inclined manometer (Fig. 2.9) is frequently used for measuring small differences in gas pressures.  It is adjusted to read zero, by moving the inclined scale, when $A$ and $B$ are open.  The inclined tube requires a greater displacement of the meniscus for given pressure difference than does a vertical tube, and so the accuracy in reading the scale is greater in the former.

**Fig. 2.9** Inclined manometer.

Surface tension causes a capillary rise in small tubes. If a U-tube is used with a meniscus in each leg, the surface tension effects cancel. The capillary rise is negligible in tubes with a diameter of 0.5 in. or greater.

### 2.5 forces on plane areas

In the preceding sections variations of pressure throughout a fluid have been considered. The distributed forces resulting from the action of fluid on a finite area may be conveniently replaced by a resultant force, in so far as external reactions to the force system are concerned. In this section the magnitude of resultant force and its line of action (pressure center) are determined by integration, by formula, and by use of the concept of the pressure prism.

*horizontal surfaces*

A plane surface in a horizontal position in a fluid at rest is subjected to a constant pressure. The magnitude of the force acting on one side of the surface is

$$\int p \, dA = p \int dA = pA$$

The elemental forces $p \, dA$ acting on $dA$ are all parallel and in the same sense; therefore, a scalar summation of all such elements yields the magnitude of the resultant force. Its direction is normal to the surface, and *toward* the surface if $p$ is *positive*. To find the line of action of the resultant, i.e., the point in the area where the moment of the distributed force about any axis through the point is zero, arbitrary $xy$-axes may be selected, as in Fig. 2.10. Then, since the moment of the resultant must equal the moment of the distributed force system about any axis, say the $y$-axis,

$$pAx' = \int_A xp \, dA$$

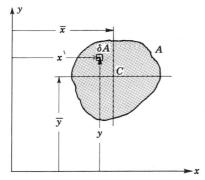

**Fig. 2.10** Notation for determining line of action of a force.

in which $x'$ is the distance from the $y$-axis to the resultant.  Since $p$ is constant,

$$x' = \frac{1}{A} \int_A x \, dA = \bar{x}$$

in which $\bar{x}$ is the distance to the centroid of the area.[1]  Hence, for a horizontal area subjected to static fluid pressure, the resultant passes through the centroid of the area.

*inclined surfaces*

In Fig. 2.11 a plane surface is indicated by its trace $A'B'$.  It is inclined $\theta°$ from the horizontal.  The intersection of the plane of the area and the free surface is taken as the $x$-axis.  The $y$-axis is taken in the plane of the area, with origin $O$, as shown, in the free surface.  The $xy$-plane portrays the arbitrary inclined area.  The magnitude, direction, and line of action of the resultant force *due to the liquid*, acting on one side of the area, are sought.

For an element with area $\delta A$ as a strip with thickness $\delta y$ with long edges horizontal, the magnitude of force $\delta F$ acting on it is

$$\delta F = p \, \delta A = \gamma h \, \delta A = \gamma y \sin \theta \, \delta A \tag{2.5.1}$$

Since all such elemental forces are parallel, the integral over the area yields the magnitude of force $F$, acting on one side of the area,

$$F = \int p \, dA = \gamma \sin \theta \int y \, dA = \gamma \sin \theta \, \bar{y} A = \gamma \bar{h} A = p_G A \tag{2.5.2}$$

with the relations from Fig. 2.11, $\bar{y} \sin \theta = \bar{h}$, and $p_G = \gamma \bar{h}$, the pressure at

[1] See Appendix A.

**Fig. 2.11**  Notation for force of liquid on one side of a plane inclined area.

the centroid of the area.   In words, the magnitude of force exerted on one side of a plane area submerged in a liquid is the product of the area and the pressure at its centroid.   In this form, it should be noted, the presence of a free surface is unnecessary.   Any means for determining the pressure at the centroid may be used.   The sense of the force is to push against the area, if $p_G$ is positive.   As all force elements are normal to the surface, the line of action of the resultant is also normal to the surface.   Any surface may be rotated about any axis through its centroid without changing the magnitude of the resultant, if the total area remains submerged in the static liquid.

*center of pressure*

The line of action of the resultant force has its piercing point in the surface at a point called the *pressure center*, with coordinates $(x_p, y_p)$ (Fig. 2.11). Unlike that for the horizontal surface, the center of pressure of an inclined surface is not at the centroid.   To find the pressure center, the moments of the resultant $x_p F$, $y_p F$ are equated to the moment of the distributed forces about the $y$-axis and $x$-axis, respectively; thus

$$x_p F = \int_A xp\, dA \tag{2.5.3}$$

$$y_p F = \int_A yp\, dA \tag{2.5.4}$$

The area element in Eq. (2.5.3) should be $\delta x\, \delta y$, and not the strip shown in Fig. 2.11.

After solving for the coordinates of pressure center,

$$x_p = \frac{1}{F} \int_A xp\, dA \tag{2.5.5}$$

$$y_p = \frac{1}{F} \int_A yp\, dA \tag{2.5.6}$$

In many applications Eqs. (2.5.5) and (2.5.6) may be evaluated most conveniently through graphical integration; for simple areas they may be transformed into general formulas as follows:[1]

$$x_p = \frac{1}{\gamma \bar{y} A \sin \theta} \int_A x\gamma y \sin \theta\, dA = \frac{1}{\bar{y} A} \int_A xy\, dA = \frac{I_{xy}}{\bar{y} A} \tag{2.5.7}$$

In Eqs. (A.10), of Appendix A, and (2.5.7),

$$x_p = \frac{\bar{I}_{xy}}{\bar{y} A} + \bar{x} \tag{2.5.8}$$

When either of the centroidal axes, $x = \bar{x}$ or $y = \bar{y}$, is an axis of symmetry for the surface, $\bar{I}_{xy}$ vanishes and the pressure center lies on $x = \bar{x}$. Since $\bar{I}_{xy}$ may be either positive or negative, the pressure center may lie on either side of the line $x = \bar{x}$. To determine $y_p$ by formula, with Eqs. (2.5.2) and (2.5.6),

$$y_p = \frac{1}{\gamma \bar{y} A \sin \theta} \int_A y\gamma y \sin \theta\, dA = \frac{1}{\bar{y} A} \int_A y^2\, dA = \frac{I_x}{\bar{y} A} \tag{2.5.9}$$

In the parallel-axis theorem for moments of inertia

$$I_x = I_G + \bar{y}^2 A$$

If $I_x$ is eliminated from Eq. (2.5.9)

$$y_p = \frac{I_G}{\bar{y} A} + \bar{y} \tag{2.5.10}$$

[1] See Appendix A.

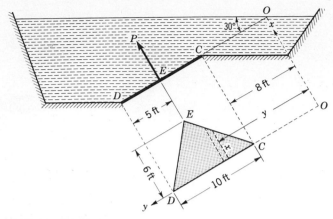

**Fig. 2.12**  Triangular gate.

or

$$y_p - \bar{y} = \frac{I_G}{\bar{y}A} \tag{2.5.11}$$

$I_G$ is always positive; hence, $y_p - \bar{y}$ is always positive, and the pressure center is always below the centroid of the surface.   It should be emphasized that $\bar{y}$ and $y_p - \bar{y}$ are distances in the plane of the surface.

**example 2.6**   The triangular gate $CDE$ (Fig. 2.12) is hinged along $CD$ and is opened by a normal force $P$ applied at $E$.   It holds oil, sp gr 0.80, above it and is open to the atmosphere on its lower side.   Neglecting the weight of the gate find (a) the magnitude of force exerted on the gate, by integration and by Eq. (2.5.2); (b) the location of pressure center; (c) the force $P$ needed to open the gate.

   (a)   By integration with reference to Fig. 2.12,

$$F = \int_A p \, dA = \gamma \sin \theta \int yx \, dy = \gamma \sin \theta \int_8^{13} xy \, dy + \gamma \sin \theta \int_{13}^{18} xy \, dy$$

When $y = 8$, $x = 0$, and when $y = 13$, $x = 6$, with $x$ varying linearly with $y$; thus

$$x = ay + b \qquad 0 = 8a + b \qquad 6 = 13a + b$$

in which the coordinates have been substituted to find $x$ in terms of $y$. After solving for $a$ and $b$,

$$a = \tfrac{6}{5} \qquad b = -\tfrac{48}{5} \qquad x = \tfrac{6}{5}(y - 8)$$

Similarly $y = 13$, $x = 6$; $y = 18$, $x = 0$; and $x = \frac{6}{5}(18 - y)$.  Hence

$$F = \gamma \sin \theta \,\frac{6}{5} \left[ \int_8^{13} (y - 8)y\, dy + \int_{13}^{18} (18 - y)y\, dy \right]$$

After integrating and substituting for $\gamma \sin \theta$,

$$F = 62.4 \times 0.8 \times 0.50 \times \frac{6}{5} \left[ \left( \frac{y^3}{3} - 4y^2 \right)_8^{13} + \left( 9y^2 - \frac{y^3}{3} \right)_{13}^{18} \right] = 9734.4 \text{ lb}$$

By Eq. (2.5.2),

$$F = p_G A = \gamma \bar{y} \sin \theta \, A = 62.4 \times 0.80 \times 0.50 \times 30 \times 13 = 9734.4 \text{ lb}$$

(b)   With the axes as shown, $\bar{x} = 2.0$, $\bar{y} = 13$.  In Eq. (2.5.8),

$$x_p = \frac{\bar{I}_{xy}}{\bar{y}A} + \bar{x}$$

$\bar{I}_{xy}$ is zero owing to symmetry about the centroidal axis parallel to the $x$-axis; hence $\bar{x} = x_p = 2.0$ ft.  In Eq. (2.5.11),

$$y_p - \bar{y} = \frac{I_G}{\bar{y}A} = 2 \times \frac{1 \times 6 \times 5^3}{12 \times 13 \times 30} = 0.32 \text{ ft}$$

i.e., the pressure center is 0.32 ft below the centroid, measured in the plane of the area.

(c)   When moments about $CD$ are taken and the action of the oil is replaced by the resultant,

$$P \times 6 = 9734.4 \times 2 \qquad P = 3244.8 \text{ lb}$$

*the pressure prism*

The concept of the pressure prism provides another means for determining the magnitude and location of the resultant force on an inclined plane surface.   The volume of the pressure prism is the magnitude of the force, and the resultant force passes through the centroid of the prism.   The surface is taken as the base of the prism, and its altitude at each point is determined by the pressure $\gamma h$ laid off to an appropriate scale (Fig. 2.13). Since the pressure increases linearly with distance from the free surface, the upper surface of the prism is in a plane with its trace $OM$ shown in Fig. 2.13.   The force acting on an elemental area $\delta A$ is

$$\delta F = \gamma h \, \delta A = \delta \upsilon \tag{2.5.12}$$

which is an element of volume of the pressure prism.   After integrating,

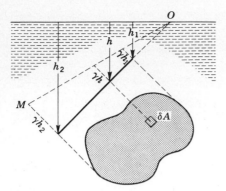

**Fig. 2.13**  Illustration of pressure prism.

$F = \mho$, the volume of the pressure prism equals the magnitude of the resultant force acting on one side of the surface.

Equations (2.5.5) and (2.5.6),

$$x_p = \frac{1}{\mho} \int_\mho x \, d\mho \qquad y_p = \frac{1}{\mho} \int_\mho y \, d\mho \tag{2.5.13}$$

show that $x_p$, $y_p$ are distances to the *centroid* of the pressure prism.[1] Hence, the line of action of the resultant passes through the centroid of the pressure prism.   For some simple areas the pressure prism is more convenient than either integration or formula.   For example, a rectangular area with one edge in the free surface has a wedge-shaped prism.   Its centroid is one-third the altitude from the base; hence, the pressure center is one-third the altitude from its lower edge.

*effects of atmospheric pressure on forces on plane areas*

In the discussion of pressure forces the pressure datum was not mentioned. The pressures were computed by $p = \gamma h$, in which $h$ is the vertical distance below the free surface.   Therefore, the datum taken was gage pressure zero, or the local atmospheric pressure.   When the opposite side of the surface is open to the atmosphere, a force is exerted on it by the atmosphere equal to the product of the atmospheric pressure $p_0$ and the area, or $p_0 A$, based on absolute zero as datum.   On the liquid side the force is

$$\int (p_0 + \gamma h) \, dA = p_0 A + \gamma \int h \, dA$$

[1] Appendix A, Eq. (A.5).

The effect $p_0A$ of the atmosphere acts equally on both sides and in no way contributes to the resultant force or its location.

So long as the same pressure datum is selected for all sides of a free body, the resultant can be determined by constructing a free surface at pressure zero on this datum and by using the above methods.

**example 2.7**  *Forces on a gravity dam.*   An application of pressure forces on plane areas is given in the design of a gravity dam.   The maximum and minimum compressive stresses in the base of the dam are computed from the forces which act on the dam.   Figure 2.14 shows a cross section through a concrete dam where the specific weight of concrete has been taken as $2.5\gamma$ and $\gamma$ is the specific weight of water.   A 1-ft section of dam is considered as a free body; the forces are due to the concrete, the water, the foundation pressure, and the hydrostatic uplift.   The determination of amount of hydrostatic uplift is beyond the scope of this treatment, but will be assumed one-half the hydrostatic head at the upstream edge, decreasing linearly to zero at the downstream edge of the dam.   Enough friction

**Fig. 2.14**  Concrete gravity dam.

or shear stress must be developed at the base of the dam to balance the thrust due to the water; that is, $R_x = 5000\gamma$. The resultant upward force on the base equals the weight of the dam less the hydrostatic uplift, $R_y = 6750\gamma + 2625\gamma - 1750\gamma = 7625\gamma$ lb. The position of $R_y$ is such that the free body is in equilibrium. For moments around $O$,

$$\Sigma M_0 = 0 = R_y x - 5000\gamma \times 33.33 - 2625\gamma \times 5 - 6750\gamma \times 30$$
$$+ 1750\gamma \times 23.33$$

and

$$x = 44.8 \text{ ft}$$

It is customary to assume that the foundation pressure varies linearly over the base of the dam, i.e., that the pressure prism is a trapezoid with a volume equal to $R_y$; thus

$$\frac{\sigma_{max} + \sigma_{min}}{2} 70 = 7625\gamma$$

in which $\sigma_{max}$, $\sigma_{min}$ are the maximum and minimum compressive stresses in pounds per square foot. The centroid of the pressure prism is at the point where $x = 44.8$ ft. By taking moments about $O$ to express the position of the centroid in terms of $\sigma_{max}$ and $\sigma_{min}$,

$$44.8 = \frac{\sigma_{min}70 \times \frac{70}{2} + (\sigma_{max} - \sigma_{min})\frac{70}{2} \times \frac{2}{3} 70}{(\sigma_{max} + \sigma_{min})\frac{70}{2}}$$

After simplifying,

$$\sigma_{max} = 11.75\sigma_{min}$$

Then

$$\sigma_{max} = 210\gamma = 12{,}500 \text{ lb/ft}^2 \qquad \sigma_{min} = 17.1\gamma = 1067 \text{ lb/ft}^2$$

When the resultant falls within the middle third of the base of the dam, $\sigma_{min}$ will always be a compressive stress. Owing to the poor tensile properties of concrete, good design requires the resultant to fall within the middle third of the base.

## 2.6  force components on curved surfaces

When the elemental forces $p\,\delta A$ vary in direction, as in the case of a curved surface, they must be added as vector quantities; i.e., their components in three mutually perpendicular directions are added as scalars, and then the

three components are added vectorially.   With two horizontal components
at right angles and with the vertical component, which are easily computed
for a curved surface, the resultant can be determined.   The lines of action
of the components are readily determined, and so the resultant and its line
of action can be completely determined.

### horizontal component of force on a curved surface

*The horizontal component of pressure force on a curved surface is equal to
the pressure force exerted on a projection of the curved surface.   The vertical
plane of projection is normal to the direction of the component.*   The surface
of Fig. 2.15 represents any three-dimensional surface, and $\delta A$ an element
of its area, with its normal making the angle $\theta$ with the negative $x$-direction.
Then

$$\delta F_x = p \; \delta A \cos \theta$$

is the $x$-component of force exerted on one side of $\delta A$.   Summing up the
$x$-components of force over the surface,

$$F_x = \int_A p \cos \theta \, dA \tag{2.6.1}$$

Considering $\cos \theta \; \delta A$, it is the projection of $\delta A$ onto a plane perpendicular
to $x$.   The element of force on the projected area is $p \cos \theta \; \delta A$, which is
also in the $x$-direction.   Projecting each element on a plane perpendicular
to $x$ is equivalent to projecting the curved surface as a whole onto the vertical plane.   Hence, the force acting on this projection of the curved surface
is the horizontal component of force exerted on the curved surface, in the
direction normal to the plane of projection.   To find the horizontal component at right angles to the $x$-direction, the curved surface is projected
onto a vertical plane parallel to $x$, and the force on the projection is
determined.

When the horizontal component of pressure force on a closed body is to
be found, the projection of the curved surface on a vertical plane is always

**Fig.  2.15** Horizontal  component  of
force on a curved surface.

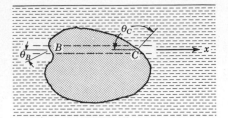

**Fig. 2.16** Projections of area elements on opposite sides of a body.

zero, since on opposite sides of the body the area-element projections have opposite signs, as indicated in Fig. 2.16.   Let a small cylinder of cross section $\delta A$ with axis parallel to $x$ intersect the closed body at $B$ and $C$.   If the element of area of the body cut by the prism at $B$ is $\delta A_B$ and at $C$ is $\delta A_C$, then

$$\delta A_B \cos \theta_B = -\delta A_C \cos \theta_C = \delta A$$

as $\cos \theta_C$ is negative.   Hence, with the pressure the same at each end of the cylinder,

$$p\delta \, A_B \cos \theta_B + p \, \delta A_C \cos \theta_C = 0$$

and similarly for all other area elements.

To find the line of action of a horizontal component of force on a curved surface, the resultant of the parallel force system composed of the force components from each area element is required.   This is exactly the resultant of the force on the projected area, since the two force systems have an identical distribution of elemental horizontal force components.   Hence, the pressure center is located on the projected area by the methods of Sec. 2.5.

**example 2.8**   An ellipsoid of revolution submerged in water has an equation given by $x^2/4 + y^2/4 + z^2/9 = 1$.   The center of the body is located 2 ft below the free surface.   Find the horizontal force components acting on the curved surface that is located in the first octant.   Consider the $xz$-plane to be horizontal and $y$ to be positive upward.

The projection of the surface on the $yz$-plane has an area of $(\pi/4) \times 2 \times 3$.   Its centroid is located $[2 - (4/3\pi) \times 2]$ ft below the free surface.   Hence

$$F_x = - \left( \frac{\pi}{4} \times 6 \right) \left( 2 - \frac{8}{3\pi} \right) \gamma = -(9.43 - 4)\gamma = -340 \text{ lb}$$

Similarly,

$$F_z = -\left(\frac{\pi}{4} \times 4\right)\left(2 - \frac{8}{3\pi}\right)\gamma = -(6.28 - 2.67)\gamma = -225 \text{ lb}$$

*vertical component of force on a curved surface*

*The vertical component of pressure force on a curved surface is equal to the weight of liquid vertically above the curved surface and extending up to the free surface.*   The vertical component of force on a curved surface can be determined by summing up the vertical components of pressure force on elemental areas $\delta A$ of the surface.   In Fig. 2.17 an area element is shown with the force $p\ \delta A$ acting normal to it.   (Let $\theta$ be the angle the normal to the area element makes with the vertical.)   Then the vertical component of force acting on the area element is $p \cos \theta\ \delta A$, and the vertical component of force on the curved surface is given by

$$F_v = \int_A p \cos \theta\ dA \qquad\qquad (2.6.2)$$

By replacing $p$ by its equivalent $\gamma h$, in which $h$ is the distance from the area element to the free surface, and noting that $\cos \theta\ \delta A$ is the projection of $\delta A$ on a horizontal plane, Eq. (2.6.2) becomes

$$F_v = \gamma \int_A h \cos \theta\ dA = \gamma \int_v dv \qquad\qquad (2.6.3)$$

in which $\delta v$ is the volume of the prism of height $h$ and base $\cos \theta\ \delta A$, or the

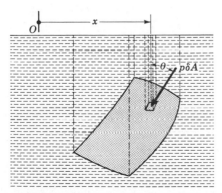

**Fig. 2.17**  Vertical component of force on a curved surface.

**Fig. 2.18** Liquid with equivalent free surface.

volume of liquid vertically above the area element. Integrating,

$$F_v = \gamma \upsilon \tag{2.6.4}$$

When the liquid is below the curved surface (Fig. 2.18) and the pressure magnitude is known at some point, e.g., $O$, an *imaginary* or equivalent free surface $s$-$s$ may be constructed $p/\gamma$ above $O$, so that the product of specific weight and vertical distance to any point in the tank is the pressure at the point. The weight of the imaginary volume of liquid vertically above the curved surface is then the vertical component of pressure force on the curved surface. In the constructing of an imaginary free surface, the imaginary liquid must be of the same specific weight as the liquid in contact with the curved surface; otherwise, the pressure distribution over the surface will not be correctly represented. With an imaginary liquid above a surface, the pressure at a point on the curved surface is equal on both sides, but the elemental force components in the vertical direction are opposite in sign. Hence, the direction of the vertical force component is reversed when an imaginary fluid is above the surface. In some cases a confined liquid may be above the curved surface, and an imaginary liquid must be added (or subtracted) to determine the free surface.

The line of action of the vertical component is determined by equating moments of the elemental vertical components about a convenient axis with the moment of the resultant force. With the axis at $O$ (Fig. 2.17),

$$F_v \bar{x} = \gamma \int_\upsilon x \, d\upsilon$$

in which $\bar{x}$ is the distance from $O$ to the line of action. Then, since $F_v = \gamma \upsilon$,

$$\bar{x} = \frac{1}{\upsilon} \int_\upsilon x \, d\upsilon$$

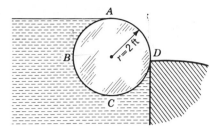

**Fig. 2.19**  Semifloating body.

the distance to the centroid of the volume.   Therefore, the line of action of the vertical force passes through the centroid of the volume, real or imaginary, that extends above the curved surface up to the real or imaginary free surface.

**example 2.9**   A cylindrical barrier (Fig. 2.19) holds water as shown.   The contact between cylinder and wall is smooth.   Considering a one-foot length of cylinder, determine ($a$) its weight and ($b$) the force exerted against the wall.

(*a*)   For equilibrium the weight of the cylinder must equal the vertical component of force exerted on it by the water.   The vertical force on $BCD$ is

$$F_{v_{BCD}} = \left(\frac{\pi r^2}{2} + 2r^2\right)\gamma = (2\pi + 8)\gamma$$

The vertical force on $AB$ is

$$F_{v_{AB}} = -\left(r^2 - \frac{\pi r^2}{4}\right)\gamma = -(4 - \pi)\gamma$$

Hence, the weight per foot of length is

$$F_{v_{BCD}} + F_{v_{AB}} = (3\pi + 4)\gamma = 838 \text{ lb}$$

(*b*)   The force exerted against the wall is the horizontal force on $ABC$ minus the horizontal force on $CD$.   The horizontal components of force on $BC$ and $CD$ cancel since the projection of $BCD$ on a vertical plane is zero. Hence,

$$F_H = F_{H_{AB}} = 2\gamma = 124.8 \text{ lb}$$

since the projected area is 2 ft² and the pressure at the centroid of the projected area is 62.4 lb/ft².

To find external reactions due to pressure forces, the action of the fluid may be replaced by the two horizontal components and one vertical component acting along their lines of action.

### *tensile stress in a pipe*

A circular pipe under the action of an internal pressure is in tension around its periphery.   Assuming that no longitudinal stress occurs, the walls are in tension as shown in Fig. 2.20.   A 1-in. section of pipe is considered, i.e., the ring between two planes normal to the axis and 1 in. apart.   Taking one-half of this ring as a free body, the tensions per inch at top and bottom are, respectively, $T_1$, $T_2$, as shown in the figure.   The horizontal component of force acts through the pressure center of the projected area and is $2pr$, in which $p$ is the pressure at the center line in pounds per square inch and $r$ is the pipe radius (internal) in inches.

For high pressures the pressure center may be taken at the pipe center; then $T_1 = T_2$, and

$$T = pr \tag{2.6.5}$$

in which $T$ is the tensile force per inch.   For wall thickness $t$ in., the *tensile stress* $\sigma$ in the pipe wall is

$$\sigma = \frac{T}{t} = \frac{pr}{t} \tag{2.6.6}$$

For larger variations in pressure between top and bottom of pipe the pressure center is computed, and two equations are needed,

$$T_1 + T_2 = 2pr$$
$$2rT_1 - 2pry = 0$$

in which the second equation is the moment equation about the lower end of the free body, neglecting the vertical component of force.   Solving,

**Fig. 2.20**  Tensile stress in pipe.

$$T_1 = py \qquad T_2 = p(2r - y)$$

in which $y$ is in inches.

**example 2.10**  A 4.0-in. ID steel pipe has a $\frac{1}{4}$-in. wall thickness.  For an allowable tensile stress of 10,000 psi what is the maximum pressure?

$$\sigma = \frac{pr}{t} = 10,000 = \frac{p2}{\frac{1}{4}}$$

and hence

$$p = 1250 \text{ psi}$$

*tensile stress in a thin spherical shell*

If a thin spherical shell is subjected to an internal pressure, neglecting the weight of the fluid within the sphere, the stress in its walls may be found by considering the forces on a free body consisting of a hemisphere, cut from the sphere by a vertical plane.  The fluid component of force normal to the plane acting on the inside of the hemisphere is $p\pi r^2$, with $r$ the radius.  The stress $\sigma$ times the cut wall area $2\pi rt$, with $t$ the thickness, must balance the fluid force, hence

$$\sigma = \frac{pr}{2t}$$

## 2.7  buoyant force

The resultant force exerted on a body *by a static fluid* in which it is submerged or floating is called the *buoyant force*.  The buoyant force always acts vertically upward.  There can be no horizontal component of the resultant because the vertical projection of the submerged body or submerged portion of the floating body is always zero.

The buoyant force on a submerged body is the difference between the vertical component of pressure force on its underside and the vertical component of pressure force on its upper side.  In Fig. 2.21 the upward force on the bottom is equal to the weight of liquid, real or imaginary, which is vertically above the surface $ABC$, indicated by the weight of liquid within $ABCEFA$.  The downward force on the upper surface equals

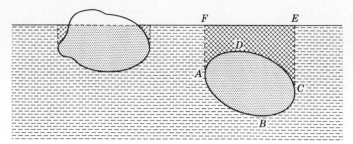

**Fig. 2.21** Buoyant force on floating and submerged bodies.

the weight of liquid $ADCEFA$. The difference between the two forces is a force, vertically upward, due to the weight of fluid $ABCD$ that is *displaced* by the solid. In equation form

$$F_B = \mathcal{V}\gamma \tag{2.7.1}$$

in which $F_B$ is the buoyant force, $\mathcal{V}$ is the volume of fluid displaced, and $\gamma$ is the specific weight of fluid. The same formula holds for floating bodies when $\mathcal{V}$ is taken as the volume of liquid displaced. This is evident from inspection of the floating body in Fig. 2.21.

In Fig. 2.22a, the vertical force exerted on an element of the body in the form of a vertical prism of cross section $\delta A$ is

$$\delta F_B = (p_2 - p_1)\, \delta A = \gamma h\, \delta A = \gamma\, \delta \mathcal{V}$$

in which $\delta \mathcal{V}$ is the volume of the prism. Integrating over the complete

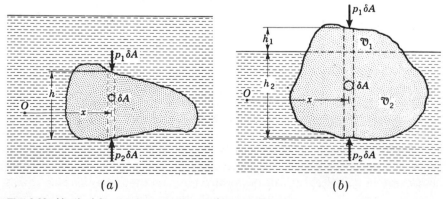

$(a)$ $(b)$

**Fig. 2.22** Vertical force components on element of body.

body,

$$F_B = \gamma \int_{\upsilon} d\upsilon = \gamma \upsilon$$

when $\gamma$ is considered constant throughout the volume.

To find the line of action of the buoyant force, moments are taken about a convenient axis $O$ and are equated to the moment of the resultant; thus,

$$\gamma \int x \, d\upsilon = \gamma \upsilon \bar{x}$$

or

$$\bar{x} = \frac{1}{\upsilon} \int x \, d\upsilon$$

in which $\bar{x}$ is the distance from the axis to the line of action.   This equation yields the distance to the centroid of the volume; hence *the buoyant force acts through the centroid of the displaced volume of fluid.*   This holds for both submerged and floating bodies.   The centroid of the displaced volume of fluid is called the *center of buoyancy.*

When the body floats at the interface of a static two-fluid system (Fig. 2.22*b*) the buoyant force on a vertical prism of cross section $\delta A$ is

$$\delta F_B = (p_2 - p_1) \, \delta A = (\gamma_2 h_2 + \gamma_1 h_1) \, \delta A$$

in which $\gamma_1$, $\gamma_2$ are the specific weights of the lighter and heavier fluids, respectively.   Integrating over the area,

$$F_B = \gamma_2 \int h_2 \, dA + \gamma_1 \int h_1 \, dA = \gamma_2 \upsilon_2 + \gamma_1 \upsilon_1$$

$\upsilon_1$ is the volume of lighter fluid displaced, and $\upsilon_2$ is the volume of heavier fluid displaced.   To locate the line of action of the buoyant force, moments are taken,

$$F_B \bar{x} = \gamma_1 \int x \, d\upsilon_1 + \gamma_2 \int x \, d\upsilon_2$$

or

$$\bar{x} = \frac{\gamma_1 \int x \, d\upsilon_1 + \gamma_2 \int x \, d\upsilon_2}{\gamma_1 \upsilon_1 + \gamma_2 \upsilon_2} = \frac{\gamma_1 \bar{x}_1 \upsilon_1 + \gamma_2 \bar{x}_2 \upsilon_2}{\gamma_1 \upsilon_1 + \gamma_2 \upsilon_2}$$

in which $\bar{x}_1$, $\bar{x}_2$ are distances to centroids of volumes $\upsilon_1$, $\upsilon_2$, respectively. The resultant does not, in general, pass through the centroid of the whole volume.

In solving a statics problem involving submerged or floating objects, the object is generally taken as a free body, and a free-body diagram is drawn.   The action of the fluid is replaced by the buoyant force.   The

**Fig. 2.23** Free-body diagram for body suspended in a fluid.

weight of the object must be shown (acting through its center of gravity) as well as all other contact forces.

Weighing an odd-shaped object when suspended in two different fluids yields sufficient data to determine its weight, volume, specific weight, and specific gravity. Figure 2.23 shows two free-body diagrams for the same object suspended and weighed in two fluids. $F_1$, $F_2$ are the weights submerged; $\gamma_1$, $\gamma_2$ are the specific weights of the fluids. $W$ and $\mho$, the weight and volume of the object, are desired.

The equations of equilibrium are written,

$$F_1 + \mho\gamma_1 = W \qquad F_2 + \mho\gamma_2 = W$$

and solved,

$$\mho = \frac{F_1 - F_2}{\gamma_2 - \gamma_1} \qquad W = \frac{F_1\gamma_2 - F_2\gamma_1}{\gamma_2 - \gamma_1}$$

A *hydrometer* uses the principle of buoyant force to determine specific gravities of liquids. Figure 2.24 shows a hydrometer in two liquids. It has a stem of prismatic cross section $a$. Considering the liquid on the

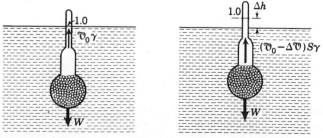

**Fig. 2.24** Hydrometer, in water and in liquid of specific gravity $S$.

left to be distilled water, $S = 1.00$, the hydrometer floats in equilibrium when

$$\mathcal{V}_0 \gamma = W \tag{2.7.2}$$

in which $\mathcal{V}_0$ is the volume submerged, $\gamma$ is the specific weight of water, and $W$ is the weight of hydrometer.  The position of the liquid surface is marked 1.00 on the stem to indicate unit specfic gravity $S$.  When the hydrometer is floated in another liquid, the equation of equilibrium becomes

$$(\mathcal{V}_0 - \Delta \mathcal{V})S\gamma = W \tag{2.7.3}$$

in which $\Delta \mathcal{V} = a \, \Delta h$.  Solving for $\Delta h$, with Eqs. (2.7.2) and (2.7.3),

$$\Delta h = \frac{\mathcal{V}_0}{a} \frac{S - 1}{S} \tag{2.7.4}$$

from which the stem may be marked off to read specific gravities.

**example 2.11**  A piece of ore weighing 7 lb in air was found to weigh 5.6 lb when submerged in water.  What is its volume and specific gravity?
The buoyant force due to air may be neglected.  From Fig. 2.23

$$7 = 5.6 + 62.4\mathcal{V} \qquad \mathcal{V} = 0.0224 \text{ ft}^3$$

$$S = \frac{7}{0.0224 \times 62.4} = 5$$

## 2.8  stability of floating and submerged bodies

A body floating in a static liquid has vertical stability.  A small upward displacement decreases the volume of liquid displaced, resulting in an unbalanced downward force which tends to return the body to its original position.  Similarly, a small downward displacement results in a greater buoyant force, which causes an unbalanced upward force.

A body has linear stability when a small linear displacement in any direction sets up restoring forces tending to return the body to its original position.  It has rotational stability when a restoring couple is set up by any small angular displacement.

Methods for determining rotational stability are developed in the following discussion.  A body may float in stable, unstable, or neutral equilibrium.  When a body is in unstable equilibrium, any small angular

(a) Stable          (b) Unstable          (c) Neutral

**Fig. 2.25** Examples of stable, unstable, and neutral equilibrium.

displacement sets up a couple that tends to increase the angular displacement. With the body in neutral equilibrium, any small angular displacement sets up no couple whatever. Figure 2.25 illustrates the three cases of equilibrium: (a) a light piece of wood with a metal weight at its bottom is stable; (b) when the metal weight is at the top, the body is in equilibrium but any slight angular displacement causes the body to assume the position in a; (c) a homogeneous sphere or right-circular cylinder is in equilibrium for any angular rotation, i.e., no couple results from an angular displacement.

A submerged object is rotationally stable only when its center of gravity is below the center of buoyancy, as in Fig. 2.26a. When the object is rotated in a counterclockwise direction as in Fig. 2.26b, the buoyant force and weight produce a couple in the clockwise direction.

Normally, when a body is too heavy to float, it submerges and goes down until it rests on the bottom. Although the specific weight of a liquid increases slightly with depth, the higher pressure tends to cause the liquid to compress the body or to penetrate into pores of solid substances, thus decreasing the buoyancy of the body. A ship, for example, is sure to go to the bottom once it is completely submerged, owing to compression of air trapped in various places within it.

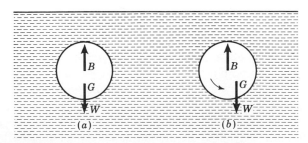

**Fig. 2.26** Rotationally stable submerged body.

*determination of rotational stability of floating objects*

Any floating object with center of gravity below its center of buoyancy (centroid of displaced volume) floats in stable equilibrium, as in Fig. 2.25a. Certain floating objects, however, are in stable equilibrium when their center of gravity is above the center of buoyancy.   The stability of prismatic bodies is first considered, followed by an analysis of general floating bodies for small angles of tip.

   Figure 2.27a is a cross section of a body with all other parallel cross sections identical.   The center of buoyancy is always at the centroid of the displaced volume, which is at the centroid of the cross-sectional area below liquid surface in this case.   Hence, when the body is tipped, as in Fig. 2.27b, the center of buoyancy is at the centroid $B'$ of the trapezoid $ABCD$; the buoyant force acts upward through $B'$, and the weight acts downward through $G$, the center of gravity of the body.   When the vertical through $B'$ intersects the original center line above $G$, as at $M$, a restoring couple is produced, and the body is in stable equilibrium.   The intersection of the buoyant force and the center line is called the *metacenter*, designated $M$.   When $M$ is above $G$, the body is stable; when below $G$, it is unstable; and when at $G$, it is in neutral equilibrium.   The distance $\overline{MG}$ is called the *metacentric height* and is a direct measure of the stability of the body.   The restoring couple is

$$\overline{WMG} \sin \theta$$

in which $\theta$ is the angular displacement and $W$ the weight of the body.

**example 2.12**   In Fig. 2.27 a scow 20 ft wide and 60 ft long has a gross weight of 225 short tons (2000 lb).   Its center of gravity is 1.0 ft above the water surface.   Find the metacentric height and restoring couple when $\Delta y = 1.0$ ft.

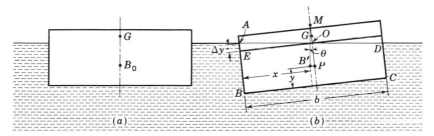

**Fig. 2.27**   Stability of prismatic body.

The depth of submergence $h$ in the water is

$$h = \frac{225 \times 2000}{20 \times 60 \times 62.4} = 6.0 \text{ ft}$$

The centroid in the tipped position is located with moments about $AB$ and $BC$,

$$x = \frac{5 \times 20 \times 10 + 2 \times 20 \times \frac{1}{2} \times \frac{20}{3}}{6 \times 20} = 9.46 \text{ ft}$$

$$y = \frac{5 \times 20 \times \frac{5}{2} + 2 \times 20 \times \frac{1}{2} \times 5\frac{2}{3}}{6 \times 20} = 3.03 \text{ ft}$$

By similar triangles $AEO$ and $B'PM$,

$$\frac{\Delta y}{b/2} = \frac{\overline{B'P}}{\overline{MP}}$$

$\Delta y = 1$, $b/2 = 10$, $\overline{B'P} = 10 - 9.46 = 0.54$ ft; then

$$\overline{MP} = \frac{0.54 \times 10}{1} = 5.40 \text{ ft}$$

$G$ is 7.0 ft from the bottom; hence

$$\overline{GP} = 7.00 - 3.03 = 3.97 \text{ ft}$$

and

$$\overline{MG} = \overline{MP} - \overline{GP} = 5.40 - 3.97 = 1.43 \text{ ft}$$

The scow is stable since $\overline{MG}$ is positive; the righting moment is

$$W\overline{GM} \sin \theta = 225 \times 2000 \times 1.43 \times \frac{1}{\sqrt{101}} = 64{,}000 \text{ lb-ft}$$

*nonprismatic cross sections*

For a floating object of variable cross section, such as a ship (Fig. 2.28$a$), a convenient formula may be developed for determination of metacentric height for very small angles of rotation $\theta$. The horizontal shift in center of buoyancy $r$ (Fig. 2.28$b$) is determined by the change in buoyant forces due to the wedge being submerged, which causes an upward force on the left, and by the other wedge decreasing the buoyant force by an equal amount $\Delta F_B$ on the right. The force system, consisting of the original

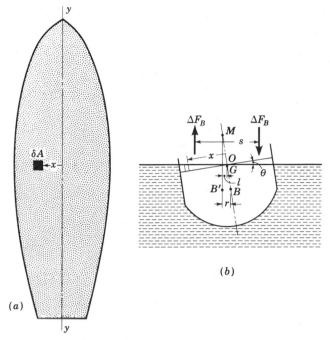

**Fig. 2.28**  Stability relations in body of variable cross section.

buoyant force at $B$ and the couple $\Delta F_B \times s$ due to the wedges, must have as resultant the equal buoyant force at $B'$.  With moments about $B$ to determine the shift $r$,

$$\Delta F_B \times s = Wr \tag{2.8.1}$$

The amount of the couple may be determined with moments about $O$, the center line of the body at the liquid surface.  For an element of area $\delta A$ on the horizontal section through the body at the liquid surface, an element of volume of the wedge is $x\theta\,\delta A$; the buoyant force due to this element is $\gamma x\theta\,\delta A$; and its moment about $O$ is $\gamma\theta x^2\,\delta A$, in which $\theta$ is the small angle of tip in radians.  By integrating over the complete original horizontal area at the liquid surface, the couple is determined to be

$$\Delta F_B \times s = \gamma\theta \int_A x^2\,dA = \gamma\theta I \tag{2.8.2}$$

in which $I$ is the moment of inertia of the area about the axis $yy$ (Fig. 2.28$a$).  Substitution into Eq. (2.8.1) produces

$$\gamma\theta I = Wr = \mathcal{U}\gamma r$$

in which $\mathcal{U}$ is the total volume of liquid displaced.

Since $\theta$ is very small,

$$\overline{MB} \sin \theta = \overline{MB}\theta = r$$

or

$$\overline{MB} = \frac{r}{\theta} = \frac{I}{\mathrm{v}}$$

The metacentric height is then

$$\overline{MG} = \overline{MB} \mp \overline{GB}$$

or

$$\overline{MG} = \frac{I}{\mathrm{v}} \mp \overline{GB} \tag{2.8.3}$$

The minus sign is used if $G$ is above $B$, the plus sign if $G$ is below $B$.

**example 2.13** A ship displacing 1000 tons has the horizontal cross section at water line shown in Fig. 2.29. Its center of buoyancy is 6.0 ft below water surface, and its center of gravity is 1.0 ft below water surface.

**Fig. 2.29** Horizontal cross section of ship at water line.

**Fig. 2.30**   Cube floating in liquid.

Determine its metacentric height for rolling (about $yy$-axis) and for pitching (about $xx$-axis).

$$\overline{GB} = 5.0 \text{ ft} \qquad \upsilon = \frac{1000 \times 2000}{62.4} = 32{,}100 \text{ ft}^3$$

$$I_{yy} = \tfrac{1}{12} \times 80 \times (30)^3 + 4 \times \tfrac{1}{12} \times 20 \times (15)^3 = 202{,}500 \text{ ft}^4$$
$$I_{xx} = \tfrac{1}{12} \times 30 \times (80)^3 + 2 \times \tfrac{1}{36} \times 30 \times (20)^3 + 600 \times (46.67)^2$$
$$= 2{,}603{,}000 \text{ ft}^4$$

For rolling:

$$\overline{MG} - \frac{I}{\upsilon} - \overline{GB} = \frac{202{,}500}{32{,}100} \quad 5 = 1.32 \text{ ft}$$

For pitching:

$$\overline{MG} = \frac{I}{\upsilon} - \overline{GB} = \frac{2{,}603{,}000}{32{,}100} - 5 = 76.2 \text{ ft}$$

**example 2.14**   A homogeneous cube of specific gravity $S_c$ floats in a liquid of specific gravity $S$.   Find the range of specific-gravity ratios $S_c/S$ for it to float with sides vertical.

In Fig. 2.30, $b$ is the length of one edge of the cube.   The depth of submergence $z$ is determined by application of the buoyant-force equation.

$$b^3 \gamma S_c = b^2 z \gamma S$$

in which $\gamma$ is the specific weight of water.   Solving for depth of submergence,

$$z = b \frac{S_c}{S}$$

The center of buoyancy is $z/2$ from the bottom, and the center of gravity

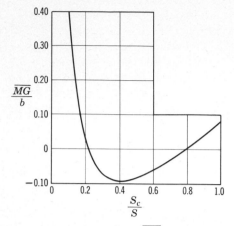

**Fig. 2.31** Plot of $S_c/S$ vs. $\overline{MG}/b$.

is $b/2$ from the bottom. Hence

$$\overline{GB} = \frac{b-z}{2} = \frac{b}{2}\left(1 - \frac{S_c}{S}\right)$$

After applying Eq. (2.8.3),

$$\overline{MG} = \frac{I}{\text{℧}} - \overline{GB} = \frac{1}{12}\frac{b \times b^3}{zb^2} - \frac{b-z}{2}$$

or

$$\overline{MG} = \frac{b}{12}\frac{S}{S_c} - \frac{b}{2}\left(1 - \frac{S_c}{S}\right)$$

When $\overline{MG}$ equals zero, $S_c/S = 0.212, 0.788$. Substitution shows that $\overline{MG}$ is positive for

$$0 < \frac{S_c}{S} < 0.212 \qquad 0.788 < \frac{S_c}{S} < 1.0$$

Figure 2.31 is a graph of $\overline{MG}/b$ vs. $S_c/S$.

## 2.9 relative equilibrium

In fluid statics the variation of pressure is simple to compute owing to the absence of shear stresses. For fluid motion such that no layer moves relative to an adjacent layer, the shear stress is also zero throughout the fluid.   A fluid with a translation at uniform velocity still follows the laws of static variation of pressure.   When a fluid is being accelerated so that no layer moves relative to an adjacent one, i.e., when the fluid moves as if it were a solid, no shear stresses occur and variation in pressure can be determined by writing the equation of motion for an appropriate free body.   Two cases are of interest, a uniform linear acceleration and a uniform rotation about a vertical axis.   When moving thus, the fluid is said to be in *relative equilibrium*.

Although relative equilibrium is not a fluid statics phenomenon, it is placed here because of the similarity of the relationships.

*uniform linear acceleration*

A liquid in an open vessel is given a uniform linear acceleration **a** as in Fig. 2.32.   After some time the liquid adjusts to the acceleration so that it moves as a solid; i.e., the distance between any two fluid particles remains fixed, and hence no shear stresses occur.

By selecting a cartesian-coordinate system with $y$ vertically upward and $x$ such that the acceleration vector **a** is in the $xy$-plane, the $z$-axis is normal to **a**, and there is no acceleration component in the $z$-direction.   An element of fluid in the form of a small rectangular parallelepiped having edges $\delta x$, $\delta y$, $\delta z$ parallel to the coordinate axes is taken as a free body, Fig. 2.33.   The center of the element is at $(x,y,z)$, and the pressure there is $p$.   The rate of change of $p$ with respect to $x$, $y$, and $z$ is desired and is first obtained for the element.   Integration then yields the pressure variation throughout the fluid.   By writing the equation of motion for the $x$-direction first

$$\Sigma f_x = ma_x$$

$$\left(p - \frac{\partial p}{\partial x}\frac{\delta x}{2}\right)\delta y\,\delta z - \left(p + \frac{\partial p}{\partial x}\frac{\delta x}{2}\right)\delta y\,\delta z = \frac{\gamma}{g}\,\delta x\,\delta y\,\delta z\,a_x$$

**Fig. 2.32** Acceleration with free surface.

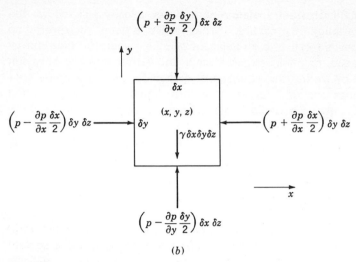

**Fig. 2.33**  Uniform linear acceleration of a fluid.

which reduces to

$$\frac{\partial p}{\partial x} = -\gamma \frac{a_x}{g}$$

when $\delta x$, $\delta y$, $\delta z$ are allowed to approach zero.   By following the same procedure for the $z$-direction, after remembering that $a_z = 0$ because of the choice of axes,

$$\frac{\partial p}{\partial z} = 0$$

In the vertical direction the weight of the element $\gamma\, \delta x\, \delta y\, \delta z$ is taken into account; thus

$$\left(p - \frac{\partial p}{\partial y}\frac{\delta y}{2}\right)\delta x\, \delta z - \left(p + \frac{\partial p}{\partial y}\frac{\delta y}{2}\right)\delta x\, \delta z - \gamma \delta x\, \delta y\, \delta z = \frac{\gamma}{g}\, \delta x\, \delta y\, \delta z\, a_y$$

Upon simplifying

$$\frac{\partial p}{\partial y} = -\gamma\left(1 + \frac{a_y}{g}\right)$$

Since $p$ is a function of position $(x,y,z)$ its total differential is (Appendix B)

$$dp = \frac{\partial p}{\partial x}\, dx + \frac{\partial p}{\partial y}\, dy + \frac{\partial p}{\partial z}\, dz$$

By substituting for the partial differentials

$$dp = -\gamma \frac{a_x}{g} dx - \gamma \left(1 + \frac{a_y}{g}\right) dy \qquad (2.9.1)$$

which may be integrated for an incompressible fluid,

$$p = -\gamma \frac{a_x}{g} x - \gamma \left(1 + \frac{a_y}{g}\right) y + c$$

To evaluate the constant of integration $c$, let $x = 0$, $y = 0$, $p = p_0$, then $c = p_0$ and

$$p = p_0 - \gamma \frac{a_x}{g} x - \gamma \left(1 + \frac{a_y}{g}\right) y \qquad (2.9.2)$$

For an isothermal gas $p/\gamma = p_0/\gamma_0$ with $p$ and $p_0$ in absolute units. Substitution into Eq. (2.9.1) yields, for $x = y = 0$, $p = p_0$, $\gamma = \gamma_0$,

$$\frac{p_0}{\gamma_0} \ln \frac{p}{p_0} = -\frac{a_x}{g} x - \left(1 + \frac{a_y}{g}\right) y$$

or

$$p - p_0 \exp\left[-\frac{xa_x/g + (1 + a_y/g)y}{p_0/\gamma_0}\right] \qquad (2.9.3)$$

The compressible equations apply only to closed containers.

When the accelerated incompressible fluid has a free surface, its equation is given by setting $p = 0$ in Eq. (2.9.2). After solving Eq. (2.9.2) for $y$

$$y = -\frac{a_x}{a_y + g} x + \frac{p_0 - p}{\gamma(1 + a_y/g)} \qquad (2.9.4)$$

The lines of constant pressure, $p = $ const, have the slope

$$-\frac{a_x}{a_y + g}$$

and are parallel to the free surface.  The $y$-intercept of the free surface is

$$\frac{p_0}{\gamma(1 + a_y/y)}$$

**example 2.15**  The tank in Fig. 2.34 is filled with oil, sp gr 0.8, and accelerated as shown.  There is a small opening in the tank at $A$.  Determine the pressure at $B$ and $C$ and the acceleration $a_x$ required to make the pressure at $B$ zero.

**Fig. 2.34**　Tank completely filled with liquid.

The planes of constant pressure have the slope

$$\tan \theta = \frac{a_x}{g} = \frac{16.1}{32.2} = 0.5$$

and at $A$ the pressure is zero.　The plane through $A$ passes 1 ft vertically above $B$; hence

$$p_B = 1 \times 62.4 \times 0.8 = 49.9 \text{ lb/ft}^2$$

Similarly, $C$ is vertically below the zero pressure plane a distance 4.75 ft, and

$$p_C = 4.75 \times 62.4 \times 0.8 = 237 \text{ lb/ft}^2$$

For zero pressure at $B$,

$$\tan \theta = \frac{4}{6} = \frac{a_x}{32.2}$$

and $a_x = \frac{2}{3} \times 32.2 = 21.47 \text{ ft/sec}^2$.

**example 2.16**　A cubical box, 2 ft on a side, half filled with oil, sp gr 0.90, is accelerated along an inclined plane at an angle of 30° with the horizontal, as shown in Fig. 2.35.　Find the slope of free surface and the pressure along the bottom.

In the coordinate system as indicated in the figure,

$$a_x = 8.05 \cos 30° = 6.98 \text{ ft/sec}^2$$

and

$$a_y = 8.05 \sin 30° = 4.02 \text{ ft/sec}^2$$

The slope of the free surface, from Eq. (2.9.4), is

$$-\frac{a_x}{a_y + g} = -\frac{6.98}{4.02 + 32.2} = -0.192$$

Since $\tan^{-1} 0.192 = 10°52'$ the free surface is inclined $40°52'$ to the bottom of the box.   The depth parallel to a side is less on the right-hand side by $2 \tan 40°52'$ or 1.73 ft.   If $s$ be the distance of $A$ from the inclined plane, then from the known liquid volume,

$$4\left(\frac{1.73}{2} + s\right) = 4 \text{ ft}^3$$

or $s = 0.135$.   The $xy$-coordinates of $A$ are

$$x = 2 \cos 30° - 0.135 \sin 30° = 1.665 \text{ ft}$$

and

$$y = 2 \sin 30° + 0.135 \cos 30° = 1.117 \text{ ft}$$

By substitution in Eq. (2.9.2), the pressure $p_0$ at the origin is obtained,

$$0 = p_0 - 0.9 \times 62.4 \times 6.98 \times \frac{1.665}{32.2} - 0.9 \times 62.4 \left(1 + \frac{4.02}{32.2}\right) 1.117$$

or

$$p_0 = 90.73 \text{ lb/ft}^2$$

Let $t$ be the distance along the bottom from the origin; then $x = 0.866t$, $y = 0.5t$ for the bottom.   By using Eq. (2.9.2) again

$$p = 90.73 - 42.07t$$

which is the pressure $t$ feet from 0 along the bottom.

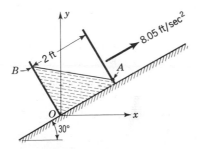

**Fig.   2.35** Uniform   acceleration along an inclined plane.

**Fig. 2.36** Rotation of fluid about a vertical axis.

*uniform rotation about a vertical axis*

Rotation of a fluid, moving as a solid, about an axis is called *forced-vortex* motion. Every particle of fluid has the same angular velocity. This motion is to be distinguished from *free-vortex* motion, where each particle moves in a circular path with a speed varying inversely as the distance from the center. Free-vortex motion is discussed in Chaps. 7 and 9. A liquid in a container, when rotated about a vertical axis at constant angular velocity, moves as a solid after some time interval. No shear stresses exist in the liquid and the only acceleration that occurs is directed radially inward toward the axis of rotation. The equation of motion in the vertical direction on a free body shows that hydrostatic conditions prevail along any vertical line; hence, the pressure at any point in the liquid is given by the product of specific weight and vertical distance from the free surface. In equation form, Fig. 2.36,

$$\frac{\partial p}{\partial y} = -\gamma$$

In the equation of motion tangent to the circular path of a particle, the acceleration is zero, and the pressure does not change along the path.

In the equation of motion in the radial (horizontal) direction (Fig. 2.36), with a free body of length $\delta r$ and cross-sectional area $\delta A$, if the pressure at $r$ be $p$, then, at the opposite face, the pressure is $p + (\partial p/\partial r)\,\delta r$. The acceleration is $-\omega^2 r$; hence

$$p\,\delta A - \left(p + \frac{\partial p}{\partial r}\,\delta r\right)\delta A = \frac{\delta A\,\delta r\,\gamma}{g}\,(-\omega^2 r)$$

After simplifying and dividing through by the volume of the element $\delta A \; \delta r$,

$$\frac{\partial p}{\partial r} = \frac{\gamma}{g} \omega^2 r$$

Since $p$ is a function of $y$ and $r$ only, the total differential $dp$ is

$$dp = \frac{\partial p}{\partial y} dy + \frac{\partial p}{\partial r} dr$$

By substituting for $\partial p / \partial y$ and $\partial p / \partial r$

$$dp = -\gamma \, dy + \frac{\gamma}{g} \omega^2 r \, dr \qquad (2.9.5)$$

For a liquid ($\gamma \approx$ const) integration yields

$$p = \frac{\gamma}{g} \omega^2 \frac{r^2}{2} - \gamma y + c$$

in which $c$ is the constant of integration.   If the value of pressure at the origin ($r = 0$, $y = 0$) be $p_0$, then $c = p_0$, and

$$p = p_0 + \gamma \frac{\omega^2 r^2}{2g} - \gamma y \; . \qquad (2.9.6)$$

When the particular horizontal plane ($y = 0$) for which $p_0 = 0$ is selected and Eq. (2.9.6) is divided by $\gamma$,

$$h = \frac{p}{\gamma} = \frac{\omega^2 r^2}{2g} \qquad (2.9.7)$$

which shows that the head, or vertical depth, varies as the square of the radius.   The surfaces of equal pressure are paraboloids of revolution.

When a free surface occurs in a container that is being rotated, the fluid volume underneath the paraboloid of revolution is the original fluid volume.   The shape of the paraboloid depends only upon the angular velocity $\omega$.

For the case of a circular cylinder rotating about its axis (Fig. 2.37) the rise of liquid from its vertex to the wall of the cylinder is, from Eq. (2.9.7), $\omega^2 r_0^2 / 2g$.   Since a paraboloid of revolution has a volume equal to one-half its circumscribing cylinder, the volume of the liquid above the horizontal plane through the vertex is

$$\pi r_0^2 \times \frac{1}{2} \frac{\omega^2 r_0^2}{2g}$$

When the liquid is at rest, this liquid is also above the plane through the

**Fig. 2.37** Rotation of circular cylinder about its axis.

vertex, to a uniform depth of

$$\frac{1}{2}\frac{\omega^2 r_0^2}{2g}$$

Hence, the liquid rises along the walls the same amount as the center drops,
thereby permitting the vertex to be located when $\omega$, $r_0$, and depth before
rotation are given.

**example 2.17**    A liquid, sp gr 1.2, is rotated at 200 rpm about a vertical axis.
At one point $A$ in the fluid 2 ft from the axis, the pressure is 10 psi.    What
is the pressure at a point $B$, 4 ft higher than $A$ and 3 ft from the axis?
   When Eq. (2.9.6) is written for the two points,

$$p_A = p_0 + \gamma\,\frac{\omega^2 r_A^2}{2g} - \gamma y \qquad p_B = p_0 + \gamma\,\frac{\omega^2 r_B^2}{2g} - \gamma(y + 4)$$

Then   $\omega = 200 \times 2\pi/60 = 20.95$   rad/sec,   $\gamma = 1.2 \times 62.4 = 74.8$   lb/ft³,
$r_A = 2$ ft, $r_B = 3$ ft, and $p_A = 1440$ lb/ft².    When the second equation is
subtracted from the first and the values are substituted,

$$p_A - p_B = 4\gamma + \frac{\gamma\omega^2}{2g}(r_A^2 - r_B^2)$$

and

$$1440 - p_B = 299 + \frac{74.8}{64.4}(20.95)^2(2^2 - 3^2)$$

Hence, $p_B = 3691$ lb/ft², or 25.6 psi.

If a closed container with no free surface, or with a partially exposed free surface, is rotated uniformly about some vertical axis, an *imaginary* free surface can be constructed, consisting of a paraboloid of revolution of shape given by Eq. (2.9.7). The vertical distance from any point in the fluid to this free surface is the pressure head at the point.

For an isothermal gas $\gamma = p\gamma_0/p_0$. Equation (2.9.5) becomes

$$\frac{p_0}{\gamma_0}\frac{dp}{p} = -dy + \frac{\omega^2 r}{g}\,dr$$

After integration, for $p = p_0$, $y = 0$, $r = 0$,

$$\frac{p_0}{\gamma_0}\ln\frac{p}{p_0} = -y + \frac{\omega^2 r^2}{2g}$$

$p$ and $p_0$ must be in absolute pressure units for the compressible case.

**example 2.18**   A straight tube 4 ft long, closed at the bottom and filled with water, is inclined 30° with the vertical and rotated about a vertical axis through its midpoint 8.02 rad/sec. Draw the paraboloid of zero pressure, and determine the pressure at the bottom and mid-point of the tube.

In Fig. 2.38, the zero-pressure paraboloid passes through point $A$. If the origin is taken at the vertex, that is, $p_0 - 0$, Eq. (2.9.7) becomes

$$h = \frac{\omega^2 r^2}{2g} \frac{(8.02)^2}{64.4} (2 \sin 30°)^2 = 1.0 \text{ ft}$$

**Fig. 2.38** Rotation of inclined tube of liquid about a vertical axis.

which locates the vertex at $O$, 1.0 ft below $A$.    The pressure at the bottom of the tube is $\gamma \times \overline{CD}$, or

4 cos 30° × 62.4 = 216 lb/ft²

At the mid-point, $\overline{OB}$ = 0.732 ft, and

$p_B$ = 0.732 × 62.4 = 45.6 lb/ft²

*fluid pressure forces in relative equilibrium*

The magnitude of the force acting on a plane area in contact with a fluid accelerating as a rigid body may be obtained by integration over the surface,

$$F = \int p \, dA$$

The nature of the acceleration and orientation of the surface governs the particular variation of $p$ over the surface.    When the pressure varies linearly over the plane surface (linear acceleration), the magnitude of force is given by the product of pressure at the centroid and area since the volume of the pressure prism is given by $p_G A$.    For nonlinear distributions the magnitude and line of action may be found by integration.

**problems**

**2.1**    Prove that the pressure is the same in all directions at a point in a static fluid for the three-dimensional case.

**2.2**    The container of Fig. 2.39 holds water and air as shown.    What is the pressure at $A$, $B$, $C$, and $D$ in pounds per square foot?

**Fig. 2.39**

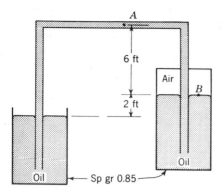

**Fig. 2.40**

**2.3**   The tube in Fig. 2.40 is filled with oil.   Determine the pressure at $A$ and $B$ in feet of water.

**2.4**   Calculate the pressure at $A$, $B$, $C$, and $D$ of Fig. 2.41 in pounds per square inch.

**2.5**   Derive the equations that give the pressure and density at any elevation in a static gas when conditions are known at one elevation and the temperature gradient $\beta$ is known.

**2.6**   By a limiting process as $\beta \rightarrow 0$, derive the isothermal case from the results of Prob. 2.5.

**2.7**   By use of the results of Prob. 2.5, determine the pressure and density at 5000 ft elevation when $p = 14.5$ psia, $t = 68°F$, and $\beta = -0.003°F/ft$ at elevation 1000 ft for air.

**2.8**   For isothermal air at 20°F, determine the pressure and density at 10,000 ft when the pressure is 15 psia at sea level.

**2.9**   In isothermal air at 80°F what is the vertical distance for reduction of density by 10 per cent?

**Fig. 2.41**

**Fig. 2.42**

**2.10** Express a pressure of 8 psi in: (a) inches of mercury, (b) feet of water, (c) feet of acetylene tetrabromide, sp gr 2.94.

**2.11** A bourdon gage reads 2 psi suction, and the barometer is 29.5 in. mercury. Express the pressure in six other customary ways.

**2.12** Express 3 atmospheres in feet of water gage. Barometer reading 29.2 in.

**2.13** Bourdon gage $A$ inside a pressure tank reads 12 psi. Another bourdon gage $B$ outside the pressure tank, connected with the tank, reads 20 psi, and an aneroid barometer reads 30 in. mercury. What is the absolute pressure measured by $A$ in inches of mercury? See Fig. 2.42.

**2.14** Determine the heights of columns of water; kerosene, sp gr 0.83; and acetylene tetrabromide, sp gr 2.94, equivalent to 18 in. mercury.

**2.15** For a reading $h = 20$ in. in Fig. 2.6a determine the pressure at $A$ in pounds per square inch. The liquid has a specific gravity of 1.90.

**2.16** Determine the reading $h$ in Fig. 2.6b for $p_A = 3.0$ psi suction if the liquid is kerosene, sp gr 0.83.

**2.17** For $h = 8$ in. in Fig. 2.6b and barometer reading 29 in., with water the liquid, find $p_A$ in feet of water absolute.

**2.18** In Fig. 2.6c $S_1 = 0.86$, $S_2 = 1.0$, $h_2 = 8.3$ in., $h_1 = 17$ in. Find $p_A$ in inches of mercury gage. If the barometer reading is 29.5 in., what is $p_A$ in feet of water absolute?

**2.19** Gas is contained in vessel $A$ of Fig. 2.6c. With water the manometer fluid and $h_1 = 5$ in., determine the pressure at $A$ in inches of mercury.

**2.20** In Fig. 2.7a $S_1 = 1.0$, $S_2 = 0.95$, $S_3 = 1.0$, $h_1 = h_2 = 1.0$ ft, and $h_3 = 3.0$ ft. Compute $p_A - p_B$ in inches of water.

**2.21** In Prob. 2.20 find the gage difference $h_2$ for $p_A - p_B = -10$ in. water.

**2.22** In Fig. 2.7b $S_1 = S_3 = 0.83$, $S_2 = 13.6$, $h_1 = 16$ in., $h_2 = 8$ in., and $h_3 = 12$ in. (a) Find $p_A$ if $p_B = 10$ psi. (b) For $p_A = 20$ psia and a barometer reading of 29.0 in. find $p_B$ in feet of water gage.

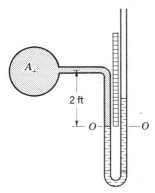

**Fig. 2.43**

**2.23** Find the gage difference $h_2$ in Prob. 2.22 for $p_A = p_B$.

**2.24** In Fig. 2.43, $A$ contains water and the manometer fluid has a specific gravity of 2.94. When the left meniscus is at zero on the scale, $p_A = 3$ in. water. Find the reading of the right meniscus for $p_A = 1$ psi with no adjustment of the U-tube or scale.

**2.25** The Empire State Building is 1250 ft high. What is the pressure difference in pounds per square inch of a water column of the same height?

**2.26** What is the pressure at a point 50 ft below the free surface in a fluid that has a variable density in slugs given by $\rho = 1.9 + ah$, in which $a = 0.01$ slug/ft$^4$ and $h$ is the distance in feet measured from the free surface?

**2.27** A vertical gas pipe in a building contains gas, $\rho = 0.002$ slug/ft$^3$ and $p = 3.0$ in. water gage in the basement. At the top of the building 800 ft higher, determine the gas pressure in inches water gage for two cases: $(a)$ gas assumed incompressible and $(b)$ gas assumed isothermal. Barometric pressure 34 ft water; $t = 70°$F.

**2.28** In Fig. 2.8 determine $R$, the gage difference for a difference in gas pressure of 1 in. water. $\gamma_2 = 62.4$; $\gamma_3 = 65.5$; $a/A = 0.01$.

**2.29** The inclined manometer of Fig. 2.9 reads zero when $A$ and $B$ are at the same pressure. The diameter of reservoir is 2.0 in., and that of the inclined tube $\frac{1}{4}$ in. For $\theta = 30°$, gage fluid sp gr 0.832, find $p_A - p_B$ in pounds per square inch as a function of gage reading $R$ in feet.

**2.30** Determine the weight $W$ that can be sustained by the 100-lb force acting on the piston of Fig. 2.44.

**2.31** Neglecting the weight of the container (Fig. 2.45), find $(a)$ the force tending to lift the circular top $CD$ and $(b)$ the compressive load on the pipe wall at $A$–$A$.

**Fig. 2.44**

**2.32**   Find the force of oil on the top surface $CD$ of Fig. 2.45 if the liquid level in the open pipe is reduced by 4.0 ft.

**2.33**   The container shown in Fig. 2.46 has a circular cross section.   Determine the upward force on the surface of the cone frustum $ABCD$.   What is the downward force on the plane $EF$?   Is this force equal to the weight of the fluid?   Explain.

**2.34**   The cylindrical container of Fig. 2.47 weighs 100 lb when empty.   It is filled with water and supported on the piston.   What force is exerted on the upper end of the cylinder?   If an additional 150-lb weight were placed on the cylinder, how much would the water force against the top of the cylinder be increased?

**2.35**   A barrel 2 ft in diameter filled with water has a vertical pipe of 0.50 in. diameter attached to the top.   Neglecting compressibility, how many

**Fig. 2.45**

2 ft diam

*B*   *C*

*A*

*D*

4 ft diam

Water

*E*   *F*

2 ft

1 ft

5 ft

**Fig. 2.46**

pounds of water must be added to the pipe to exert a force of 1000 lb on the top of the barrel?

**2.36** A right-angled triangular surface has a vertex in the free surface of a liquid (Fig. 2.48). Find the force on one side $(a)$ by integration and $(b)$ by formula.

**2.37** Determine the magnitude of the force acting on triangle $ABC$ of Fig. 2.49 $(a)$ by integration and $(b)$ by formula.

**2.38** Find the moment about $AB$ of the force acting on one side of the surface $ABC$ of Fig. 2.48.

**2.39** Find the moment about $AB$ of the force acting on one side of the surface $ABC$ of Fig. 2.49.

**2.40** Locate a horizontal line below $AB$ of Fig. 2.49 such that the magnitude of pressure force on the surface is equal above and below the line.

24 in. diam

*A*

Water

24 in.

*C*   *B*

1 in.²

**Fig. 2.47**

**Fig. 2.48**

**Fig. 2.49**

**2.41** Determine the force acting on one side of the vertical surface of Fig. 2.50.

**2.42** Calculate the force exerted by water on one side of the vertical annular area shown in Fig. 2.51.

**2.43** Determine the moment at $A$ required to hold the gate as shown in Fig. 2.52.

**2.44** If there is water on the other side of the gate (Fig. 2.52) up to $A$, determine the resultant force due to water on both sides of the gate, including its line of action.

**2.45** The shaft of the gate in Fig. 2.53 will fail at a moment of 100,000 lb-ft. Determine the maximum value of liquid depth $h$.

**Fig. 2.50**

**Fig. 2.51**

**Fig. 2.52**

**2.46** The dam of Fig. 2.54 has a strut $AB$ every 10 ft. Determine the compressive force in the strut, neglecting the weight of the dam.

**2.47** Locate the distance the pressure center is below the liquid surface in the triangular area $ABC$ of Fig. 2.49 by integration and by formula.

**2.48** By integration locate the pressure center horizontally in Fig. 2.49.

**Fig. 2.53**

**Fig. 2.54**

**2.49** By using the pressure prism, determine the resultant force and location for the triangle of Fig. 2.48.

**2.50** By integration, determine the pressure center for Fig. 2.48.

**2.51** Locate the pressure center for the annular area of Fig. 2.51.

**2.52** Locate the pressure center for the gate of Fig. 2.52.

**2.53** A vertical square area 5 by 5 ft is submerged in water with upper edge 2 ft below the surface. Locate a horizontal line on the surface of the square such that ($a$) the force on the upper portion equals the force on the lower portion and ($b$) the moment of force about the line due to the upper portion equals the moment due to the lower portion.

**2.54** An equilateral triangle with one edge in a water surface extends downward at a 45° angle. Locate the pressure center in terms of the length of a side $b$.

**2.55** In Fig. 2.53 develop the expression for $y_p$ in terms of $h$.

**2.56** Locate the pressure center of Fig. 2.50.

**2.57** Locate the pressure center for the vertical area of Fig. 2.55.

**2.58** Demonstrate the fact that the magnitude of the resultant force on a totally submerged plane area is unchanged if the area is rotated about an axis through its centroid.

**Fig. 2.55**

**Fig. 2.56**

**2.59** The gate of Fig. 2.56 weighs 300 lb/ft normal to the paper.   Its center of gravity is 1.5 ft from the left face and 2.0 ft above the lower face.   It is hinged at $O$.   Determine the water-surface position for the gate just to start to come up.   (Water surface is below the hinge.)

**2.60** Find $h$ of Prob. 2.59 for the gate just to come up to the vertical position shown.

**2.61** Determine the value of $h$ and the force against the stop when this force is a maximum for the gate of Prob. 2.59.

**2.62** Determine $y$ of Fig. 2.57 so that the flashboards will tumble when water reaches their top.

**2.63** Determine the hinge location $y$ of the rectangular gate of Fig. 2.58 so that it will open when the liquid surface is as shown.

**Fig. 2.57**

**Fig. 2.58**

**2.64** By use of the pressure prism, show that the pressure center approaches the centroid of an area as its depth of submergence is increased.

**2.65** (*a*) Find the magnitude and line of action of force on each side of the gate of Fig. 2.59. (*b*) Find the resultant force due to the liquid on both sides of the gate. (*c*) Determine $F$ to open the gate if it is uniform and weighs 6000 lb.

**2.66** For linear stress variation over the base of the dam of Fig. 2.60, (*a*) locate where the resultant crosses the base and (*b*) compute the maximum and minimum compressive stresses at the base. Neglect hydrostatic uplift.

**2.67** Work Prob. 2.66 with the addition that the hydrostatic uplift varies linearly from 60 ft at $A$ to zero at the toe of the dam.

**2.68** Find the moment $M$ at $O$ (Fig. 2.61) to hold the gate closed.

**Fig. 2.59**

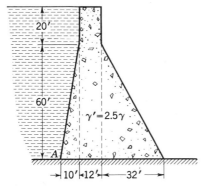

**Fig. 2.60**

**2.69**   The gate shown in Fig. 2.62 is in equilibrium.   Compute $W$, the weight of counterweight per foot of width, neglecting the weight of the gate. Is this gate in stable equilibrium?

**2.70**   The gate of Fig. 2.63 weighs 150 lb/ft normal to the page.   It is in equilibrium as shown.   Neglecting the weight of the arm and brace supporting the counterweight, ($a$) determine $W$ and ($b$) determine whether the gate is in stable equilibrium.   The weight is made of concrete, sp gr 2.50.

**2.71**   The plane gate (Fig. 2.64) weighs 500 lb per foot of length, with its center of gravity 6.0 ft from the hinge at $O$.   ($a$) Find $h$ as a function of $\theta$ for equilibrium of the gate.   ($b$) Is the gate in stable equilibrium for any values of $\theta$?

**2.72**   A 16-ft-diameter pressure pipe carries liquid at 150 psi.   What thickness pipe wall is required for maximum stress of 10,000 psi?

**2.73**   To obtain the same flow area, which pipe system requires the least steel: a single pipe or four pipes having half the diameter?   The maximum allowable pipe wall stress is the same in each case.

**Fig. 2.61**

**Fig. 2.62**

**2.74** A thin-walled hollow sphere 8 ft in diameter holds gas at 200 psi. For allowable stress of 8000 psi determine the minimum wall thickness.

**2.75** A cylindrical container 8 ft high and 4 ft in diameter provides for pipe tension with two hoops a foot from each end. When filled with water, what is the tension in each hoop due to the water?

**2.76** A 1-in.-diameter steel ball covers a $\frac{3}{4}$-in. hole in a pressure chamber where the pressure is 4000 psi. What force is required to lift the ball from the opening?

**Fig. 2.63**

**Fig. 2.64**

**Fig. 2.65**

**2.77**  If the horizontal component of force on a curved surface did *not* equal the force on a projection of the surface onto a vertical plane, what conclusions could you draw regarding the propulsion of a boat (Fig. 2.65)?

**2.78**  (*a*) Determine the horizontal component of force acting on the radial gate (Fig. 2.66) and its line of action.  (*b*) Determine the vertical component of force and its line of action.  (*c*) What force $F$ is required to open the gate, neglecting its weight?  (*d*) What is the moment about an axis normal to the paper and through point $O$?

**2.79**  Calculate the force $F$ required to hold the gate of Fig. 2.67 in a closed position $R = 2$ ft.

**2.80**  Calculate the force $F$ required to open or hold closed the gate of Fig. 2.67 when $R = 1.5$ ft.

**2.81**  What is $R$ of Fig. 2.67 for no force $F$ required to hold the gate closed or to open it?

**2.82**  Find the vertical component of force on the curved gate of Fig. 2.68, including its line of action.

**2.83**  What is the force on the surface whose trace is $OA$ of Fig. 2.50? The length normal to the paper is 10 ft.

**2.84**  A right circular cylinder with a diameter of 2 ft is illustrated in Fig. 2.69.  The pressure, in pounds per square foot, varies over the segment $ABC$ as $p = 2\rho(1 - 4 \sin^2 \theta) + 10$ due to the flow.  Calculate the force on $ABC$.

**Fig. 2.66**

Hinge

Gate 4 ft wide

Oil sp gr 0.80

$r = 2$ ft

$F$—

2 ft

Water

2 ft

$R$

$S = 3.0$

**Fig. 2.67**

$y$

$x = y^2/4$

$\gamma = 60$ lb/ft$^3$

4 ft

Gate 5 ft wide

$M$

$0$

$x$

**Fig. 2.68**

$A$

Cylinder 5 ft long

$\theta$

$B$

$C$

**Fig. 2.69**

**Fig. 2.70**

**2.85** If the pressure variation on the cylinder in Fig. 2.69 is $p = 2\rho \times [1 - 4(1 + \sin \theta)^2] + 10$, determine the force on the cylinder.

**2.86** Determine the moment $M$ to hold the gate of Fig. 2.68, neglecting its weight.

**2.87** Find the resultant force, including its line of action, acting on the outer surface of the first quadrant of a spherical shell of radius 2.0 ft with center at the origin.   Its center is 3 ft below the water surface.

**2.88** The volume of the ellipsoid given by $x^2/a^2 + y^2/b^2 + z^2/c^2 = 1$ is $4\pi abc/3$, and the area of the ellipse $x^2/a^2 + z^2/c^2 = 1$ is $\pi ac$.   Determine the vertical force on the surface given in Example 2.8.

**2.89** The log holds the water as shown in Fig. 2.70.   Determine (a) the force per foot pushing it against the dam, (b) the weight of the log per foot of length, and (c) its specific gravity.

**2.90** The cylinder of Fig. 2.71 is filled with liquid as shown.   Find (a) the horizontal component of force on $AB$ per foot of length, including its line of action, and (b) the vertical component of force on $AB$ per foot of length, including its line of action.

**Fig. 2.71**

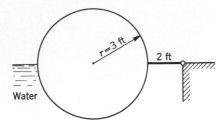

**Fig. 2.72**

**2.91** The cylinder gate of Fig. 2.72 is made up from a circular cylinder and a plate, hinged at the dam. The gate position is controlled by pumping water into or out of the cylinder. The center of gravity of the empty gate is on the line of symmetry 4 ft from the hinge. It is in equilibrium when empty in the position shown. How many cubic feet of water must be added per foot of cylinder to hold the gate in its position when the water surface is raised 3 ft?

**2.92** A hydrometer weighs 0.008 lb and has a stem 0.20 in. in diameter. Compute the distance between specific gravity markings 1.0 and 1.1.

**2.93** Design a hydrometer to read specific gravities in the range from 0.80 to 1.10 when the scale is to be 3 in. long.

**2.94** A sphere 1 ft in diameter, sp gr 1.4, is immersed in a liquid having a density varying with the depth $y$ below the surface given by $\rho = 2 + 0.1y$. Determine the equilibrium position of the sphere in the liquid.

**2.95** Repeat the calculations for Prob. 2.94 for a horizontal circular cylinder with a specific gravity of 1.4 and a diameter of 1 ft.

**2.96** A cube, 2 ft on an edge, has its lower half of specific gravity 1.4 and upper half of specific gravity 0.6. It is submerged into a two-layered fluid, the lower of specific gravity 1.2 and the upper of specific gravity 0.9. Determine the height of the top of the cube above the interface.

**2.97** Determine the density, specific volume, and volume of an object that weighs 3 lb in water and 4 lb in oil, sp gr 0.83.

**2.98** Two cubes, of the same size, 27 ft³, one of sp gr 0.80, the other of sp gr 1.1, are connected by a short wire and placed in water. What portion of the lighter cube is above the water surface, and what is the tension in the wire?

**2.99** In Fig. 2.73 the hollow triangular prism is in equilibrium as shown when $z = 1$ ft and $y = 0$. Find the weight of prism per foot of length and $z$ in terms of $y$ for equilibrium. Both liquids are water. Determine the value of $y$ for $z = 1.5$ ft.

**Fig. 2.73**

**2.100** How many pounds of concrete, $\gamma = 150$ lb/ft³, must be attached to a beam having a volume of 4 ft³ and specific gravity 0.65 to cause both to sink in water?

**2.101** Two beams, each 6 ft by 12 by 4 in., are attached at their ends and float as shown in Fig. 2.74. Determine the specific gravity of each beam.

**2.102** A wooden cylinder 24 in. in diameter, sp gr 0.50, has a concrete cylinder 2 ft long of the same diameter, sp gr 2.50, attached to one end. Determine the lengths of wooden cylinder for the system to float in stable equilibrium with axis vertical.

**2.103** What are the proportions $r_0/h$ of a right circular cylinder of specific gravity $S$ so that it will float in water with end faces horizontal in stable equilibrium?

**2.104** Will a beam 10 ft long with square cross section, sp gr 0.75, float in stable equilibrium in water with two sides horizontal?

**2.105** Determine the metacentric height of the torus shown in Fig. 2.75.

**Fig. 2.74**

**Fig. 2.75**

**Fig. 2.76**

**2.106**   Determine whether the thick-walled cylinder of Fig. 2.76 is stable in the position shown.

**2.107**   A spherical balloon 40 ft in diameter is open at the bottom and filled with hydrogen.   For barometer reading of 28 in. mercury and 80°F, what is the total weight of the balloon and the load to hold it stationary?

**2.108**   A tank of liquid $S = 0.86$ is accelerated uniformly in a horizontal direction so that the pressure decreases within the liquid 1 psi/ft in the direction of motion.   Determine the acceleration.

**2.109**   The free surface of a liquid makes an angle of 20° with the horizontal when accelerated uniformly in a horizontal direction.   What is the acceleration?

**2.110**   In Fig. 2.77, $a_x = 8.05$ ft/sec², $a_y = 0$.   Find the imaginary free liquid surface and the pressure at $B$, $C$, $D$, and $E$.

**2.111**   In Fig. 2.77, $a_x = 0$, $a_y = -16.1$ ft/sec².   Find the pressure at $B$, $C$, $D$, and $E$.

**Fig. 2.77**

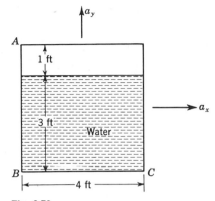

**Fig. 2.78**

**2.112**   In Fig. 2.77, $a_x = 8.05$ ft/sec$^2$, $a_y = 16.1$ ft/sec$^2$.   Find the imaginary free surface and the pressure at $B$, $C$, $D$, and $E$.

**2.113**   In Fig. 2.78, $a_x = 32.2$ ft/sec$^2$, $a_y = 0$.   Find the pressure at $A$, $B$, and $C$.

**2.114**   In Fig. 2.78, $a_x = 16.1$ ft/sec$^2$, $a_y = 16.1$ ft/sec$^2$.   Find the pressure at $A$, $B$, and $C$.

**2.115**   A circular cross-sectional tank of 6-ft depth and 4-ft diameter is filled with liquid and accelerated uniformly in a horizontal direction.   If one-third of the liquid spills out, determine the acceleration.

**2.116**   Derive an expression for pressure variation in a constant-temperature gas undergoing an acceleration $a_x$ in the $x$-direction.

**2.117**   The tube of Fig. 2.79 is filled with liquid, sp gr 2.40.   When accelerated to the right 8.05 ft/sec$^2$, draw the imaginary free surface and determine the pressure at $A$.   For $p_A = 8$ psi vacuum determine $a_x$.

**2.118**   A cubical box 3 ft on an edge, open at the top and half filled with water, is placed on an inclined plane making a 30° angle with the horizontal. The box alone weighs 100 lb and has a coefficient of friction with the plane

**Fig. 2.79**

of 0.30.   Determine the acceleration of the box and the angle the free water surface makes with the horizontal.

**2.119**   Show that the pressure is the same in all directions at a point in a liquid moving as a solid.

**2.120**   A closed box contains two immiscible liquids.   When accelerated uniformly in the $x$-direction, prove that the interface and zero pressure surface are parallel.

**2.121**   Verify the statement made in Sec. 2.9 on uniform rotation about a vertical axis that when a fluid rotates in the manner of a solid body, no shear stresses exist in the fluid.

**2.122**   A vessel containing liquid, sp gr 1.2, is rotated about a vertical axis. The pressure at one point 2 ft radially from the axis is the same as at another point 4 ft from the axis and with elevation 2 ft higher.   Calculate the rotational speed.

**2.123**   The U-tube of Fig. 2.79 is rotated about a vertical axis 6 in. to the right of $A$ at such a speed that the pressure at $A$ is zero gage.   What is the rotational speed?

**2.124**   Locate the vertical axis of rotation and the speed of rotation of the U-tube of Fig. 2.79 so that the pressure of liquid at the mid-point of the U-tube and at $A$ are both zero.

**2.125**   An incompressible fluid of density $\rho$ moving as a solid rotates at speed $\omega$ about an axis inclined at $\theta°$ with the vertical.   Knowing the pressure at one point in the fluid, how do you find the pressure at any other point?

**2.126**   A right circular cylinder of radius $r_0$ and height $h_0$ with axis vertical is open at the top and filled with liquid.   At what speed must it rotate so that half the area of the bottom is exposed?

**2.127**   A liquid rotating about a *horizontal* axis as a solid has a pressure of 10 psi at the axis.   Determine the pressure variation along a vertical line through the axis for density $\rho$ and speed $\omega$.

**2.128**   Determine the equation for the surfaces of constant pressure for the situation described in Prob. 2.127.

**2.129**   Prove by integration that a paraboloid of revolution has a volume equal to half its circumscribing cylinder.

**2.130**   A tank containing two immiscible liquids is rotated about a vertical axis.   Prove that the interface has the same shape as the zero pressure surface.

**2.131**   A hollow sphere of radius $r_0$ is filled with liquid and rotated about its vertical axis at speed $\omega$.   Locate the circular line of maximum pressure.

**2.132**  A gas following the law $p\rho^{-n} = $ const is rotated about a vertical axis as a solid.   Derive an expression for pressure in a radial direction for speed $\omega$, pressure $p_0$, and density $\rho_0$ at a point on the axis.

**2.133**  A vessel containing water is rotated about a vertical axis with an angular velocity of 50 rad/sec.   At the same time the container has a downward acceleration of 16.1 ft/sec².   What is the equation for a surface of constant pressure?

**2.134**  The U-tube of Fig. 2.79 is rotated about a vertical axis through $A$ at such a speed that the water in the tube begins to vaporize at the closed end above $A$, which is at 70°F.   What is the angular velocity?   What would happen if the angular velocity were to be increased?

**2.135**  A cubical box 4 ft on an edge is open at the top and filled with water. When accelerated upward 8.05 ft/sec², find the magnitude of water force on one side of the box.

**2.136**  A cube 1 ft on an edge is filled with liquid, sp gr 0.65, and is accelerated downward 8.05 ft/sec².   Find the resultant force on one side of the cube due to liquid pressure.

**2.137**  Find the force on side $OB$ of Fig. 2.35 for the situation described in Example 2.16.

**2.138**  A cylinder 2 ft in diameter and 6 ft long is accelerated uniformly along its axis in a horizontal direction 16.1 ft/sec².   It is filled with liquid, $\gamma = 50$ lb/ft³, and has a pressure along its axis of 10 psi before acceleration commences.   Find the net force exerted against the liquid in the cylinder.

**2.139**  A closed cube, 1 ft on an edge, has a small opening at the center of its top.   When it is filled with water and rotated uniformly about a vertical axis through its center at $\omega$ rad/sec, find the force on a side due to the water in terms of $\omega$.

**2.140**  The normal stress is the same in all directions at a point in a fluid

(a)  *only* when the fluid is frictionless
(b)  *only* when the fluid is frictionless and incompressible
(c)  *only* when the fluid has zero viscosity and is at rest
(d)  when there is no motion of one fluid layer relative to an adjacent layer
(e)  regardless of the motion of one fluid layer relative to an adjacent layer

**2.141**  The pressure in the air space above an oil (sp gr 0.75) surface in a tank is 2 psi.   The pressure 5.0 ft below the surface of the oil, in feet of water, is

(a)  7.0      (b)  8.37      (c)  9.62      (d)  11.16      (e)  none of these
answers

**2.142**   The pressure, in inches of mercury gage, equivalent to 8 in. of water plus 6 in. manometer fluid, sp gr 2.94, is

($a$) 1.03      ($b$) 1.88      ($c$) 2.04      ($d$) 3.06      ($e$) none of these answers

**2.143**   The differential equation for pressure variation in a static fluid may be written ($y$ measured vertically upward)

($a$) $dp = -\gamma\, dy$      ($b$) $d\rho = -\gamma\, dy$      ($c$) $dy = -\rho\, dp$
($d$) $dp = -\rho\, dy$      ($e$) $dp = -y\, d\rho$

**2.144**   In an isothermal atmosphere, the pressure

($a$) remains constant
($b$) decreases linearly with elevation
($c$) increases exponentially with elevation
($d$) varies in the same way as the density
($e$) and density remain constant

**2.145**   Select the correct statement.

($a$) Local atmospheric pressure is always below standard atmospheric pressure.
($b$) Local atmospheric pressure depends upon elevation of locality only.
($c$) Standard atmospheric pressure is the mean local atmospheric pressure at sea level.
($d$) A barometer reads the difference between local and standard atmospheric pressure.
($e$) Standard atmospheric pressure is 34 in. mercury abs.

**2.146**   Select the three pressures that are equivalent.

($a$) 10.0 psi, 23.1 ft water, 4.91 in. mercury
($b$) 10.0 psi, 4.33 ft water, 20.3 in. mercury
($c$) 10.0 psi, 20.3 ft water, 23.1 in. mercury
($d$) 4.33 psi, 10.0 ft water, 20.3 in. mercury
($e$) 4.33 psi, 10.0 ft water, 8.83 in. mercury

**2.147**   2 psi suction, with barometer reading 28 in. mercury, is the same as

($a$) 4.08 in. mercury abs        ($b$) 4.08 in. mercury
($c$) 4.62 ft water vacuum        ($d$) 32.08 in. mercury abs
($e$) 36.42 ft water abs

**2.148**   With the barometer reading 29 in. mercury, 7.0 psia is equivalent to

($a$) 0.476 atmosphere        ($b$) 0.493 atmosphere
($c$) 7.9 psi suction        ($d$) 7.7 psi
($e$) 13.8 in. mercury abs

**2.149** In Fig. 2.6$b$ the liquid is oil, sp gr 0.80. When $h = 2$ ft, the pressure at $A$ may be expressed as

($a$) $-1.6$ ft water abs         ($b$) 1.6 ft water
($c$) 1.6 ft water suction       ($d$) 2.5 ft water vacuum
($e$) none of these answers

**2.150** In Fig. 2.6$c$ air is contained in the pipe, water is the manometer liquid, and $h_1 = 2.0$ ft, $h_2 = 1.0$ ft. The pressure at $A$ is

($a$) 2.0 ft water abs         ($b$) 2.0 ft water vacuum
($c$) 1.0 ft water             ($d$) 0.866 psi
($e$) 0.433 psi

**2.151** In Fig. 2.7$a$, $h_1 = 2.0$ ft, $h_2 = 1.0$ ft, $h_3 = 4.0$ ft, $S_1 = 0.80$, $S_2 = 0.65$, $S_3 = 1.0$. Then $h_B - h_A$ in feet of water is

($a$) $-3.05$    ($b$) $-1.75$    ($c$) 3.05    ($d$) 6.25    ($e$) none of these answers

**2.152** In Fig. 2.7$b$, $h_1 = 1.5$ ft, $h_2 = 1.0$ ft, $h_3 = 2.0$ ft, $S_1 = 1.0$, $S_2 = 3.0$, $S_3 = 1.0$. Then $p_A - p_B$ in pounds per square inch is

($a$) $-1.08$    ($b$) 1.52    ($c$) 8.08    ($d$) 218    ($e$) none of these answers

**2.153** A mercury-water manometer has a gage difference of 2.0 ft (difference in elevation of menlsci). The difference in pressure, measured in feet of water, is

($a$) 2.0    ($b$) 25.2    ($c$) 26.2    ($d$) 27.2    ($e$) none of these answers

**2.154** In the inclined manometer of Fig. 2.9 the reservoir is so large that its surface may be assumed to remain at a fixed elevation. $\theta = 30°$. Used as a simple manometer for measuring air pressure, it contains water, and $R = 1.2$ ft. The pressure at $A$, in inches of water, is

($a$) 7.2    ($b$) 7.2 vacuum    ($c$) 12.5    ($d$) 14.4    ($e$) none of these answers

**2.155** A closed cubical box, 2 ft on each edge, is half filled with water, the other half being filled with oil, sp gr 0.75. When accelerated vertically upward 16.1 ft/sec$^2$, the pressure difference between bottom and top, in pounds per square foot, is

($a$) 187.2    ($b$) 163.8    ($c$) 109.0    ($d$) 54.6    ($e$) none of these answers

**2.156**   When the box of Prob. 2.155 is accelerated uniformly, in a horizontal direction parallel to one side, 16.1 ft/sec², the slope of the interface is

(a) 0      (b) $-\frac{1}{4}$      (c) $-\frac{1}{2}$      (d) $-1$      (e) none of these answers

**2.157**   When the minimum pressure in the box of Prob. 2.156 is zero gage, the maximum pressure in feet of water is

(a) 0.75      (b) 1.0      (c) 1.625      (d) 1.875      (e) 2.75

**2.158**   The magnitude of force on one side of a circular surface of unit area, with centroid 10 ft below a free water surface, is

(a) less than $10\gamma$
(b) dependent upon orientation of the area
(c) greater than $10\gamma$
(d) the product of $\gamma$ and the vertical distance from free surface to pressure center
(e) none of the above

**2.159**   A rectangular surface 3 by 4 ft has the lower 3-ft edge horizontal and 6 ft below a free oil surface, sp gr 0.80.   The surface is inclined 30° with the horizontal.   The force on one side of the surface is

(a) $38.4\gamma$      (b) $48\gamma$      (c) $51.2\gamma$      (d) $60\gamma$      (e) none of these answers

**2.160**   The pressure center of the surface of Prob. 2.159 is vertically below the liquid surface

(a) 10.133 ft      (b) 5.133 ft      (c) 5.067 ft      (d) 5.00 ft      (e) none of these answers

**2.161**   The pressure center is

(a) at the centroid of the submerged area
(b) the centroid of the pressure prism
(c) independent of the orientation of the area
(d) a point on the line of action of the resultant force
(e) always above the centroid of the area

**2.162**   What is the force exerted on the vertical annular area enclosed by concentric circles of radii 1.0 and 2.0 ft?   The center is 3.0 ft below a free water surface.   $\gamma$ = sp wt.

(a) $3\pi\gamma$      (b) $9\pi\gamma$      (c) $10.25\pi\gamma$      (d) $12\pi\gamma$      (e) none of these answers

**2.163**  The pressure center for the annular area of Prob. 2.162 is below the centroid of the area

(a) 0 ft      (b) 0.42 ft      (c) 0.44 ft      (d) 0.47 ft      (e) none of these answers

**2.164**  A vertical triangular area has one side in a free surface, with vertex downward.   Its altitude is $h$.   The pressure center is below the free surface

(a) $h/4$      (b) $h/3$      (c) $h/2$      (d) $2h/3$      (e) $3h/4$

**2.165**  A vertical gate 4 ft by 4 ft holds water with free surface at its top. The moment about the bottom of the gate is

(a) $42.7\gamma$      (b) $57\gamma$      (c) $64\gamma$      (d) $85.3\gamma$      (e) none of these answers

**2.166**  The magnitude of the resultant force acting on both sides of the gate (Fig. 2.80) is

(a) $768\gamma$      (b) $1593\gamma$      (c) $1810\gamma$      (d) $3820\gamma$      (e) none of these answers

**2.167**  The line of action of the resultant force on both sides of the gate in Fig. 2.80 is above the bottom of the gate

(a) 2.67 ft      (b) 3.33 ft      (c) 3.68 ft      (d) 4.00 ft.      (e) none of these answers

**2.168**  The horizontal component of force on a curved surface is equal to the

(a)  weight of liquid vertically above the curved surface
(b)  weight of liquid retained by the curved surface
(c)  product of pressure at its centroid and area
(d)  force on a vertical projection of the curved surface
(e)  scalar sum of all elemental horizontal components

**Fig. 2.80**

**2.169**  A pipe 16 ft in diameter is to carry water at 200 psi.   For an allowable tensile stress of 8000 psi, the thickness of pipe wall is

($a$)  1.2 in.      ($b$)  1.6 in.      ($c$)  2.4 in.      ($d$)  3.2 in.      ($e$)  none of these answers

**2.170**  The vertical component of pressure force on a submerged curved surface is equal to

($a$)  its horizontal component
($b$)  the force on a vertical projection of the curved surface
($c$)  the product of pressure at centroid and surface area
($d$)  the weight of liquid vertically above the curved surface
($e$)  none of the above answers

**2.171**  The vertical component of force on the quadrant of the cylinder $AB$ (Fig. 2.81) is

($a$)  $224\gamma$      ($b$)  $96.5\gamma$      ($c$)  $81\gamma$      ($d$)  $42.5\gamma$      ($e$)  none of these answers

**2.172**  The vertical component of force on the upper half of a horizontal right-circular cylinder, 3 ft in diameter and 10 ft long, filled with water, and with a pressure of 0.433 psi at the axis, is

($a$)  $-458$ lb      ($b$)  $-331$ lb      ($c$)  124.8 lb      ($d$)  1872 lb      ($e$)  none of these answers

**2.173**  A cylindrical wooden barrel is held together by hoops at top and bottom.   When the barrel is filled with liquid, the ratio of tension in the top hoop to tension in the bottom hoop, due to the liquid, is

($a$)  $\frac{1}{2}$      ($b$)  1      ($c$)  2      ($d$)  3      ($e$)  none of these answers

**2.174**  A 1-in. ID pipe with $\frac{1}{8}$-in. wall thickness carries water at 250 psi. The tensile stress in the pipe wall, in pounds per square inch, is

($a$)  125      ($b$)  250      ($c$)  500      ($d$)  2000      ($e$)  none of these answers

Water  3 ft
$A$
$r = 3$ ft
$B$   Surface 6 ft long

**Fig. 2.81**

**2.175**   A slab of wood 4 by 4 by 1 ft, sp gr 0.50, floats in water with a 400-lb load on it.   The volume of slab submerged, in cubic feet, is

(a) 1.6      (b) 6.4      (c) 8.0      (d) 14.4      (e) none of these answers

**2.176**   The line of action of the buoyant force acts through the

(a) center of gravity of any submerged body
(b) centroid of the volume of any floating body
(c) centroid of the displaced volume of fluid
(d) centroid of the volume of fluid vertically above the body
(e) centroid of the horizontal projection of the body

**2.177**   Buoyant force is

(a) the resultant force on a body due to the fluid surrounding it
(b) the resultant force acting on a floating body
(c) the force necessary to maintain equilibrium of a submerged body
(d) a nonvertical force for nonsymmetrical bodies
(e) equal to the volume of liquid displaced

**2.178**   A body floats in stable equilibrium

(a) when its metacentric height is zero
(b) *only* when its center of gravity is below its center of buoyancy
(c) when $\overline{GB} - I/\upsilon$ is positive and $G$ is above $B$
(d) when $I/\upsilon$ is positive
(e) when the metacenter is above the center of gravity

**2.179**   A closed cubical metal box 3 ft on an edge is made of uniform sheet and weighs 1200 lb.   Its metacentric height when placed in oil, sp gr 0.90, with sides vertical, is

(a) 0 ft      (b) −0.08 ft      (c) 0.62 ft      (d) 0.78 ft      (e) none of
      these answers

**2.180**   Liquid in a cylinder 10 ft long is accelerated horizontally $20g$ ft/sec² along the axis of the cylinder.   The difference in pressure intensities at the ends of the cylinder, in pounds per square foot, if $\gamma$ = sp wt of liquid, is

(a) $20\gamma$      (b) $200\gamma$      (c) $20g\gamma$      (d) $200\gamma/g$      (e) none of these
      answers

**2.181**   When a liquid rotates at constant angular velocity about a vertical axis as a rigid body, the pressure

(a) decreases as the square of the radial distance
(b) increases linearly as the radial distance
(c) decreases as the square of increase in elevation along any vertical line
(d) varies inversely as the elevation along any vertical line
(e) varies as the square of the radial distance

**2.182**    When a liquid rotates about a vertical axis as a rigid body so that points on the axis have the same pressure as points 2 ft higher and 2 ft from the axis, the angular velocity in radians per second is

(a) 8.02      (b) 11.34      (c) 64.4      (d) not determinable from data
    given      (e) none of these answers

**2.183**    A right-circular cylinder, open at the top, is filled with liquid, sp gr 1.2, and rotated about its vertical axis at such speed that half the liquid spills out.   The pressure at the center of the bottom is

(a) zero
(b) one-fourth its value when cylinder was full
(c) indeterminable; insufficient data
(d) greater than a similar case with water as liquid
(e) none of these answers

**2.184**    A forced vortex

(a) turns in an opposite direction to a free vortex
(b) always occurs in conjunction with a free vortex
(c) has the velocity decreasing with the radius
(d) occurs when fluid rotates as a solid
(e) has the velocity decreasing inversely with the radius

# 3

# fluid-flow concepts and
# basic equations

The statics of fluids, treated in the preceding chapter, is almost an exact science, specific weight (or density) being the only quantity that must be determined experimentally. On the other hand, the nature of *flow* of a real fluid is very complex. The basic laws describing the complete motion of a fluid are not easily formulated and handled mathematically, and so recourse to experimentation is required. By an analysis based on mechanics, thermodynamics, and orderly experimentation, large hydraulic structures and efficient fluid machines have been produced.

This chapter introduces the concepts needed for analysis of fluid motion. The basic equations that enable us to predict fluid behavior are stated or derived: These are equations of motion, continuity, and momentum, and the first and second laws of thermodynamics as applied to steady flow of a perfect gas. In this chapter the control-volume approach is utilized in the derivation of the continuity, energy, and momentum equations. Viscous effects, the experimental determination of losses, and the dimensionless presentation of loss data are presented in Chap. 5 after dimensional analysis has been introduced in Chap. 4. In general, one-dimensional-flow theory is developed in this chapter, with applications limited to incompressible cases where viscous effects do not predominate. Chapter 6 deals with compressible flow, and Chap. 7 with two- and three-dimensional flow.

## 3.1   the concepts of system and control volume

The free-body diagram was used in Chap. 2 as a convenient way to show forces exerted on some arbitrary fixed mass. This is a special case of a *system*. A system refers to a definite mass of material and distinguishes it from all other matter, called its *surroundings*. The boundaries of a system form a closed surface, and this surface may vary with time, so that it contains the same mass during changes in its condition; e.g., a slug of gas may be confined in a cylinder and be compressed by motion of a piston; the system boundary coinciding with the end of the piston then moves with the piston. The system may contain an infinitesimal mass or a large finite mass of fluids and solids at the will of the investigator.

The law of conservation of mass states that the mass within a system remains constant with time (disregarding relativity effects). In equation form

$$\frac{dm}{dt} = 0 \qquad\qquad (3.1.1)$$

with $m$ the total mass.

Newton's second law of motion is usually expressed for a system as

$$\Sigma \mathbf{F} = \frac{d}{dt}(m\mathbf{v}) \qquad\qquad (3.1.2)$$

in which it must be remembered that $m$ is the constant mass of the system. $\Sigma\mathbf{F}$ refers to the resultant of all external forces acting on the system, including body forces, such as gravity, and $\mathbf{v}$ is the velocity of the center of mass of the system.

A *control volume* refers to a region in space and is useful in the analysis of situations where flow occurs into and out of the space. The boundary of a control volume is its *control surface*. The size and shape of the control volume are entirely arbitrary, but frequently they are made to coincide with solid boundaries in parts, and in other parts they are drawn normal to the flow directions as a matter of simplification. By superposition of a uniform velocity on a system and its surroundings a convenient situation for application of the control volume may sometimes be found, e.g., determination of sound-wave velocity in a medium. The control-volume concept is used in the derivation of continuity, momentum, and energy equations, as well as in the solution of many types of problems. The control volume is also referred to as an *open system*.

Regardless of the nature of the flow, all flow situations are found to be subject to the following relationships, which may be expressed in analytic form:

1. Newton's laws of motion must hold for every particle at every instant.
2. The continuity relationship. i.e., the law of conservation of mass.
3. The first and second laws of thermodynamics.
4. Boundary conditions, analytical statements that a real fluid has zero velocity relative to a boundary at a boundary or that ideal fluids cannot penetrate a boundary.

Other relations and equations may enter, such as an equation of state or Newton's law of viscosity.

The control-volume concept is related to the system in terms of a general property of the system.   It is then applied specifically to obtain continuity, energy, and linear momentum relationships.

To formulate the relationship among equations applied to a system and those applied to a control volume, consider some general flow situation, Fig. 3.1, in which the velocity of a fluid is given relative to an $xyz$-coordinate system.   At time $t$ consider a certain mass of fluid that is contained within

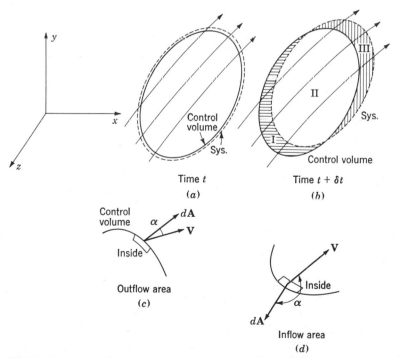

**Fig. 3.1** System with identical control volume at time $t$ in a velocity field.

a system, having the dotted-line boundaries indicated.   Also consider a control volume, fixed relative to the $xyz$-axes, that exactly coincides with the system at time $t$.   At time $t + \delta t$ the system has moved somewhat since each mass particle moves at the velocity associated with its location.

Let $N$ be the total amount of some property (mass, energy, momentum) within the system at time $t$, and let $\eta$ be the amount of this property, per unit mass, throughout the fluid.   The time rate of increase of $N$ for the system is now formulated in terms of the control volume.

At $t + \delta t$, Fig. 3.1$b$, the system is comprised of volumes II and III, while at time $t$ it occupied volumes I and II.   The increase in property $N$ in the system in time $\delta t$ is given by

$$N_{\text{sys}_{t+\delta t}} - N_{\text{sys}_t} = \left( \int_{\text{II}} \eta \rho \, d\mathcal{v} + \int_{\text{III}} \eta \rho \, d\mathcal{v} \right)_{t+\delta t} - \left( \int_{\text{I}} \eta \rho \, d\mathcal{v} + \int_{\text{II}} \eta \rho \, d\mathcal{v} \right)_t$$

By rearrangement, after dividing through by $\delta t$

$$\frac{N_{\text{sys}_{t+\delta t}} - N_{\text{sys}_t}}{\delta t} = \frac{\int_{\text{II}_{t+\delta t}} \eta \rho \, d\mathcal{v} - \int_{\text{II}_t} \eta \rho \, d\mathcal{v}}{\delta t} + \frac{\int_{\text{III}_{t+\delta t}} \eta \rho \, d\mathcal{v}}{\delta t} - \frac{\int_{\text{I}_t} \eta \rho \, d\mathcal{v}}{\delta t}$$

$$(3.1.3)$$

The term on the left is the average time rate of increase of $N$ within the system during time $\delta t$.   In the limit as $\delta t$ approaches zero it becomes $dN/dt$.   If the limit is taken for the first set of terms on the right-hand side of the equation, comprising volume II, by definition of a partial derivative it becomes

$$\frac{\partial}{\partial t} \int_{cv} \eta \rho \, d\mathcal{v}$$

as the volume II becomes the control volume in the limit as $\delta t \rightarrow 0$.

The next term, which is the time rate of flow of $N$ out of the control volume, in the limit, may be written as

$$\lim_{\delta t \to 0} \frac{\int_{\text{III}_{t+\delta t}} \eta \rho \, d\mathcal{v}}{\delta t} = \int_{\text{outflow area}} \eta \rho \mathbf{v} \cdot d\mathbf{A} = \int \eta \rho v \cos \alpha \, dA \qquad (3.1.4)$$

in which $d\mathbf{A}$, Fig. 3.1$c$, is the vector representing an area element of the outflow area.   It has a direction normal to the surface of the control volume, positive outward.   $\alpha$ is the angle between the velocity vector and the elemental area vector.

Similarly, the last term of Eq. (3.1.3) is the negative of the time rate of flow of $N$ into the control volume.   In the limit

$$\lim_{\delta t \to 0} \frac{\int_{I_t} \eta\rho \, d\mathcal{V}}{\delta t} = \int_{\text{inflow area}} \eta\rho\mathbf{v} \cdot d\mathbf{A} = \int \eta\rho v \cos \alpha \, dA \qquad (3.1.5)$$

As shown in Fig. 3.1$d$, cos $\alpha$ is negative in this case.   The two terms, given by Eqs. (3.1.4) and (3.1.5), may be combined into a single term which is an integral over the complete control-volume area (the control surface) since the signs are properly accounted for, and $\mathbf{v} \cdot d\mathbf{A}$ is zero wherever there is no flow across the boundary.

Collecting the reorganized terms of Eq. (3.1.3),

$$\frac{dN}{dt} = \frac{\partial}{\partial t} \int_{cv} \eta\rho \, d\mathcal{V} + \int_{cs} \eta\rho\mathbf{v} \cdot d\mathbf{A} \qquad (3.1.6)$$

In words, this equation states that the time rate of increase of $N$ within a system is just equal to the time rate of increase of the property $N$ within the control volume (fixed relative to $xyz$) plus the net rate of efflux of $N$ across the control-volume boundary.

Equation (3.1.6) is used throughout this chapter in converting laws and principles from the system form to the control-volume form.   The system form, which in effect follows the motion of the particles, is referred to as the Lagrangian method of analysis; the control-volume approach is called the Eulerian method of analysis, as it observes flow from a reference system fixed relative to the control volume.

Since the $xyz$-frame of reference may be given an arbitrary constant velocity without affecting the dynamics of the system and its surroundings, Eq. (3.1.6) is valid if the control volume, fixed in size and shape, has a uniform velocity of translation.

## 3.2   application of the control volume to continuity, energy, and momentum

In this section the general relation of system and control volume to a property, developed in Sec. 3.1, is applied first to continuity, then to energy, and finally to linear momentum.   In the following sections the uses of equations are brought out and illustrated.

*continuity*

The continuity equations are developed from the general principle of conservation of mass, Eq. (3.1.1), which states that the mass within a system remains constant with time; i.e.,

$$\frac{dm}{dt} = 0$$

In Eq. (3.1.6) let $N$ be the mass of the system $m$.   $\eta$ is then the mass per unit mass, or

$$0 = \frac{\partial}{\partial t} \int_{cv} \rho \, d\mathcal{V} + \int_{cs} \rho \mathbf{v} \cdot d\mathbf{A} \qquad (3.2.1)$$

In words the continuity equation for a control volume states that the time rate of increase of mass within a control volume is just equal to the net rate of mass inflow to the control volume.   This equation is examined further in Sec. 3.4.

*energy equation*

The first law of thermodynamics for a system states that the heat $Q_H$ added to a system minus the work $W$ done by the system depends only upon the initial and final states of the system.   The difference in states of the system, being independent of the path from initial to final state, must be a property of the system.   It is called the internal energy $E$. The first law in equation form is

$$Q_H - W = E_2 - E_1 \qquad (3.2.2)$$

The internal energy per unit mass is called $e$, hence, applying Eq. (3.1.6), $N = E$ and $\eta = \rho e / \rho$,

$$\frac{dE}{dt} = \frac{\partial}{\partial t} \int_{cv} \rho e \, d\mathcal{V} + \int_{cs} \rho e \mathbf{v} \cdot d\mathbf{A} \qquad (3.2.3)$$

or by use of Eq. (3.2.2)

$$\frac{\delta Q_H}{\delta t} - \frac{\delta W}{\delta t} = \frac{dE}{dt} = \frac{\partial}{\partial t} \int_{cv} \rho e \, d\mathcal{V} + \int_{cs} \rho e \mathbf{v} \cdot d\mathbf{A} \qquad (3.2.4)$$

The work done by the system on its surroundings may be broken into two parts: the work $W_{pr}$ done by pressure forces on the moving boundaries, and the work $W_S$ done by shear forces such as the torque exerted on a rotating shaft.   The work done by pressure forces in time $\delta t$ is

$$\delta W_{pr} = \delta t \int p \mathbf{v} \cdot d\mathbf{A} \qquad (3.2.5)$$

By use of the definitions of the work terms, Eq. (3.2.4) becomes

$$\frac{\delta Q_H}{\delta t} - \frac{\delta W_S}{\delta t} = \frac{\partial}{\partial t} \int_{cv} \rho e \, d\mathcal{V} + \int_{cs} \left( \frac{p}{\rho} + e \right) \rho \mathbf{v} \cdot d\mathbf{A} \qquad (3.2.6)$$

In the absence of nuclear, electrical, magnetic, and surface-tension effects, the internal energy $e$ of a pure substance is the sum of potential, kinetic, and "intrinsic" energies.  The intrinsic energy $u$ per unit mass is due to molecular spacing and forces (dependent upon $p$, $\rho$, or $T$):

$$e = gz + \frac{v^2}{2} + u \qquad (3.2.7)$$

*linear momentum equation*

Newton's second law for a system, Eq. (3.1.2), is used as the basis for finding the linear momentum equation for a control volume by use of Eq. (3.1.6).  Let $N$ be the linear momentum $m\mathbf{v}$ of the system and let $\eta$ be the linear momentum per unit mass $\rho\mathbf{v}/\rho$.  Then by use of Eqs. (3.1.2) and (3.1.6)

$$\Sigma \mathbf{F} = \frac{d(m\mathbf{v})}{dt} = \frac{\partial}{\partial t} \int_{cv} \rho \mathbf{v} \, d\mathcal{V} + \int_{cs} \rho \mathbf{v} \mathbf{v} \cdot d\mathbf{A} \qquad (3.2.8)$$

In words, the resultant force acting on a control volume is equal to the time rate of increase of linear momentum within the control volume plus the net efflux of linear momentum from the control volume.

Equations (3.2.1), (3.2.6), and (3.2.8) provide the relationships for analysis of many of the problems of fluid mechanics.  In effect, they provide a bridge from the solid dynamics relations of the system to the convenient control-volume relations of fluid flow.

Flow characteristics and definitions are next discussed, before the basic control-volume equations are examined and applied.

## 3.3  flow characteristics, definitions

Flow may be classified in many ways, such as turbulent, laminar; real, ideal; reversible, irreversible; steady, unsteady; uniform, nonuniform; rotational, irrotational.  In this and the following section various types of flow are distinguished.

Turbulent-flow situations are most prevalent in engineering practice. In turbulent flow the fluid particles (small molar masses) move in very irregular paths, causing an exchange of momentum from one portion of the fluid to another in a manner somewhat similar to the molecular momentum transfer described in Sec. 1.3, but on a much larger scale. The fluid particles can range in size from very small (say a few thousand molecules) to very large (thousands of cubic feet in a large swirl in a river or in an atmospheric gust).   In a situation in which the flow could be either turbulent or nonturbulent (laminar), the turbulence sets up greater shear stresses throughout the fluid and causes more irreversibilities or losses. Also, in turbulent flow, the losses vary about as the square of the velocity, while in laminar flow, they vary as the first power of the velocity.

In *laminar* flow, fluid particles move along smooth paths in laminas, or layers, with one layer gliding smoothly over an adjacent layer.   Laminar flow is governed by Newton's law of viscosity [Eq. (1.1.1) or extensions of it to three-dimensional flow], which relates shear stress to rate of angular deformation.   In laminar flow, the action of viscosity damps out turbulent tendencies (see Sec. 5.3 for criteria for laminar flow).   Laminar flow is not stable in situations involving combinations of low viscosity, high velocity, or large flow passages and breaks down into turbulent flow.   An equation similar in form to Newton's law of viscosity may be written for turbulent flow:

$$\tau = \eta \frac{du}{dy} \tag{3.3.1}$$

The factor $\eta$, however, is not a fluid property alone but depends upon the fluid motion and the density.   It is called the eddy viscosity.

In many practical flow situations, both viscosity and turbulence contribute to the shear stress:

$$\tau = (\mu + \eta) \frac{du}{dy} \tag{3.3.2}$$

Experimentation is required for determination of this type of flow.

An *ideal fluid* is frictionless and incompressible and should not be confused with a perfect gas (Sec. 1.6).   The assumption of an ideal fluid is helpful in analyzing flow situations involving large expanses of fluids, as in the motion of an airplane or a submarine.   A frictionless fluid is nonviscous, and its flow processes are reversible.

The layer of fluid in the immediate neighborhood of an actual flow boundary that has had its velocity relative to the boundary affected by viscous shear is called the *boundary layer*.   Boundary layers may be laminar or turbulent, depending generally upon their length, the viscosity, the velocity of the flow near them, and the boundary roughness.

*Adiabatic* flow is that flow of a fluid in which no heat is transferred to or from the fluid.  *Reversible adiabatic* (frictionless adiabatic) flow is called *isentropic* flow.   To proceed in an orderly manner into the analysis of fluid flow requires a clear understanding of the terminology involved. Several of the more important technical terms are defined and illustrated in this section.

*Steady* flow occurs when conditions at any point in the fluid do not change with the time.   For example, if the velocity at a certain point is 10 ft/sec in the $+x$-direction in steady flow, it remains exactly that amount and in that direction indefinitely.   This can be expressed as $\partial \mathbf{v}/\partial t = 0$, in which space ($x$, $y$, $z$ coordinates of the point) is held constant.   Likewise, in steady flow there is no change in density $\rho$, pressure $p$, or temperature $T$, with time at any point; thus

$$\frac{\partial \rho}{\partial t} = 0 \qquad \frac{\partial p}{\partial t} = 0 \qquad \frac{\partial T}{\partial t} = 0$$

In turbulent flow, owing to the erratic motion of the fluid particles, there are always small fluctuations occurring at any point.   The definition for steady flow must be generalized somewhat to provide for these fluctuations.   To illustrate this, a plot of velocity against time, at some point in turbulent flow, is given in Fig. 3.2.   When the temporal mean velocity

$$v_t = \frac{1}{t} \int_0^t v \, dt$$

indicated in the figure by the horizontal line, does not change with the time, the flow is said to be steady.   The same generalization applies to

Time

**Fig. 3.2** Velocity at a point in steady turbulent flow.

density, pressure, temperature, etc., when they are substituted for $v$ in the above formula.

The flow is *unsteady* when conditions at any point change with the time, $\partial \mathbf{v}/\partial t \neq 0$. Water being pumped through a fixed system at a constant rate is an example of steady flow. Water being pumped through a fixed system at an increasing rate is an example of unsteady flow.

*Uniform* flow occurs when at every point the velocity vector is identical (in magnitude and direction) for any given instant, or, in equation form, $\partial \mathbf{v}/\partial s = 0$, in which time is held constant and $\delta s$ is a displacement in any direction. The equation states that there is no change in the velocity vector in any direction throughout the fluid at any one instant. It states nothing about the change in velocity at a point with time.

In flow of a real fluid in an open or closed conduit, the definition of uniform flow may also be extended in most cases even though the velocity vector at the boundary is always zero. When all parallel cross sections through the conduit are identical (i.e., when the conduit is prismatic) and the average velocity at each cross section is the same at any given instant, the flow is said to be *uniform*.

Flow such that the velocity vector varies from place to place at any instant ($\partial \mathbf{v}/\partial s \neq 0$) is *nonuniform* flow. A liquid being pumped through a long, straight pipe has uniform flow. A liquid flowing through a reducing section or through a curved pipe has nonuniform flow.

Examples of steady and unsteady flow and of uniform and nonuniform flow are: liquid flow through a long pipe at a constant rate is *steady uniform* flow; liquid flow through a long pipe at a decreasing rate is *unsteady uniform* flow; flow through an expanding tube at a constant rate is *steady nonuniform* flow; and flow through an expanding tube at an increasing rate is *unsteady nonuniform* flow.

*Rotation* of a fluid particle about a given axis, say the $z$-axis, is defined as the average angular velocity of two infinitesimal line elements in the particle that are at right angles to each other and to the given axis. If the fluid particles within a region have rotation about any axis, the flow is called *rotational flow*, or *vortex flow*. If the fluid within a region has no rotation, the flow is called *irrotational flow*. It is shown in texts on hydrodynamics that if a fluid is at rest, and is frictionless, any later motion of this fluid will be irrotational.

*One-dimensional* flow neglects variations or changes in velocity, pressure, etc., transverse to the main flow direction. Conditions at a cross section are expressed in terms of average values of velocity, density, and other properties. Flow through a pipe, for example, may usually be characterized as one-dimensional. Many practical problems may be handled by this method of analysis, which is much simpler than two- and three-dimensional methods of analysis.  In *two-dimensional* flow all particles are assumed to flow in parallel planes along identical paths in each of these planes; hence, there are no changes in flow normal to these planes.  The flow net, developed in Chap. 7, is the most useful method for analysis of two-dimensional-flow situations.  *Three-dimensional* flow is the most general flow in which the velocity components $u$, $v$, $w$ in mutually perpendicular directions are functions of space coordinates and time $x$, $y$, $z$, and $t$. Methods of analysis are generally complex mathematically, and only simple geometrical flow boundaries may be handled.

A *streamline* is a continuous line drawn through the fluid so that it has the direction of the velocity vector at every point.  There can be no flow across a streamline.  Since a particle moves in the direction of the streamline at any instant, its displacement $\delta\mathbf{s}$, having components $\delta x$, $\delta y$, $\delta z$, has the direction of the velocity vector $\mathbf{q}$ that has components $u$, $v$, $w$ in the $x$-, $y$-, $z$-directions, respectively.  Then

$$\frac{\delta x}{u} = \frac{\delta y}{v} = \frac{\delta z}{w}$$

states that the corresponding components are proportional and hence that $\delta\mathbf{s}$ and $\mathbf{q}$ have the same direction.  Expressing the displacements in differential form,

$$\frac{dx}{u} = \frac{dy}{v} = \frac{dz}{w} \tag{3.3.3}$$

produces the differential equations of a streamline.  Equations (3.3.3) are two independent equations.  Any continuous line that satisfies them is a streamline.

In steady flow, since there is no change in direction of the velocity vector at any point, the streamline has a fixed inclination at every point and is, therefore, *fixed in space*.  A particle always moves tangent to the streamline; hence, in steady flow the *path of a particle* is a streamline.  In unsteady flow, since the direction of the velocity vector at any point may change with time, a streamline may shift in space from instant to instant. A particle then follows one streamline one instant, another one the next instant, and so on, so that the path of the particle may have no resemblance to any given instantaneous streamline.

A dye, or smoke, is frequently injected into a fluid in order to trace its subsequent motion.  The resulting dye, or smoke, trails are called *streak lines*.  In steady flow a streak line is a streamline and the path of a particle.

Streamlines in two-dimensional flow may be obtained by inserting fine, bright particles (aluminum dust) into the fluid, brilliantly lighting one plane,

**Fig. 3.3** Streamlines for steady flow around a cylinder between parallel walls.

and taking a photograph of the streaks made in a short time interval. Tracing on the picture continuous lines that have the direction of the streaks at every point portrays the streamlines for either steady or unsteady flow.

In illustration of an incompressible two-dimensional flow, as in Fig. 3.3, the streamlines are drawn so that per unit time the volume flowing between adjacent streamlines is the same, if unit depth is considered normal to the plane of the figure. Hence, when the streamlines are closer together, the velocity must be greater, and vice versa. If $v$ is the average velocity between two adjacent streamlines at some position where they are $h$ apart, the flow rate $\Delta q$ is

$$\Delta q = vh \tag{3.3.4}$$

At any other position on the chart where the distance between streamlines is $h_1$, the average velocity is $v_1 = \Delta q/h_1$. By increasing the number of streamlines drawn, i.e., by decreasing $\Delta q$, in the limiting case the velocity at a point is obtained.

A *stream tube* is the tube made by all the streamlines passing through a small, closed curve. In steady flow it is fixed in space and can have no flow through its walls because the velocity vector has no component normal to the tube surface.

**example 3.1** In two-dimensional, incompressible, steady flow around an airfoil the streamlines are drawn so that they are 1 in. apart at a great distance from the airfoil where the velocity is 120 ft/sec. What is the velocity near the airfoil where the streamlines are 0.75 in. apart?

The flow per unit width is the same at both positions; hence

$120 \times 1 = v \times 0.75$

and $v = 120/0.75 = 160$ ft/sec.

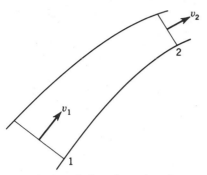

**Fig. 3.4**  Steady flow through a stream tube.

## 3.4  continuity equation

The use of Eq. (3.2.1) is developed in this section.   First, consider steady flow through a portion of the stream tube of Fig. 3.4.   The control volume comprises the walls of the stream tube between sections 1 and 2, plus the end areas of sections 1 and 2.   Because the flow is steady the first term of Eq. (3.2.1) is zero, hence

$$\int_{cs} \rho \mathbf{v} \cdot d\mathbf{A} = 0 \tag{3.4.1}$$

which states that the net mass outflow from the control volume must be zero.   At section 1 the net mass outflow is $-\rho_1 v_1 \, \delta A_1$ and at section 2 it is $\rho_2 v_2 \, \delta A_2$.   Since there is no flow through the wall of the stream tube,

$$\rho_1 v_1 \, \delta A_1 = \rho_2 v_2 \, \delta A_2 \tag{3.4.2}$$

is the continuity equation applied to two sections along a stream tube in steady flow.

For a collection of stream tubes, as in Fig. 3.5, if $\rho_1$ is the average density

**Fig. 3.5**  Collection of stream tubes between fixed boundaries.

at section 1 and $\rho_2$ the average density at section 2, then

$$\dot{m} = \rho_1 V_1 A_1 = \rho_2 V_2 A_2 \qquad (3.4.3)$$

in which $V_1$, $V_2$ represent average velocities over the cross sections and $\dot{m}$ is the rate of mass flow.    The average velocity over a cross section is given by

$$V = \frac{1}{A} \int v \, dA$$

By defining the discharge $Q$ as

$$Q = AV \qquad (3.4.4)$$

the continuity equation may take the form

$$\dot{m} = \rho_1 Q_1 = \rho_2 Q_2 \qquad (3.4.5)$$

For incompressible, steady flow

$$Q = A_1 V_1 = A_2 V_2 \qquad (3.4.6)$$

is a useful form of the equation.
For constant-density flow, steady or unsteady, Eq. (3.2.1) becomes

$$\int_{cs} \mathbf{v} \cdot d\mathbf{A} = 0 \qquad (3.4.7)$$

which states that the net volume efflux is zero (this implies that the control volume is filled with liquid at all times).

**example 3.2**    At section 1 of a pipe system carrying water (Fig. 3.6) the velocity is 3.0 ft/sec and the diameter is 2.0 ft.    This same flow passes another section 2 where the diameter is 3.0 ft.    Find the discharge and the velocity at section 2.
From Eq. (3.4.6)

$$Q = V_1 A_1 = 3.0\pi = 9.42 \text{ cfs}$$

**Fig. 3.6**  Control volume for flow through series pipes.

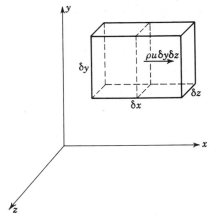

**Fig. 3.7** Control volume for derivation of three-dimensional continuity equation in cartesian coordinates.

and

$$V_2 = \frac{Q}{A_2} = \frac{9.42}{2.25\pi} = 1.33 \text{ ft/sec}$$

For two- and three-dimensional-flow studies, differential expressions of the continuity equation are used. For three-dimensional cartesian coordinates, Eq. (3.2.1) is applied to the control-volume element $\delta x\ \delta y\ \delta z$ of Fig. 3.7 with center at $(x,y,z)$ where the velocity components in the $x$-, $y$-, $z$-directions are $u$, $v$, $w$, respectively, and $\rho$ is the density. Consider first the flux through the pair of faces normal to the $x$-direction. On the right-hand face the flux outward is

$$\left[\rho u + \frac{\partial}{\partial x}(\rho u)\frac{\delta x}{2}\right]\delta y\ \delta z$$

since both $\rho$ and $u$ are assumed to vary continuously throughout the fluid. In the expression, $\rho u\ \delta y\ \delta z$ is the mass flux through the center face normal to the $x$-axis. The second term is the rate of increase of mass flux with respect to $x$, multiplied by the distance $\delta x/2$ to the right-hand face. Similarly on the left-hand face the flux into the volume is

$$\left[\rho u - \frac{\partial}{\partial x}(\rho u)\frac{\delta x}{2}\right]\delta y\ \delta z$$

since the step is $-\delta x/2$.  The net flux out through these two faces is

$$\frac{\partial}{\partial x}(\rho u)\ \delta x\ \delta y\ \delta z$$

The other two directions yield similar expressions; hence the net mass out-flow is

$$\left[\frac{\partial}{\partial x}(\rho u) + \frac{\partial}{\partial y}(\rho v) + \frac{\partial}{\partial z}(\rho w)\right]\delta x\ \delta y\ \delta z$$

which takes the place of the right-hand part of Eq. (3.2.1).  The left-hand part of Eq. (3.2.1) becomes, for an element,

$$-\frac{\partial \rho}{\partial t}\ \delta x\ \delta y\ \delta z$$

By equating these two expressions and after dividing through by the volume element and taking the limit as $\delta x\ \delta y\ \delta z$ approaches zero, the continuity equation at a point becomes

$$\frac{\partial}{\partial x}(\rho u) + \frac{\partial}{\partial y}(\rho v) + \frac{\partial}{\partial z}(\rho w) = -\frac{\partial \rho}{\partial t} \tag{3.4.8}$$

which must hold for every point in the flow, steady or unsteady, compressible or incompressible.[1]   For incompressible flow, however, it simplifies to

$$\frac{\partial u}{\partial x} + \frac{\partial v}{\partial y} + \frac{\partial w}{\partial z} = 0 \tag{3.4.9}$$

Equations (3.4.8) and (3.4.9) may be compactly written in vector notation. By using fixed unit vectors in $x$-, $y$-, $z$-directions, **i**, **j**, **k**, respectively, the operator $\nabla$ (pronounced "del") is defined as

$$\nabla = \mathbf{i}\,\frac{\partial}{\partial x} + \mathbf{j}\,\frac{\partial}{\partial y} + \mathbf{k}\,\frac{\partial}{\partial z} \tag{3.4.10}$$

and the velocity vector **q** is given by

$$\mathbf{q} = \mathbf{i}u + \mathbf{j}v + \mathbf{k}w \tag{3.4.11}$$

[1] Equation (3.4.8) may be derived from Eq. (3.2.1) by application of Gauss' theorem.  See L. Page, "Introduction to Theorectical Physics," 2d ed., pp. 32–36, D. Van Nostrand Company, Inc., Princeton, N.J., 1935.

Then

$$\nabla \cdot (\rho \mathbf{q}) = \left( \mathbf{i} \frac{\partial}{\partial x} + \mathbf{j} \frac{\partial}{\partial y} + \mathbf{k} \frac{\partial}{\partial z} \right) \cdot (\mathbf{i}\rho u + \mathbf{j}\rho v + \mathbf{k}\rho w)$$

$$= \frac{\partial}{\partial x} (\rho u) + \frac{\partial}{\partial y} (\rho v) + \frac{\partial}{\partial z} (\rho w)$$

because $\mathbf{i} \cdot \mathbf{i} = 1$, $\mathbf{i} \cdot \mathbf{j} = 0$, etc.    Equation (3.4.8) becomes

$$\nabla \cdot (\rho \mathbf{q}) = - \frac{\partial \rho}{\partial t} \tag{3.4.12}$$

and Eq. (3.4.9) becomes

$$\nabla \cdot \mathbf{q} = 0 \tag{3.4.13}$$

The dot product $\nabla \cdot \mathbf{q}$ is called the *divergence* of the velocity vector $\mathbf{q}$.    In words it is the net volume efflux at a point and must be zero for incompressible flow.    See Sec. 7.2 for further discussion of the operator $\nabla$.

In two-dimensional flow, generally assumed to be in planes parallel to the $xy$-plane, $w = 0$ and there is no change with respect to $z$, so $\partial/\partial z = 0$, which reduces the three-dimensional equations given for continuity.

**example 3.3**    The velocity distribution for a two-dimensional incompressible flow is given by

$$u - - \frac{x}{x^2 + y^2} \qquad v - - \frac{y}{x^2 + y^2}$$

Show that it satisfies continuity.

In two dimensions the continuity equation is, from Eq. (3.4.9),

$$\frac{\partial u}{\partial x} + \frac{\partial v}{\partial y} = 0$$

Then

$$\frac{\partial u}{\partial x} = - \frac{1}{x^2 + y^2} + \frac{2x^2}{(x^2 + y^2)^2} \qquad \frac{\partial v}{\partial y} = - \frac{1}{x^2 + y^2} + \frac{2y^2}{(x^2 + y^2)^2}$$

and their sum does equal zero, satisfying continuity.

### 3.5  Euler's equation of motion along a streamline

In addition to the continuity equation, other general controlling equations are Euler's equation, Bernoulli's equation, the energy equation, the momen-

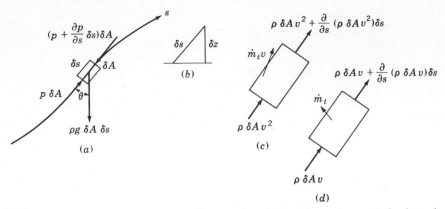

**Fig. 3.8** Application of continuity and momentum to flow through a control volume in the $s$-direction.

tum equations, and the first and second laws of thermodynamics.    In this section Euler's equation is derived in differential form.    In Sec. 3.9 it is integrated to obtain Bernoulli's equation.    The first law of thermodynamics is then developed for steady flow, and some of the interrelations of the equations are explored, including an introduction to the second law of thermodynamics.    In Chap. 7 Euler's equation is derived for general three-dimensional flow.    Here it is restricted to flow along a streamline.

In Fig. 3.8 a prismatic control volume of very small size is selected, with cross-sectional area $\delta A$ and length $\delta s$.    Fluid velocity is along the stream-line $s$.    By assuming that the viscosity is zero, or that the flow is friction-less, the only forces acting on the control volume in the $s$-direction are the end or normal forces and the weight.    The momentum equation for a control volume [Eq. (3.2.8)] is applied to the $s$-component of the vector equation, which is

$$\Sigma F_s = \frac{\partial}{\partial t} (\rho v \; \delta s \; \delta A) + \int_{cs} \rho v \mathbf{v} \cdot d\mathbf{A}$$

The forces acting are

$$\Sigma F_s = p \; \delta A - \left( p \; \delta A + \frac{\partial p}{\partial s} \; \delta s \; \delta A \right) - \rho g \; \delta s \; \delta A \cos \theta$$

As $s$ increases, the vertical coordinate increases in such a manner that $\cos \theta = \partial z / \partial s$.

The first term on the right-hand side of the equation may be written

$$\frac{\partial(\rho v)}{\partial t} \, \delta s \, \delta A$$

as $\delta s$ and $\delta A$ are independent of $t$.

The net efflux of $s$-momentum must consider mass flow $\dot{m}_t$ through the transverse faces plus mass flow through the end faces.    The $s$-momentum efflux from the end faces is, Fig. 3.8$c$,

$$-\rho \, \delta A \, v^2 + \left[ \rho \, \delta A \, v^2 + \frac{\partial}{\partial s} (\rho \, \delta A \, v^2) \, \delta s \right]$$

and the $s$-momentum efflux from the transverse walls is

$$\dot{m}_t v$$

To find the value of $\dot{m}_t$, by use of the general continuity equation (3.2.1) for a small control volume,

$$\frac{\partial}{\partial t} (\rho) \, \delta A \, \delta s + \frac{\partial}{\partial s} (\rho v) \, \delta A \, \delta s + \dot{m}_t = 0 \tag{3.5.1}$$

The middle term is the net rate of efflux of mass from the end areas, Fig. 3.8$d$.    By substituting for $\dot{m}_t$ from continuity, the terms of the momentum equation become

$$\frac{-\partial p}{\partial s} \, \delta s \, \delta A - \rho g \, \delta s \, \delta A \, \frac{\partial z}{\partial s}$$

$$= \frac{\partial(\rho v)}{\partial t} \, \delta s \, \delta A + \frac{\partial}{\partial s} (\rho \, \delta A \, v^2) \, \delta s - v \left[ \frac{\partial \rho}{\partial t} \, \delta A \, \delta s + \frac{\partial(\rho v)}{\partial s} \, \delta A \, \delta s \right]$$

After dividing through by the mass $\rho \, \delta A \, \delta s$ of the control volume and taking the limit as $\delta A$ and $\delta s$ become zero, the equation reduces to

$$\frac{1}{\rho} \frac{\partial p}{\partial s} + g \frac{\partial z}{\partial s} + v \frac{\partial v}{\partial s} + \frac{\partial v}{\partial t} = 0 \tag{3.5.2}$$

Two assumptions have been made: (1) that the flow is along a streamline, and (2) that the flow is frictionless.    If the flow is steady, Eq. (3.5.2) reduces to

$$\frac{1}{\rho} \frac{\partial p}{\partial s} + g \frac{\partial z}{\partial s} + v \frac{\partial v}{\partial s} = 0 \tag{3.5.3}$$

Now $s$ is the only independent variable, and total differentials may replace the partials

$$\frac{dp}{\rho} + g\,dz + v\,dv = 0 \tag{3.5.4}$$

This is one form of the Euler equation of motion; it could have been derived from $\Sigma\mathbf{F} = \delta m\,d\mathbf{v}/dt$ in a simpler manner, but the use of the control-volume equations was preferred.

## 3.6   reversibility, irreversibility, and losses

A *process* may be defined as the path of the succession of states through which the system passes, such as the changes in velocity, elevation, pressure, density, temperature, etc.   The expansion of air in a cylinder as the piston moves out and heat is transferred through the walls is an example of a process.   Normally, the process causes some change in the surroundings, such as displacing it or transferring heat to or from its boundaries. When a process can be made to take place in such a manner that it can be *reversed*, i.e., made to return to its original state without a final change in either the system or its surroundings, it is said to be *reversible*.   In any actual flow of a real fluid or change in a mechanical system, the effects of viscous friction, Coulomb friction, unrestrained expansion, hysteresis, etc., prohibit the process from being reversible.   It is, however, an ideal to be strived for in design processes, and their efficiency is usually defined in terms of their nearness to reversibility.

When a certain process has a sole effect upon its surroundings that is equivalent to the raising of a weight, it is said to have done *work* on its surroundings.   Any actual process is *irreversible*.   The difference between the amount of work a substance can do by changing from one state to another state along a path reversibly and the actual work it produces for the same path is the *irreversibility* of the process.   It may be defined in terms of work per unit mass or weight or work per unit time.   Under certain conditions the irreversibility of a process is referred to as its *lost work*,[1] that is, the loss of ability to do work because of friction and other causes.   In this treatise when *losses* are referred to, they mean irreversibility or lost work and do not mean an actual loss of energy.

**example 3.4**   A hydroelectric power plant has a head (difference in elevation of headwater and tailwater) of 100 ft and a flow of 100 ft$^3$/sec of water through turbines, which rotate at 180 rpm.   The torque in the turbine

---

[1] Reference to a text on thermodynamics is advised for a full discussion of these concepts.

shaft is measured to be 28,700 lb-ft, and the horsepower output of the generator is 945.  Determine the irreversibility, or losses, and the reversible work for the system.  $g = 32.17$ ft/sec$^2$.

The potential energy of the water is 100 ft-lb/lb$_m$.  Hence for perfect conversion the reversible work is 100 ft-lb/lb$_m$ or $100 \times 100 \times 62.4 = 6.24 \times 10^5$ ft-lb/sec.  The work done on the shaft by the water is

$$T\omega = 28,700 \times \tfrac{180}{60} 2\pi = 5.41 \times 10^5 \text{ ft-lb/sec}$$

The irreversibility through the turbine is then

$$(6.24 - 5.41) \times 10^5 = 83,000 \text{ ft-lb/sec}$$

or

$$\frac{83,000}{100 \times 62.4} = 13.38 \text{ ft-lb/lb}_m$$

The irreversibility through the generator is

$$5.41 \times 10^5 - 945 \times 550 = 21,000 \text{ ft-lb/sec}$$

or

$$\frac{21,000}{100 \times 62.4} = 3.37 \text{ ft-lb/lb}_m$$

Efficiency of the turbine $\eta_t$ Is

$$\eta_t = 100 \times \frac{100 - 13.38}{100} = 86.6\%$$

and efficiency of the generator $\eta_g$ is

$$\eta_g = 100 \times \frac{86.62 - 3.37}{86.62} = 96.1\%$$

## 3.7  the steady-state energy equation

When Eq. (3.2.6) is applied to steady flow through a control volume similar to Fig. 3.9, the volume integral drops out, and it becomes

$$\frac{\delta Q_H}{\delta t} + \left( \frac{p_1}{\rho_1} + gz_1 + \frac{v_1{}^2}{2} + u_1 \right) \rho_1 v_1 A_1$$
$$= \frac{\delta W_s}{\delta t} + \left( \frac{p_2}{\rho_2} + gz_2 + \frac{v_2{}^2}{2} + u_2 \right) \rho_2 v_2 A_2$$

**Fig. 3.9** Control volume with flow across control surface normal to surface.

Since the flow is steady in this equation, it is convenient to divide through by the mass per second flowing through the system $\rho_1 A_1 v_1 = \rho_2 A_2 v_2$, getting

$$q_H + \frac{p_1}{\rho_1} + g z_1 + \frac{v_1{}^2}{2} + u_1 = w_s + \frac{p_2}{\rho_2} + g z_2 + \frac{v_2{}^2}{2} + u_2 \qquad (3.7.1)$$

$q_H$ is the heat added per unit mass of fluid flowing, and $w_s$ is the shaft work per unit mass of fluid flowing. This is the *energy* equation for steady flow through a control volume.

The energy equation (3.7.1) in differential form, for flow through a stream tube (Fig. 3.10) with no shaft work, is

$$d \frac{p}{\rho} + g \, dz + v \, dv + du - dq_H = 0 \qquad (3.7.2)$$

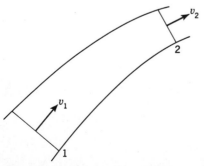

**Fig. 3.10** Steady stream tube as control volume.

By rearranging

$$\frac{dp}{\rho} + g\,dz + v\,dv + du + p\,d\frac{1}{\rho} - dq_H = 0 \qquad (3.7.3)$$

The first three terms are the Euler equation (3.5.4); the last three terms are one form of the first law of thermodynamics for a system,

$$dq_H = p\,d\frac{1}{\rho} + du \qquad (3.7.4)$$

Now, for reversible flow, *entropy s* per unit mass is defined by

$$ds = \left(\frac{dq_H}{T}\right)_{\text{rev}} \qquad (3.7.5)$$

in which $T$ is the absolute temperature.    Entropy is shown to be a fluid property in texts on thermodynamics.    In this equation it may have the units Btu per slug per degree Rankine, or foot-pounds per slug per degree Rankine, as heat may be expressed in foot-pounds (1 Btu = 778 ft-lb). Since Eq. (3.7.4) is for a frictionless fluid (reversible), $dq_H$ may be eliminated from Eqs. (3.7.4) and (3.7.5),

$$T\,ds = du + p\,d\frac{1}{\rho} \qquad (3.7.6)$$

which is a very important thermodynamic relation.    Although it was derived for a reversible process, since all terms are thermodynamic properties, it must also hold for irreversible-flow cases as well.    By use of Eq. (3.7.6) together with the *Clausius inequality*[1] and various combinations of Euler's equation and the first law, a clearer understanding of entropy and losses is gained.

## 3.8  interrelationships between Euler's equations and the thermodynamic relations

The first law in differential form, from Eq. (3.7.3), with shaft work included, is

$$dw_s + \frac{dp}{\rho} + v\,dv + g\,dz + p\,d\frac{1}{\rho} + du - dq_H = 0 \qquad (3.8.1)$$

---

[1] See any text on thermodynamics.

After substituting for $du + p\,d(1/\rho)$ in Eq. (3.7.6),

$$dw_s + \frac{dp}{\rho} + v\,dv + g\,dz + T\,ds - dq_H = 0 \qquad (3.8.2)$$

The Clausius inequality states that

$$ds \geq \frac{dq_H}{T}$$

or

$$T\,ds \geq dq_H \qquad (3.8.3)$$

Thus $T\,ds - dq_H \geq 0$. The equals sign applies to a reversible process [or a frictionless fluid, yielding Eq. (3.5.4) with a work term]. If the quantity called "losses" or "irreversibilities" is identified as

$$d\,\text{(losses)} \equiv T\,ds - dq_H \qquad (3.8.4)$$

it is seen that $d$ (losses) is positive in irreversible flow, is zero in reversible flow, and can never be negative. By substituting Eq. (3.8.4) into Eq. (3.8.2)

$$dw_s + \frac{dp}{\rho} + v\,dv + g\,dz + d\,\text{(losses)} = 0 \qquad (3.8.5)$$

This is a most important form of the energy equation. In general, the losses must be determined by recourse to experimentation. It implies that some of the available energy is converted into internal energy during an irreversible process. This equation, in the absence of the shaft work, differs from Euler's equation by the loss term only. In integrated form,

$$\frac{v_1^2}{2} + gz_1 = \int_1^2 \frac{dp}{\rho} + \frac{v_2^2}{2} + gz_2 + w_s + \text{losses}_{1-2} \qquad (3.8.6)$$

If work is done on the fluid in the control volume, as with a pump, then $w_s$ is negative. Section 1 is upstream, and section 2 is downstream.

### 3.9 the Bernoulli equation

Integration of Eq. (3.5.4) for constant density yields the Bernoulli equation

$$gz + \frac{v^2}{2} + \frac{p}{\rho} = \text{const} \qquad (3.9.1)$$

The constant of integration (called the Bernoulli constant) in general varies from one streamline to another but remains constant along a *streamline* in *steady, frictionless, incompressible* flow. These four assumptions are needed and must be kept in mind when applying this equation. Each term has the dimensions $(L/T)^2$ or the units ft²/sec², which is equivalent to ft-lb/slug:

ft-lb/slug $=$ ft-lb/(lb-sec²/ft) $=$ ft²/sec²

as 1 slug $\equiv$ 1 lb-sec²/ft. Therefore Eq. (3.9.1) is energy per unit mass. By dividing it through by $g$,

$$z + \frac{v^2}{2g} + \frac{p}{\gamma} = \text{const} \tag{3.9.2}$$

since $\gamma = \rho g$, or

$$z_1 + \frac{v_1{}^2}{2g} + \frac{p_1}{\gamma} = z_2 + \frac{v_2{}^2}{2g} + \frac{p_2}{\gamma} \tag{3.9.3}$$

it may now be interpreted as energy per unit weight, or ft-lb/lb. This form is particularly convenient for dealing with liquid problems with a free surface. By multiplying Eq. (3.9.1) by $\rho$,

$$\gamma z + \frac{\rho v^2}{2} + p = \text{const} \tag{3.9.4}$$

which is convenient for gas flow, since elevation changes are frequently unimportant and $\gamma z$ may be dropped out. In this form each term is ft-lb/ft³ or energy per unit volume.

Each of the terms of Bernoulli's equation may be interpreted as a form of energy. In Eq. (3.9.1) the first term is potential energy per unit mass. With reference to Fig. 3.11 the work needed to lift $W$ lb $z$ ft is $Wz$. The mass of $W$ lb weight is $W/g$ slugs; hence the potential energy per slug is

$$\frac{Wz}{W/g} = gz$$

**Fig. 3.11** Potential energy.

**Fig. 3.12** Work done by sustained pressure.

The next term, $v^2/2$, is interpreted as follows: Kinetic energy of a particle of mass is $\delta m \, v^2/2$.   To place this on a unit mass basis, divide by $\delta m$; thus $v^2/2$ is ft-lb/slug kinetic energy.

The last term, $p/\rho$, is the *flow work* or *flow energy* per unit mass.   Flow work is net work done by the fluid element on its surroundings while it is flowing.   For example, in Fig. 3.12, imagine a turbine consisting of a vaned unit that rotates as fluid passes through it, exerting a torque on its shaft. For a small rotation the pressure drop across a vane times the exposed area of vane is a force on the rotor.   When multiplied by the distance from center of force to axis of the rotor, a torque is obtained.   Elemental work done is $p \, \delta A \, ds$ by $\rho \, \delta A \, ds$ units of mass of flowing fluid; hence, the work per unit mass is $p/\rho$.   The three energy terms in Eq. (3.9.1) are referred to as *available* energy.

**example 3.5**   Show that the energy per unit mass is everywhere constant in a reservoir.

For any point $A$ in the reservoir (Fig. 3.13) the energy is given by Eq. (3.9.1).

$$gz + \frac{v^2}{2} + \frac{p}{\rho} = gy + 0 + (H - y)\frac{\gamma}{\rho} = gH$$

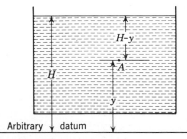

Arbitrary datum

**Fig. 3.13** Liquid reservoir.

Since $y$ drops out of the equation, the energy per unit mass is $gH$ for all locations.

By applying Eq. (3.9.3) to two points on a streamline,

$$z_1 + \frac{p_1}{\gamma} + \frac{v_1^2}{2g} = z_2 + \frac{p_2}{\gamma} + \frac{v_2^2}{2g} \qquad (3.9.5)$$

or

$$z_1 - z_2 + \frac{p_1 - p_2}{\gamma} + \frac{v_1^2 - v_2^2}{2g} = 0$$

This equation shows that it is the difference in potential energy, flow energy, and kinetic energy that actually has significance in the equation. Thus $z_1 - z_2$ is independent of the particular elevation datum, as it is the difference in elevation of the two points. Similarly $p_1/\gamma - p_2/\gamma$ is the difference in pressure heads expressed in feet of the fluid flowing and is not altered by the particular pressure datum selected. Since the velocity terms are not linear, their datum is fixed.

**example 3.6** Water is flowing in an open channel at a depth of 4 ft and a velocity of 8.02 ft/sec. It then flows down a chute into another open channel, where the depth is 2 ft and the velocity is 40.1 ft/sec. Assuming frictionless flow, determine the difference in elevation of the channel floors.

If the difference in elevation of floors is $y$, then Bernoulli's equation from the upper water surface to the lower water surface may be written

$$\frac{V_1^2}{2g} + \frac{p_1}{\gamma} + z_1 = \frac{V_2^2}{2g} + \frac{p_2}{\gamma} + z_2$$

$V_1$ and $V_2$ are average velocities. With gage pressure zero as datum and the floor of the lower channel as elevation datum, then $z_1 = y + 4$, $z_2 = 2$, $V_1 = 8.02$, $V_2 = 40.1$, $p_1 = p_2 = 0$, and

$$\frac{(8.02)^2}{64.4} + 0 + y + 4 = \frac{(40.1)^2}{64.4} + 0 + 2$$

and $y = 22$ ft.

*modification of assumptions underlying Bernoulli's equation*

Under special conditions each of the four assumptions underlying Bernoulli's equation may be waived.

1. When all streamlines originate from a reservoir, where the energy content is everywhere the same, the constant of integration does not change from one streamline to another and points 1 and 2 for application of Bernoulli's equation may be selected arbitrarily, i.e., not necessarily on the same streamline.
2. In the flow of a gas, as in a ventilation system, where the change in pressure is only a small fraction (a few per cent) of the absolute pressure, the gas may be considered incompressible. Equation (3.9.3) may be applied, with an average specific weight $\gamma$.
3. For unsteady flow with gradually changing conditions, such as the emptying of a reservoir, Bernoulli's equation may be applied without appreciable error.
4. Bernoulli's equation is of use in analyzing real fluid cases by first neglecting viscous shear to obtain theoretical results. The resulting equation may then be modified by a coefficient, determined by experiment, which corrects the theoretical equation so that it conforms to the actual physical case. In general, losses are handled by use of the energy equation, Eq. (3.8.6).

**example 3.7**  ($a$) Determine the velocity of efflux from the nozzle in the wall of the reservoir of Fig. 3.14.  ($b$) Find the discharge through the nozzle.

($a$)  The jet issues as a cylinder with atmospheric pressure around its periphery. The pressure along its center line is at atmospheric pressure for all practical purposes. Bernoulli's equation is applied between a point on the water surface and a point downstream from the nozzle,

$$\frac{V_1^2}{2g} + \frac{p_1}{\gamma} + z_1 = \frac{V_2^2}{2g} + \frac{p_2}{\gamma} + z_2$$

With the pressure datum as local atmospheric pressure, $p_1 = p_2 = 0$; with the elevation datum through point 2, $z_2 = 0$, $z_1 = H$. The velocity on the

**Fig. 3.14** Flow through nozzle from reservoir.

**Fig. 3.15**   Venturi meter.

surface of the reservoir is zero (practically); hence

$$0 + 0 + H = \frac{V_2{}^2}{2g} + 0 + 0$$

and

$$V_2 = \sqrt{2gH} = \sqrt{2 \times 32.2 \times 16} = 32.08 \text{ ft/sec}$$

which states that the velocity of efflux is equal to the velocity of free fall from the surface of the reservoir.   This is known as *Torricelli's theorem.*

(b)   The discharge $Q$ is the product of velocity of efflux and area of stream,

$$Q = A_2 V_2 = \frac{\pi}{36} \, 32.08 = 2.80 \text{ cfs}$$

**example 3.8**   A venturi meter, consisting of a converging portion followed by a throat portion of constant diameter, and then a gradually diverging portion, is used to determine rate of flow in a pipe (Fig. 3.15).   The diameter at section 1 is 6.0 in. and at section 2 is 4.0 in.   Find the discharge through the pipe when $p_1 - p_2 = 3$ psi and oil, sp gr 0.90, is flowing.

From the continuity equation, Eq. (3.4.6),

$$Q = A_1 V_1 = A_2 V_2 = \frac{\pi}{16} V_1 = \frac{\pi}{36} V_2$$

in which $Q$ is the discharge (volume per unit time flowing).   By applying Eq. (3.9.3) for $z_1 = z_2$,

$$p_1 - p_2 = 3 \times 144 = 432 \text{ lb/ft}^2 \qquad \gamma = 0.90 \times 62.4 = 56.16 \text{ lb/ft}^3$$

$$\frac{p_1 - p_2}{\gamma} = \frac{V_2{}^2}{2g} - \frac{V_1{}^2}{2g}$$

or

$$\frac{432}{56.16} = \frac{Q^2}{\pi^2} \frac{1}{2g} [(36)^2 - (16)^2]$$

Solving for discharge, $Q = 2.20$ cfs (cubic feet per second).

## 3.10 application of the Bernoulli and energy equations to steady fluid-flow situations

For an incompressible fluid Eq. (3.8.6) may be simplified to

$$\frac{p_1}{\gamma} + \frac{v_1{}^2}{2g} + z_1 = \frac{p_2}{\gamma} + \frac{v_2{}^2}{2g} + z_2 + \text{losses}_{1-2} \tag{3.10.1}$$

in which each term now is energy in foot-pounds per pound, including the loss term. The work term has been omitted but may be inserted if needed.

*kinetic-energy correction factor*

In dealing with flow situations in open- or closed-channel flow, the so-called "one-dimensional" form of analysis is frequently used. The whole flow is considered to be one large stream tube with average velocity $V$ at each cross section. The kinetic energy per unit weight given by $V^2/2g$, however, is not the average of $v^2/2g$ taken over the cross section. It is necessary to compute a correction factor $\alpha$ for $V^2/2g$, so that $\alpha V^2/2g$ is the average kinetic energy per unit weight passing the section. Referring to Fig. 3.16, the kinetic energy passing the cross section per unit time is

$$\gamma \int_A \frac{v^2}{2g} v \, dA$$

in which $\gamma v \, \delta A$ is the weight per unit time passing $\delta A$ and $v^2/2g$ is the kinetic energy per unit weight. By equating this to the kinetic energy per unit time passing the section, in terms of $\alpha V^2/2g$,

$$\alpha \frac{V^2}{2g} \gamma V A = \gamma \int_A \frac{v^3}{2g} dA$$

**Fig. 3.16** Velocity distribution and average velocity.

By solving for $\alpha$, the *kinetic-energy correction factor*,

$$\alpha = \frac{1}{A} \int_A \left(\frac{v}{V}\right)^3 dA \tag{3.10.2}$$

Bernoulli's equation becomes

$$z_1 + \frac{p_1}{\gamma} + \alpha_1 \frac{V_1{}^2}{2g} = z_2 + \frac{p_2}{\gamma} + \alpha_2 \frac{V_2{}^2}{2g} \tag{3.10.3}$$

For laminar flow in a pipe, $\alpha = 2$, as shown in Sec. 5.2.   For turbulent flow[1] in a pipe, $\alpha$ varies from about 1.01 to 1.10 and is usually neglected except for precise work.

**example 3.9**   The velocity distribution in turbulent flow in a pipe is given approximately by Prandtl's one-seventh power law,

$$\frac{v}{v_{max}} = \left(\frac{y}{r_0}\right)^{1/7}$$

with $y$ the distance from the pipe wall and $r_0$ the pipe radius.   Find the kinetic-energy correction factor.
   The average velocity $V$ is expressed by

$$\pi r_0{}^2 V = 2\pi \int_0^{r_0} rv \, dr$$

in which $r = r_0 - y$.   By substituting for $r$ and $v$,

$$\pi r_0{}^2 V = 2\pi v_{max} \int_0^{r_0} (r_0 - y) \left(\frac{y}{r_0}\right)^{1/7} dy = \pi r_0{}^2 v_{max} \frac{98}{120}$$

or

$$V = \frac{98}{120} v_{max} \qquad v = \frac{120}{98} \left(\frac{y}{r_0}\right)^{1/7}$$

By substituting into Eq. (3.10.2)

$$\alpha = \frac{1}{\pi r_0{}^2} \int_0^{r_0} 2\pi r \left(\frac{120}{98}\right)^3 \left(\frac{y}{r_0}\right)^{3/7} dr = 2 \left(\frac{120}{98}\right)^3 \frac{1}{r_0{}^2} \int_0^{r_0} (r_0 - y) \left(\frac{y}{r_0}\right)^{3/7}$$
$$dy = 1.06$$

   All the terms in the energy equation (3.10.1) except the term losses are *available energy*.   For real fluids flowing through a system the available energy decreases in the downstream direction; it is available to do work,

[1] V. L. Streeter, The Kinetic Energy and Momentum Correction Factors for Pipes and Open Channels of Great Width, *Civil Eng. N.Y.*, vol. 12, no. 4, pp. 212–213, 1942.

as in passing through a water turbine.   A plot showing the available energy along a stream tube portrays the *energy grade line* (see Sec. 10.1).   A plot of the two terms $z + p/\gamma$ along a stream tube portrays the *hydraulic grade line*.   The energy grade line always slopes downward in real fluid flow, except at a pump or other source of energy.   Reductions in energy grade line are also referred to as head losses.

**example 3.10**   The siphon of Fig. 3.17 is filled with water and discharging at 2.80 cfs.   Find the losses from point 1 to point 3 in terms of the velocity head $V^2/2g$.   Find the pressure at point 2 if two-thirds of the losses occur between points 1 and 2.

The energy equation is applied to the control volume between points 1 and 3, with elevation datum at point 3 and gage pressure zero for pressure datum:

$$\frac{V_1^2}{2g} + \frac{p_1}{\gamma} + z_1 = \frac{V_3^2}{2g} + \frac{p_3}{\gamma} + z_3 + \text{losses}$$

or

$$0 + 0 + 4 = \frac{V_3^2}{2g} + 0 + 0 + \frac{KV_3^2}{2g}$$

in which the losses from 1 to 3 have been expressed as $KV_3^2/2g$.   From

**Fig. 3.17**   Siphon.

**Fig. 3.18**  Pitot tube.

the discharge

$$V_3 = \frac{Q}{A} = \frac{2.80}{\pi/9} = 8.02 \text{ ft/sec}$$

and $V_3^2/2g = 1.0$ ft.   Hence $K = 3$ and the losses are $3V_3^2/2g$ or 3 ft-lb/lb.

The energy equation applied to the control volume between points 1 and 2, with losses $2V_3^2/2g = 2.0$ ft, is

$$0 + 0 + 0 = 1 + \frac{p_2}{\gamma} + 8 + 2$$

The pressure at 2 is $-11$ ft of water, or 4.76 psi vacuum.

**example 3.11**   The device shown in Fig. 3.18 is used to determine the velocity of liquid at point 1.   It is a tube with its lower end directed upstream and its other leg vertical and open to the atmosphere.   The impact of liquid against the opening 2 forces liquid to rise in the vertical leg to the height $\Delta z$ above the free surface.   Determine the velocity at 1.

Point 2 is a stagnation point, where the velocity of the flow is reduced to zero.   This creates an impact pressure, called the dynamic pressure, which forces the fluid into the vertical leg.   By writing Bernoulli's equation between points 1 and 2, neglecting losses, which are very small,

$$\frac{V_1^2}{2g} + \frac{p_1}{\gamma} + 0 = 0 + \frac{p_2}{\gamma} + 0$$

$p_1/\gamma$ is given by the fluid above point 1 and equals $k$ ft of fluid flowing. $p_2/\gamma$ is given by the manometer as $k + \Delta z$, neglecting capillary rise.   After substituting these values into the equation, $V_1^2/2g = \Delta z$ and

$$V_1 = \sqrt{2g\,\Delta z}$$

This is the pitot tube in a simple form.

Examples of compressible flow are given in Chap. 6.

### 3.11 applications of the linear momentum equation

Newton's second law, the equation of motion, was developed into the linear momentum equation in Sec. 3.2,

$$\Sigma\mathbf{F} = \frac{\partial}{\partial t}\int_{cv} \rho\mathbf{v}\,d\mathcal{V} + \int_{cs} \rho\mathbf{v}\mathbf{v}\cdot d\mathbf{A} \tag{3.11.1}$$

This vector relation may be applied for any component, say the $x$-direction, reducing to

$$\Sigma F_x = \frac{\partial}{\partial t}\int \rho v_x\,d\mathcal{V} + \int \rho v_x\mathbf{v}\cdot d\mathbf{A} \tag{3.11.2}$$

In selecting the arbitrary control volume, it is generally advantageous to take the surface normal to the velocity wherever it cuts across the flow. In addition, if the velocity is constant over the surface, the surface integral can be dispensed with.   In Fig. 3.19, with the control surface as shown, and with steady flow, the $\Sigma F_x$ acting on the control volume is given by Eq. (3.11.2) as

$$\Sigma F_x = \rho_2 A_2 V_2 V_{x2} - \rho_1 A_1 V_1 V_{x1}$$

or

$$\Sigma F_x = \rho Q(V_{x2} - V_{x1})$$

as the mass per second entering and leaving is $\rho Q = \rho_1 Q_1 = \rho_2 Q_2$.

When the velocity varies over a plane cross section of the control surface, by introduction of a momentum correction factor $\beta$, the average velocity

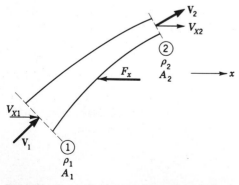

**Fig. 3.19** Control volume with uniform inflow and outflow normal to control surface.

**Fig.   3.20** Nonuniform   flow
through a control surface.

may be utilized, Fig. 3.20,

$$\int_A \rho v^2 \, dA = \beta \rho V^2 A \tag{3.11.3}$$

in which $\beta$ is dimensionless.   By solving for $\beta$,

$$\beta = \frac{1}{A} \int_A \left(\frac{v}{V}\right)^2 dA \tag{3.11.4}$$

which is analogous to $\alpha$, the kinetic-energy correction factor, Eq. (3.10.2).
For laminar flow in a straight round tube, $\beta$ is shown to equal $\frac{4}{3}$ in Chap. 5.
It equals 1 for uniform flow, and cannot have a value less than 1.

In applying Eq. (3.11.1) or a component equation such as Eq. (3.11.2)
care should be taken to clearly define the control volume and the forces
acting on it.   Also the sign of the inflow or outflow term must be carefully
evaluated.   The first example is an unsteady one using Eq. (3.11.2) and
the general continuity equation (3.2.1).

**example 3.12**   The horizontal pipe of Fig. 3.21 is filled with water for the
distance $x$.   A jet of constant velocity $V_1$ impinges against the filled portion.   Fluid frictional force on the pipe wall is given by $cx V_2^2/D_2$.   Determine the equations to analyze this flow condition when initial conditions
are known, i.e., $t = 0$, $x = x_0$, $V_2 = V_{2_0}$.   Specifically, for $V_1 = 50$ ft/sec,

**Fig. 3.21**   Jet impact on pipe flowing full over partial length.

$D_1 = 2.0$ in., $V_2 = 2.0$ ft/sec, $D_2 = 12$ in., $x = 500$ ft, $\rho = 1.935$, $c/D_2 = 0.03$, find the rate of change of $V_2$ and $x$ with time.

The continuity and momentum equations are used to analyze this unsteady-flow problem. Take as control volume the inside surface of the pipe, with the two end sections $l$ ft apart, as shown. The continuity equation

$$0 = \frac{\partial}{\partial t} \int_{cv} \rho \, d\upsilon + \int_{cs} \rho \mathbf{v} \cdot d\mathbf{A}$$

becomes, using $A_1 = \pi D_1^2/4$, $A_2 = \pi D_2^2/4$,

$$\frac{\partial}{\partial t} [\rho A_2 x + \rho A_1(l - x)] + \rho(V_2 A_2 - V_1 A_1) = 0$$

After simplifying,

$$\frac{\partial x}{\partial t}(A_2 - A_1) + V_2 A_2 - V_1 A_1 = 0$$

The momentum equation for the horizontal direction $x$,

$$\Sigma F_x = \frac{\partial}{\partial t} \int_{cv} \rho v_x \, d\upsilon + \int_{cs} \rho v_x \mathbf{v} \cdot d\mathbf{A}$$

becomes

$$-\frac{cx}{D_2} V_2^2 = \frac{\partial}{\partial t} [\rho A_2 x V_2 + \rho A_1(l - x) V_1] + \rho A_2 V_2^2 - \rho A_1 V_1^2$$

after simplifying

$$\frac{cx V_2^2}{\rho D_2} + A_2 \frac{\partial}{\partial t}(x V_2) - A_1 V_1 \frac{\partial x}{\partial t} + A_2 V_2^2 - A_1 V_1^2 = 0$$

As $t$ is the only independent variable, the partials may be replaced by totals. The continuity equation is

$$\frac{dx}{\partial t} = -\frac{V_2 A_2 - V_1 A_1}{A_2 - A_1}$$

By expanding the momentum equation, and substituting for $dx/dt$, it becomes

$$\frac{dV_2}{dt} = \frac{1}{x A_2} \left[ A_1 V_1^2 - A_2 V_2^2 - \frac{cx V_2^2}{\rho D_2} + \frac{(A_2 V_2 - A_1 V_1)^2}{A_2 - A_1} \right]$$

These two equations, being nonlinear, may be solved simultaneously by numerical methods, such as Runge-Kutta methods described in Appendix E, when initial conditions are known.   The rate of change of $x$ and $V_2$ may be found directly from the equations for the specific problem

$$\frac{dx}{dt} = -\frac{2 \times 0.7854 \times 1^2 - 50 \times 0.7854(\frac{2}{12})^2}{0.7854[1^2 - (\frac{2}{12})^2]} = -0.63 \text{ ft/sec}$$

$$\frac{dV_2}{dt} = \frac{1}{500 \times 0.7854 \times 1^2} \left\{ 0.7854 \left( \frac{1}{6^2} 50^2 - 1^2 \times 2^2 \right) - \frac{0.03 \times 500 \times 2^2}{1.935} \right.$$

$$\left. + \frac{[0.7854 \times 1 \times 2 - 0.7854 \times (1/6^2)50]^2}{0.7854(1^2 - 1/6^2)} \right\} = 0.0886 \text{ ft/sec}^2$$

**example 3.13**   In Fig. 3.22 a fluid jet impinges on a body as shown; the momentum per second of each of the jets is given by **M** and is the vector located at the center of the jets.   By vector addition find the resultant force needed to hold the body at rest.

The vector form of the linear momentum equation (3.11.1) is to be applied to a control volume comprising the fluid bounded by the body and the three dotted cross sections.   As the problem is steady, Eq. (3.11.1) reduces to

$$\Sigma \mathbf{F} = \int \rho \mathbf{v} \mathbf{v} \cdot d\mathbf{A} = \sum_{\text{out}} \mathbf{M}_i$$

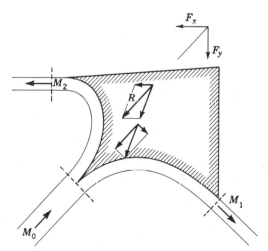

**Fig. 3.22**  Solution of linear momentum problem by addition of vectors.

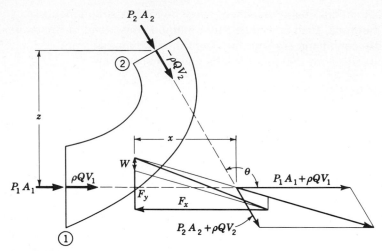

**Fig. 3.23** Forces on a reducing elbow, including the vector solution.

By taking $\mathbf{M}_1$ and $\mathbf{M}_0$ first, the vector $\mathbf{M}_1 - \mathbf{M}_0$ is the net momentum efflux for these two vectors, shown graphically on their lines of action. The resultant of these two vectors is then added to momentum efflux $\mathbf{M}_2$, along its line of action, to obtain $\mathbf{R}$. $\mathbf{R}$ is the momentum efflux over the control surface, and is just equal to the force that must be exerted on the control surface. The same force must then be exerted on the body, to resist the control-volume force on it.

**example 3.14** The reducing bend of Fig. 3.23 is in a vertical plane. Water is flowing, $D_1 = 6$ ft, $D_2 = 4$ ft, $Q = 300$ cfs, $W = 18{,}000$ lb, $z = 10$ ft, $\theta = 120°$, $p_1 = 40$ psi, $x = 6$ ft, and losses through the bend are $0.5 V_2^2/2g$ ft-lb/lb. Determine $F_x$, $F_y$, and the line of action of the resultant force. $\beta_1 = \beta_2 = 1$.

The inside surface of the reducing bend comprises the control-volume surface for the portion of the surface with no flow across it. The normal sections 1 and 2 complete the control surface.

$$V_1 = \frac{Q}{A_1} = \frac{300}{\pi(6)^2/4} = 10.61 \text{ ft/sec}$$

$$V_2 = \frac{Q}{A_2} = \frac{300}{\pi(4)^2/4} = 23.88 \text{ ft/sec}$$

By application of the energy equation, Eq. (3.10.1),

$$\frac{p_1}{\gamma} + \frac{V_1{}^2}{2g} + z_1 = \frac{p_2}{\gamma} + \frac{V_2{}^2}{2g} + z_2 + \text{losses}_{1-2}$$

$$\frac{40 \times 144}{62.4} + \frac{(10.61)^2}{64.4} + 0 = \frac{p_2}{62.4} + \frac{(23.88)^2}{64.4} + 10 + 0.5 \times \frac{(23.88)^2}{64.4}$$

from which $p_2 = 4420 \text{ lb/ft}^2 = 30.7$ psi.
To determine $F_x$, Eq. (3.11.2) yields

$$p_1A_1 - p_2A_2 \cos\theta - F_x = \rho Q(V_2 \cos\theta - V_1)$$
$$40 \times 144\pi(3)^2 - 4420\pi(2)^2 \cos 120° - F_x = 1.935 \times 300(23.88 \cos 120° -$$
$$10.61)$$

Since $\cos 120° = -0.5$,

$$162,900 + 27,750 - F_x = 580.5(-11.94 - 10.61)$$
$$F_x = 203,740 \text{ lb}$$

For the $y$-direction

$$\Sigma F_y = \rho Q(V_{y2} - V_{y1})$$
$$F_y - W - p_2A_2 \sin\theta = \rho Q V_2 \sin\theta$$
$$F_y - 18,000 - 4420\pi(2)^2 \sin 120° = 1.935 \times 300 \times 23.88 \sin 120°$$
$$F_y = 78,100 \text{ lb}$$

To find the line of action of the resultant force, using the momentum flux vectors (Fig. 3.23), $\rho Q V_1 = 6160$ lb, $\rho Q V_2 = 13,860$ lb, $p_1A_1 = 162,900$ lb, $p_2A_2 = 55,560$ lb. Combining these vectors and the weight $W$ in Fig. 3.23 yields the final force, 218,000 lb, which must be opposed by $F_x$ and $F_y$.

In this example gage pressures were used. If absolute pressures had been used, a different answer would result. $F_x$ and $F_y$ would be changed, but when atmospheric pressure on the surface of the bend is considered, the same forces for the anchor would be obtained, since the integration of atmospheric pressure over the entire control surface will yield a zero force component in the $x$-, $y$-, and $z$-directions.

As demonstrated in Example 3.14, a change in direction of a pipeline causes forces to be exerted on the line unless the bend or elbow is anchored in place. These forces are due to both static pressure in the line and dynamic reactions in the turning fluid stream. Expansion joints are placed in large pipelines to avoid stress in the pipe in an axial direction, whether caused by fluid or by temperature change. These expansion joints permit relatively free movement of the line in an axial direction, and hence the static and dynamic forces must be provided for at the bends.

**Fig. 3.24** Nozzle mounted on boat.

**example 3.15** A jet of water 3 in. in diameter with a velocity of 120 ft/sec is discharged in a horizontal direction from a nozzle mounted on a boat. What force is required to hold the boat stationary?

Selecting the control volume as shown in Fig. 3.24, the net efflux of momentum is [Eq. (3.11.2)]

$$F_x = \rho Q(V_{x2} - V_{x1}) = \rho Q V = 1.935 \times \frac{\pi}{64} \, 120(120 - 0) = 1370 \text{ lb}$$

The force exerted against the boat is 1370 lb along the $x$-direction.

**example 3.16** Find the force exerted by the nozzle on the pipe of Fig. 3.25a. Neglect losses. The fluid is oil, sp gr 0.85, and $p_1 = 100$ psi.

To determine the discharge, Bernoulli's equation is written for the stream from section 1 to the downstream end of the nozzle, where the pressure is zero.

$$z_1 + \frac{V_1^2}{2g} + \frac{100}{0.85 \times 0.433} = z_2 + \frac{V_2^2}{2g} + 0$$

Since $z_1 = z_2$, and $V_2 = (D_1/D_2)^2 V_1 = 9V_1$, after substituting,

$$\frac{V_1^2}{2g}(1 - 81) + \frac{100}{0.85 \times 0.433} = 0$$

and $V_1 = 14.78$ ft/sec, $V_2 = 133$ ft/sec, $Q = 14.78 \dfrac{\pi}{4}\left(\dfrac{1}{4}\right)^2 = 0.725$ cfs.

| (a) | (b) |

**Fig. 3.25** Nozzle at the end of a pipe.

Let $P_x$ (Fig. 3.25$b$) be the force exerted on the liquid control volume by the nozzle; then, with Eq. (3.11.2),

$$100\,\frac{\pi}{4}\,9 - P_x = 1.935 \times 0.85 \times 0.725(133 - 14.78)$$

or $P_x = 565$ lb.   The oil exerts a force on the nozzle of 565 lb to the right, and a tension force of 565 lb is exerted by the nozzle on the pipe.

In many situations an unsteady-flow problem can be converted to a steady-flow problem by superposing a constant velocity upon the system and its surroundings, i.e., by changing the reference velocity. The dynamics of a system and its surroundings are unchanged by the super-position of a constant velocity, hence, pressures and forces are unchanged. In the next flow situation studied, advantage is taken of this principle.

*the momentum theory for propellers*

The action of a propeller is to change the momentum of the fluid within which it is submerged and thus to develop a thrust that is used for propulsion.   Propellers cannot be designed according to the momentum theory, although some of the relations governing them are made evident by its application.   A propeller, with its slipstream and velocity distributions at two sections a fixed distance from it, is shown in Fig. 3.26.   The propeller

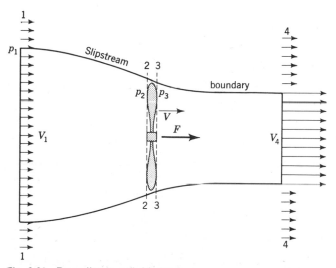

**Fig. 3.26**  Propeller in a fluid stream.

may be either (1) stationary in a flow as indicated or (2) moving to the left with a velocity $V_1$ through a stationary fluid since the relative picture is the same. The fluid is assumed to be frictionless and incompressible.

The flow is undisturbed at section 1 upstream from the propeller and is accelerated as it approaches the propeller, owing to the reduced pressure on its upstream side. In passing through the propeller, the fluid has its pressure increased, which further accelerates the flow and reduces the cross section at 4. The velocity $V$ does not change across the propeller, from 2 to 3. The pressure at 1 and 4 is that of the undisturbed fluid, which is also the pressure along the slipstream boundary.

When the momentum equation (3.11.2) is applied to the control volume within sections 1 and 4 and the slipstream boundary of Fig. 3.26, the force $F$ exerted by the propeller is the only external force acting in the axial direction since the pressure is everywhere the same on the control surface. Therefore

$$F = \rho Q(V_4 - V_1) = (p_3 - p_2)A \qquad (3.11.5)$$

in which $A$ is the area swept over by the propeller blades. The force on the propeller must be equal and opposite to the force on the fluid. After substituting $Q = AV$ and simplifying,

$$\rho V(V_4 - V_1) = p_3 - p_2 \qquad (3.11.6)$$

When Bernoulli's equation is written for the stream between sections 1 and 2 and between sections 3 and 4,

$$p_1 + \tfrac{1}{2}\rho V_1{}^2 = p_2 + \tfrac{1}{2}\rho V^2 \qquad p_3 + \tfrac{1}{2}\rho V^2 = p_4 + \tfrac{1}{2}\rho V_4{}^2$$

since $z_1 = z_2 = z_3 = z_4$. In solving for $p_3 - p_2$, with $p_1 = p_4$,

$$p_3 - p_2 = \tfrac{1}{2}\rho(V_4{}^2 - V_1{}^2) \qquad (3.11.7)$$

By eliminating $p_3 - p_2$ in Eqs. (3.11.6) and 3.11.7),

$$V = \frac{V_1 + V_4}{2} \qquad (3.11.8)$$

which shows that the velocity through the propeller area is the average of the velocities upstream and downstream from it.

The useful work done by a propeller moving through still fluid is the product of propeller thrust and velocity, i.e.,

$$\text{Power} = FV_1 = \rho Q(V_4 - V_1)V_1 \qquad (3.11.9)$$

The power input is that required to increase the velocity of fluid from $V_1$

to $V_4$, or the useful work plus the kinetic energy per unit time remaining in the slipstream.

$$\text{Power input} = \rho \frac{Q}{2} (V_4{}^2 - V_1{}^2) = \rho Q (V_4 - V_1) V_1$$

$$+ \rho \frac{Q}{2} (V_4 - V_1)^2 \quad (3.11.10)$$

With the ratio of Eqs. (3.11.9) and (3.11.10) used to obtain the theoretical efficiency $e_t$,

$$e_t = \frac{2V_1}{V_4 + V_1} = \frac{V_1}{V} \quad (3.11.11)$$

If $\Delta V = V_4 - V_1$ is the increase in slipstream velocity, substituting into Eq. (3.11.11) produces

$$e_t = \frac{V_1}{V_1 + \Delta V / 2} \quad (3.11.12)$$

which shows that maximum efficiency is obtained with a propeller that increases the velocity of slipstream as little as possible, or for which $\Delta V / V_1$ is a minimum.

Owing to compressibility effects, the efficiency of an airplane propeller drops rapidly with speeds above 400 mph.  Airplane propellers under optimum conditions have actual efficiencies close to the theoretical efficiencies, in the neighborhood of 85 per cent.  Ship propeller efficiencies are less, around 60 per cent, owing to restrictions in diameter.

The windmill may be analyzed by application of the momentum relations. The jet has its speed reduced, and the diameter of slipstream is increased.

**example 3.17**   An airplane traveling 250 mph through still air, $\gamma = 0.080$ lb/ft³, discharges 33,000 cfs through its two 7.0-ft-diameter propellers. Determine (a) the theoretical efficiency, (b) the thrust, (c) the pressure difference across the blades, and (d) the theoretical horsepower required.

(a)   $V_1 = \dfrac{250 \times 88}{60} = 366 \text{ ft/sec} \qquad V = \dfrac{16,500}{49\pi/4} = 428 \text{ ft/sec}$

From Eq. (3.11.11)

$$e_t = \frac{V_1}{V} = \frac{366}{428} = 85.5 \%$$

(b)   From Eq. (3.11.8)

$$V_4 = 2V - V_1 = 2 \times 428 - 366 = 490 \text{ ft/sec}$$

The thrust from both propellers is, from Eq. (3.11.5),

$$F = \frac{0.080}{32.2} \times 33,000(490 - 366) = 10,170 \text{ lb}$$

(c)   The pressure difference, from Eq. (3.11.6), is

$$p_3 - p_2 = \frac{0.080}{32.2} 428(490 - 366) = 132 \text{ lb/ft}^2$$

(d)   The theoretical horsepower is

$$\frac{FV_1}{550e_t} = \frac{10,170 \times 366}{550 \times 0.855} = 7920$$

*jet propulsion*

The propeller is one form of jet propulsion in that it creates a jet and by so doing has a thrust exerted upon it that is the propelling force.   In jet engines, air (initially at rest) is taken into the engine and burned with a small amount of fuel; the gases are then ejected with a much higher velocity than in a propeller slipstream.   The jet diameter is necessarily smaller than the propeller slipstream.   For the mechanical energy only, the theoretical efficiency is given by the ratio of useful work to work input or by useful work divided by the sum of useful work and kinetic energy per unit time remaining in the jet.   If the mass of fuel burned is neglected, the propelling force $F$ [Eq. (3.11.5)] is

$$F = \rho Q(V_2 - V_1) = \rho Q V_{\text{abs}} \tag{3.11.13}$$

in which $V_{\text{abs}}$ (Fig. 3.27) is the absolute velocity of fluid in the jet and $\rho Q$ is the mass per unit time being discharged.   The useful work is $FV_1$, in which $V_1$ is the speed of the body.   The kinetic energy per unit time being

**Fig. 3.27**  Walls of flow passages through jet engine taken as impenetrable part of control surface for plane when viewed as a steady-state problem.

discharged in the jet is $\gamma Q V_{abs}^2/2g = \rho Q V_{abs}^2/2$, since $\gamma Q$ is the weight per unit time being discharged and $V_{abs}^2/2g$ is the kinetic energy per unit weight. Hence, the theoretical mechanical efficiency is

$$e_t = \frac{\text{output}}{\text{output} + \text{loss}} = \frac{FV_1}{FV_1 + \rho Q V_{abs}^2/2}$$

$$= \frac{\rho Q V_{abs} V_1}{\rho Q V_{abs} V_1 + \rho Q V_{abs}^2/2} = \frac{1}{1 + V_{abs}/2V_1} \tag{3.11.14}$$

which is the same expression as that for efficiency of the propeller. It is obvious that, other things being equal, $V_{abs}/V_1$ should be as small as possible. For a given speed $V_1$, the resistance force $F$ is determined by the body and fluid in which it moves; hence, for $V_{abs}$ in Eq. (3.11.13) to be very small, $\rho Q$ must be very large.

An example is the type of propulsion system to be used on a boat. If the boat requires a force of 400 lb to move it through water at 15 mph, first a method of jet propulsion can be considered in which water is taken in at the bow and discharged out the stern by a 100-per-cent-efficient pumping system. To analyze the propulsion system the problem is converted to steady state by superposition of the boat speed $-V_1$ on boat and surroundings (Fig. 3.28).

If a 6-in.-diameter jet pipe is used, $V_2 = 16Q/\pi$. By use of Eq. (3.11.2), for $V_1 = 15$ mph $= 22$ ft/sec,

$$400 = 1.935Q \left( \frac{16Q}{\pi} - 22 \right)$$

Hence $Q = 8.89$ cfs, $V_{abs} = 23.2$, and the efficiency is

$$e_t = \frac{1}{1 + V_{abs}/2V_1} = \frac{1}{1 + 23.2/44} = 65.5\%$$

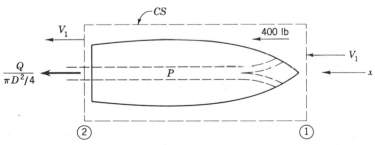

**Fig. 3.28** Steady-state flow around boat.

The horsepower required is

$$\frac{FV_1}{550e_t} = \frac{400 \times 22}{550 \times 0.655} = 24.4$$

With an 8-in.-diameter jet pipe, $V_2 = 9Q/\pi$, and

$$400 = 1.935Q \left(\frac{9Q}{\pi} - 22\right)$$

so that $Q = 13.14$ cfs, $V_2 = 15.72$, $e_t = 73.7$ per cent, and the horsepower required is 21.7.

 With additional enlarging of the jet pipe and the pumping of more water with less velocity head, the efficiency can be further increased.   The type of pump best suited for large flows at small head is the axial-flow propeller pump.   Increasing the size of pump and jet pipe would increase weight greatly and take up useful space in the boat; the logical limit is to drop the propeller down below or behind the boat and thus eliminate the jet pipe, which is the usual propeller for boats.   Jet propulsion of a boat by a jet pipe is practical, however, in very shallow water where a propeller would be damaged by striking bottom or other obstructions.

 To take the weight of fuel into account in jet propulsion of aircraft, let $\dot{m}_{air}$ be the mass of air per unit time and $r$ the ratio of mass of fuel burned to mass of air.   Then (Fig. 3.27), the propulsive force $F$ is

$$F = \dot{m}_{air}(V_2 - V_1) + r\dot{m}_{air}V_2$$

The second term on the right is the mass of fuel per unit time multiplied by its change in velocity.   By rearranging,

$$F = \dot{m}_{air}[V_2(1 + r) - V_1] \tag{3.11.15}$$

Defining the mechanical efficiency again as the useful work divided by the sum of useful work and kinetic energy remaining,

$$e_t = \frac{FV_1}{FV_1 + \dot{m}_{air}(1 + r)(V_2 - V_1)^2/2}$$

By use of Eq. (3.11.15)

$$e_t = \frac{1}{1 + \dfrac{(1 + r)[(V_2/V_1) - 1]^2}{2[(1 + r)(V_2/V_1) - 1]}} \tag{3.11.16}$$

The efficiency becomes unity for $V_1 = V_2$, as the combustion products are then brought to rest and no kinetic energy remains in the jet.

**example 3.18**   An airplane consumes 1 lb$_m$ fuel for each 20 lb$_m$ air and discharges hot gases from the tail pipe at $V_2 = 6000$ ft/sec.   Determine the mechanical efficiency for airplane speeds of 1000 and 500 ft/sec.

For 1000 ft/sec, $V_2/V_1 = \frac{6000}{1000} = 6$, $r = 0.05$.   From Eq. (3.11.16),

$$e_t = \cfrac{1}{1 + \cfrac{(1 + 0.05)(6 - 1)^2}{2[6(1 + 0.05) - 1]}} = 0.287$$

For 500 ft/sec, $V_2/V_1 = \frac{6000}{500} = 12$ and

$$e_t = \cfrac{1}{1 + \cfrac{(1 + 0.05)(12 - 1)^2}{2[12(1 + 0.05) - 1]}} = 0.154$$

*jet propulsion of aircraft or missiles*

Propulsion through air or water in each case is caused by reaction to the formation of a jet behind the body.   The various means include the propeller, turbojet, turboprop, ram jet, and rocket motor, which are briefly described in the following paragraphs.

The momentum relations for a propeller determine that its theoretical efficiency increases as the speed of the aircraft increases and the absolute velocity of the slipstream decreases.   As the speed of the blade tips approaches the speed of sound, however, compressibility effects greatly increase the drag on the blades and thus decrease the over-all efficiency of the propulsion system.

A *turbojet* is an engine consisting of a compressor, a combustion chamber, a turbine, and a jet pipe.   Air is scooped through the front of the engine and is compressed, and fuel is added and burned with a great excess of air. The air and combustion gases then pass through a gas turbine that drives the compressor.   Only a portion of the energy of the hot gases is removed by the turbine, since the only means of propulsion is the issuance of the hot gas through the jet pipe.   The over-all efficiency of a jet engine increases with speed of the aircraft.   Although there is very little information available on propeller systems near the speed of sound, it appears that the over-all efficiencies of the turbojet and propeller systems are about the same at the speed of sound.

The *turboprop* is a system combining thrust from a propeller with thrust from the ejection of hot gases.   The gas turbine must drive both compressor and propeller.   The proportion of thrust between the propeller and the jet may be selected arbitrarily by the designer.

The *ram jet* is a high-speed engine that has neither compressor nor turbine. The ram pressure of the air forces air into the front of the engine, where some of the kinetic energy is converted into pressure energy by enlarging the flow cross section. It then enters a combustion chamber, where fuel is burned, and the air and gases of combustion are ejected through a jet pipe. It is a supersonic device requiring very high speed for compression of the air. An intermittent ram jet was used by the Germans in the V-1 *buzz bomb*. Air is admitted through spring-closed flap valves in the nose. Fuel is ignited to build up pressure that closes the flap valves and ejects the hot gases as a jet. The ram pressure then opens the valves in the nose to repeat the cycle. The cyclic rate is around 40 per second. Such a device must be launched at high speed to initiate operation of the ram jet.

### rocket mechanics

The rocket motor carries with it an oxidizing agent to mix with its fuel so that it develops a thrust that is independent of the medium through which it travels. In contrast, a gas turbine can eject a mass many times the mass of fuel it carries because it takes in air to mix with the fuel.

To determine the acceleration of a rocket during flight, Fig. 3.29, it is

**Fig. 3.29** Control surface for analysis of rocket acceleration. Frame of reference has the velocity $V_1$ of the rocket.

convenient to take the control volume as the outer surface of the rocket, with a plane area normal to the jet across the nozzle exit.  The control volume has a velocity equal to the velocity of the rocket at the instant the analysis is made.  Let $R$ be the air resistance, $m_R$ the mass of the rocket body, $m_f$ the mass of fuel, $\dot{m}$ the rate at which fuel is being burned, and $v_r$ the exit gas velocity relative to the rocket.  $V_1$ is the actual velocity of the rocket (and of the frame of reference) and $V$ is the velocity of the rocket relative to the frame of reference.  $V$ is zero but $dV/dt = dV_1/dt$ is the rocket acceleration.  The basic linear momentum equation for the $y$-direction

$$\Sigma F_y = \frac{\partial}{\partial t} \int_{cv} \rho v_y \, d\mathcal{V} + \int_{cs} \rho v_y \mathbf{v} \cdot d\mathbf{A} \qquad (3.11.17)$$

becomes

$$-R - (m_R + m_f)g = \frac{\partial}{\partial t}\left[(m_R + m_f)V\right] - \dot{m}v_r \qquad (3.11.18)$$

Since $V$ is a function of $t$ only, the equation can be written as a total differential equation

$$\frac{dV}{dt} = \frac{dV_1}{dt} = \frac{\dot{m}v_r - g(m_f + m_R) - R}{m_R + m_f} \qquad (3.11.19)$$

The mass of propellant reduces with time; for constant burning rate $\dot{m}$, $m_f = m_{f_0} - \dot{m}t$, with $m_{f_0}$ the initial mass of fuel and oxidizer.  Gravity is a function of $y$, and the air resistance depends on the Reynolds number and Mach number (Chap. 4), as well as on the shape and size of the rocket.

By considering the mass of rocket and fuel together [Eq. (3.11.19)], the thrust $\dot{m}v_r$ minus the weight and the air resistance just equals the combined mass times its acceleration.

The theoretical efficiency of a rocket motor (based on available energy) is shown to increase with rocket speed.  $E$ represents the available energy in the propellant per unit mass.  When the propellant is ignited, its available energy is converted into kinetic energy; $E = v_r^2/2$, in which $v_r$ is the jet velocity relative to the rocket, or $v_r = \sqrt{2E}$.  For rocket speed $V_1$ referred to axes fixed in the earth, the useful work is $\dot{m}v_r V_1$.  The kinetic energy being used up per unit time is due to mass loss $\dot{m}V_1^2/2$ of the unburned propellant and to the burning $\dot{m}E$, or

$$\text{Available energy input per unit time} = \dot{m}\left(E + \frac{V_1^2}{2}\right) \qquad (3.11.20)$$

The mechanical efficiency $e$ is

$$e = \frac{\dot{m} V_1 \sqrt{2E}}{\dot{m}(E + V_1{}^2/2)} = \frac{2v_r/V_1}{1 + (v_r/V_1)^2} \qquad (3.11.21)$$

When $v_r/V_1 = 1$, the maximum efficiency $e = 1$ is obtained. In this case the absolute velocity of ejected gas is zero.

When the thrust on a vertical rocket is greater than the total weight plus resistance, the rocket accelerates. Its mass is continuously reduced. To lift a rocket off its pad, its thrust $\dot{m}v_r$ must exceed its total weight.

**example 3.19** ($a$) Determine the burning time for a rocket that initially weighs 1,000,000 lb, of which 70 per cent is propellant. It consumes a fuel at constant rate, and its initial thrust is 10 per cent greater than its weight. $v_r = 11,000$ ft/sec. ($b$) Considering $g$ constant at 32.17 ft/sec² and the flight to be vertical without air resistance, find the speed of the rocket at burnout time, its height above ground, and the maximum height it will attain.

($a$)   From the thrust-weight relation,

$$\dot{m}v_r = 1.1W_0 = 1,100,000 = \dot{m}11,000$$

and $\dot{m} = 100$ slugs/sec.   The available mass of propellant is

$$\frac{0.7 \times 1,000,000}{32.17} = 21,750 \text{ slugs}$$

Hence the burning time is

$$\frac{21,750}{100} = 217.5 \text{ sec}$$

($b$)   From Eq. (3.11.19)

$$100 \times 11,000 = 32.17(21,750 - 100t) + 300,000$$
$$+ \left(21,750 - 100t + \frac{300,000}{32.17}\right) \frac{dV_1}{dt}$$

Simplifying,

$$\frac{dV_1}{dt} = \frac{1000 + 32.17t}{310.8 - t} = -32.17 + \frac{11,000}{310.8 - t}$$

$$V_1 = -32.71t - 11,000 \ln (310.8 - t) + \text{const}$$

When $t = 0$, $V_1 = 0$, hence

$$V_1 = -32.17t - 11,000 \ln \left(1 - \frac{t}{310.8}\right)$$

When $t = 217.5$, $V_1 = 6243$ ft/sec $= 4258$ mph.   The height at $t = 217.5$ is

$$y = \int_0^{217.5} V_1 \, dt = -32.17 \left. \frac{t^2}{2} \right]_0^{217.5} - 11,000 \int_0^{217.5} \ln \left( 1 - \frac{t}{310.8} \right) dt$$

$$= 397,000 \text{ ft} = 75.2 \text{ miles}$$

The rocket will glide $V_1^2/2g$ ft higher after burnout, or

$$397,000 + \frac{(6243)^2}{64.34} = 1,003,000 \text{ ft} = 190 \text{ miles}$$

*fixed and moving vanes*

The theory of turbomachines is based on the relationships between jets
and vanes.   The mechanics of transfer of work and energy from fluid jets
to moving vanes is studied as an application of the momentum principles.
When a free jet impinges onto a smooth vane that is curved, as in Fig. 3.30,
the jet is deflected, its momentum is changed, and a force is exerted on the
vane.   The jet is assumed to flow onto the vane in a tangential direction,
without shock; and furthermore, the frictional resistance between jet and
vane is neglected.   The velocity is assumed to be uniform throughout the
jet upstream and downstream from the vane.   Since the jet is open to the
air, it has the same pressure at each end of the vane.   Neglecting the small
change in elevation between ends, if any, application of Bernoulli's equation
shows that the magnitude of the velocity is unchanged for *fixed* vanes.

**example 3.20**   Find the force exerted on a fixed vane when a jet discharging
2 cfs water at 150 ft/sec is deflected through 135°.
   By referring to Fig. 3.30 and by applying Eq. (3.11.2) in the $x$- and $y$-

**Fig. 3.30**  Free jet impinging on smooth, fixed vane.

directions, it is found that

$$-F_x = \rho Q(V_0 \cos \theta - V_0)$$
$$F_y = \rho Q V_0 \sin \theta$$

Hence,

$$F_x = -1.935 \times 2(150 \cos 135° - 150) = 990 \text{ lb}$$
$$F_y = 1.935 \times 2 \times 150 \sin 135° = 410 \text{ lb}$$

The force components on the fixed vane are then equal and opposite to $F_x$ and $F_y$.

**example 3.21**    Fluid issues from a long slot and strikes against a smooth inclined flat plate (Fig. 3.31).    Determine the division of flow and the force exerted on the plate, neglecting losses due to impact.

As there are no changes in elevation or pressure before and after impact the magnitude of the velocity leaving is the same as the initial speed of jet. The division of flow $Q_1$, $Q_2$ can be computed by applying the momentum equation in the $s$-direction, parallel to the plate.    No force is exerted on the fluid by the plate in this direction; hence, the final momentum component must equal the initial momentum component in the $s$-direction.    By rewriting the momentum equation so that it contains two terms for final momentum,

$$F_s = 0 = \rho Q_1 V_0 - \rho Q_2 V_0 - \rho Q_0 V_0 \cos \theta$$

After simplifying,

$$Q_1 - Q_2 = Q_0 \cos \theta$$

**Fig. 3.31**  Two-dimensional jet impinging on an inclined, fixed plane surface.

and with the continuity equation,

$$Q_1 + Q_2 = Q_0$$

The two equations may be solved for $Q_1$ and $Q_2$,

$$Q_1 = \frac{Q_0}{2}(1 + \cos \theta)$$

$$Q_2 = \frac{Q_0}{2}(1 - \cos \theta)$$

The force $F$ exerted on the plate must be normal to it.  For the momentum equation normal to the plate,

$$F = \rho Q_0 V_0 \sin \theta$$

*moving vanes*

Turbomachinery utilizes the forces resulting from the motion over moving vanes.  No work can be done on or by a fluid that flows over a fixed vane. When vanes can be displaced, work can be done either on the vane or on the fluid.  In Fig. 3.32a a moving vane is shown with fluid flowing onto it tangentially.  Forces exerted on the fluid by the vane are indicated by $F_x$

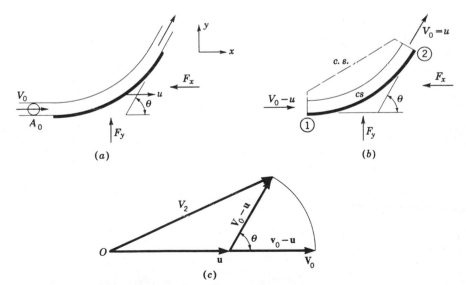

**Fig. 3.32**  (*a*) Moving vane.  (*b*) Vane flow viewed as steady-state problem by superposition of velocity $u$ to the left.  (*c*) Polar vector diagram.

and $F_y$. To analyze the flow the problem is reduced to steady state by superposition of vane velocity $u$ to the left (Fig. 3.32$b$) on both vane and fluid. The control volume then encloses the fluid in contact with the vane, with its control surface normal to the flow at sections 1 and 2. Figure 3.32$c$ shows the *polar vector diagram* for flow through the vane. The absolute velocity vectors originate at the origin $O$, and the relative velocity vector $\mathbf{V}_0 - \mathbf{u}$ is turned through the angle $\theta$ of the vane as shown. $\mathbf{V}_2$ is the final absolute velocity leaving the vane. The relative velocity is unchanged in magnitude as it traverses the vane. The mass per unit time is given by $\rho A_0 v_r$, and is not the mass rate being discharged from the nozzle in the case of a single moving vane. If a *series of vanes* is employed, as on the periphery of a wheel, arranged so that one or another of the jets intercepts all flow from the nozzle and so that the velocity is substantially $u$, then the mass per second is the total mass per second being discharged.

**example 3.22**  Determine for a single moving vane of Fig. 3.33$a$ the force components due to the water jet and the rate of work done on the vane.

Figure 3.33$b$ is the steady-state reduction with a control volume shown. The polar vector diagram is shown in Fig. 3.33$c$. The mass per second entering the control volume is

$$\rho A v_r = 1.935 \times 60 \times \frac{3}{144} = 2.42 \text{ slugs/sec}$$

$$A = 3 \text{ in.}^2$$

(a)

(b)

(c)

**Fig. 3.33**  Jet acting on a moving vane.

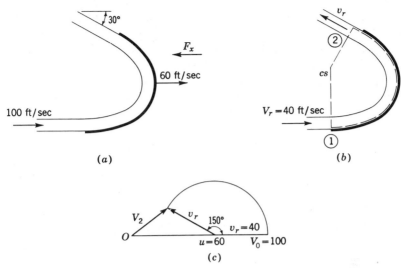

**Fig. 3.34**  Flow through moving vanes.

By applying Eq. (3.11.2) in the $x$- and $y$-directions to the control volume,

$$-F_x = 2.42(-60 \cos 10° - 60) = -288 \text{ lb}$$
$$F_y = 2.42 \times 60 \sin 10° = 25.3 \text{ lb}$$

The work done on the vane is

$$uF_x = 60 \times 288 = 17,280 \text{ ft-lb/sec}$$

**example 3.23**  Determine the horsepower that may be obtained from a series of vanes (Fig. 3.34$a$), curved through 150°, moving 60 ft/sec away from a 3.0-cfs water jet having a cross section of 0.03 ft². Draw the polar vector diagram and calculate the energy remaining in the jet.

The jet velocity is $V_0 = 3/0.03 = 100$ ft/sec. The steady-state vane control volume is shown in Fig. 3.34$b$ and the polar vector diagram in Fig. 3.34$c$. The force on a vane (or several vanes if the flow is split among them) is given by

$$-F_x = 1.935 \times 3 \times (-40 \cos 30° - 40) = -433 \text{ lb}$$

The horsepower is

$$\text{hp} = \frac{433 \times 60}{550} = 47.3$$

The components of absolute velocity leaving the vane are, from Fig. 3.34c,

$V_{2x} = 60 - 40 \cos 30° = 25.4 \text{ ft/sec}$
$V_{2y} = 40 \sin 30° = 20 \text{ ft/sec}$

and the exit velocity head is

$$\frac{V_2^2}{2g} = \frac{(25.4)^2 + (20)^2}{64.4} = 16.2 \text{ ft-lb/lb}$$

The kinetic energy remaining in the jet, in foot pounds per second, is

$$Q\gamma \frac{V_2^2}{2g} = 3 \times 62.4 \times 16.2 = 3030 \text{ ft-lb/sec}$$

The initial kinetic energy available was

$$3 \times 62.4 \times \frac{(100)^2}{64.4} = 29{,}030 \text{ ft-lb/sec}$$

which is the sum of the work done and the energy remaining per second.

When a vane, or series of vanes, moves toward a jet, work is done by the vane system on the fluid, thereby increasing the energy of the fluid. Figure 3.35 illustrates this situation; the polar vector diagram shows the exit velocity to be greater than the entering velocity.

In turbulent flow, losses generally must be determined from experimental tests on the system or a geometrically similar model of the system.    In the following two cases, application of the continuity, energy, and momentum equations permits the losses to be evaluated analytically.

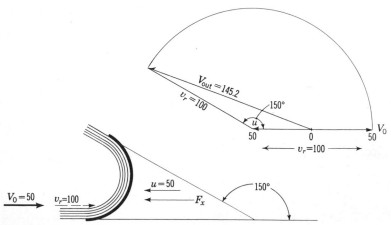

**Fig. 3.35** Vector diagram for vane doing work on jet.

**Fig. 3.36**   Sudden expansion in a pipe.

*losses due to sudden expansion in a pipe*

The losses due to sudden enlargement in a pipeline may be calculated with both the energy and momentum equations.   For steady, incompressible, turbulent flow through the control volume between sections 1 and 2 of the sudden expansion of Fig. 3.36a, b, the small shear force exerted on the walls between the two sections may be neglected.   By assuming uniform velocity over the flow cross sections, which is approached in turbulent flow, application of Eq. (3.11.2) produces

$$p_1A_2 - p_2A_2 = \frac{Q\gamma}{g}(V_2 - V_1)$$

At section 1 the radial acceleration of fluid particles in the eddy along the surface is small, and so generally a hydrostatic pressure variation occurs across the section.   The energy equation (3.10.1) applied to sections 1 and 2, with the loss term $h_l$, is (for $\alpha - 1$)

$$\frac{V_1^2}{2g} + \frac{p_1}{\gamma} = \frac{V_2^2}{2g} + \frac{p_2}{\gamma} + h_l$$

Solving for $(p_1 - p_2)/\gamma$ in each equation and equating the results,

$$\frac{Q}{A_2g}(V_2 - V_1) = \frac{V_2^2 - V_1^2}{2g} + h_l$$

As $Q/A_2 = V_2$,

$$h_l = \frac{(V_1 - V_2)^2}{2g} = \frac{V_1^2}{2g}\left(1 - \frac{A_1}{A_2}\right)^2 \tag{3.11.22}$$

which indicates that the losses in turbulent flow are proportional to the square of the velocity.

*hydraulic jump*

The hydraulic jump is the second application of the basic equations to determine losses due to a turbulent-flow situation.   Under proper condi-

**Fig. 3.37** Hydraulic jump in a rectangular channel.

tions a rapidly flowing stream of liquid in an open channel suddenly changes to a slowly flowing stream with a larger cross-sectional area and a sudden rise in elevation of liquid surface. This phenomenon is known as the *hydraulic jump* and is an example of steady nonuniform flow. In effect, the rapidly flowing liquid jet expands (Fig. 3.37) and converts kinetic energy into potential energy and losses or irreversibilities. A roller develops on the inclined surface of the expanding liquid jet and draws air into the liquid. The surface of the jump is very rough and turbulent, the losses being greater as the jump height is greater. For small heights, the form of the jump changes to a standing wave (Fig. 3.38). The jump is discussed further in Sec. 10.4.

The relations among the variables for the hydraulic jump in a horizontal rectangular channel are easily obtained by use of the continuity, momentum, and energy equations. For convenience the width of channel is taken as unity. The continuity equation (Fig. 3.37) is

$$V_1 y_1 = V_2 y_2$$

The momentum equation is

$$\frac{\gamma y_1^2}{2} - \frac{\gamma y_2^2}{2} = \frac{V_1 y_1 \gamma}{g}(V_2 - V_1)$$

and the energy equation (for points on the liquid surface) is

$$\frac{V_1^2}{2g} + y_1 = \frac{V_2^2}{2g} + y_2 + h_j$$

in which $h_j$ represents losses due to the jump. By eliminating $V_2$ in the

**Fig. 3.38** Standing wave.

first two equations,

$$y_2 = -\frac{y_1}{2} + \sqrt{\left(\frac{y_1}{2}\right)^2 + \frac{2V_1^2 y_1}{g}} \qquad (3.11.23)$$

in which the plus sign has been taken before the radical (a negative $y_2$ has no physical significance).  The depths $y_1$ and $y_2$ are referred to as *conjugate depths*.  By solving the energy equation for $h_j$ and eliminating $V_1$ and $V_2$,

$$h_j = \frac{(y_2 - y_1)^3}{4y_1 y_2} \qquad (3.11.24)$$

The hydraulic jump, which is a very effective device for creating irreversibilities, is commonly used at the end of chutes or the bottom of spillways to destroy much of the kinetic energy in the flow.  It is also an effective mixing chamber, because of the violent agitation that takes place in the roller.  Experimental measurements of hydraulic jumps show that the equations yield the correct value of $y_2$ to within 1 per cent.  The reasons the jump equations are not precise are due to neglect of shear stress on walls and to nonuniform velocity distribution.

**example 3.24**    120 cfs water per foot of width flows down a spillway onto a horizontal floor.  The velocity is 50 ft/sec.  Determine the depth of tail water required to cause a hydraulic jump and the losses in horsepower by the jump per foot of width.

$$y_1 = \frac{120}{50} = 2.4 \text{ ft}$$

By substituting into Eq. (3.11.23),

$$y_2 = -1.2 + \sqrt{(1.2)^2 + \frac{2 \times (50)^2 \times 2.4}{32.2}} = 18.1 \text{ ft}$$

With Eq. (3.11.24),

$$\text{Losses} = \frac{(18.1 - 2.4)^3}{4 \times 2.4 \times 18.1} = 22.3 \text{ ft-lb/lb}$$

or

$$\text{hp/ft} = \frac{120 \times 62.4 \times 22.3}{550} = 304$$

Before taking up the moment-of-momentum relations, an additional example of the application of the unsteady form of the linear momentum equation is considered.

**Fig. 3.39** Acceleration of liquid in a pipe.

**example 3.25** Find the head $H$ in the reservoir of Fig. 3.39 needed to accelerate the flow of oil, $S = 0.85$, at the rate of 0.5 ft/sec² when the flow is 8.02 ft/sec. At 8.02 ft/sec the steady-state head on the pipe is 20 ft. Neglect entrance loss.

The oil may be considered to be incompressible and to be moving uniformly in the pipeline. By applying Eq. (3.11.2), the last term is zero, as the net efflux is zero,

$$\gamma A \left( H - \frac{V^2}{2g} \right) - \gamma A \left[ 20 - \frac{(8.02)^2}{2g} \right] = \frac{\partial}{\partial t} \left( \frac{\gamma}{g} A L V \right)$$

or

$$H = 20 + \frac{1000}{32.2} \times 0.5 = 35.52 \text{ ft}$$

## 3.12 the moment-of-momentum equation

The general unsteady linear momentum equation applied to a control volume may be obtained from the component equations of the form of Eq. (3.11.1),

$$\mathbf{F} = \frac{\partial}{\partial t} \int_{cv} \rho \mathbf{v} \, d\upsilon + \int_{cs} \rho \mathbf{v} \mathbf{v} \cdot d\mathbf{A} \tag{3.12.1}$$

The moment of a force $\mathbf{F}$ about a point $O$ (Fig. 3.40) is given by

$$\mathbf{r} \times \mathbf{F}$$

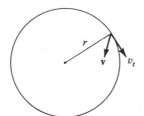

**Fig. 3.40** Notation for moment of a vector.

**Fig. 3.41** Notation for two-dimensional flow.

which is the cross, or vector, product of **F** and the position vector **r** of a point on the line of action of the vector from $O$. The cross product of two vectors is a vector at right angles to the plane defined by the first two vectors and with magnitude

$Fr \sin \theta$

which is the product of $F$ and the shortest distance from $O$ to the line of action of **F**. The sense of the final vector follows the right-hand rule. In Fig. 3.40 the force tends to cause a counterclockwise rotation around $O$. If this were a right-hand screw thread turning in this direction, it would tend to come up, and so the vector is likewise directed up out of the paper. If one curls the fingers of the right hand in the direction the force tends to cause rotation, the thumb yields the direction, or sense, of the vector.

By taking **r** ✕ **F**, using Eq. (3.12.1),

$$\mathbf{r} \times \mathbf{F} = \frac{\partial}{\partial t} \int_{cv} \rho \mathbf{r} \times \mathbf{v} \, d\mathrm{U} + \int_{cs} \rho \mathbf{r} \times \mathbf{vv} \cdot d\mathbf{A} \qquad (3.12.2)$$

The left-hand side of the equation is the torque exerted by any forces on the control volume, and terms on the right-hand side represent the rate of change of *moment of momentum* within the control volume plus the net efflux of moment of momentum from the control volume. This is the general moment-of-momentum equation for a control volume. It has great value in the analysis of certain flow problems, e.g., in turbomachinery, where torques are more significant than forces.

When Eq. (3.12.2) is applied to a case of flow in the $xy$-plane, with $r$ the shortest distance to the tangential component of the velocity $v_t$, as in Fig. 3.41, and $v_n$ is the normal component of velocity,

$$F_t r = T_z = \int_{cs} \rho r v_t v_n \, dA + \frac{\partial}{\partial t} \int_{cv} \rho r v_t \, d\mathrm{U} \qquad (3.12.3)$$

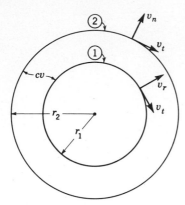

**Fig. 3.42** Flow through annular passage such as a centrifugal pump impeller.

in which $T_z$ is the torque. A useful form of Eq. (3.12.3) applied to an annular control volume, in steady flow (Fig. 3.42), is

$$T_z = \int_{A_2} \rho_2 r_2 v_{t_2} v_{n_2}\, dA_2 - \int_{A_1} \rho_1 r_1 v_{t_1} v_{n_1}\, dA_1 \tag{3.12.4}$$

For complete circular symmetry, where $r$, $\rho$, $v_t$, and $v_n$ are constant over the inlet and outlet control surfaces, it takes the simple form

$$T_z = \rho Q[(rv_t)_2 - (rv_t)_1] \tag{3.12.5}$$

since $\int \rho v_n\, dA = \rho Q$, the same at inlet or outlet.

**example 3.26** The sprinkler shown in Fig. 3.43 discharges water upward and outward from the horizontal plane so that it makes an angle of $\theta°$ with the $t$-axis when the sprinkler arm is at rest. It has a constant cross-sectional flow area of $A_0$ and discharges $q$ cfs starting with $\omega = 0$ and $t = 0$. The resisting torque due to bearings and seals is the constant $T_0$, and the moment of inertia of the rotating empty sprinkler head is $I_s$. Determine the equation for $\omega$ as a function of time.

Equation (3.12.2) may be applied. The control volume is the cylindrical area enclosing the rotating sprinkler head. The inflow is along the axis, so that it has no moment of momentum; hence the torque $-T_0$ due to friction is equal to the time rate of change of moment of momentum of sprinkler head and fluid within the sprinkler head plus the net efflux of moment of momentum from the control volume. Let $V_r = q/2A_0$

$$-T_0 = 2\frac{d}{dt}\int_0^{r_0} A_0 \rho \omega r^2\, dr + I_s \frac{d\omega}{dt} - \frac{2\rho q r_0}{2}(V_r \cos\theta - \omega r_0)$$

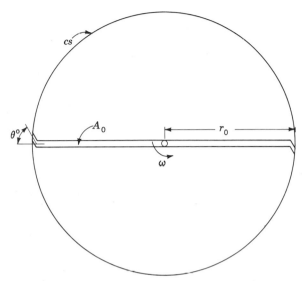

**Fig. 3.43**  Plan view of sprinkler and control surface.

The total derivative may be used.  After simplifying

$$\frac{d\omega}{dt}\left(I_s + \frac{2}{3}\rho A_0 r_0^3\right) = \rho q r_0 (V_r \cos\theta - \omega r_0) - T_0$$

For rotation to start $\rho q r_0 V_r \cos\theta$ must be greater than $T_0$.  The equation is easily integrated to find $\omega$ as a function of $t$.  The final value of $\omega$ is obtained by setting $d\omega/dt = 0$ in the equation.

**example 3.27**  A turbine discharging 400 cfs is to be designed so that a torque of 10,000 lb·ft is to be exerted on an impeller turning at 200 rpm that takes all the moment of momentum out of the fluid.  At the outer periphery of the impeller, $r = 3.0$ ft.  What must the tangential component of velocity be at this location?
  Equation (3.12.5) is

$$T = \rho Q (r v_t)_{in}$$

in this case, since the outflow has $v_t = 0$.  By solving for $v_{t_{in}}$

$$v_{t_{in}} = \frac{T}{\rho Q r} = \frac{10,000}{1.935 \times 400 \times 3} = 4.30 \text{ ft/sec}$$

**Fig. 3.44** Rotating jet system.

**example 3.28** The sprinkler of Fig. 3.44 discharges 0.01 cfs through each nozzle. Neglecting friction, find its speed of rotation. The area of each nozzle opening is 0.001 ft².

The fluid entering the sprinkler has no moment of momentum, and no torque is exerted on the system externally; hence the moment of momentum of fluid leaving must be zero. Let $\omega$ be the speed of rotation; then the moment of momentum leaving is

$$\rho Q_1 r_1 v_{t1} + \rho Q_2 r_2 v_{t2}$$

in which $v_{t1}$ and $v_{t2}$ are absolute velocities. Then

$$v_{t1} = v_{r1} - \omega r_1 = \frac{Q_1}{0.001} - \omega r_1 = 10 - \omega$$

and

$$v_{t2} = v_{r2} - \omega r_2 = 10 - \tfrac{2}{3}\omega$$

For moment of momentum to be zero,

$$\rho Q(r_1 v_{t1} + r_2 v_{t2}) = 0$$

or

$$10 - \omega + \tfrac{2}{3}(10 - \tfrac{2}{3}\omega) = 0$$

and $\omega = 11.54$ rad/sec, $N = 110.2$ rpm.

## problems

**3.1** A pipeline leads from one water reservoir to another which has its water surface 20 ft lower. For a discharge of 1.0 cfs, determine the losses in foot-pounds per slug and in horsepower.

**3.2** A pump which is located 10 ft above the surface of a lake expels a jet of water vertically upward a distance of 50 ft. If 0.5 cfs is being pumped by a 5-hp electric motor running at rated capacity, what is the efficiency of the motor-pump combination? What is the irreversibility of the pump system when comparing the zenith of the jet and the lake surface?    What is the irreversibility after the water falls to the lake surface?

**3.3**   A blower delivers 5000 cfm (cubic feet per minute) air, $\rho = 0.0024$ slug/ft$^3$, at an increase in pressure of 4.0 in. water.   It is 72 per cent efficient.   Determine the irreversibility of the blower in foot-pounds per slug and in horsepower, and determine the torque in the shaft if the blower turns at 1800 rpm.

**3.4**   A three-dimensional velocity distribution is given by $u = -x$, $v = 2y$, $w = 5 - z$.   Find the equation of the streamline through (2,1,1).

**3.5**   A two-dimensional flow can be described by $u = -y/b^2$, $v = x/a^2$. Verify that this is the flow of an incompressible fluid and that the ellipse

$$\frac{x^2}{a^2} + \frac{y^2}{b^2} = 1$$

is a streamline.

**3.6**   Oil is flowing in a laminar way in a pipeline at the rate of 300 gpm (gallons per minute).   The irreversibilities are measured at 20 ft-lb/lb$_m$. What losses should be expected if the flow is reduced to 200 gpm?   What losses should be encountered for a flow of 450 gpm?

**3.7**   In a flow of liquid through a pipeline the losses are 3 hp for average velocity of 6 ft/sec and 6 hp for 9 ft/sec.   What is the nature of the flow?

**3.8**   When tripling the flow in a line causes the losses to increase by 7.64 times, how do the losses vary with velocity and what is the nature of the flow?

**3.9**   In two-dimensional flow around a circular cylinder (Fig. 3.3), the discharge between streamlines is 0.01 cfs/ft.   At a great distance the streamlines are 0.20 in. apart, and at a point near the cylinder they are 0.12 in. apart.   Calculate the magnitude of the velocity at these two points.

**3.10**   A pipeline carries oil, sp gr 0.86, at $V = 6$ ft/sec through 8.0-in. ID pipe.   At another section the diameter is 10.0 in.   Find the velocity at this section and the mass rate of flow in slugs per second.

**3.11**   Hydrogen is flowing in a 2.0-in.-diameter pipe at the mass rate of 0.03 lb$_m$/sec.   At section 1 the pressure is 40 psia and $t = 40°$F.   What is the average velocity?

**3.12**   A nozzle with a base diameter of 3.0 in. and with $1\frac{1}{8}$-in.-diameter tip discharges 300 gpm.   Derive an expression for the fluid velocity along the axis of the nozzle.   Measure the distance $x$ along the axis from the plane of the larger diameter.

**3.13**   An 18-ft-diameter pressure pipe has a velocity of 10 ft/sec.   After passing through a reducing bend the flow is in a 16-ft-diameter pipe.   If the losses vary as the square of the velocity, how much greater are they through the 16-ft pipe than through the 18-ft pipe per 1000 ft of pipe?

**3.14** Does the velocity distribution of Prob. 3.4 for incompressible flow satisfy the continuity equation?

**3.15** Does the velocity distribution

$$\mathbf{q} = \mathbf{i}(5x) + \mathbf{j}(5y) + \mathbf{k}(-10z)$$

satisfy the law of mass conservation for incompressible flow?

**3.16** Consider a cube with 1-ft edges parallel to the coordinate axes located in the first quadrant with one corner at the origin. By using the velocity distribution of Prob. 3.15, find the flow through each face and show that no mass is being accumulated within the cube if the fluid is of constant density.

**3.17** Find the flow (per foot in the $z$-direction) through each side of the square with corners at (0,0), (0,1), (1,1), (1,0) due to

$$\mathbf{q} = \mathbf{i}(16y - 12x) + \mathbf{j}(12y - 9x)$$

and show that continuity is satisfied.

**3.18** Show that the velocity

$$\mathbf{q} = \mathbf{i}\,\frac{4x}{x^2 + y^2} + \mathbf{j}\,\frac{4y}{x^2 + y^2}$$

satisfies continuity at every point except the origin.

**3.19** Problem 3.18 is a velocity distribution that is everywhere radial from the origin with magnitude $v_r = 4/r$. Show that the flow through each circle concentric with the origin (per foot in the $z$-direction) is the same.

**3.20** Perform the operation $\nabla \cdot \mathbf{q}$ on the velocity vectors of Probs. 3.15, 3.17, and 3.18.

**3.21** By introducing the following relationships between cartesian coordinates and plane polar coordinates, obtain a form of the continuity equation in plane polar coordinates:

$$x^2 + y^2 = r^2 \qquad \frac{y}{x} = \tan \theta$$

$$\frac{\partial}{\partial x} = \frac{\partial}{\partial r}\frac{\partial r}{\partial x} + \frac{\partial}{\partial \theta}\frac{\partial \theta}{\partial x}$$

$$u = v_r \cos \theta - v_\theta \sin \theta$$
$$v = v_r \sin \theta + v_\theta \cos \theta$$

Does the velocity given in Prob. 3.19 satisfy the equation that has been derived?

**3.22**   A standpipe 20 ft in diameter and 50 ft high is filled with water.   How much potential energy is in this water if the elevation datum is taken 10 ft below the base of the standpipe?

**3.23**   How much work could be obtained from the water of Prob. 3.22 if run through a 100 per cent efficient turbine that discharged into a reservoir with elevation 30 ft below the base of the standpipe?

**3.24**   What is the kinetic energy in foot-pounds per second of 200 gpm of oil, sp gr 0.80, discharging through a 2.0-in.-diameter nozzle?

**3.25**   By neglecting air resistance, determine the height a vertical jet of water will rise, with velocity 40 ft/sec.

**3.26**   If the water jet of Prob. 3.25 is directed upward 45° with the horizontal and air resistance is neglected, how high will it rise and what is the velocity at its high point?

**3.27**   Show that the work a liquid can do by virtue of its pressure is $\int p \, d\mathcal{v}$, in which $\mathcal{v}$ is the volume of liquid displaced.

**3.28**   What angle $\alpha$ of jet is required to reach the roof of the building of Fig. 3.45 with minimum jet velocity $V_0$ at the nozzle?   What is the value of $V_0$?

**3.29**   The velocity distribution in laminar flow in a pipe is given by $v = V_{max}[1 - (r/r_0)^2]$.   Determine the average velocity and the kinetic-energy correction factor.

**3.30**   For highly turbulent flow the velocity distribution in a pipe is given by

$$\frac{v}{v_{max}} = \left(\frac{y}{r_0}\right)^{1/9}$$

with $y$ the wall distance and $r_0$ the pipe radius.   Determine the kinetic-energy correction factor for this flow.

**Fig. 3.45**

**Fig. 3.46**

**3.31**  The velocity distribution between two parallel plates separated by a distance $a$ is

$$u = -10\frac{y}{a} + 20\frac{y}{a}\left(1 - \frac{y}{a}\right)$$

in which $u$ is the velocity component parallel to the plate and $y$ is measured from, and normal to, the lower plate.   Determine the volume rate of flow and the average velocity.   What is the time rate of flow of kinetic energy between the plates?   In what direction is the kinetic energy flowing?

**3.32**  What is the efflux of kinetic energy out of the cube given by Prob. 3.16 for the velocity prescribed in Prob. 3.15?

**3.33**  Water is flowing in a channel, as shown in Fig. 3.46.   Neglecting all losses, determine the two possible depths of flow $y_1$ and $y_2$.

**3.34**  High-velocity water flows up an inclined plane as shown in Fig. 3.47. Neglecting all losses, calculate the two possible depths of flow at section $B$.

**3.35**  If the losses from section $A$ to section $B$ of Fig. 3.46 are 1.5 ft-lb/lb, determine the two possible depths at section $B$.

**3.36**  In Fig. 3.47 the situation exists under which each pound of water increases in temperature 0.001°F due to losses incurred in flowing between $A$ and $B$.   Determine the lower depth of flow at section $B$.

**3.37**  Neglecting all losses, in Fig. 3.46 the channel narrows in the drop to

**Fig. 3.47**

**Fig. 3.48**

6 ft wide at section $B$.  For uniform flow across section $B$, determine the two possible depths of flow.

**3.38**  In Fig. 3.47 the channel changes in width from 6 ft at section $A$ to 8 ft at section $B$.  For losses of 1 ft-lb/lb between sections $A$ and $B$, find the two possible depths at section $B$.

**3.39**  Some steam locomotives had scoops installed that took water from a tank between the tracks and lifted it into the water reservoir in the tender.  To lift the water 12 ft with a scoop, neglecting all losses, what speed is required?  (*Note:* Consider the locomotive stationary and the water moving toward it, to reduce to a steady-flow situation.)

**3.40**  In Fig. 3.48 oil discharges from a "two-dimensional" slot as indicated at $A$ into the air.  At $B$ oil discharges from under a gate onto a floor.  Neglecting all losses, determine the discharges of $A$ and at $B$ per foot of width.  Why do they differ?

**3.41**  At point $A$ in a pipeline carrying water the diameter is 4.0 ft, the pressure 10 psi, and the velocity 4 ft/sec.  At point $B$, 6 ft higher than $A$, the diameter is 2.0 ft and the pressure 2 psi.  Determine the direction of flow.

**3.42**  Neglecting losses, determine the discharge in Fig. 3.49.

**Fig. 3.49**

**Fig. 3.50**

**Fig. 3.51**

**3.43** For losses of 0.3 ft-lb/lb, find the velocity at $A$ in Fig. 3.50. Barometer reading 29.5 in. mercury.

**3.44** The losses in Fig. 3.51 for $H = 20$ ft are $3V^2/2g$ ft-lb/lb. What is the discharge?

**3.45** For flow of 750 gpm in Fig. 3.51, determine $H$ for losses of $15V^2/2g$ ft-lb/lb.

**3.46** For 1500-gpm flow and $H = 32$ ft in Fig. 3.51, calculate the losses through the system in velocity heads, $KV^2/2g$.

**3.47** In Fig. 3.52 the losses up to section $A$ are $4V_1^2/2g$ and the nozzle losses are $0.05V_2^2/2g$. Determine the discharge and the pressure at $A$. $H = 25$ ft.

**3.48** For pressure at $A$ of 4 psi in Fig. 3.52, with the losses in Prob. 3.47, determine the discharge and the head $H$.

**Fig. 3.52**

**Fig. 3.53**

**3.49**   The pumping system shown in Fig. 3.53 must have pressure of 5 psi
in the discharge line when cavitation is incipient at the pump inlet.   Calculate the length of pipe from the reservoir to the pump for this operating
condition if the loss in this pipe can be expressed as $V_1^2/2g$ (0.03) $L/D$.
What horsepower is being supplied to the fluid by the pump?   What percentage of this power is being used to overcome losses?

*use absolute pressures*
*psa 70°F   no losses*
*in*
*nozzle*

**3.50**   Neglecting losses and surface-tension effects, derive an equation for
the water surface $r$ of the jet of Fig. 3.54, in terms of $y/H$.

**3.51**   In the siphon of Fig. 3.55, $h_1 = 3$ ft, $h_2 = 9$ ft, $D_1 = 10$ ft, $D_2 = 14$ ft,
and the losses are $1.6 V_2^2/2g$, with 10 per cent of the losses occurring before
section 1.   Find the discharge and the pressure at section 1.

**Fig. 3.54**

**Fig. 3.55**

**Fig. 3.56**

**3.52** Find the pressure at $A$ of Prob. 3.51 if it is a stagnation point (velocity zero).

**3.53** The siphon of Fig. 3.17 has a nozzle 6 in. long attached at section 3, reducing the diameter to 6 in. For no losses, compute the discharge, and the pressure at sections 2 and 3.

**3.54** With exit velocity $V_E$ in Prob. 3.53 and losses from 1 to 2 of $1.7V_2^2/2g$, from 2 to 3 of $0.9V_2^2/2g$, and through the nozzle $0.06V_E^2/2g$, calculate the discharge and the pressure at sections 2 and 3.

**3.55** Determine the shaft horsepower for an 80-per-cent-efficient pump to discharge 1 cfs through the system of Fig. 3.56. The system losses, exclusive of pump losses, are $10V^2/2g$ and $H = 50$ ft.

**3.56** The fluid horsepower ($Q\gamma H_p/550$) produced by the pump of Fig. 3.56 is 10. For $H = 60$ ft and system losses of $8V^2/2g$, determine the discharge and the pump head $H_p$. Draw the hydraulic and energy grade lines.

**3.57** If the over-all efficiency of the system and turbine in Fig. 3.57 is 80 per cent, what horsepower is produced for $H = 200$ ft and $Q = 1000$ cfs?

**3.58** Losses through the system of Fig. 3.57 are $4V^2/2g$, exclusive of the turbine. The turbine is 90 per cent efficient and runs at 240 rpm. To produce 1000 hp for $H = 300$ ft, determine the discharge and torque in the turbine shaft. Draw the energy and hydraulic grade lines.

**3.59** Neglecting losses, find the discharge through the venturi meter of Fig. 3.58.

**Fig. 3.57**

**Fig. 3.58**

**Fig. 3.59**

**3.60**  For the venturi meter and manometer installation shown in Fig. 3.59 derive an expression relating the volume rate of flow with the manometer reading.

**3.61**  With losses of $0.2V_1^2/2g$ between sections 1 and 2 of Fig. 3.58, calculate the flow in gallons per minute.

**3.62**  In Fig. 3.60 determine $V$ for $R = 12$ in.

**Fig. 3.60**

**Fig. 3.61**

**3.63**   In Fig. 3.61 $H = 20.0$ ft and $h = 19.6$ ft.   Calculate the discharge and the losses in foot-pounds per pound and in horsepower.

**3.64**   Neglecting losses, calculate $H$ in terms of $R$ for Fig. 3.62.

**3.65**   For losses of $0.1H$ through the nozzle of Fig. 3.62, what is the gage difference $R$ in terms of $H$?

**3.66**   A liquid flows through a long pipeline with losses of 4 ft-lb/lb per 100 ft of pipe.   What is the slope of the hydraulic and energy grade lines?

**3.67**   In Fig. 3.63, 4 cfs water flows from section 1 to section 2 with losses of $0.4(V_1 - V_2)^2/2g$; $p_1 = 10$ psi.   Compute $p_2$, and plot the energy and hydraulic grade lines through the diffuser.

**3.68**   In an isothermal, reversible flow at 200°F, 2 Btu/sec heat is added to 14 slug/sec flowing through a control volume.   Calculate the entropy increase in foot-pounds per slug per degree Rankine.

**Fig. 3.62**

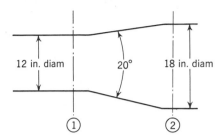

**Fig. 3.63**

**3.69**  In isothermal flow of a real fluid through a pipe system the losses are 60 ft-lb/slug per 100 ft, and 0.02 Btu/sec per 100 ft heat transfer from the fluid is required to hold the temperature at 40°F.   What is the entropy change $\Delta s$ in foot-pounds per slug per degree Rankine per 100 ft of pipe system for 10 $lb_m$/sec flowing?

**3.70**  Determine the momentum correction factor for the velocity distribution of Prob. 3.29.

**3.71**  Calculate the average velocity and momentum correction factor for the velocity distribution in a pipe,

$$\frac{v}{v_{\max}} = \left(\frac{y}{r_0}\right)^{1/n}$$

with $y$ the wall distance and $r_0$ the pipe radius.

**3.72**  By introducing $V + v'$ for $v$ into Eq. (3.11.4) show that $\beta \geq 1$.   The term $v'$ is the variation of $v$ from the average velocity $V$ and can be positive or negative.

**3.73**  Determine the time rate of $x$-momentum passing out of the cube of Prob. 3.16.   (*Hint:* Consider all six faces of the cube.)

**3.74**  Calculate the $y$-momentum efflux from the figure described in Prob. 3.17 for the velocity given there.

**3.75**  If gravity acts in the negative $z$-direction, determine the $z$-component of the force acting on the fluid within the cube described in Prob. 3.16 for the velocity specified there.

**3.76**  Find the $y$-component of the force acting on the control volume given in Prob. 3.17 for the velocity given there.   Consider gravity to be acting in the negative $y$-direction.

**3.77**  What force components $F_x$, $F_y$ are required to hold the "black box" of Fig. 3.64 stationary?   All pressures are zero gage.

**3.78**  What force $F$ (Fig. 3.65) is required to hold the plate for oil flow, sp gr 0.83, for $V_0 = 40$ ft/sec?

**Fig. 3.64**

**Fig. 3.65**

**3.79**  How much is the apparent weight of the tank full of water (Fig. 3.66) increased by the steady jet flow into the tank?

**3.80**  Does a nozzle on a fire hose place the hose in tension or in compression?

**3.81**  When a jet from a nozzle is used to aid in maneuvering a fireboat, can more force be obtained by directing the jet against a solid surface such as a wharf than by allowing it to discharge into air?

**Fig. 3.66**

**3.82**    Work Example 3.16 with the flow direction reversed, and compare results.

**3.83**    In the reducing bend of Fig. 3.23, $D_1 = 12$ ft, $D_2 = 9$ ft, $\theta = -45°$, $Q = 2000$ cfs, $W = 80,000$ lb, $z = 7$ ft, $p_2 = 20$ psi, $x = 8$ ft, and losses may be neglected.    Find the force components and line of action of the force which must be resisted by an anchor block.

**3.84**    20 ft³/sec of water flows through an 18-in.-diameter pipeline that contains a horizontal 90° bend.    The pressure at the entrance to the bend is 10 psi.    Determine the force components, parallel and normal to the approach velocity, required to hold the bend in place.    Neglect losses.

**3.85**    Oil, sp gr 0.83, flows through a 90° expanding pipe bend from 18- to 24-in.-diameter pipe.    The pressure at the bend entrance is 20 psi, and losses are to be neglected.    For 10,000 gpm, determine the force components (parallel and normal to the approach velocity) necessary to support the bend.

**3.86**    Work Prob. 3.85 with elbow losses of $0.6 V_1{}^2/2g$, with $V_1$ the approach velocity, and compare results.

**3.87**    A 4-in.-diameter steam line carries saturated steam at 1400 ft/sec velocity.    Water is entrained by the steam at the rate of 0.3 lb/sec.    What force is required to hold a 90° bend in place owing to the entrained water?

**3.88**    Neglecting losses, determine the $x$- and $y$-components of force needed to hold the tee (Fig. 3.67) in place.    The plane of the tee is horizontal.

**3.89**    Determine the net force on the sluice gate shown in Fig. 3.68.    Neglect losses.    By noting that the pressure at $A$ and $B$ is atmospheric,

**Fig. 3.67**

**Fig. 3.68**

sketch the pressure distribution on the surface $AB$.   Is it a hydrostatic distribution?   How is it related to the force just calculated?

**3.90**   The vertical reducing section shown in Fig. 3.69 contains oil, sp gr 0.86, flowing upward at the rate of 15 cfs.   The pressure at the larger section is 20 psi.   Neglecting losses but including gravity, determine the force on the contraction.

**3.91**   Apply the momentum and energy equations to a windmill as if it were a propeller, noting that the slipstream is slowed down and expands as it passes through the blades.   Show that the velocity through the plane of the blades is the average of the velocities in the slipstream at the downstream and upstream sections.   By defining the theoretical efficiency (neglecting all losses) as the power output divided by the power available in an undisturbed jet having the area at the plane of the blades, determine the maximum theoretical efficiency of a windmill.

**3.92**   An airplane with propeller diameter of 8.0 ft travels through still air ($\rho = 0.0022$ slug/ft³) at 210 mph.   The speed of air through the plane of the propeller is 280 mph relative to the airplane.   Calculate ($a$) the thrust on the plane, ($b$) the kinetic energy per second remaining in the slipstream,

**Fig. 3.69**

(c) the theoretical horsepower required to drive the propeller, (d) the propeller efficiency, and (e) the pressure difference across the blades.

**3.93**   A boat traveling at 25 mph has a 2-ft-diameter propeller that discharges 160 cfs through its blades.   Determine the thrust on the boat, the theoretical efficiency of the propulsion system, and the horsepower input to the propeller.

**3.94**   A ship propeller has a theoretical efficiency of 60 per cent.   If it is 4 ft in diameter and the ship travels 20 mph, what is the thrust developed and what is the theoretical horsepower required?

**3.95**   A jet-propelled airplane traveling 600 mph takes in 87 $\text{lb}_m/\text{sec}$ air and discharges it at 1800 ft/sec relative to the airplane.   Neglecting the weight of fuel, what thrust is produced?

**3.96**   A jet-propelled airplane travels 700 mph.   It takes in 165 $\text{lb}_m/\text{sec}$ of air, and burns 3 $\text{lb}_m/\text{sec}$ of fuel, and develops 8000 lb of thrust.   What is the velocity of the exhaust gas?

**3.97**   What is the theoretical mechanical efficiency of the jet engine of Prob. 3.96?

**3.98**   A boat requires a 4000-lb thrust to keep it moving at 16 mph.   How many cubic feet per second water must be taken in and ejected through an 18-in. pipe to maintain this motion?   What is the over-all efficiency if the pumping system is 60 per cent efficient?

**3.99**   In Prob. 3.98 what would be the required discharge if water were taken from a tank inside the boat and ejected from the stern through an 18-in. pipe?

**3.100**   Determine the size of jet pipe and the theoretical horsepower necessary to produce a thrust of 2000 lb on a boat moving 40 ft/sec when the propulsive efficiency is 68 per cent.

**3.101**   In Fig. 3.70, a jet, $\rho = 2$ slugs/ft³, is deflected by a vane through 180°.   Assume that the cart is frictionless and free to move in a horizontal direction.   The cart weighs 200 lb.   Determine the velocity and the distance traveled by the cart 10 sec after the jet is directed against the vane. $A_0 = 0.02$ ft²; $V_0 = 100$ ft/sec.

**Fig. 3.70**

**3.102**   A rocket burns 260 $lb_m$/sec fuel, ejecting hot gases at 6560 ft/sec relative to the rocket.   How much thrust is produced at 1500 and 3000 mph?

**3.103**   What is the mechanical efficiency of a rocket moving at 4000 ft/sec that ejects gas at 6000 ft/sec relative to the rocket?

**3.104**   Can a rocket travel faster than the velocity of ejected gas?   What is the mechanical efficiency when it travels 12,000 ft/sec and the gas is ejected at 8000 ft/sec relative to the rocket?   Is a positive thrust developed?

**3.105**   In Example 3.19 what is the thrust just before the completion of burning?

**3.106**   Neglecting air resistance, what velocity would a vertically directed $V$-2 rocket attain in 68 sec if it starts from rest, initially weighs 28,660 lb, burns 275 $lb_m$/sec fuel, and ejects gas at $v_r = 6400$ ft/sec?   Consider $g = 34.17$ ft/sec².

**3.107**   What altitude has the rocket of Prob. 3.106 reached after 68 sec?

**3.108**   If the fuel supply is exhausted after 68 sec (burnout), what is the maximum height of the rocket of Prob. 3.106?

**3.109**   What is the thrust of the rocket of Prob. 3.106 after 68 sec?

**3.110**   Draw the polar vector diagram for a vane, angle $\theta$, doing work on a jet.   Label all vectors.

**3.111**   Determine the resultant force exerted on the vane of Fig. 3.30. $A_0 = 0.1$ ft²; $V_0 = 100$ ft/sec; $\theta = 60°$, $\gamma = 55$ lb/ft³.   How can the line of action be determined?

**3.112**   In Fig. 3.31, 45 per cent of the flow is deflected in one direction. What is the plate angle $\theta$?

**3.113**   A flat plate is moving with velocity $u$ into a jet, as shown in Fig. 3.71. Derive the expression for power required to move the plate.

**3.114**   At what speed $u$ should the cart of Fig. 3.71 move away from the jet in order to produce maximum work from the jet?

**Fig. 3.71**

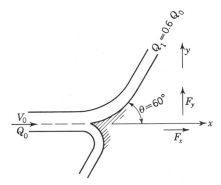

**Fig. 3.72**

**3.115** Calculate the force components $F_x$, $F_y$ needed to hold the stationary vane of Fig. 3.72. $Q_0 = 3$ cfs; $\rho = 2$ slugs/ft$^2$; $V_0 = 300$ ft/sec.

**3.116** If the vane of Fig. 3.72 moves in the $x$-direction at $u = 40$ ft/sec, for $Q = 2$ cfs, $\rho = 1.935$ slugs/ft$^3$, $V_0 = 150$ ft/sec, what are the force components $F_x$, $F_y$?

**3.117** For the flow divider of Fig. 3.73 find the force components for the following conditions: $Q_0 = 0.3$ cfs, $Q_1 = 0.1$ cfs, $\theta_0 = 45°$, $\theta_1 = -30°$, $\theta_2 = 120°$, $V_0 = 20$ ft/sec.

**3.118** Solve the preceding problem by graphical vector addition.

**3.119** At what speed $u$ should the vane of Fig. 3.32 travel for maximum power from the jet?   What should be the angle $\theta$ for maximum power?

**3.120** Draw the polar vector diagram for the moving vane of Fig. 3.32 for $V_0 - 100$ ft/sec, $u = 60$ ft/sec, and $\theta = 160°$.

**3.121** Draw the polar vector diagram for the moving vane of Fig. 3.32 for $V_0 = 120$ ft/sec, $u = -50$ ft/sec, and $\theta = 150°$.

**Fig. 3.73**

**Fig. 3.74**

**3.122**   What horsepower can be developed from $(a)$ a single vane and $(b)$ a series of vanes (Fig. 3.32) when $A_0 = 10$ in.$^2$, $V_0 = 240$ ft/sec, $u = 80$ ft/sec, and $\theta = 173°$, for water flowing?

**3.123**   Determine the blade angles $\theta_1$ and $\theta_2$ of Fig. 3.74 so that the flow enters the vane tangent to its leading edge and leaves with no $x$-component of absolute velocity.

**3.124**   Determine the vane angle required to deflect the absolute velocity of a jet 120° (Fig. 3.75).

**3.125**   In Prob. 3.39 for pickup of 1 cfs water at locomotive speed of 40 mph, what force is exerted parallel to the tracks?

**3.126**   In Fig. 3.76 an orifice called a Borda mouthpiece is shown.   The tube

**Fig. 3.75**

**Fig. 3.76**

is long enough so that the fluid velocity near the bottom of the tank is nearly zero.   Calculate the ratio of the jet area to the tube area.   Neglect gravity.

**3.127**   Determine the irreversibility in foot-pounds per pound mass for 6 cfs flow of liquid, $\rho = 1.6$ slugs/ft³, through a sudden expansion from a 12- to 24-in.-diameter pipe.   $g = 30$ ft/sec².

**3.128**   Air flows through a 24-in.-diameter duct at $p = 10$ psia, $t = 40°F$, $V = 200$ ft/sec.   The duct suddenly expands to 30 in. diameter.   Considering the gas as incompressible, calculate the losses in foot-pounds per pound of air and the pressure difference in inches of water.

**3.129**   What are the losses when 180 cfs water discharges from a submerged 48-in.-diameter pipe into a reservoir?

**3.130**   Show that in the limiting case, as $y_1 = y_2$ in Eq. (3.11.23), the relation $V = \sqrt{gy}$ is obtained.

**3.131**   A jump occurs in a 20-ft-wide channel carrying 600 cfs water at a depth of 1 ft.   Determine $y_2$, $V_2$, and the losses in foot-pounds per pound, in horsepower, and in Btu per pound.

**3.132**   Derive an expression similar to Eq. (3.11.23) for a hydraulic jump in a channel having an equilateral triangle as its cross section (symmetric with the vertical).

**3.133**   Derive Eq. (3.11.24).

**3.134**   Assuming no losses through the gate of Fig. 3.77 and neglecting $V_0^2/2g$, for $y_0 = 20$ ft and $y_1 = 2$ ft, find $y_2$ and losses through the jump. What is the basis for neglecting $V_0^2/2g$?

**3.135**   Under the same assumption as in Prob. 3.134, for $y_1 = 1.5$ ft and $y_2 = 6$ ft, determine $y_0$.

**3.136**   Under the same assumptions as in Prob. 3.134, $y_0 = 22$ ft and $y_2 = 8$ ft.   Find the discharge per foot.

**3.137**   For losses down the spillway of Fig. 3.78 of 8 ft-lb/lb and discharge per foot of 120 cfs, determine the floor elevation for the jump to occur.

**3.138**   Water is flowing through the pipe of Fig. 3.79 with velocity $V = 8.02$ ft/sec and losses of 10-ft-lb/lb up to section 1.   When the obstruction at the end of the pipe is removed, calculate the acceleration of water in the pipe.

**Fig. 3.77**

**Fig. 3.78**

**Fig. 3.79**

**3.139** Water fills the piping system of Fig. 3.80. At one instant $p_1 = 10$ psi, $p_2 = 0$, $V_1 = 10$ ft/sec, and the flow rate is increasing by 3000 gpm per minute. Find the force $F_x$ required to hold the piping system stationary.

**3.140** If in Fig. 3.66 $Q_2$ is 1.0 cfs, what is the apparent weight of the tank? Assume that overflow has not occurred. Weight of tank is 20 lb.

**3.141** In Fig. 3.42, $r_1 = 4$ in., $r_2 = 7$ in., $v_{t1} = 0$, and $v_{t2} = 10$ ft/sec for a centrifugal pump impeller discharging 0.6 cfs of water. What torque must be exerted on the impeller?

**3.142** In a centrifugal pump 400 gpm water leaves an 8-in.-diameter impeller with a tangential velocity component of 30 ft/sec. It enters the impeller in a radial direction. For pump speed of 1200 rpm and neglecting all losses,

**Fig. 3.80**

**Fig. 3.81**

determine the torque in the pump shaft, the horsepower input, and the energy added to the flow in foot-pounds per pound.

**3.143**   A water turbine at 240 rpm discharges 1500 cfs.   To produce 60,000 hp, what must be the tangential component of velocity at the entrance to the impeller at $r = 6$ ft?   All whirl is taken from the water when it leaves the turbine.   Neglect all losses.   What head is required for the turbine?

**3.144**   The symmetrical sprinkler of Fig. 3.81 has a total discharge of 14 gpm and is frictionless.   Determine its rpm if the nozzle tips are $\frac{1}{4}$-in. diameter.

**3.145**   What torque would be required to hold the sprinkler of Prob. 3.144 stationary?   Total flow 40 gpm water.

**3.146**   If there is a torque resistance of 0.50 lb-ft in the shaft of Prob. 3.144, what is its speed of rotation?

**3.147**   For torque resistance of $0.01\omega^2$ in the shaft, determine the speed of rotation of the sprinkler of Prob. 3.144.

**3.148**   A *reversible* process requires that

(*a*)   there be no heat transfer
(*b*)   Newton's law of viscosity be satisfied
(*c*)   temperature of system and surroundings be equal
(*d*)   there be no viscous or Coloumb friction in the system
(*e*)   heat transfer occurs from surroundings to system only

**3.149**   An *open system* implies

(*a*)   the presence of a free surface
(*b*)   that a specified mass is considered
(*c*)   the use of a control volume
(*d*)   no interchange between system and surroundings
(*e*)   none of the above answers

**3.150**   A *control volume* refers to

(*a*)   a fixed region in space      (*b*)   a specified mass
(*c*)   an isolated system      (*d*)   a reversible process only
(*e*)   a closed system

**3.151**   Which three of the following are synonymous?

1. losses
2. irreversibilities

**Fig. 3.82**

3. energy losses
4. available energy losses
5. drop in hydraulic grade line

($a$) 1, 2, 3,      ($b$) 1, 2, 5      ($c$) 1, 2, 4      ($d$) 2, 3, 4      ($e$) 3, 4, 5

**3.152**  Irreversibility of the system of Fig. 3.82 is

($a$) 9.2 hp      ($b$) 36.8 hp      ($c$) 8.45 ft      ($d$) 11.55 ft

($e$)  none of these answers

**3.153**  Isentropic flow is

($a$)  irreversible adiabatic flow      ($b$)  perfect-gas flow
($c$)  ideal-fluid flow      ($d$)  reversible adiabatic flow
($e$)  frictionless reversible flow

**3.154**  One-dimensional flow is

($a$)  steady uniform flow
($b$)  uniform flow
($c$)  flow which neglects changes in a transverse direction
($d$)  restricted to flow in a straight line
($e$)  none of these answers

**3.155**  The continuity equation may take the form

($a$) $Q = pAv$      ($b$) $\rho_1 A_1 = \rho_2 A_2$      ($c$) $p_1 A_1 v_1 = p_2 A_2 v_2$
($d$) $\nabla \cdot \mathbf{p} = 0$      ($e$) $A_1 v_1 = A_2 v_2$

**3.156**  The first law of thermodynamics, for steady flow,

($a$)  accounts for all energy entering and leaving a control volume
($b$)  is an energy balance for a specified mass of fluid
($c$)  is an expression of the conservation of linear momentum
($d$)  is primarily concerned with heat transfer
($e$)  is restricted in its application to perfect gases

**3.157**  Entropy, for reversible flow, is defined by the expression

($a$) $ds = du + p\,d(1/\rho)$      ($b$) $ds = T\,dq_H$      ($c$) $s = u + pv_s$
($d$) $ds = dq_H/T$      ($e$)  none of these answers

**3.158**  The equation $d$ (losses) $= T\,ds$ is restricted to

($a$) insentropic flow     ($b$) reversible flow     ($c$) adiabatic flow
($d$) perfect-gas flow     ($e$) none of these answers

**3.159**  In turbulent flow

($a$) the fluid particles move in an orderly manner
($b$) cohesion is more effective than momentum transfer in causing shear stress
($c$) momentum transfer is on a molecular scale only
($d$) one lamina of fluid glides smoothly over another
($e$) the shear stresses are generally larger than in a similar laminar flow

**3.160**  The ratio $\eta = \tau/(du/dy)$ for turbulent flow is

($a$) a physical property of the fluid
($b$) dependent upon the flow and the density
($c$) the viscosity divided by the density
($d$) a function of temperature and pressure of fluid
($e$) independent of the nature of the flow

**3.161**  Turbulent flow generally occurs for cases involving

($a$) very viscous fluids
($b$) very narrow passages or capillary tubes
($c$) very slow motions
($d$) combinations of ($a$), ($b$), and ($c$)
($e$) none of these answers

**3.162**  In laminar flow

($a$) experimentation is required for the simplest flow cases
($b$) Newton's law of viscosity applies
($c$) the fluid particles move in irregular and haphazard paths
($d$) the viscosity is unimportant
($e$) the ratio $\tau/(du/dy)$ depends upon the flow

**3.163**  An ideal fluid is

($a$) very viscous
($b$) one which obeys Newton's law of viscosity
($c$) a useful assumption in problems in conduit flow
($d$) frictionless and incompressible
($e$) none of these answers

**3.164**  Which of the following must be fulfilled by the flow of any fluid, real or ideal?

1. Newton's law of viscosity
2. Newton's second law of motion

3. The continuity equation

4. $\tau = (\mu + \eta)\, du/dy$

5. Velocity at boundary must be zero relative to boundary

6. Fluid cannot penetrate a boundary

(a) 1, 2, 3       (b) 1, 3, 6       (c) 2, 3, 5       (d) 2, 3, 6       (e) 2, 4, 5

**3.165**   Steady flow occurs when

(a) conditions do not change with time at any point
(b) conditions are the same at adjacent points at any instant
(c) conditions change steadily with the time
(d) $\partial v/\partial t$ is constant
(e) $\partial v/\partial s$ is constant

**3.166**   Uniform flow occurs

(a) whenever the flow is steady
(b) when $\partial \bar{v}/\partial t$ is everywhere zero
(c) only when the velocity vector at any point remains constant
(d) when $\partial \bar{v}/\partial s = 0$
(e) when the discharge through a curved pipe of constant cross-sectional area is constant

**3.167**   Select the correct practical example of steady nonuniform flow:

(a) motion of water around a ship in a lake
(b) motion of a river around bridge piers
(c) steadily increasing flow through a pipe
(d) steadily decreasing flow through a reducing section
(e) constant discharge through a long, straight pipe

**3.168**   A streamline

(a) is the line connecting the mid-points of flow cross sections
(b) is defined for uniform flow only
(c) is drawn normal to the velocity vector at every point
(d) is always the path of a particle
(e) is fixed in space in steady flow

**3.169**   In two-dimensional flow around a cylinder the streamlines are 2 in. apart at a great distance from the cylinder, where the velocity is 100 ft/sec. At one point near the cylinder the streamlines are 1.5 in. apart. The average velocity there is

(a) 75 ft/sec       (b) 133 ft/sec       (c) 150 ft/sec       (d) 200 ft/sec
(e) 300 ft/sec

**3.170** An oil has a specific gravity of 0.80. Its density in slugs per cubic foot is

(a) 0.775     (b) 0.80     (c) 1.55     (d) 1.935     (e) 49.92

**3.171** The continuity equation

(a) requires that Newton's second law of motion be satisfied at every point in the fluid
(b) expresses the relation between energy and work
(c) states that the velocity at a boundary must be zero relative to the boundary for a real fluid
(d) relates the momentum per unit volume for two points on a streamline
(e) relates mass rate of flow along a stream tube

**3.172** Water has an average velocity of 10 ft/sec through a 24-in. pipe. The discharge through the pipe, in cubic feet per second, is

(a) 7.85     (b) 31.42     (c) 40     (d) 125.68     (e) none of these answers

**3.173** The assumptions about flow required in deriving the equation $gz + v^2/2 + \int dp/\rho = \text{const}$ are that it is

(a) steady, frictionless, incompressible, along a streamline
(b) uniform, frictionless, along a streamline, $\rho$ a function of $p$
(c) steady, uniform, incompressible, along a streamline
(d) steady, frictionless, $\rho$ a function of $p$, along a streamline
(e) none of these answers

**3.174** The equation $z + p/\gamma + v^2/2g = C$ has the units of

(a) ft-lb/sec     (b) lb     (c) ft-lb/slug     (d) ft-lb/ft³     (e) ft-lb/lb

**3.175** The work that a liquid is capable of doing by virtue of its sustained pressure is, in foot-pounds per pound,

(a) $z$     (h) $p$     (c) $p/\gamma$     (d) $v^2/2g$     (e) $\sqrt{2gh}$

**3.176** The velocity head is

(a) $v^2/2g$     (b) $z$     (c) $v$     (d) $\sqrt{2gh}$     (e) none of these answers

**3.177** The kinetic-energy correction factor

(a) applies to the continuity equation
(b) has the units of velocity head

(c) is expressed by $\dfrac{1}{A} \int_A \left(\dfrac{v}{V}\right) dA$

(d) is expressed by $\dfrac{1}{A}\displaystyle\int_A \left(\dfrac{v}{V}\right)^2 dA$

(e) is expressed by $\dfrac{1}{A}\displaystyle\int_A \left(\dfrac{v}{V}\right)^3 dA$

**3.178**  The kinetic-energy correction factor for the velocity distribution given by Fig. 1.1 is

(a) 0    (b) 1    (c) $\frac{4}{3}$    (d) 2    (e) none of these answers

**3.179**  The equation $\Sigma F_x = \rho Q(V_{x_{out}} - V_{x_{in}})$ requires the following assumptions for its derivation:

1. Velocity constant over the end cross sections
2. Steady flow
3. Uniform flow
4. Compressible fluid
5. Frictionless fluid

(a) 1, 2    (b) 1, 5    (c) 1, 3    (d) 3, 5    (e) 2, 4

**3.180**  The momentum correction factor is expressed by

(a) $\dfrac{1}{A}\displaystyle\int_A \left(\dfrac{v}{V}\right) dA$    (b) $\dfrac{1}{A}\displaystyle\int_A \left(\dfrac{v}{V}\right)^2 dA$    (c) $\dfrac{1}{A}\displaystyle\int_A \left(\dfrac{v}{V}\right)^3 dA$

(d) $\dfrac{1}{A}\displaystyle\int_A \left(\dfrac{v}{V}\right)^4 dA$    (e) none of these answers

**3.181**  The momentum correction factor for the velocity distribution given by Fig. 1.1 is

(a) 0    (b) 1    (c) $\frac{4}{3}$    (d) 2    (e) none of these answers

**3.182**  The velocity over one-third of a cross section is zero and is uniform over the remaining two-thirds of the area.  The momentum correction factor is

(a) 1    (b) $\frac{4}{3}$    (c) $\frac{3}{2}$    (d) $\frac{9}{4}$    (e) none of these answers

**3.183**  The magnitude of the resultant force necessary to hold a 6-in.-diameter 90° elbow under no-flow conditions when the pressure is 100 psi is, in pounds,

(a) 5644    (b) 3996    (c) 2822    (d) 0    (e) none of these answers

**3.184**  A 12-in.-diameter 90° elbow carries water with average velocity of 15 ft/sec and pressure of −5 psi.  The force component in the direction of the approach velocity necessary to hold the elbow in place is, in pounds,

(a) −342    (b) 223    (c) 565    (d) 907    (e) none of these answers

**3.185** A 3-in.-diameter 180° bend carries a liquid, $\rho = 2.0$, at 20 ft/sec at a pressure of zero gage. The force tending to push the bend off the pipe is, in pounds,

($a$) 0    ($b$) 39.2    ($c$) 78.5    ($d$) 286.5    ($e$) none of these answers

**3.186** The thickness of wall for a large high-pressure pipeline is determined by consideration of

($a$) axial tensile stresses in the pipe
($b$) forces exerted by dynamic action at bends
($c$) forces exerted by static and dynamic action at bends
($d$) circumferential pipe wall tension
($e$) temperature stresses

**3.187** Select from the following list the correct assumptions for analyzing flow of a jet that is deflected by a fixed or moving vane:

1. The momentum of the jet is unchanged.
2. The absolute speed does not change along the vane.
3. The fluid flows onto the vane without shock.
4. The flow from the nozzle is steady.
5. The cross-sectional area of jet is unchanged.
6. Friction between jet and vane is neglected.
7. The jet leaves without velocity.
8. The velocity is uniform over the cross section of the jet before and after contacting the vane.

($a$) 1, 3, 4, 6    ($b$) 2, 3, 6, 7    ($c$) 3, 4, 5, 6    ($d$) 3, 4, 6, 8
($e$) 3, 5, 6, 8

**3.188** When a steady jet impinges on a fixed inclined plane surface

($a$) the momentum in the direction of the approach velocity is unchanged
($b$) no force is exerted on the jet by the vane
($c$) the flow is divided into parts directly proportional to the angle of inclination of the surface
($d$) the speed is reduced for that portion of the jet turned through more than 90° and increased for the other portion
($e$) the momentum component is unchanged parallel to the surface

**3.189** A jet with initial velocity of 100 ft/sec in the $+x$-direction is deflected by a fixed vane with a blade angle of 120°. The velocity components leaving the vane parallel to and normal to the approach velocity are

($a$) $v_x = -50$, $v_y = 86.6$    ($b$) $v_x = 100$, $v_y = 0$    ($c$) $v_x = 50$, $v_y = 50$
($d$) $v_x = 50$, $v_y = 86.6$    ($e$) $v_x = -86.6$, $v_y = 50$

**3.190**    An oil jet, sp gr 0.80, discharges 0.50 slug/sec onto a fixed vane that turns the flow through 90°.   The speed of the jet is 100 ft/sec as it leaves the vane.   The force component on the vane in the direction of the approach velocity is, in pounds,

(*a*) 70.7      (*b*) 50      (*c*) 40      (*d*) 35.35      (*e*) none of these answers

**3.191**    A water jet having a velocity of 120 ft/sec and cross-sectional area 0.05 ft² flows onto a vane moving 40 ft/sec in the same direction as the jet. The mass having its momentum changed per unit time, in slugs per second, is

(*a*) 4      (*b*) 7.74      (*c*) 11.61      (*d*) 15.48      (*e*) none of these answers

**3.192**    A jet having a velocity of 100 ft/sec flows onto a vane, angle $\theta = 150°$, having a velocity of 50 ft/sec in the same direction as the jet.   The final absolute velocity components parallel and normal to the approach velocity are

(*a*) $v_x = 6.7, v_y = 25$      (*b*) $v_x = 24, v_y = 43.3$
(*c*) $v_x = -36.6, v_y = 50$      (*d*) $v_x = 14.65, v_y = 35.35$
(*e*) none of these answers

**3.193**    A vane moves toward a nozzle 30 ft/sec, and the jet issuing from the nozzle has a velocity of 40 ft/sec.   The vane angle is $\theta = 90°$.   The absolute velocity components of the jet as it leaves the vane, parallel and normal to the undisturbed jet, are

(*a*) $v_x = 10, v_y = 10$      (*b*) $v_x = -30, v_y = 10$
(*c*) $v_x = -30, v_y = 40$      (*d*) $v_x = -30, v_y = 70$
(*e*) none of these answers

**3.194**    A force of 60 lb is exerted upon a moving blade in the direction of its motion, $u = 55$ ft/sec.   The horsepower obtained is

(*a*) 0.1      (*b*) 3      (*c*) 5.5      (*d*) 10      (*e*) none of these answers

**3.195**    A series of moving vanes, $u = 50$ ft/sec, $\theta = 90°$, intercepts a jet, $Q = 1$ cfs, $\rho = 1.5$ slugs/ft³, $V_0 = 100$ ft/sec.   The work done on the vanes, in foot-pounds per second, is

(*a*) 1875      (*b*) 2500      (*c*) 3750      (*d*) 7500      (*e*) none of these answers

**3.196**    The horsepower available in a water jet of cross-sectional area 0.04 ft² and velocity 80.2 ft/sec is

(*a*) 1.13      (*b*) 36.35      (*c*) 39      (*d*) 72.7      (*e*) none of these answers

**3.197**   A ship moves through water at 30 ft/sec.   The velocity of water in the slipstream behind the boat is 20 ft/sec, and the propeller diameter is 3.0 ft.   The theoretical efficiency of the propeller is, in per cent,

(a) 0      (b) 60      (c) 75      (d) 86      (e) none of these answers

**3.198**   The thrust on the ship of Prob. 3.197, in pounds, is

(a) 1362      (b) 4090      (c) 5450      (d) 8180      (e) none of these answers

**3.199**   A rocket exerts a constant horizontal thrust of 40 lb on a missile for 3 sec.   If the missile weighs 8 lb and starts from rest, its speed at the end of the period, neglecting the downward acceleration of gravity and reduction in weight of the rocket, is, in feet per second,

(a) 386      (b) 483      (c) 580      (d) 600      (e) none of these answers

**3.200**   What is the reduction in weight of the rocket of Prob. 3.199 if the jet leaves at 6000 ft/sec relative to the rocket?

(a) 0.02 lb      (b) 0.04 lb      (c) 0.32 lb      (d) 0.64 lb      (e) none of these answers

**3.201**   A glass tube with a 90° bend is open at both ends.   It is inserted into a flowing stream of oil, sp gr 0.90, so that one opening is directed upstream and the other is directed upward.   Oil inside the tube is 2 in. higher than the surface of flowing oil.   The velocity measured by the tube is, in feet per second,

(a) 2.95      (b) 3.28      (c) 3.64      (d) 4.64      (e) none of these answers

**3.202**   In Fig. 8.7 the gage difference $R'$ for $v_1 = 5$ ft/sec, $S = 0.08$, $S_0 = 1.2$ is, in feet,

(a) 0.39      (b) 0.62      (c) 0.78      (d) 1.17      (e) none of these answers

**3.203**   The theoretical velocity of oil, sp gr 0.75, flowing from an orifice in a reservoir under a head of 9.0 ft is, in feet per second,

(a) 18.1      (b) 24.06      (c) 32.1      (d) not determinable from data given      (e) none of these answers

**3.204**   In which of the following cases is it possible for flow to occur from low pressure to high pressure?

(a) flow through a converging section
(b) adiabatic flow in a horizontal pipe
(c) flow of a liquid upward in a vertical pipe

(d) flow of air downward in a pipe

(e) impossible in a constant-cross-section conduit

**3.205**   The head loss in turbulent flow in a pipe

(a) varies directly as the velocity

(b) varies inversely as the square of the velocity

(c) varies inversely as the square of the diameter

(d) depends upon the orientation of the pipe

(e) varies approximately as the square of the velocity

**3.206**   The losses due to a sudden expansion are expressed by

(a) $\dfrac{V_1{}^2 - V_2{}^2}{2g}$ 　　(b) $\dfrac{V_1 - V_2}{2g}$ 　　(c) $\dfrac{V_2{}^2 - V_1{}^2}{g}$

(d) $\dfrac{(V_1 - V_2)^2}{g}$ 　　(e) $\dfrac{(V_1 - V_2)^2}{2g}$

**3.207**   If all losses are neglected, the pressure at the summit of a siphon

(a) is a minimum for the siphon

(b) depends upon height of summit above upstream reservoir only

(c) is independent of the length of the downstream leg

(d) is independent of the discharge through the siphon

(e) is independent of the liquid density

**3.208**   The depth conjugate to $y = 1$ ft and $V = 20$ ft/sec is

(a) 2.32 ft 　　(b) 4.5 ft 　　(c) 5.0 ft 　　(d) 5.5 ft 　　(e) none of these answers

**3.209**   The depth conjugate to $y = 10$ ft and $V = 20$ ft/sec is

(a) 10.72 ft 　　(b) 11.5 ft 　　(c) 16.5 ft 　　(d) 21.5 ft 　　(e) none of these answers

**3.210**   The depth conjugate to $y = 10$ ft and $V = 1$ ft/sec is

(a) 0.06 ft 　　(b) 1.46 ft 　　(c) 5.06 ft 　　(d) 10.06 ft 　　(e) none of these answers

**3.211**   The continuity equation in ideal fluid flow

(a) states that the net rate of inflow into any small volume must be zero

(b) states that the energy is constant along a streamline

(c) states that the energy is constant everywhere in the fluid

(d) applies to irrotational flow only

(e) implies the existence of a velocity potential

# 4

# dimensional analysis and dynamic similitude

Dimensionless parameters have aided significantly in our understanding of fluid-flow phenomena in a way which is analogous to the case of a hydraulic jack, where the ratio of piston diameters determines the mechanical advantage, a dimensionless number which is independent of the over-all size of the jack. They permit limited experimental results to be applied to situations involving different physical dimensions and often different fluid properties. The concepts of dimensional analysis that are introduced in this chapter plus an understanding of the mechanics of the type of flow under study make possible this generalization of experimental data. The consequence of such generalization is manifold, since one is now able to describe the phenomenon in its entirety and is not restricted to discussing the specialized experiment that was performed. Thus, it is possible to conduct fewer, although highly selective, experiments to uncover the hidden facets of the problem and thereby achieve important savings in time and money. The results of an investigation can also be presented to other engineers and scientists in a more compact and meaningful way so as to facilitate their use. Equally important is the fact that through such incisive and uncluttered presentations of information researchers are able to discover new features and missing areas of knowledge of the problem at hand. This directed advancement of our understanding of a phenomenon would be impaired if the tools of dimensional analysis were not available. In the following chapter, dealing primarily with viscous effects, one parameter is highly significant, viz., the Reynolds number. In Chap. 6, dealing with compressible flow, the Mach number is the most important dimensionless parameter.   In Chap. 11, dealing with open channels, the Froude number has the greatest significance.

Many of the dimensionless parameters may be viewed as a ratio of a pair of fluid forces, the relative magnitude indicating the relative importance of one of the forces with respect to the other.   If some forces, in a particular flow situation, are very much larger than a few others, it is often possible to neglect the effect of the smaller forces and treat the phenomenon as though it were completely determined by the major forces that exist.   This means that simpler, although not necessarily easy, mathematical and experimental procedures can be used to solve the problem.   For situations with several forces of the same magnitude, such as inertial, viscous, and gravitational forces, special techniques are required.   After a discussion of dimensions, dimensional analysis, and dimensionless parameters, dynamic similitude and model studies are presented.

### 4.1   dimensional homogeneity and dimensionless ratios

The solving of practical design problems in fluid mechanics usually requires both theoretical developments and experimental results.   By means of a grouping of significant quantities into dimensionless parameters it is possible to reduce the number of variables appearing and to make this compact result (equations or data plots) applicable to all similar situations.

If one were to write the equation of motion $\Sigma\mathbf{F} = m\mathbf{a}$ for a fluid particle, including all types of force terms that could act, such as gravity, pressure, viscous, elastic, and surface-tension forces, an equation of the sum of these forces equated to $m\mathbf{a}$, the inertial force, would result.   As with all physical equations, each term must have the same dimensions, in this case, force. The division of each term of the equation by any one of the terms would make the equation dimensionless.   For example, dividing through by the inertial force term would yield a sum of dimensionless parameters equated to unity.   The relative size of any one parameter, compared with unity, would indicate its importance.   If one were to divide the force equation through by a different term, say the viscous-force term, then another set of dimensionless parameters would result.   Without experience in the flow case it is difficult to determine which parameters will be most useful.

An example of the use of dimensional analysis and its advantages is given by considering the hydraulic jump that was treated in Sec. 3.11.   The momentum equation for this case is repeated here for convenience:

$$\frac{\gamma y_1{}^2}{2} - \frac{\gamma y_2{}^2}{2} = \frac{V_1 y_1 \gamma}{g}\,(V_2 - V_1) \tag{4.1.1}$$

which can be rewritten as

$$\frac{\gamma}{2} y_1{}^2 \left[ 1 - \left(\frac{y_2}{y_1}\right)^2 \right] = V_1{}^2 \frac{\gamma}{g} y_1 \left(1 - \frac{y_2}{y_1}\right) \frac{y_1}{y_2}$$

Clearly the right-hand side represents the inertial forces and the left-hand side, the pressure forces that exist due to gravity.   These two forces are of equal magnitude since one determines the other in this equation.   Furthermore, the term $\gamma y_1{}^2/2$ has the dimensions of force, and it multiplies a dimensionless number which is specified by the geometry of the hydraulic jump.

If one divides this equation by the geometric term $(1 - y_2/y_1)$ and a number representative of the gravity forces, one has

$$\frac{V_1{}^2}{g y_1} = \frac{1}{2} \frac{y_2}{y_1} \left(1 + \frac{y_2}{y_1}\right) \tag{4.1.2}$$

It is now clear that the left-hand side is the ratio of the inertia and gravity forces, even though the explicit representation of the forces has been obscured through the cancellation of terms that are common in both the numerator and denominator.   This ratio is equivalent to a dimensionless parameter called the Froude number, which will be discussed in further detail later in this chapter.   It is also interesting to note that this ratio of forces is known once the ratio $y_2/y_1$ is given, regardless of what the values $y_2$ and $y_1$ are.   From this observation one can obtain an appreciation of the increased scope that Eq. (4.1.2) affords over Eq. (4.1.1) even though one is only a rearrangement of the other.

In writing the momentum equation which led to Eq. (4.1.2) only inertia and gravity forces were included in the original problem statement.   But other forces are present, such as surface tension and viscosity.   These were neglected as being small in comparison with gravity and inertia forces; however, only experience with the phenomenon, or ones similar to it, would justify such an initial simplification.   For example, if viscosity had been included because one was not sure of the magnitude of its effect, the momentum equation would become

$$\frac{\gamma y_1{}^2}{2} - \frac{\gamma y_2{}^2}{2} - F_{\text{viscous}} = V_1 \frac{y_1 \gamma}{g} (V_2 - V_1)$$

with the result that

$$\frac{V_1{}^2}{g y_1} + \frac{F_{\text{viscous}} y_2}{\gamma y_1{}^2 (y_1 - y_2)} = \frac{1}{2} \left(\frac{y_2}{y_1}\right) \left(1 + \frac{y_2}{y_1}\right)$$

This statement is more complete than that given by Eq. (4.1.2).   However, experiments would show that the second term on the left-hand side is usually a small fraction of the first term and could be neglected in making initial tests on a hydraulic jump.

In the last equation one can consider the ratio $y_2/y_1$ to be a dependent variable which is determined for each of the various values of the force ratios, $V_1^2/gy_1$ and $F_{\text{viscous}}/\gamma y_1^2$, which are the independent variables. From the previous discussion it appears that the latter variable plays only a minor role in determining the values of $y_2/y_1$. Nevertheless, if one observed that the ratios of the forces, $V_1^2/gy_1$ and $F_{\text{viscous}}/\gamma y_1^2$, had the same values in two different tests, one would expect, on the basis of the last equation, that the values of $y_2/y_1$ would be the same in the two situations. If the ratio of $V_1^2/gy_1$ was the same in the two tests but the ratio $F_{\text{viscous}}/\gamma y_1$, which has only a minor influence for this case, was not equal, one would conclude that the values of $y_2/y_1$ for the two cases would be almost the same.

This is the key to much of what follows. For if one can create in a model experiment the same geometric and force ratios that occur on the full-scale unit, then the dimensionless solution for the model is valid also for the prototype. Often, as will be seen, it is not possible to have all the ratios equal in the model and prototype. Then one attempts to plan the experimentation in such a way that the dominant force ratios are as nearly equal as possible. The results obtained with such incomplete modeling are often sufficient to describe the phenomenon in the detail that is desired.

The writing of a force equation for a complex situation may not be feasible, and another process, *dimensional analysis*, is then used if one knows the pertinent quantities that enter into the problem.

In a given situation several of the forces may be of little significance, leaving perhaps two or three forces of the same order of magnitude. With three forces of the same order of magnitude, two dimensionless parameters are obtained; one set of experimental data on a geometrically similar model provides the relationships between parameters holding for all other similar flow cases.

## 4.2  dimensions and units

The dimensions of mechanics are force, mass, length, and time, related to Newton's second law of motion,

$$\mathbf{F} = M\mathbf{a} \tag{4.2.1}$$

Force and mass units are discussed in Sec. 1.2. For all physical systems, it would probably be necessary to introduce two more dimensions, one

**Table 4.1   Dimensions of physical quantities used in fluid mechanics**

| Quantity | Symbol | Dimensions $(M, L, T)$ |
|---|---|---|
| Length | $l$ | $L$ |
| Time | $t$ | $T$ |
| Mass | $M$ | $M$ |
| Force | $F$ | $MLT^{-2}$ |
| Velocity | $V$ | $LT^{-1}$ |
| Acceleration | $a$ | $LT^{-2}$ |
| Area | $A$ | $L^2$ |
| Discharge | $Q$ | $L^3 T^{-1}$ |
| Pressure | $\Delta p$ | $ML^{-1}T^{-2}$ |
| Gravity | $g$ | $LT^{-2}$ |
| Density | $\rho$ | $ML^{-3}$ |
| Specific weight | $\gamma$ | $ML^{-2}T^{-2}$ |
| Dynamic viscosity | $\mu$ | $ML^{-1}T^{-1}$ |
| Kinematic viscosity | $\nu$ | $L^2 T^{-1}$ |
| Surface tension | $\sigma$ | $MT^{-2}$ |
| Bulk modulus of elasticity | $K$ | $ML^{-1}T^{-2}$ |

dealing with electromagnetics and the other with thermal effects.   For the compressible work in this text, it is unnecessary to include a thermal unit, as the equations of state link pressure, density, and temperature.

Newton's second law of motion in dimensional form is

$$F = MLT^{-2} \tag{4.2.2}$$

which shows that only three of the dimensions are independent.   $F$ is the force dimension, $M$ the mass dimension, $L$ the length dimension, and $T$ the time dimension.   One common system employed in dimensional analysis is the $M$-, $L$-, $T$-system.   Table 4.1 is a listing of some of the quantities used in fluid flow, together with their symbols and dimensions.

## 4.3   the Π-theorem

The Buckingham[1] Π-theorem proves that in a physical problem including $n$ quantities in which there are $m$ dimensions, the quantities may be arranged into $n - m$ independent dimensionless parameters.   Let $A_1$, $A_2$, $A_3$, . . . , $A_n$ be the quantities involved, such as pressure, viscosity, velocity,

[1] E. Buckingham, Model Experiments and the Form of Empirical Equations, *Trans. ASME*, vol. 37, pp. 263–296, 1915.

etc.  All the quantities are known to be essential to the solution, and hence some functional relation must exist.

$$F(A_1, A_2, A_3, \ldots, A_n) = 0 \qquad (4.3.1)$$

If $\Pi_1$, $\Pi_2$, etc., represent dimensionless groupings of the quantities $A_1$, $A_2$, $A_3$, etc., then with $m$ dimensions involved, an equation of the form

$$f(\Pi_1, \Pi_2, \Pi_3, \ldots, \Pi_{n-m}) = 0 \qquad (4.3.2)$$

exists.

Proof of the $\Pi$-theorem may be found in Buckingham's paper, as well as in Sedov's book listed in the references at the end of this chapter.  The method of determining the $\Pi$-parameters is to select $m$ of the $A$-quantities, with different dimensions, that contain among them the $m$ dimensions, and to use them as repeating variables together with one of the other $A$-quantities for each $\Pi$.  For example, let $A_1$, $A_2$, $A_3$ contain $M$, $L$, and $T$, not necessarily in each one, but collectively.  Then, the first $\Pi$-parameter is made up as

$$\Pi_1 = A_1^{x_1} A_2^{y_1} A_3^{z_1} A_4 \qquad (4.3.3)$$

the second one as

$$\Pi_2 = A_1^{x_2} A_2^{y_2} A_3^{z_2} A_5$$

and so on, until

$$\Pi_{n-m} = A_1^{x_{n-m}} A_2^{y_{n-m}} A_3^{z_{n-m}} A_n$$

In these equations the exponents are to be determined so that each $\Pi$ is dimensionless.  The dimensions of the $A$-quantities are substituted and the exponents $M$, $L$, and $T$ are set equal to zero respectively.  These produce three equations in three unknowns for each $\Pi$-parameter, so that the $x$, $y$, $z$ exponents can be determined, and hence the $\Pi$-parameter.

If only two dimensions are involved, then two of the $A$-quantities are selected as repeating variables, and two equations in the two unknown exponents are obtained for each $\Pi$ term.

In many cases the grouping of $A$-terms is such that the dimensionless arrangement is evident by inspection.  The simplest case is that, when two quantities have the same dimensions, e.g., length, then the ratio of these two terms is the $\Pi$-parameter.

The procedure is best illustrated by several examples.

**example 4.1**  The discharge through a horizontal capillary tube is thought to depend upon the pressure drop per unit length, the diameter, and the viscosity.  Find the form of the equation.

The quantities are listed with their dimensions:

| Quantity | Symbol | Dimensions |
|----------|--------|------------|
| Discharge | $Q$ | $L^3T^{-1}$ |
| Pressure drop/length | $\Delta p/l$ | $ML^{-2}T^{-2}$ |
| Diameter | $D$ | $L$ |
| Viscosity | $\mu$ | $ML^{-1}T^{-1}$ |

Then

$$F\left(Q, \frac{\Delta p}{l}, D, \mu\right) = 0$$

Three dimensions are used, and with four quantities there will be one $\Pi$-parameter:

$$\Pi = Q^{x_1}\left(\frac{\Delta p}{l}\right)^{y_1} D^{z_1}\mu$$

By substituting in the dimensions,

$$\Pi = (L^3T^{-1})^{x_1}(ML^{-2}T^{-2})^{y_1}L^{z_1}ML^{-1}T^{-1} = M^0L^0T^0$$

The exponents of each dimension must be the same on both sides of the equation.   With $L$ first,

$$3x_1 - 2y_1 + z_1 - 1 = 0$$

and similarly for $M$ and $T$

$$y_1 + 1 = 0$$
$$-x_1 - 2y_1 - 1 = 0$$

from which $x_1 = 1$, $y_1 = -1$, $z_1 = -4$, and

$$\Pi = \frac{Q\mu}{D^4 \, \Delta p/l}$$

After solving for $Q$,

$$Q = C\frac{\Delta p}{l}\frac{D^4}{\mu}$$

from which dimensional analysis yields no information about the numerical value of the dimensionless constant $C$, experiment (or analysis) shows that it is $\pi/128$ [Eq. (5.2.10a)].

When dimensional analysis is used, the variables in a problem must be known.    In the last example if kinematic viscosity had been used in place of dynamic viscosity an incorrect formula would have resulted.

**example 4.2**    A V-notch weir is a vertical plate with a notch of angle $\phi$ cut into the top of it and placed across an open channel.    The liquid in the channel is backed up and forced to flow through the notch.    The discharge $Q$ is some function of the elevation $H$ of upstream liquid surface above the bottom of the notch.    In addition the discharge depends upon gravity and upon the velocity of approach $V_0$ to the weir.    Determine the form of discharge equation.

A functional relationship

$$F(Q,H,g,V_0,\phi) = 0$$

is to be grouped into dimensionless parameters.    $\phi$ is dimensionless, hence it is one $\Pi$-parameter.    Only two dimensions are used, $L$ and $T$. If $g$ and $H$ are the repeating variables,

$$\Pi_1 = H^{x_1}g^{y_1}Q = L^{x_1}(LT^{-2})^{y_1}L^3T^{-1}$$
$$\Pi_2 = H^{x_2}g^{y_2}V_0 = L^{x_2}(LT^{-2})^{y_2}LT^{-1}$$

Then

$$x_1 + y_1 + 3 = 0 \qquad x_2 + y_2 + 1 = 0$$
$$-2y_1 - 1 = 0 \qquad\quad -2y_2 - 1 = 0$$

from which $x_1 = -\frac{5}{2}$, $y_1 = -\frac{1}{2}$, $x_2 = -\frac{1}{2}$, $y_2 = -\frac{1}{2}$, and

$$\Pi_1 = \frac{Q}{\sqrt{g}\,H^{5/2}} \qquad \Pi_2 = \frac{V_0}{\sqrt{gH}} \qquad \Pi_3 = \phi$$

or

$$f\left(\frac{Q}{\sqrt{g}\,H^{5/2}}, \frac{V_0}{\sqrt{gH}}, \phi\right) = 0$$

This may be written

$$\frac{Q}{\sqrt{g}\,H^{5/2}} = f_1\left(\frac{V_0}{\sqrt{gH}}, \phi\right)$$

in which both $f$, $f_1$ are unknown functions.    After solving for $Q$,

$$Q = \sqrt{g}\,H^{5/2}f_1\left(\frac{V_0}{\sqrt{gH}}, \phi\right)$$

Either experiment or analysis is required to yield additional information as to the function $f_1$.

If $H$ and $V_0$ were selected as repeating variables in place of $g$ and $H$,

$$\Pi_1 = H^{x_1}V_0^{y_1}Q = L^{x_1}(LT^{-1})^{x_1}L^3T^{-1}$$
$$\Pi_2 = H^{x_2}V_0^{y_2}g = L^{x_2}(LT^{-1})^{y_2}LT^{-2}$$

Then

$$x_1 + y_1 + 3 = 0 \qquad x_2 + y_2 + 1 = 0$$
$$- y_1 - 1 = 0 \qquad\qquad - y_2 - 2 = 0$$

from which $x_1 = -2$, $y_1 = -1$, $x_2 = 1$, $y_2 = -2$, and

$$\Pi_1 = \frac{Q}{H^2V_0} \qquad \Pi_2 = \frac{gH}{V_0^2} \qquad \Pi_3 = \phi$$

or

$$f\left(\frac{Q}{H^2V_0}, \frac{gH}{V_0^2}, \phi\right) = 0$$

Since any of the $\Pi$-parameters may be inverted or raised to any power without affecting their dimensionless status,

$$Q = V_0H^2f_2\left(\frac{V_0}{\sqrt{gH}}, \phi\right)$$

The unknown function $f_2$ has the same parameters as $f_1$, but it could not be the same function.   The last form is not very useful, in general, because frequently $V_0$ may be neglected with V-notch weirs.   This shows that a term of minor importance should not be selected as a repeating variable.

Another method of determining alternate sets of $\Pi$-parameters would be the arbitrary recombination of the first set.   If four independent $\Pi$ param eters $\Pi_1$, $\Pi_2$, $\Pi_3$, $\Pi_4$ are known, the term

$$\Pi_a = \Pi_1^{a_1}\Pi_2^{a_2}\Pi_3^{a_3}\Pi_4^{a_4}$$

with the exponents chosen at will, would yield a new parameter.   Then $\Pi_a$, $\Pi_2$, $\Pi_3$, $\Pi_4$ would constitute a new set.   This procedure may be con-tinued to find all possible sets.

**example 4.3**   The losses $\Delta h/l$ per unit length of pipe in turbulent flow through a smooth pipe depend upon velocity $V$, diameter $D$, gravity $g$, dynamic viscosity $\mu$, and density $\rho$.   With dimensional analysis, determine the general form of the equation

$$F\left(\frac{\Delta h}{l},\ V,D,\rho,\mu,g\right) = 0$$

Clearly, $\Delta h/l$ is a $\Pi$-parameter.   If $V$, $D$, and $\rho$ are repeating variables,

$$\Pi_1 = V^{x_1}D^{y_1}\rho^{z_1}\mu = (LT^{-1})^{x_1}L^{y_1}(ML^{-3})^{z_1}ML^{-1}T^{-1}$$
$$x_1 + y_1 - 3z_1 - 1 = 0$$
$$-x_1 \qquad\qquad\quad - 1 = 0$$
$$z_1 + 1 = 0$$

from which $x_1 = -1$, $y_1 = -1$, $z_1 = -1$.

$$\Pi_2 = V^{x_2}D^{y_2}\rho^{z_2}g = (LT^{-1})^{x_2}L^{y_2}(ML^{-3})^{z_2}LT^{-2}$$
$$x_2 + y_2 - 3z_2 + 1 = 0$$
$$-x_2 \qquad\qquad\quad - 2 = 0$$
$$z_2 \qquad\quad = 0$$

from which $x_2 = -2$, $y_2 = 1$, $z_2 = 0$.

$$\Pi_1 = \frac{\mu}{VD\rho} \qquad \Pi_2 = \frac{gD}{V^2} \qquad \Pi_3 = \frac{\Delta h}{l}$$

or

$$f\left(\frac{VD\rho}{\mu},\ \frac{V^2}{gD},\ \frac{\Delta h}{l}\right) = 0$$

since the $\Pi$-quantities may be inverted if desired.   The first parameter, $VD\rho/\mu$, is the *Reynolds number,* one of the most important of the dimensionless parameters in fluid mechanics.   The size of the Reynolds number determines the nature of the flow.   It is discussed in Sec. 5.3.   After solving for $\Delta h/l$,

$$\frac{\Delta h}{l} = f_1\left(\mathbf{R},\ \frac{V^2}{gD}\right)$$

The usual formula employed is

$$\frac{\Delta h}{l} = f(\mathbf{R})\,\frac{1}{D}\frac{V^2}{2g}$$

**example 4.4**   A fluid-flow situation depends upon the velocity $V$, the density $\rho$, several linear dimensions $l$, $l_1$, $l_2$, pressure drop $\Delta p$, gravity $g$, viscosity $\mu$, surface tension $\sigma$, and bulk modulus of elasticity $K$.   Apply dimensional analysis to these variables to find a set of $\Pi$-parameters.

$$F(V,\rho,l,l_1,l_2,\Delta p,g,\mu,\sigma,K) = 0$$

As three dimensions are involved, three repeating variables are selected. For complex situations, $V$, $\rho$, and $l$ are generally helpful.   There are seven $\Pi$-parameters:

$$\Pi_1 = V^{x_1}\rho^{y_1}l^{z_1}\,\Delta p \qquad \Pi_2 = V^{x_2}\rho^{y_2}l^{z_2}g \qquad \Pi_3 = V^{x_3}\rho^{y_3}l^{z_3}\mu$$
$$\Pi_4 = V^{x_4}\rho^{y_4}l^{z_4}\sigma \qquad \Pi_5 = V^{x_5}\rho^{y_5}l^{z_5}K \qquad \Pi_6 = l/l_1$$
$$\Pi_7 = l/l_2$$

By expanding the $\Pi$-quantities into dimensions,

$$\Pi_1 = (LT^{-1})^{x_1}(ML^{-3})^{y_1}L^{z_1}ML^{-1}T^{-2}$$

$$\begin{aligned} x_1 - 3y_1 + z_1 - 1 &= 0 \\ -x_1 \qquad\qquad\quad -2 &= 0 \\ y_1 \qquad\qquad +1 &= 0 \end{aligned}$$

from which $x_1 = -2$, $y_1 = -1$, $z_1 = 0$.

$$\Pi_2 = (LT^{-1})^{x_2}(ML^{-3})^{y_2}L^{z_2}LT^{-2}$$

$$\begin{aligned} x_2 - 3y_2 + z_2 + 1 &= 0 \\ -x_2 \qquad\qquad\quad -2 &= 0 \\ y_2 \qquad\qquad\qquad &= 0 \end{aligned}$$

from which $x_2 = -2$, $y_2 = 0$, $z_2 = 1$.

$$\Pi_3 = (LT^{-1})^{x_3}(ML^{-3})^{y_3}L^{z_3}ML^{-1}T^{-1}$$

$$\begin{aligned} x_3 - 3y_3 + z_3 - 1 &= 0 \\ -x_3 \qquad\qquad\quad -1 &= 0 \\ y_3 \qquad\qquad +1 &= 0 \end{aligned}$$

from which $x_3 = -1$, $y_3 = -1$, $z_3 = -1$.

$$\Pi_4 = (LT^{-1})^{x_4}(ML^{-3})^{y_4}L^{z_4}MT^{-2}$$

$$\begin{aligned} x_4 - 3y_4 + z_4 \qquad &= 0 \\ -x_4 \qquad\qquad\quad -2 &= 0 \\ y_4 \qquad\qquad +1 &= 0 \end{aligned}$$

from which $x_4 = -2$, $y_4 = -1$, $z_4 = -1$.

$$\Pi_5 = (LT^{-1})^{x_5}(ML^{-3})^{y_5}L^{z_5}ML^{-1}T^{-2}$$

$$\begin{aligned} x_5 - 3y_5 + z_5 - 1 &= 0 \\ -x_5 \qquad\qquad\quad -2 &= 0 \\ y_5 \qquad\qquad +1 &= 0 \end{aligned}$$

from which $x_5 = -2$, $y_5 = -1$, $z_5 = 0$.

Hence

$$\Pi_1 = \frac{\Delta p}{\rho V^2} \qquad \Pi_2 = \frac{gl}{V^2} \qquad \Pi_3 = \frac{\mu}{Vl\rho} \qquad \Pi_4 = \frac{\sigma}{V^2 \rho l}$$

$$\Pi_5 = \frac{K}{\rho V^2} \qquad \Pi_6 = \frac{l}{l_1} \qquad \Pi_7 = \frac{l}{l_2}$$

and

$$f\left(\frac{\Delta p}{\rho V^2}, \frac{gl}{V^2}, \frac{\mu}{Vl\rho}, \frac{\sigma}{V^2 \rho l}, \frac{K}{\rho V^2}, \frac{l}{l_1}, \frac{l}{l_2}\right) = 0$$

It is convenient to invert some of the parameters and to take the square root of $\Pi_5$,

$$f_1\left(\frac{\Delta p}{\rho V^2}, \frac{V^2}{gl}, \frac{Vl\rho}{\mu}, \frac{V^2 l\rho}{\sigma}, \frac{V}{\sqrt{K/\rho}}, \frac{l}{l_1}, \frac{l}{l_2}\right) = 0$$

The first parameter, usually written $\Delta p/(\rho V^2/2)$, is the *pressure coefficient;* the second parameter is the *Froude* number **F**; the third is the *Reynolds* number **R**; the fourth is the *Weber* number **W**; and the fifth is the *Mach* number **M**.  Hence

$$f_1\left(\frac{\Delta p}{\rho V^2}, \textbf{F,R,W,M}, \frac{l_1}{l}, \frac{l}{l_2}\right) = 0$$

After solving for pressure drop

$$\Delta p = \rho V^2 f_2\left(\textbf{F,R,W,M}, \frac{l}{l_1}, \frac{l}{l_2}\right)$$

in which $f_1$, $f_2$ must be determined from analysis or experiment.  By selecting other repeating variables, a different set of II-parameters could be obtained.

Figure 5.32 is a representation of a functional relationship of the type just given as it applies to the flow in pipes.  Here the parameters **F**, **W**, and **M** are neglected as being unimportant; $l$ is the pipe diameter $D$, $l_1$ is the length of the pipe $L$, and $l_2$ is a dimension which is representative of the effective height of the surface roughness of the pipe and is given by $\epsilon$. Thus

$$\frac{\Delta p}{\rho V^2} = f_3\left(\textbf{R}, \frac{L}{D}, \frac{\epsilon}{D}\right)$$

The fact that the pressure drop in the pipeline varies linearly with the length (i.e., doubling the length of pipe doubles the loss in pressure) appears reasonable, so that one has

$$\frac{\Delta p}{\rho V^2} = \frac{L}{D} f_4 \left( \mathbf{R}, \frac{\epsilon}{D} \right)$$

or

$$\frac{\Delta p}{\rho V^2 (L/D)} = f_4 \left( \mathbf{R}, \frac{\epsilon}{D} \right)$$

The term on the left-hand side is commonly given the notation $f$, as in Fig. 5.32. The curves shown in this figure have $f$ and $\mathbf{R}$ as ordinate and abscissa, respectively, with $\epsilon/D$ a parameter which assumes a given value for each curve. The nature of these curves was determined through experiment. Such experiments show that when the parameter $\mathbf{R}$ is below the value of 2000, all the curves for the various values of $\epsilon/D$ coalesce into one. Hence $f$ is independent of $\epsilon/D$, and the result is

$$f = f_5(\mathbf{R})$$

This relationship will be predicted in Chap. 5 on the basis of theoretical considerations, but it remained for an experimental verification of these predictions to indicate the power of the theoretical methods that were developed.

**example 4.5**   The thrust due to any one of a family of geometrically similar airplane propellers is to be determined experimentally from a wind-tunnel test on a model. By means of dimensional analysis find suitable parameters for plotting test results.

The thrust $F_T$ depends upon speed of rotation $\omega$, speed of advance $V_0$, diameter $D$, air viscosity $\mu$, density $\rho$, and speed of sound $c$. The function

$$f(F_T, V_0, D, \omega, \mu, \rho, c) = 0$$

is to be arranged into four dimensionless parameters, since there are seven quantities and three dimensions. Starting first by selecting $\rho$, $\omega$, and $D$ as repeating variables,

$$\Pi_1 = \rho^{x_1} \omega^{y_1} D^{z_1} F_T = (ML^{-3})^{x_1} (T^{-1})^{y_1} L^{z_1} MLT^{-2}$$
$$\Pi_2 = \rho^{x_2} \omega^{y_2} D^{z_2} V_0 = (ML^{-3})^{x_2} (T^{-1})^{y_2} L^{z_2} LT^{-1}$$
$$\Pi_3 = \rho^{x_3} \omega^{y_3} D^{z_3} \mu = (ML^{-3})^{x_3} (T^{-1})^{y_3} L^{z_3} ML^{-1}T^{-1}$$
$$\Pi_4 = \rho^{x_4} \omega^{y_4} D^{z_4} c = (ML^{-3})^{x_4} (T^{-1})^{y_4} L^{z_4} LT^{-1}$$

By writing the simultaneous equations in $x_1$, $y_1$, $z_1$, etc., as before and solving them,

$$\Pi_1 = \frac{F_T}{\rho \omega^2 D^2} \qquad \Pi_2 = \frac{V_0}{\omega D} \qquad \Pi_3 = \frac{\mu}{\rho \omega D^2} \qquad \Pi_4 = \frac{c}{\omega D}$$

Solving for the thrust parameter,

$$\frac{F_T}{\rho\omega^2 D^4} = f_1\left(\frac{V_0}{\omega D}, \frac{\rho\omega D^2}{\mu}, \frac{c}{\omega D}\right)$$

Since the parameters may be recombined to obtain other forms, the second term is replaced by the product of the first and second terms, $VD\rho/\mu$, and the third term is replaced by the first term divided by the third term, $V_0/c$; thus

$$\frac{F_T}{\rho\omega^2 D^4} = f_2\left(\frac{V_0}{\omega D}, \frac{V_0 D\rho}{\mu}, \frac{V_0}{c}\right)$$

Of the dimensionless parameters, the first is probably of the most importance, since it relates speed of advance to speed of rotation. The second parameter is a Reynolds number and accounts for viscous effects. The last parameter, speed of advance divided by speed of sound, is a Mach number, which would be important for speeds near or higher than the speed of sound. Reynolds effects are usually small, so that a plot of $F_T/\rho\omega^2 D^4$ against $V_0/\omega D$ should be most informative.

The steps in a dimensional analysis may be summarized as follows:

1.  Select the pertinent variables. This requires some knowledge of the process.
2.  Write the functional relationships, e.g.,

    $$f(V,D,\rho,\mu,c,H) = 0$$

3.  Select the repeating variables. (Do not make the dependent quantity a repeating variable.) These variables should contain all the $m$ dimensions of the problem. Often one variable is chosen because it specifies the scale, another the kinematic conditions, and in the cases of major interest in this chapter, one variable is chosen which is related to the forces or mass of the system, e.g., $D$, $V$, $\rho$.
4.  Write the Π-parameters in terms of unknown exponents, e.g.,

    $$\Pi_1 = V^{x_1}D^{y_1}\rho^{z_1}\mu = (LT^{-1})^{x_1}L^{y_1}(ML^{-3})^{z_1}ML^{-1}T^1$$

5.  For each of the Π-expressions write the equations of the exponents, so that the sum of the exponents of each dimension will be zero.
6.  Solve the equations simultaneously.
7.  Substitute back into the Π-expressions of step 4 the exponents to obtain the dimensionless Π-parameters.

8. Establish the functional relation

$$f_1(\Pi_1, \Pi_2, \Pi_3, \ldots, \Pi_{n-m}) = 0$$

or solve for one of the $\Pi$'s explicitly:

$$\Pi_2 = f(\Pi_1, \Pi_3, \ldots, \Pi_{n-m})$$

9. Recombine, if desired, to alter the forms of the $\Pi$-parameters, keeping the same number of independent parameters.

*alternate formulation of* $\Pi$-*parameters*

A rapid method for obtaining $\Pi$-parameters, developed by Hunsaker and Rightmire (referenced at end of chapter), uses the repeating variables as primary quantities and solves for $M$, $L$, and $T$ in terms of them.   In Example 4.3 the repeating variables are $V$, $D$, and $\rho$; therefore

$$
\begin{array}{lll}
(V) = (LT^{-1}) & (D) = (L) & (\rho) = (ML^{-3}) \\
(L) = (D) & (T) = (DV^{-1}) & (M) = (\rho D^3)
\end{array}
\tag{4.3.4}
$$

Now, by use of Eqs. (4.3.4)

$$(\mu) = (ML^{-1}T^{-1}) = (\rho D^3 D^{-1} D^{-1} V) = \rho D V$$

hence the $\pi$-parameter is

$$\Pi_1 - \frac{\mu}{\rho D V}$$

Equations (4.3.4) may be used directly to find the other $\Pi$-parameters. For $\Pi_2$

$$(g) = (LT^{-2}) = (DD^{-2}V^2) = (V^2 D^{-1})$$

and

$$\Pi_2 = \frac{g}{V^2 D^{-1}} = \frac{gD}{V^2}$$

This method does not require the repeated solution of three equations in three unknowns for each $\Pi$-parameter determination.

## 4.4  discussion of dimensionless parameters

The five dimensionless parameters, pressure coefficient, Reynolds number, Froude number, Weber number, and Mach number, are of importance in correlating experimental data. They are discussed in this section, with particular emphasis placed on the relation of pressure coefficient to the other parameters.

*pressure coefficient*

The pressure coefficient $\Delta p/(\rho V^2/2)$ is the ratio of pressure to dynamic pressure. When multiplied by area it is the ratio of pressure force to inertial force, as $(\rho V^2/2)A$ would be the force needed to reduce the velocity to zero. It may also be written as $\Delta h/(V^2/2g)$ by division by $\gamma$. For pipe flow the Darcy-Weisbach equation relates losses $h_l$ to length of pipe $L$, diameter $D$, and velocity $V$ by a dimensionless friction factor, $f$[1]

$$h_l = f\frac{L}{D}\frac{V^2}{2g}$$

or

$$\frac{fL}{D} = \frac{h_l}{V^2/2g} = f_2\left(\mathbf{R,F,W,M},\frac{l}{l_1},\frac{l}{l_2}\right)$$

as $fL/D$ is shown to be equal to the pressure coefficient (see Example 4.4). In pipe flow, gravity has no influence on losses; therefore **F** may be dropped out. Similarly surface tension has no effect and **W** drops out. For steady liquid flow, compressibility is not important and **M** is dropped. $l$ may refer to $D$, $l_1$ to roughness height projection $\epsilon$ in the pipe wall, and $l_2$ to their spacing $\epsilon'$; hence

$$\frac{fL}{D} = f_2\left(\mathbf{R},\frac{\epsilon}{D},\frac{\epsilon'}{D}\right) \qquad\qquad (4.4.1)$$

Pipe-flow problems are discussed in Chaps. 5, 6, and 10. If compressibility is important,

$$\frac{fL}{D} = f_2\left(\mathbf{R,M},\frac{\epsilon}{D},\frac{\epsilon'}{D}\right) \qquad\qquad (4.4.2)$$

Compressible-flow problems are studied in Chap. 6. With orifice flow, studied in Chap. 8, $V = C_v\sqrt{2gH}$,

$$\frac{H}{V^2/2g} = \frac{1}{C_v^2} = f_2\left(\mathbf{R,W,M},\frac{l}{l_1},\frac{l}{l_2}\right) \qquad\qquad (4.4.3)$$

---

[1] There are several friction factors in general use. This is the Darcy-Weisbach friction factor, which is four times the size of the *Fanning* friction factor, also called $f$.

in which $l$ may refer to orifice diameter and $l_1$ and $l_2$ to upstream dimensions. Viscosity and surface tension are unimportant for large orifices and low-viscosity fluids. Mach number effects may be very important for gas flow with large pressure drops, i.e., Mach numbers approaching unity.

In steady, uniform open-channel flow, discussed in Chap. 5, the Chézy formula relates average velocity $V$, slope of channel $S$, and hydraulic radius of cross section $R$ (area of section divided by wetted perimeter) by

$$V = C\sqrt{RS} = C\sqrt{R\frac{\Delta h}{L}} \tag{4.4.4}$$

$C$ is a coefficient depending upon size, shape, and roughness of channel. Then

$$\frac{\Delta h}{V^2/2g} = \frac{2gL}{R}\frac{1}{C^2} = f_2\left(\mathbf{F},\mathbf{R},\frac{l}{l_1},\frac{l}{l_2}\right) \tag{4.4.5}$$

since surface tension and compressible effects are usually unimportant.

The drag $F$ on a body is expressed by $F = C_D A\rho V^2/2$, in which $A$ is a typical area of the body, usually the projection of the body onto a plane normal to the flow. Then $F/A$ is equivalent to $\Delta p$, and

$$\frac{F}{A\rho V^2/2} = C_D = f_2\left(\mathbf{R},\mathbf{F},\mathbf{M},\frac{l}{l_1},\frac{l}{l_2}\right) \tag{4.4.6}$$

The term $\mathbf{R}$ is related to *skin-friction* drag due to viscous shear as well as to *form*, or *profile*, drag resulting from *separation* of the flow streamlines from the body; $\mathbf{F}$ is related to wave drag if there is a free surface; for large Mach numbers $C_D$ may vary more markedly with $\mathbf{M}$ than with the other parameters; the length ratios may refer to shape or roughness of the surface.

*the Reynolds number*

The Reynolds number $VD\rho/\mu$ is the ratio of inertial forces to viscous forces. A "critical" Reynolds number distinguishes among flow regimes, such as laminar or turbulent flow in pipes, in the boundary layer, or around immersed objects. The particular value depends upon the situation. In compressible flow, the Mach number is generally more significant than the Reynolds number.

### the Froude number

The Froude number $V^2/gl$, when multiplied and divided by $\rho A$, is a ratio of dynamic (or inertial) force to weight.   With free liquid-surface flow the nature of the flow (rapid[1] or tranquil) depends upon whether the Froude number is greater or less than unity.   It is useful in calculations of hydraulic jump, in design of hydraulic structures, and in ship design.

### the Weber number

The Weber number $V^2 l\rho/\sigma$ is the ratio of inertial forces to surface-tension forces (evident when numerator and denominator are multiplied by $l$). It is important at gas-liquid or liquid-liquid interfaces and also where these interfaces are in contact with a boundary.   Surface tension causes small (capillary) waves and droplet formation and has an effect on discharge of orifices and weirs at very small heads.   The effect of surface tension on wave propagation is shown in Fig. 4.1.   To the left of the curve's minimum the wave speed is controlled by surface tension (the waves are called ripples), and to the right of the minimum gravity effects are dominant.

### the Mach number

The speed of sound in a liquid is written $\sqrt{K/\rho}$, if $K$ is the bulk modulus of elasticity (Secs. 1.7 and 6.2) or $c = \sqrt{kRT}$ ($k$ is the specific heat ratio and $T$ the absolute temperature, for a perfect gas).   $V/c$ or $V/\sqrt{K/\rho}$

---

[1] Open-channel flow at depth $y$ is *rapid* when the flow velocity is greater than the speed $\sqrt{gy}$ of an elementary wave in quiet liquid.   *Tranquil* flow occurs when the flow velocity is less than $\sqrt{gy}$.

**Fig. 4.1**  Wave speed vs. wavelength for surface waves.

is the Mach number.  It is a measure of the ratio of inertial forces to elastic forces.  By squaring $V/c$ and multiplying by $\rho A/2$ in numerator and denominator, the numerator is the dynamic force and the denominator is the dynamic force at sonic flow.  It may also be shown to be a measure of the ratio of kinetic energy of the flow to internal energy of the fluid. It is the most important correlating parameter when velocities are near or above local sonic velocities.

## 4.5  similitude—model studies

Model studies of proposed hydraulic structures and machines are frequently undertaken as an aid to the designer.  They permit visual observation of the flow and make possible the obtaining of certain numerical data, e.g., calibrations of weirs and gates, depths of flow, velocity distributions, forces on gates, efficiencies and capacities of pumps and turbines, pressure distributions, and losses.

If accurate quantitative data are to be obtained from a model study there must be dynamic similitude between model and prototype.  This similitude requires (1) that there be exact geometric similitude, and (2) that the ratio of dynamic pressures at corresponding points be a constant. Part 2 may also be expressed as a kinematic similitude, i.e., the streamlines must be geometrically similar.

Geometric similitude extends to the actual surface roughness of model and prototype.  If the model is one tenth the size of the prototype in every linear dimension, then the height of roughness projections must be in the same ratio.  For dynamic pressures to be in the same ratio at corresponding points in model and prototype, the ratios of the various types of forces must be the same at corresponding points.  Hence, for strict dynamic similitude, the Mach, Reynolds, Froude, and Weber numbers must be the same in both model and prototype.

Strict fulfillment of these requirements is generally impossible of achievement, except with a 1:1 scale ratio.  Fortunately, in many situations only two of the forces are of the same magnitude.  Discussion of a few cases will make this clear.

### wind- and water-tunnel tests

This equipment is used to examine the streamlines and the forces that are induced as the fluid flows past a fully submerged body.  The type of test that is being conducted and the availability of the equipment determine which kind of tunnel will be used.  Because the kinematic viscosity of

**Fig. 4.2** Wind-tunnel tests on an aircraft-carrier superstructure. Model is inverted and suspended from ceiling. (*Photograph taken in Aeronautical and Astronautical Laboratories of The University of Michigan for the Dynasciences Corp.*)

water is about one-tenth that of air, a water tunnel can be used for model studies at relatively high Reynolds numbers.   The drag effect of various parachutes was studied in a water tunnel!   At very high air velocities the effects of compressibility, and consequently Mach number, must be taken into consideration, and indeed may be the chief reason for undertaking an investigation.   Figure 4.2 shows a model of an aircraft carrier being tested in a low-speed tunnel to study the flow pattern around the ship's superstructure.   The model has been inverted and suspended from the ceiling so that the wool tufts can be used to give an indication of the flow direction.   Behind the model there is an apparatus for sensing the air speed and direction at various locations along an aircraft's glide path.

*pipe flow*

In steady flow in a pipe, viscous and inertial forces are the only ones of consequence; hence, when geometric similitude is observed, the same

Reynolds number in model and prototype provides dynamic similitude. The various corresponding pressure coefficients are the same. For testing with fluids having the same kinematic viscosity in model and prototype, the product, $VD$, must be the same. Frequently this requires very high velocities in small models.

*open hydraulic structures*

Structures such as spillways, stilling pools, channel transitions, and weirs generally have forces due to gravity (from changes in elevation of liquid surfaces) and inertial forces that are greater than viscous and turbulent shear forces. In these cases geometric similitude and the same value of Froude's number in model and prototype produce a good approximation to dynamic similitude; thus

$$\frac{V_m{}^2}{g_m l_m} = \frac{V_p{}^2}{g_p l_p}$$

Since gravity is the same, the velocity ratio varies as the square root of the scale ratio $\lambda = l_p/l_m$,

$$V_p = V_m \sqrt{\lambda}$$

The corresponding times for events to take place (as time for passage of a particle through a transition) are related; thus

$$t_m = \frac{l_m}{V_m} \qquad t_p = \frac{l_p}{V_p}$$

and

$$t_p = t_m \frac{l_p}{l_m} \frac{V_m}{V_p} = t_m \sqrt{\lambda}$$

The discharge ratio $Q_p/Q_m$ is

$$\frac{Q_p}{Q_m} = \frac{l_p{}^3/t_p}{l_m{}^3/t_m} = \lambda^{5/2}$$

Force ratios, e.g., on gates, $F_p/F_m$, are

$$\frac{F'_p}{F_m} = \frac{\gamma h_p l_p{}^2}{\gamma h_m l_m{}^2} = \lambda^3$$

In a similar fashion other pertinent ratios may be derived so that model results can be interpreted as prototype performance.

Figure 4.3 shows a model test conducted to determine the effect of a breakwater on the wave formation in a harbor.

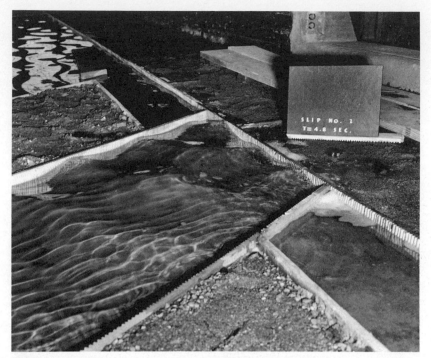

**Fig. 4.3** Model test on a harbor to determine the effect of a breakwater. (*Department of Civil Engineering, The University of Michigan.*)

*ship's resistance*

The resistance to motion of a ship through water is composed of pressure drag, skin friction, and wave resistance.   Model studies are complicated by the three types of forces that are important, inertia, viscosity, and gravity.   Skin-friction studies should be based on equal Reynolds numbers in model and prototype, but wave resistance depends upon the Froude number.   To satisfy both requirements, model and prototype have to be the same size.

The difficulty is surmounted by using a small model and measuring the total drag on it when towed.   The skin friction is then computed for the model and subtracted from the total drag.   The remainder is stepped up to prototype size by Froude's law, and the prototype skin friction is computed and added to yield total resistance due to the water.   Figure 4.4 shows the dramatic change in the wave profile which resulted from a redesigned bow.   From such tests it is possible to predict through

**Fig. 4.4**  Model tests showing the influence of a bulbous bow on bow-wave formation. *(Department of Naval Architecture and Marine Engineering, The University of Michigan.)*

Froude's law the wave formation and drag that would occur on the prototype.

*hydraulic machinery*

Due to the moving parts in a hydraulic machine, an extra parameter is required to ensure that the streamline patterns are similar in model and prototype. This parameter must relate the throughflow (discharge) to the speed of moving parts. For geometrically similar machines if the vector diagrams of velocity entering or leaving the moving parts are similar, the units are *homologous;* i.e., for practical purposes dynamic similitude exists. The Froude number is unimportant, but the Reynolds number effects (called *scale effects* because it is impossible to maintain the same Reynolds number in homologous units) may cause a discrepancy of 2 or 3 per cent in efficiency between model and prototype. The Mach number is also of importance in axial-flow compressors and gas turbines.

**example 4.6**  The Reynolds number for a sphere is commonly determined by the speed of the fluid at a great distance from the sphere, the diameter of the sphere, and the kinematic viscosity of the fluid. When this Reynolds number is less than unity, the drag force on the sphere is given by $3\pi\mu DU$. Discuss the feasibility of modeling in water the case of $\frac{1}{64}$-in.-diameter spheres falling in air at a speed of 0.10 ft/sec. Air temperature is 33°F.

$$\mathbf{R}_p = \frac{UD}{\nu} = \frac{0.01 \times (\frac{1}{64} \times \frac{1}{12})}{1.5 \times 10^{-4}} = 0.87$$

$$\frac{\text{Drag}}{(\pi D^2/4)(\rho U^2/2)} = C_D = \frac{3\pi\mu DU}{\pi D^2(\rho U^2/8)} = \frac{24}{\mathbf{R}}$$

Let $\nu$ for water equal $1.5 \times 10^{-5}$ ft²/sec:

$$U_m D_m = U_p D_p \frac{1.5 \times 10^{-5}}{1.5 \times 10^{-4}} = 0.1 U_p D_p$$

At the same $\mathbf{R}$, $C_D$ for the model and prototype is equal, so that

$$\frac{24}{\mathbf{R}_m} = \frac{24}{\mathbf{R}_p}$$

Hence no new restrictions are placed on the system for this case. For convenience let $D_m = D_p$; then $U_m = 0.1 U_p$. The drag on the model is

$$F = 3\pi (1.5 \times 10^{-5} \times 1.94) \frac{0.0156}{12} 0.01 = 3.56 \times 10^{-9} \text{ lb}$$

The drag on the sphere must equal its submerged weight when terminal velocity is reached, so that

$$\gamma = F/(\pi D^3/6)$$

$$\gamma = \frac{3.56 \times 10^{-9} \times 6/\pi}{(0.0156/12)^3} = 3.09 \text{ lb/ft}^3$$

Consequently spheres must be found so that

$$S = \frac{62.4 + 3.09}{62.4} = 1.048$$

## problems

**4.1**  Show that Eqs. (3.5.3), (3.9.3), and (3.11.1) are dimensionally homogeneous.

**4.2**  Arrange the following groups into dimensionless parameters:

$(a)$ $\Delta p$, $\rho$, $V$      $(b)$ $\rho$, $g$, $V$, $F$      $(c)$ $\mu$, $F$, $\Delta p$, $t$

**4.3**  By inspection, arrange the following groups into dimensionless parameters:

$(a)$ $a$, $l$, $t$      $(b)$ $v$, $l$, $t$      $(c)$ $A$, $Q$, $\omega$      $(d)$ $K$, $\sigma$, $A$

**4.4**  Derive the unit of mass consistent with the units inches, minutes, tons.

**4.5**  In terms of $M$, $L$, $T$, determine the dimensions of radians, angular velocity, power, work, torque, and moment of momentum.

**4.6**  Find the dimensions of the quantities in Prob. 4.5 in the $F$-, $L$-, $T$-system.

**4.7**  Work Example 4.2 using $Q$ and $H$ as repeating variables.

**4.8**  Using the variables $Q$, $D$, $\Delta h/l$, $\rho$, $\mu$, $g$ as pertinent to smooth pipe flow, arrange them into dimensionless parameters with $Q$, $\rho$, $\mu$ as repeating variables.

**4.9**  If the shear stress $\tau$ is known to depend upon viscosity and rate of angular deformation $du/dy$ in one-dimensional laminar flow, determine the form of Newton's law of viscosity by dimensional reasoning.

**4.10**  The variation $\Delta p$ of pressure in static liquids is known to depend upon specific weight $\gamma$ and elevation difference $\Delta z$. By dimensional reasoning determine the form of the hydrostatic law of variation of pressure.

**4.11**  Neglecting viscous and surface-tension effects, the velocity $V$ of efflux of liquid from a reservoir is thought to depend upon the pressure drop $\Delta p$ of the liquid and its density $\rho$.    Determine the form of expression for $V$.

**4.12**  The buoyant force $F_B$ on a body is thought to depend upon its volume submerged $\upsilon$ and the gravitational body force acting on the fluid.    Determine the form of the buoyant-force equation.

**4.13**  In a fluid rotated as a solid about a vertical axis with angular velocity $\omega$, the pressure rise $p$ in a radial direction depends upon speed $\omega$, radius $r$, and fluid density $\rho$.    Obtain the form of equation for $p$.

**4.14**  In Example 4.3, work out two other sets of dimensionless parameters by recombination of the dimensionless parameters given.

**4.15**  Find the dimensionless parameters of Example 4.4 using $\Delta p$, $\rho$, and $l$ as repeating variables.

**4.16**  The Mach number **M** for flow of a perfect gas in a pipe depends upon the specific heat ratio $k$ (dimensionless), the pressure $p$, the density $\rho$, and the velocity $V$.    Obtain by dimensional reasoning the form of the Mach number expression.

**4.17**  Work out the scaling ratio for torque $T$ on a disk of radius $r$ that rotates in fluid of viscosity $\mu$ with angular velocity $\omega$ and clearance $y$ between disk and fixed plate.

**4.18**  The velocity at a point in a model of a spillway for a dam is 3.3 ft/sec. For a ratio of prototype to model of 10:1, what is the velocity at the corresponding point in the prototype under similar conditions?

**4.19**  The power input to a pump depends upon the discharge $Q$, the pressure rise $\Delta p$, the fluid density $\rho$, size $D$, and efficiency $e$.    Find the expression for power by the use of dimensional analysis.

**4.20**  The torque delivered by a water turbine depends upon discharge $Q$, head $H$, specific weight $\gamma$, angular velocity $\omega$, and efficiency $e$.    Determine the form of equation for torque.

**4.21**  A model of a venturi meter has linear dimensions one-fifth those of the prototype.    The prototype operates on water at 68°F, and the model on water at 200°F.    For a throat diameter of 24 in. and a velocity at the throat of 20 ft/sec in the prototype, what discharge is needed through the model for similitude?

**4.22**  The drag $F$ on a high-velocity projectile depends upon speed $V$ of projectile, density of fluid $\rho$, acoustic velocity $c$, diameter of projectile $D$, and viscosity $\mu$.    Develop an expression for the drag.

**4.23**  The wave drag on a model of a ship is 3.52 lb at a speed of 8 ft/sec. For a prototype fifteen times as long what would be the corresponding speed and wave drag if the liquid is the same in each case?

**4.24**  Determine the specific gravity of the prototype particles used in Example 4.6.

**4.25**  A small sphere of radius $r_0$ and density $\rho_0$ settles at velocity $U$ in another liquid of density $\rho$ and viscosity $\mu$.   The tests are conducted inside vertical tubes of radius $r$.   By dimensional analysis determine a set of dimensionless parameters to be used in determining the influence of the tube wall on the settling velocity.

**4.26**  The losses in a Y in a 48-in.-diameter pipe system carrying gas ($\rho = 0.08$ slug/ft$^3$, $\mu = 0.002$ poise, $V = 75$ ft/sec) are to be determined by testing a model with water at 70°F.   The laboratory has a water capacity of 1200 gpm.   What model scale should be used, and how are the results converted into prototype losses?

**4.27**  Ripples have a velocity of propagation that is dependent upon the surface tension and density of the fluid as well as the wavelength.   By dimensional analysis justify the shape of Fig. 4.1 for small wavelengths.

**4.28**  In very deep water the velocity of propagation of waves is dependent upon the wavelength, but in shallow water it is independent of this dimension.   Upon what variables does the speed of advance depend for shallow-water waves?   Is Fig. 4.1 in agreement with this problem?

**4.29**  If a vertical circular conduit which is not flowing full is rotated at high speed, the fluid will attach itself uniformly to the inside wall as it flows downward (see Sec. 2.9).   Under these conditions the radial acceleration of the fluid yields a radial force field which is similar to gravitational attraction, and a hydraulic jump can occur on the inside of the tube, whereby the fluid thickness suddenly changes.   Determine a set of dimensionless parameters for studying this rotating hydraulic jump.

**4.30**  A nearly spherical fluid drop oscillates as it falls.   Surface tension plays a dominant role.   Determine a meaningful dimensionless parameter for this natural frequency.

**4.31**  The lift and drag coefficients for a wing are shown in Fig. 5.23.   If the wing has a chord of 10 ft determine the lift and drag per foot of length when the wing is operating at zero angle of attack at a Reynolds number, based on the chord length, of $4.5 \times 10^7$ in air at 50°F.   What force would be on a 1:20 scale model if the tests were conducted in water at 70°F.   What would be the speed of the water?   Comment on the desirability of conducting the model tests in water.

**4.32**   A 1:5 scale model of a water pumping station piping system is to be tested to determine over-all head losses.   Air at 80°F, 14 psia is available. For a prototype velocity of 1.5 ft/sec in a 14-ft-diameter section with water at 60°F, determine the air velocity and quantity needed and how losses determined from the model are converted to prototype losses.

**4.33**   Full-scale wind-tunnel tests of the lift and drag on hydrofoils for a boat are to be made.   The boat will travel at 35 mph through water at 60°F. What velocity of air ($p = 30$ psia, $t = 90°F$) is required to determine the lift and drag?   (*Note:* The lift coefficient $C_L$ is dimensionless.   Lift = $C_L A \rho V^2/2$.)

**4.34**   The resistance to ascent of a balloon is to be determined by studying the ascent of a 1:50 scale model in water.   How would such a model study be conducted and the results converted to prototype behavior?

**4.35**   The moment exerted on a submarine by its rudder is to be studied with a 1:20 scale model in a water tunnel.   If the torque measured on the model is 3.50 lb-ft for a tunnel velocity of 50 ft/sec, what are the corresponding torque and speed for the prototype?

**4.36**   For two hydraulic machines to be homologous they must (*a*) be geometrically similar; (*b*) have the same discharge coefficient when viewed as an orifice, $Q_1/(A_1 \sqrt{2gH_1}) = Q_2/(A_2 \sqrt{2gH_2})$; and (*c*) have the same ratio of peripheral speed to fluid velocity, $\omega D/(Q/A)$.   Show that the scaling ratios may be expressed as $Q/ND^3 = $ const and $H/(ND)^2 = $ const. $N$ is the rotational speed.

**4.37**   By use of the scaling ratios of Prob. 4.36, determine the head and discharge of a 1:4 model of a centrifugal pump that produces 20 cfs at 96 ft head when turning 240 rpm.   The model operates at 1200 rpm.

**4.38**   An *incorrect* arbitrary recombination of the $\Pi$-parameters

$$F\left(\frac{V_0}{\omega D}, \frac{\rho \omega D^2}{\mu}, \frac{c}{\omega D}\right) = 0$$

is

(*a*) $F\left(\dfrac{c}{V_0}, \dfrac{\rho C D}{\mu}, \dfrac{c}{\omega D}\right) = 0$

(*b*) $F\left(\dfrac{V_0}{\omega D}, \dfrac{\rho c D^2}{\mu}, \dfrac{c}{\omega D}\right) = 0$

(*c*) $F\left(\dfrac{V_0}{\omega D}, \dfrac{V_0 C \rho}{\omega \mu}, \dfrac{\rho c D}{\mu}\right) = 0$

(d)  $F\left(\dfrac{V_0\mu}{\omega^2 D^3\rho}, \dfrac{V_0\rho D}{\mu}, \dfrac{c}{\omega D}\right) = 0$

(e)  none of these answers

**4.39**  The repeating variables in a dimensional analysis should

(a)  include the dependent variable
(b)  have two variables with the same dimensions if possible
(c)  exclude one of the dimensions from each variable if possible
(d)  include those variables not considered very important factors
(e)  satisfy none of these answers

**4.40**  Select a common dimensionless parameter in fluid mechanics from the following:

(a)  angular velocity    (b)  kinematic viscosity    (c)  specific gravity
(d)  specific weight    (e)  none of these answers

**4.41**  Select the quantity in the following that is *not* a dimensionless parameter:

(a)  pressure coefficient    (b)  Froude number    (c)  Darcy-Weisbach
     friction factor    (d)  kinematic viscosity    (e)  Weber number

**4.42**  Which of the following has the form of a Reynolds number?

(a)  $ul/\nu$    (b)  $VD\mu/\rho$    (c)  $u_w\nu/l$    (d)  $V/gD$    (e)  $\Delta p/\rho V^2$

**4.43**  The Reynolds number may be defined as the ratio of

(a)  viscous forces to inertial forces
(b)  viscous forces to gravity forces
(c)  gravity forces to inertial forces
(d)  elastic forces to pressure forces
(e)  none of these answers

**4.44**  The pressure coefficient may take the form

(a)  $\Delta p/\gamma H$    (b)  $\Delta p/(\rho V^2/2)$    (c)  $\Delta p/l\mu V$    (d)  $\Delta p\, \rho/\mu^2 l^4$
(e)  none of these answers

**4.45**  The pressure coefficient is a ratio of pressure forces to

(a)  viscous forces
(b)  inertial forces
(c)  gravity forces
(d)  surface-tension forces
(e)  elastic-energy forces

**4.46**  How many $\Pi$-parameters are needed to express the function

$F(a,V,t,\nu,L) = 0$?

(a) 5     (b) 4     (c) 3     (d) 2     (e) 1

**4.47**  Which of the following could be a $\Pi$-parameter of the function

$F(Q,H,g,V_0,\phi) = 0$

when $Q$ and $g$ are taken as repeating variables?

(a) $Q^2/gH^4$     (b) $V_0^2/g^2Q$     (c) $Q/g\phi^2$     (d) $Q/\sqrt{gH}$
(e)  none of these answers

**4.48**  Select the situation in which inertial forces would be *unimportant:*

(a)  flow over a spillway crest
(b)  flow through an open-channel transition
(c)  waves breaking against a sea wall
(d)  flow through a long capillary tube
(e)  flow through a half-opened valve

**4.49**  Which two forces are most important in laminar flow between closely
spaced parallel plates?

(a) inertial, viscous     (b) pressure, inertial     (c) gravity, pressure
(d) viscous, pressure     (e) none of these answers

**4.50**  A dimensionless combination of $\Delta p$, $\rho$, $l$, $Q$ is

(a) $\sqrt{\dfrac{\Delta p}{\rho}\dfrac{Q}{l^2}}$     (b) $\dfrac{\rho Q}{\Delta p\, l^2}$     (c) $\dfrac{pl}{\Delta p\, Q^2}$     (d) $\dfrac{\Delta p\, lQ}{\rho}$     (e) $\sqrt{\dfrac{\rho}{\Delta p}\dfrac{Q}{l^2}}$

**4.51**  What velocity of oil, $\rho = 1.6$ slugs/ft³, $\mu = 0.20$ poise, must occur in
a 1-in.-diameter pipe to be dynamically similar to 10 ft/sec water velocity at
68°F in a $\frac{1}{4}$-in.-diameter tube?

(a) 0.60 ft/sec     (b) 9.6 ft/sec     (c) 4.0 ft/sec     (d) 60 ft/sec
(e)  none of these answers

**4.52**  The velocity at a point on a model dam crest was measured to be 2.5
ft/sec.   The corresponding prototype velocity for $\lambda = 25$ is, in ft/sec,

(a) 62.5     (b) 12.5     (c) 0.5     (d) 0.10     (e) none of these
answers

**4.53**  The height of a hydraulic jump in a stilling pool was found to be 4.0
in. in a model, $\lambda = 36$.   The prototype jump height is

(a) 12 ft     (b) 2 ft     (c) not determinable from data given
(d) less than 4 in.     (e) none of these answers

**4.54**   A ship's model, scale 1 : 100, had a wave resistance of 2.5 lb at its design speed.   The corresponding prototype wave resistance is, in pounds,

($a$)  2500        ($b$)  25,000        ($c$)  250,000        ($d$)  2,500,000
($e$)  none of these answers

**4.55**   A 1 : 5 scale model of a projectile has a drag coefficient of 3.5 at **M** = 2.0.   How many times greater would the prototype resistance be when fired at the same Mach number in air of the same temperature and half the density?

($a$)  3.12        ($b$)  12.5        ($c$)  25        ($d$)  100        ($e$)  none of these
answers

**4.56**   If the capillary rise $\Delta h$ of a liquid in a circular tube of diameter $D$ depends upon surface tension $\sigma$ and specific weight $\gamma$, the formula for capillary rise could take the form

($a$)  $\Delta h = \sqrt{\dfrac{\sigma}{\gamma}}\, F\left(\dfrac{\sigma}{\gamma D^2}\right)$        ($b$)  $\Delta h = c\left(\dfrac{\sigma}{\gamma D^2}\right)^n$        ($c$)  $\Delta h = cD\left(\dfrac{\sigma}{\gamma}\right)^n$

($d$)  $\Delta h = \sqrt{\dfrac{\gamma}{\sigma}}\, F\left(\dfrac{\gamma D^2}{\sigma}\right)$        ($e$)  none of these answers

## references

Bridgman, P. W.: "Dimensional Analysis," Yale University Press, New Haven, Conn., 1922.

Chick, A. C.: "Dimensional Analysis and the Principle of Similitude as Applied to Hydraulic Experiments with Models," ASME Hydraulic Laboratory Practice, pp. 775–827, 1929.

Holt, M.: Dimensional Analysis, sec. 15 in "Handbook of Fluid Dynamics," ed. by V. L. Streeter, McGraw-Hill Book Company, New York, 1961.

Hunsaker, J. C., and B. G. Rightmire: "Engineering Applications of Fluid Mechanics," McGraw-Hill Book Company, New York, 1947, pp. 110, 111.

"Hydraulic Models," ASCE Manual of Engineering Practice, no. 25, 1942.

Ipsen, D. C.: "Units, Dimensions, and Dimensionless Numbers," McGraw-Hill Book Company, New York, 1960.

Langhaar, H. L.: "Dimensional Analysis and Theory of Models," John Wiley & Sons, Inc., New York, 1951.

Murphy, G.: "Similitude in Engineering," The Ronald Press Company, New York, 1950.

Sedov, L. I.: "Similarity and Dimensional Methods in Mechanics" (English translation ed. by M. Holt), Academic Press Inc., New York, 1959.

# 5

# viscous effects: fluid resistance

In Chap. 3 the basic equations used in the analysis of fluid-flow situations were discussed. The fluid was considered frictionless, or in some cases, losses were assumed or computed without probing into their underlying causes. This chapter deals with real fluids, i.e., with situations in which irreversibilities are important. Viscosity is the fluid property that causes shear stresses in a moving fluid; it is also one means by which irreversibilities or losses are developed. Without viscosity in a fluid there is no fluid resistance. Simple cases of steady laminar incompressible flow are first developed in this chapter, since in these cases the losses may be computed. The concept of the Reynolds number, introduced in Chap. 4, is then further developed. Turbulent-flow shear relationships are introduced by use of the Prandtl mixing-length theory and are applied to turbulent velocity distributions. This is followed by boundary-layer concepts and by drag on immersed bodies. Resistance to steady, uniform, incompressible, turbulent flow is then examined for open and closed conduits, with a section devoted to open channels and to pipe flow. The chapter closes with a section on lubrication mechanics.

The equations of motion for a real fluid may be developed from consideration of the forces acting on a small element of the fluid, including the shear stresses generated by fluid motion and viscosity. The derivation of these equations, called the *Navier-Stokes* equations, is beyond the scope of this treatment. They are listed, however, for the sake of completeness, and many of the developments of this chapter could be made directly from them. First, Newton's law of viscosity, Eq. (1.1.1), for one-dimensional laminar flow may be generalized to three-dimensional flow (Stokes' law of viscosity)

$$\tau_{xy} = \mu \left( \frac{\partial u}{\partial y} + \frac{\partial v}{\partial x} \right)$$

$$\tau_{yz} = \mu \left( \frac{\partial v}{\partial z} + \frac{\partial w}{\partial y} \right)$$

$$\tau_{zx} = \mu \left( \frac{\partial w}{\partial x} + \frac{\partial u}{\partial z} \right)$$

The first subscript of the shear stress is the normal direction to the face over which the stress component is acting.    The second subscript is the direction of the stress component.

By limiting the Navier-Stokes equations to incompressible flow, with gravity the only body force acting (let $h$ be measured vertically upward), they become

$$-\frac{1}{\rho}\frac{\partial}{\partial x}(p + \gamma h) + \nu\nabla^2 u = \frac{Du}{Dt}$$

$$-\frac{1}{\rho}\frac{\partial}{\partial y}(p + \gamma h) + \nu\nabla^2 v = \frac{Dv}{Dt}$$

$$-\frac{1}{\rho}\frac{\partial}{\partial z}(p + \gamma h) + \nu\nabla^2 w = \frac{Dw}{Dt}$$

in which $\nu$ is the kinematic viscosity, $D/Dt$ is differentiation with respect to the motion

$$\frac{D}{Dt} = u\frac{\partial}{\partial x} + v\frac{\partial}{\partial y} + w\frac{\partial}{\partial z} + \frac{\partial}{\partial t}$$

as explained in Sec. 7.3, and the operator $\nabla^2$ is

$$\nabla^2 = \frac{\partial^2}{\partial x^2} + \frac{\partial^2}{\partial y^2} + \frac{\partial^2}{\partial z^2}$$

For a nonviscous fluid, the Navier-Stokes equations reduce to the Euler equations of motion in three dimensions, given by Eqs. (7.3.8), (7.3.9), and (7.3.10).    For one-dimensional flow of a real fluid in the $x$-direction, with $z$

vertically upward the equations reduce to ($u$ varies with $z$ and $t$ only)

$$-\frac{1}{\rho}\frac{\partial p}{\partial x} + \frac{\mu}{\rho}\frac{\partial^2 u}{\partial z^2} = \frac{\partial u}{\partial t}$$

$$\frac{\partial p}{\partial y} = 0$$

$$\frac{\partial}{\partial z}(p + \gamma z) = 0$$

and for steady flow the first equation reduces to

$$\frac{\partial p}{\partial x} = \mu\frac{\partial^2 u}{\partial z^2}$$

## 5.1  laminar, incompressible, steady flow between parallel plates

The general case of steady flow between parallel, inclined plates is first developed for laminar flow, with the upper plate having a constant velocity $U$ (Fig. 5.1).    Flow between fixed plates is a special case obtained by setting $U = 0$.    In Fig. 5.1 the upper plate moves parallel to the flow direction, and there is a pressure variation in the $l$-direction.    The flow is analyzed by

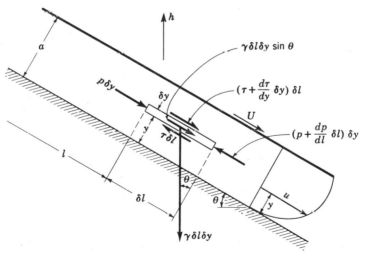

**Fig. 5.1**  Flow between inclined, parallel plates with the upper plate in motion.

taking a thin lamina of unit width as a free body.    In steady flow the lamina moves at constant velocity $u$.    The equation of motion yields

$$p \; \delta y - \left(p \; \delta y + \frac{dp}{dl} \; \delta l \; \delta y\right) - \tau \; \delta l + \left(\tau \; \delta l + \frac{d\tau}{dy} \; \delta y \; \delta l\right) + \gamma \; \delta l \; \delta y \sin \theta = 0$$

After dividing through by the volume of the element and after simplifying,

$$\frac{d\tau}{dy} = \frac{d}{dl}(p + \gamma h) \tag{5.1.1}$$

in which $\sin \theta = -dh/dl$ has been substituted.    Since there is no accelera-tion in the $y$-direction, the right-hand side of the equation is not a function of $y$.    By integrating with respect to $y$,

$$\tau = y \frac{d}{dl}(p + \gamma h) + A$$

Now, by substitution of Newton's law of viscosity [Eq. (1.1.1)],

$$\tau = \mu \frac{du}{dy}$$

for $\tau$,

$$\frac{du}{dy} = \frac{1}{\mu} \frac{d}{dl}(p + \gamma h)y + \frac{A}{\mu}$$

By integrating again with respect to $y$,

$$u = \frac{1}{2\mu} \frac{d}{dl}(p + \gamma h)y^2 + \frac{A}{\mu}y + B$$

in which $A$ and $B$ are constants of integration.    To evaluate them take $y = 0$, $u = 0$ and $y = a$, $u = U$, and obtain

$$B = 0 \qquad U = \frac{1}{2\mu} \frac{d}{dl}(p + \gamma h)a^2 + \frac{Aa}{\mu} + B$$

After eliminating $A$ and $B$,

$$u = \frac{Uy}{a} - \frac{1}{2\mu} \frac{d}{dl}(p + \gamma h)(ay - y^2) \tag{5.1.2}$$

For horizontal plates, $h = C$; for no gradient due to pressure or elevation, i.e., hydrostatic pressure distribution, $p + \gamma h = C$ and the velocity has a straight-line distribution.    For fixed plates, $U = 0$, and the velocity dis-tribution is parabolic.

The discharge past a fixed cross section is obtained by integration of Eq. (5.1.2) with respect to $y$:

$$Q = \int_0^a u\,dy = \frac{Ua}{2} - \frac{1}{12\mu}\frac{d}{dl}(p + \gamma h)a^3 \tag{5.1.3}$$

In general the maximum velocity is not at the midplane.

**example 5.1**   In Fig. 5.2 one plate moves relative to the other as shown. $\mu = 0.80$ poise, $\rho = 1.7$ slugs/ft³.   Determine the velocity distribution, the discharge, and the shear stress exerted on the upper plate.
At the upper point

$$p + \gamma h = 20 \times 144 + 1.7 \times 32.2 \times 10 = 3426 \text{ lb/ft}^2$$

and at the lower point

$$p + \gamma h = 12 \times 144 = 1728 \text{ lb/ft}^2$$

to the same datum.   Hence

$$\frac{d(p + \gamma h)}{dl} = \frac{1728 - 3427}{10\sqrt{2}} = -120 \text{ lb/ft}^3$$

From the figure, $a = 0.24/12 = 0.02$ ft, $U = -3.0$ ft/sec, and from Eq. (5.1.2)

$$u = -\frac{3y}{0.02} + \frac{120}{2(0.80/479)}(0.02y - y^2)$$

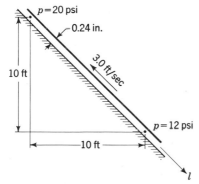

**Fig. 5.2**   Flow between inclined flat plates.

After simplifying,

$$u = 566y - 35{,}800y^2$$

the maximum velocity occurs where $du/dy = 0$, or $y = 0.0079$ ft and is $u_{max} = 2.24$ ft/sec, so that the minimum velocity occurs at the upper plate. The discharge is

$$Q = \int_0^{0.02} u \, dy = 283y^2 - 11{,}933y^3 \Big]_0^{0.02} = 0.0177 \text{ cfs/ft}$$

and is downward.

To find the shear stress on the upper plate,

$$\frac{du}{dy}\Big]_{y=0.02} = 566 - 71{,}600y \Big]_{y=0.02} = -866$$

and

$$\tau = \mu \frac{du}{dy} = \frac{0.80}{479}(-866) = -1.45 \text{ lb/ft}^2$$

This is the fluid shear at the plate; hence, the shear force on the plate is 1.45 lb/ft² resisting the motion of the plate.

*losses in laminar flow*

An expression for the irreversibilities is developed for one-dimensional, incompressible, steady, laminar flow, in which the equation of motion and the principle of work and energy are utilized.  There is no increase in kinetic energy in steady flow in a tube or between parallel plates.  The pressure drop in horizontal flow, which represents work done on the fluid per unit volume, is converted into irreversibilities by the action of viscous shear.  The losses in the length $L$ are $Q \, \Delta p$ per unit time, in which $\Delta p$ is the pressure drop.

After examination of the work done on the fluid in one-dimensional flow, an expression for the losses can be developed.  First, the equation of motion applied to an element (Fig. 5.3) relates the shear stress and pressure drop.  There is no acceleration; hence, $\Sigma f_x = 0$, and

$$p \, \delta y - \left(p + \frac{dp}{dx}\delta x\right)\delta y - \tau \, \delta x + \left(\tau + \frac{d\tau}{dy}\delta y\right)\delta x = 0$$

After simplifying,

$$\frac{dp}{dx} = \frac{d\tau}{dy} \tag{5.1.4}$$

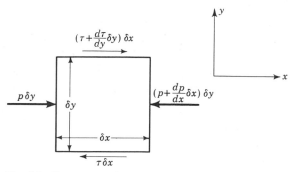

**Fig. 5.3**  Forces on a fluid element.

which implies that the rate of change of pressure in the $x$-direction must equal the rate of change of shear in the $y$-direction.   Clearly, $dp/dx$ is independent of $y$, and $d\tau/dy$ is independent of $x$.

The work done per unit time, or power input, to a fluid element (Fig. 5.4) for one-dimensional flow consists in the work done on the element by pressure and by shear stress, minus the work that the element does on the surrounding fluid, or

$$p\left(u + \frac{du}{dy}\frac{\delta y}{2}\right)\delta y - \left(p + \frac{dp}{dx}\delta x\right)\left(u + \frac{du}{dy}\frac{\delta y}{2}\right)\delta y + \tau u\,\delta x$$

$$+ \frac{d}{dy}(\tau u)\,\delta y\,\delta x - \tau u\,\delta x$$

After simplifying,

$$\frac{\text{Net power input}}{\text{Unit volume}} = \frac{d}{dy}(\tau u) - u\frac{dp}{dx} \tag{5.1.5}$$

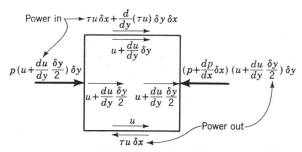

**Fig. 5.4**  Work done on a fluid element in one-dimensional motion.

By expanding Eq. (5.1.5) and substituting Eq. (5.1.4)

$$\frac{\text{Net power input}}{\text{Unit volume}} = \tau \frac{du}{dy} + u \frac{d\tau}{dy} - u \frac{dp}{dx} = \tau \frac{du}{dy} \tag{5.1.6}$$

With Newton's law of viscosity,

$$\frac{\text{Net power input}}{\text{Unit volume}} = \tau \frac{du}{dy} = \mu \left(\frac{du}{dy}\right)^2 = \frac{\tau^2}{\mu} \tag{5.1.7}$$

This power is used up by viscous friction and is converted into irreversibilities.

By integrating the expression over a length $L$ between two fixed parallel plates, with Eq. (5.1.2) for $U = 0$ and with Eq. (5.1.7),

$$\text{Net power input} = \int_0^a \mu \left(\frac{du}{dy}\right)^2 L \, dy = \mu L \int_0^a \left[\frac{1}{2\mu}\frac{dp}{dl}(2y - a)\right]^2 dy$$

$$= \left(\frac{dp}{dl}\right)^2 \frac{a^3 L}{12\mu}$$

By substituting for $Q$ from Eq. (5.1.3) for $U = 0$,

$$\text{Losses} = \text{net power input} = -Q \frac{dp}{dl} L = Q \, \Delta p$$

in which $\Delta p$ is the pressure drop in the length $L$. The expression for power input per unit volume [Eq. (5.1.7)] is also applicable to cases of laminar flow in a tube. The irreversibilities are greatest when $du/dy$ is greatest. The distribution of shear stress, velocity, and losses is shown in Fig. 5.5 for a round tube.

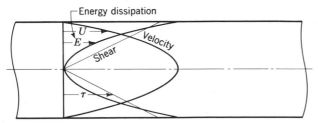

**Fig. 5.5** Distribution of velocity, shear, and losses for a round tube.

**Fig. 5.6**  Free-body diagram of cylindrical sleeve element for laminar flow in an inclined circular tube.

## 5.2  laminar flow through circular tubes and circular annuli

For steady, incompressible, laminar flow through a circular tube or an annulus, a cylindrical infinitesimal sleeve (Fig. 5.6) is taken as a free body, and the equation of motion is applied in the $l$-direction, with acceleration equal to zero.  From the figure,

$$2\pi r\ \delta r\ p - \left[2\pi r\ \delta r\ p + 2\pi r\ \delta r\ \frac{dp}{dl}\ \delta l\right] + 2\pi r\ \delta l\ \tau$$

$$- \left[2\pi r\ \delta l\ \tau + \frac{d}{dr}\ (2\pi r\ \delta l\ \tau)\ \delta r\right] + \gamma 2\pi r\ \delta r\ \delta l\ \sin\theta = 0$$

After replacing $\sin\theta$ by $-dh/dl$ and after dividing by the volume of the free body, $2\pi r\ \delta r\ \delta l$,

$$\frac{d}{dl}\ (p + \gamma h) + \frac{1}{r}\frac{d}{dr}\ (\tau r) = 0 \qquad\qquad (5.2.1)$$

Since $d(p + \gamma h)/dl$ is not a function of $r$, the equation may be multiplied by $r \, \delta r$ and integrated with respect to $r$, yielding

$$\frac{r^2}{2} \frac{d}{dl} (p + \gamma h) + \tau r = A \qquad (5.2.2)$$

in which $A$ is the constant of integration. For a circular tube this equation must be satisfied when $r = 0$; hence $A = 0$ for this case. By substituting,

$$\tau = -\mu \frac{du}{dr}$$

noting that the minus sign is required to obtain the sign of the $\tau$ term in Fig. 5.6. ($u$ is considered to decrease with $r$, hence $du/dr$ is negative.)

$$du = \frac{1}{2\mu} \frac{d}{dl} (p + \gamma h) r \, dr - \frac{A}{\mu} \frac{dr}{r}$$

After integrating again,

$$u = \frac{r^2}{4\mu} \frac{d}{dl} (p + \gamma h) - \frac{A}{\mu} \ln r + B \qquad (5.2.3)$$

For the annular case, to evaluate $A$ and $B$, $u = 0$ when $r = b$, the inner tube radius, and $u = 0$ when $r = a$ (Fig. 5.7). When $A$ and $B$ are eliminated,

$$u = -\frac{1}{4\mu} \frac{d}{dl} (p + \gamma h) \left( a^2 - r^2 + \frac{a^2 - b^2}{\ln b/a} \ln \frac{a}{r} \right) \qquad (5.2.4)$$

**Fig. 5.7** Flow through an annulus.

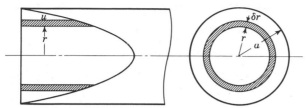

**Fig. 5.8**   Ring element of area used to compute discharge.

and for discharge through an annulus (Fig. 5.8),

$$Q = \int_b^a 2\pi r u \, dr = -\frac{\pi}{8\mu}\frac{d}{dl}(p + \gamma h)\left[a^4 - b^4 - \frac{(a^2 - b^2)^2}{\ln a/b}\right] \tag{5.2.5}$$

*circular tube.   Hagen-Poiseuille equation*

For the circular tube, $A = 0$ in Eq. (5.2.3) and $u = 0$ for $r = a$,

$$u = -\frac{(a^2 - r^2)}{4\mu}\frac{d}{dl}(p + \gamma h) \tag{5.2.6}$$

The maximum velocity $u_{max}$ is given for $r = 0$ as

$$u_{max} = -\frac{a^2}{4\mu}\frac{d}{dl}(p + \gamma h) \tag{5.2.7}$$

Since the velocity distribution is a paraboloid of revolution (Fig. 5.5), its volume is one-half that of its circumscribing cylinder; therefore the average velocity is one-half of the maximum velocity,

$$V = -\frac{a^2}{8\mu}\frac{d}{dl}(p + \gamma h) \tag{5.2.8}$$

The discharge $Q$ is equal to $V\pi a^2$,

$$Q = -\frac{\pi a^4}{8\mu}\frac{d}{dl}(p + \gamma h) \tag{5.2.9}$$

The discharge may also be obtained by integration of the velocity $u$ over the area, i.e., by use of Fig. 5.8:

$$Q = \int_a^0 2\pi r u \, dr$$

For a horizontal tube, $h = $ const; by writing the pressure drop $\Delta p$ in the length $L$,

$$\frac{\Delta p}{L} = -\frac{dp}{dl}$$

and substituting diameter $D$,

$$Q = \frac{\Delta p \,\pi D^4}{128\mu L} \tag{5.2.10a}$$

In terms of average velocity,

$$V = \frac{\Delta p \, D^2}{32\mu L} \tag{5.2.10b}$$

Equation (5.2.10a) can then be solved for pressure drop, which represents losses per unit volume,

$$\Delta p = \frac{128\mu L Q}{\pi D^4} \tag{5.2.11}$$

The losses are seen to vary directly as the viscosity, the length, and the discharge, and to vary inversely as the fourth power of the diameter. It should be noted that tube roughness does not enter into the equations. Equation (5.2.10a) is known as the *Hagen-Poiseuille equation;* it was determined experimentally by Hagen in 1839 and independently by Poiseuille in 1840.   The analytical derivation was made by Wiedemann in 1856.

The results as given by Eqs. (5.2.1) to (5.2.10) are not valid near the entrance of a pipe.   If the flow enters the pipe from a reservoir through a well-rounded entrance, the velocity at first is almost uniform over the cross section.   The action of wall shear stress (as the velocity must be zero at the wall) is to slow down the fluid near the wall.   As a consequence of continuity the velocity must then increase in the central region.   The transition length $L'$ for the characteristic parabolic velocity distribution to develop is a function of the Reynolds number.   Langhaar[1] developed the theoretical formula

$$\frac{L'}{D} = 0.058\mathbf{R}$$

which agrees well with observation.

**example 5.2**   Determine the direction of flow through the tube shown in Fig. 5.9, in which $\gamma = 50$ lb/ft$^3$, $\mu = 0.40$ poise.   Find the quantity flowing

[1] H. L. Langhaar, Steady Flow in the Transition Length of a Straight Tube, *J. Appl. Mech.*, vol. 9, pp. 55–58, 1942.

**Fig. 5.9** Flow through an inclined tube.

in gallons per minute, and compute the Reynolds number for the flow.
At section 1

$$p + \gamma h = 20 \times 144 + 50 \times 15 = 3630 \text{ lb/ft}^2$$

and at section 2

$$p + \gamma h = 30 \times 144 = 4320 \text{ lb/ft}^2$$

if datum for $h$ is taken through section 2. The flow is from 2 to 1 since the energy is greater at 2 (kinetic energy must be the same at both sections) than at 1. To determine the quantity flowing, the expression is written

$$-\frac{d}{dl}(p + \gamma h) = -\frac{3630 - 4230}{30} = 23 \text{ lb/ft}^3$$

After substituting into Eq. (5.2.10a),

$$Q = \frac{23\pi(\frac{1}{4})^4}{8 \times (12)^4(0.40/479)} = 0.00203 \text{ cfs}$$

By converting to gallons per minute,

$$Q = 0.00203 \times 7.46 \times 60 = 0.91 \text{ gpm}$$

The average velocity is $Q/\pi r_0^2$, or

$$V = \frac{0.00203}{\pi(\frac{1}{48})^2} = 1.486 \text{ ft/sec}$$

and the Reynolds number is (Sec. 4.4)

$$\mathbf{R} = \frac{VD\rho}{\mu} = \frac{1.486 \times 1 \times 50 \times 479}{24 \times 32.2 \times 0.40} = 115$$

If the Reynolds number had been above 2000, the Hagen-Poiseuille equation would no longer apply, as discussed in Sec. 5.3.

The kinetic-energy correction factor $\alpha$ [Eq. (3.10.2)] may be determined for laminar flow in a tube by use of Eqs. (5.2.6) and (5.2.7),

$$\frac{u}{V} = 2\frac{u}{u_{max}} = 2\left[1 - \left(\frac{r}{a}\right)^2\right] \tag{5.2.12}$$

By substituting into the expression for $\alpha$,

$$\alpha = \frac{1}{A}\int \left(\frac{u}{V}\right)^3 dA = \frac{1}{\pi a^2}\int_0^a \left\{2\left[1 - \left(\frac{r}{a}\right)^2\right]\right\}^3 2\pi r\, dr = 2 \tag{5.2.13}$$

There is twice as much energy in the flow as in uniform flow at the same average velocity.

## 5.3 the Reynolds number

Laminar flow is defined as flow in which the fluid moves in layers, or laminas, one layer gliding smoothly over an adjacent layer with only a molecular interchange of momentum.   Any tendencies toward instability and turbulence are damped out by viscous shear forces that resist relative motion of adjacent fluid layers.   Turbulent flow, however, has very erratic motion of fluid particles, with a violent transverse interchange of momentum.   The nature of the flow, i.e., whether laminar or turbulent, and its relative position along a scale indicating the relative importance of turbulent to laminar tendencies are indicated by the *Reynolds number*.   The concept of the Reynolds number and its interpretation are discussed in this section.   In Sec. 3.5 an equation of motion was developed with the assumption that the fluid is frictionless, i.e., that the viscosity is zero.   More general equations have been developed that include viscosity, by including shear stresses. These equations (see introduction to this chapter) are complicated, non-linear, partial differential equations for which no general solution has been obtained.   In the last century Osborne Reynolds[1] studied these equations to try to determine when two different flow situations would be similar.

Two flow cases are said to be *dynamically similar* when

1.   they are geometrically similar, i.e., corresponding linear dimensions have a constant ratio and
2.   the corresponding streamlines are geometrically similar, or pressures at corresponding points have a constant ratio.

[1] O. Reynolds, An Experimental Investigation of the Circumstances Which Determine whether the Motion of Water Shall Be Direct or Sinuous, and of the Laws of Resistance in Parallel Channels, *Trans. Roy. Soc. London*, vol. 174, 1883.

In considering two geometrically similar flow situations, Reynolds deduced that they would be dynamically similar if the general differential equations describing their flow were identical.    By changing the units of mass, length, and time in one set of equations and determining the conditions that must be satisfied to make them identical to the original equations, Reynolds found that the dimensionless group $ul\rho/\mu$ must be the same for both cases.    Of these, $u$ is a characteristic velocity, $l$ a characteristic length, $\rho$ the mass density, and $\mu$ the viscosity.    This group, or parameter, is now called the Reynolds number **R**,

$$\mathbf{R} = \frac{ul\rho}{\mu} \qquad\qquad (5.3.1)$$

To determine the significance of the dimensionless group, Reynolds conducted his experiments on flow of water through glass tubes, illustrated in Fig. 5.10.    A glass tube was mounted horizontally with one end in a tank and a valve on the opposite end.    A smooth bellmouth entrance was attached to the upstream end, with a dye jet arranged so that a fine stream of dye could be ejected at any point in front of the bellmouth.    Reynolds took the average velocity $V$ as characteristic velocity and the diameter of tube $D$ as characteristic length, so that $\mathbf{R} = VD\rho/\mu$.

For small flows the dye stream moved as a straight line through the tube, showing that the flow was laminar.    As the flow rate increased, the Reynolds number increased, since $D$, $\rho$, $\mu$ were constant, and $V$ was directly proportional to the rate of flow.    With increasing discharge a condition was reached at which the dye stream wavered and then suddenly broke up and was diffused throughout the tube.    The flow had changed to turbulent flow with its violent interchange of momentum that had completely disrupted the orderly movement of laminar flow.    By careful manipulation Reynolds was able to obtain a valve **R** = 12,000 before turbulence set in.    A later investigator, using Reynolds' original equipment,

**Fig. 5.10**  Reynolds apparatus.

obtained a value of 40,000 by allowing the water to stand in the tank for several days before the experiment and by taking precautions to avoid vibration of the water or equipment. These numbers, referred to as the *Reynolds upper critical numbers*, have no practical significance in that the ordinary pipe installation has irregularities that cause turbulent flow at a much smaller value of the Reynolds number.

Starting with turbulent flow in the glass tube, Reynolds found that it would always become laminar when the velocity was reduced to make **R** less than 2000. This is the *Reynolds lower critical number* for pipe flow and is of practical importance. With the usual piping installation, the flow will change from laminar to turbulent in the range of the Reynolds numbers from 2000 to 4000. For the purpose of this treatment it is assumed that the change occurs at **R** = 2000. In laminar flow the losses are directly proportional to the average velocity, while in turbulent flow the losses are proportional to the velocity to a power varying from 1.7 to 2.0.

There are many Reynolds numbers in use today in addition to the one for straight, round tubes. For example, the motion of a sphere through a fluid may be characterized by $UD\rho/\mu$, in which $U$ is the velocity of sphere, $D$ is the diameter of sphere, and $\rho$ and $\mu$ are the fluid density and viscosity.

The Reynolds number may be viewed as a ratio of shear stress $\tau_t$ due to turbulence to shear stress $\tau_v$ due to viscosity. By applying the momentum equation to the flow through an element of area $\delta A$ (Fig. 5.11) the apparent shear stress due to turbulence can be determined. If $v'$ is the velocity normal to $\delta A$ and $u'$ is the difference in velocity, or the velocity fluctuation, on the two sides of the area, then, with Eq. (3.11.1), the shear force $\delta F$ acting is computed to be

$$\delta F = \rho v' \, \delta A \, u'$$

in which $\rho v' \, \delta A$ is the mass per second having its momentum changed and $u'$ is the final velocity minus the initial velocity in the $s$-direction. By dividing through by $\delta A$, the shear stress $\tau_t$ due to turbulent fluctuations

**Fig. 5.11** Notation for shear stress due to turbulent flow.

is obtained,

$$\tau_t = \rho u'v' \tag{5.3.2}$$

The shear stress due to viscosity may be written

$$\tau_v = \frac{\mu u'}{l} \tag{5.3.3}$$

in which $u'$ is interpreted as the change in velocity in the distance $l$, measured normal to the velocity.   Then the ratio

$$\frac{\tau_t}{\tau_v} = \frac{v'l\rho}{\mu}$$

has the form of a Reynolds number.

The *nature* of a given flow of an incompressible fluid is characterized by its Reynolds number.   For large values of **R** one or all of the terms in the numerator are large compared with the denominator.   This implies a large expanse of fluid, high velocity, great density, extremely small viscosity, or combinations of these extremes.   The numerator terms are related to *inertial* forces, or to forces set up by acceleration or deceleration of the fluid.   The denominator term is the cause of viscous shear forces.   Thus, the Reynolds number parameter may also be considered as a ratio of inertial to viscous forces.   A large **R** indicates a highly turbulent flow with losses proportional to the square of the velocity.   The turbulence may be *fine scale*, composed of a great many small eddies that rapidly convert mechanical energy into irreversibilities through viscous action; or it may be *large scale*, like the huge vortices and swirls in a river or gusts in the atmosphere.   The large eddies generate smaller eddies, which in turn create fine-scale turbulence.   Turbulent flow may be thought of as a smooth, possibly uniform flow, with a secondary flow superposed on it.   A fine-scale turbulent flow has small fluctuations in velocity that occur with high frequency.   The root-mean-square value of the fluctuations and the frequency of change of sign of the fluctuations are quantitative measures of turbulence.   In general the intensity of turbulence increases as the Reynolds number increases.

For intermediate values of **R** both viscous and inertial effects are important, and changes in viscosity change the velocity distribution and the resistance to flow.

For the same **R**, two geometrically similar closed-conduit systems (one, say, twice the size of the other) will have the same ratio of losses to velocity head.   Use of the Reynolds number provides a means for using experimental results with one fluid for predicting results in a similar case with another fluid.

In addition to the applications of laminar flow shown in this and the preceding section, the results may also apply to greatly different situations, because the equations describing the cases are analogous.   As an example the two-dimensional laminar flow between closely spaced plates is called Hele-Shaw flow.[1]   If some of the space is filled between the plates, by use of dye in the fluid the streamlines for flow around the obstructions are made visible.   These streamlines in laminar flow are the same as the streamlines for similar flow of a frictionless (irrotational) fluid around the same obstructions.   Likewise the two-dimensional frictionless flow cases (Chap. 7) are analogous and similar to two-dimensional percolation through porous media.

## 5.4   Prandtl mixing length.   velocity distribution in turbulent flow

Pressure drop and velocity distribution for several cases of laminar flow were worked out in the preceding sections.   In this section the mixing-length theory of turbulence is developed, including its application to several flow situations.   The apparent shear stress in turbulent flow is expressed by [Eq. (3.3.2)]

$$\tau = (\mu + \eta) \frac{du}{dy} \tag{5.4.1}$$

including direct viscous effects.   Prandtl[2] has developed a most useful theory of turbulence called the *mixing-length* theory.   In Sec. 5.3 the shear stress $\tau$, due to turbulence, was shown to be

$$\tau = \rho u'v' \tag{5.3.2}$$

in which $u'$, $v'$ are the velocity fluctuations at a point.   In Prandtl's[3] theory, expressions for $u'$ and $v'$ are obtained in terms of a mixing-length distance $l$ and the velocity gradient $du/d\imath$ in which $u$ is the temporal mean velocity at a point and $y$ is the distance normal to $u$, usually measured from the boundary.   In a gas, one molecule, before striking another, travels an

---

[1] H. J. S. Hele-Shaw, Investigation of the Nature of the Surface Resistance of Water and of Streamline Motion under Certain Experimental Conditions, *Trans. Inst. Naval Architects*, vol. 40, 1898.

[2] For an account of the development of turbulence theory the reader is referred to L. Prandtl, "Essentials of Fluid Dynamics," pp. 105–145, Hafner Publishing Company, Inc., New York, 1952.

[3] L. Prandtl, Bericht über Untersuchungen zur ausgebildeten Turbulenz, *Z. Angew. Math. Mech.*, vol. 5, no. 2, p. 136, 1925.

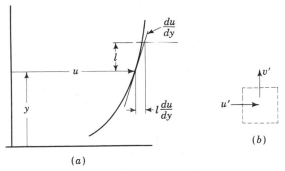

(a)

(b)

**Fig. 5.12**   Notation for mixing-length theory.

average distance known as the *mean free path* of the gas.   Using this as an analogy (Fig. 5.12a), Prandtl assumed that a particle of fluid is displaced a distance $l$ before its momentum is changed by the new environment.   The fluctuation $u'$ is then related to $l$ by

$$u' \sim l \frac{du}{dy}$$

which means that the amount of the change in velocity depends upon the change in temporal mean velocity at two points distant $l$ apart in the $y$-direction.   From the continuity equation, he reasoned that there must be a correlation between $u'$ and $v'$ (Fig. 5.12b), so that $v'$ is proportional to $u'$,

$$v' \sim u' \sim l \frac{du}{dy}$$

By substituting for $u'$ and $v'$ in Eq. (5.3.2) and by letting $l$ absorb the proportionality factor, the defining equation for mixing length is obtained:

$$\tau = \rho l^2 \left(\frac{du}{dy}\right)^2 \qquad\qquad (5.4.2)$$

$\tau$ always acts in the sense that causes the velocity distribution to become more uniform.   When Eq. (5.4.2) is compared with Eq. (3.3.1) it is found that

$$\eta = \rho l^2 \frac{du}{dy} \qquad\qquad (5.4.3)$$

But $\eta$ is not a fluid property as is dynamic viscosity.   Rather, $\eta$ depends upon the density, the velocity gradient, and the mixing length $l$.   In turbulent flow there is a violent interchange of globules of fluid except at a boundary, or very near to it, where this interchange is reduced to zero; hence, $l$ must approach zero at a fluid boundary.   The particular relationship of $l$ to wall distance $y$ is not given by Prandtl's derivation.   Von Kármán[1] suggested, after considering similitude relationships in a turbulent fluid, that

$$l = \kappa \frac{du/dy}{d^2u/dy^2} \tag{5.4.4}$$

in which $\kappa$ is a universal constant in turbulent flow, regardless of the boundary configuration or value of the Reynolds number.

In turbulent flows, $\eta$, sometimes referred to as the *eddy viscosity*, is generally much larger than $\mu$.   It may be considered as a coefficient of momentum transfer, expressing the transfer of momentum from points where the concentration is high to points where it is lower.   It is convenient to utilize a *kinematic eddy viscosity* $\epsilon = \eta/\rho$ which is a property of the flow alone and is analogous to kinematic viscosity.

## velocity distributions

Utilizing the mixing-length concept, turbulent velocity distributions are discussed for the flat plate and the pipe.   For turbulent flow over a smooth plane surface (such as the wind blowing over smooth ground) the shear stress in the fluid is constant, say $\tau_0$.   Equation (5.4.1) is applicable, but $\eta$ approaches zero at the surface and $\mu$ becomes negligible away from the surface.   If $\eta$ is negligible for the film thickness $y = \delta$, in which $\mu$ predominates, Eq. (5.4.1) becomes

$$\frac{\tau_0}{\rho} = \frac{\mu}{\rho} \frac{u}{y} = \nu \frac{u}{y} \qquad y \leq \delta \tag{5.4.5}$$

The term $\sqrt{\tau_0/\rho}$ has the dimensions of a velocity and is called the shear-stress velocity $u_*$.   Hence

$$\frac{u}{u_*} = \frac{u_* y}{\nu} \qquad y \leq \delta \tag{5.4.6}$$

shows a linear relation between $u$ and $y$ in the laminar film.   For $y > \delta$, $\mu$ is neglected, and Eq. (5.4.1) produces

$$\tau_0 = \rho l^2 \left(\frac{du}{dy}\right)^2 \tag{5.4.7}$$

---

[1] Th. von Kármán, Turbulence and Skin Friction, *J. Aeron. Sci.*, vol. 1, no. 1, p. 1, 1934.

Since $l$ has the dimensions of a length and from dimensional considerations would be proportional to $y$ (the only significant linear dimension), assume $l = \kappa y$.   By substituting into Eq. (5.4.7) and rearranging,

$$\frac{du}{u*} = \frac{1}{\kappa}\frac{dy}{y} \tag{5.4.8}$$

After integrating,

$$\frac{u}{u*} = \frac{1}{\kappa}\ln y + \text{const} \tag{5.4.9}$$

It is to be noted that this value of $u$ substituted in Eq. (5.4.4) also determines $l$ proportional to $y$ $(d^2u/dy^2$ is negative since the velocity gradient decreases as $y$ increases).   Equation (5.4.9) agrees well with experiment and, in fact, is also useful when $\tau$ is a function of $y$, because most of the velocity change occurs near the wall where $\tau$ is substantially constant.   It is quite satisfactory to apply the equation to turbulent flow in pipes.

**example 5.3**   By integration of Eq. (5.4.9) find the relation between the average velocity $V$ and the maximum velocity $u_m$ in turbulent flow in a pipe.
When $y = r_0$, $u = u_m$, so that

$$\frac{u}{u*} = \frac{u_m}{u*} + \frac{1}{\kappa}\ln\frac{y}{r_0}$$

The discharge $V\pi r_0^2$ is obtained by integrating the velocity distribution,

$$V\pi r_0^2 = 2\pi\int_0^{r_0-\delta} ur\,dr = 2\pi\int_\delta^{r_0}\left(u_m + \frac{u*}{\kappa}\ln\frac{y}{r_0}\right)(r_0 - y)\,dy$$

The integration cannot be carried out to $y = 0$, since the equation holds in the turbulent zone only.   The volume per second flowing in the laminar zone is so small that it may be neglected.   Then

$$V = 2\int_{\delta/r_0}^1\left(u_m + \frac{u*}{\kappa}\ln\frac{y}{r_0}\right)\left(1 - \frac{y}{r_0}\right)d\left(\frac{y}{r_0}\right)$$

in which the variable of integration is $y/r_0$.   By integrating,

$$V = 2\left\{u_m\left[\frac{y}{r_0} - \frac{1}{2}\left(\frac{y}{r_0}\right)^2\right]\right.$$
$$\left. + \frac{u*}{\kappa}\left[\frac{y}{r_0}\ln\frac{y}{r_0} - \frac{y}{r_0} - \frac{1}{2}\left(\frac{y}{r_0}\right)^2\ln\frac{y}{r_0} + \frac{1}{4}\left(\frac{y}{r_0}\right)^2\right]\right\}_{\delta/r_0}^1$$

Since $\delta/r_0$ is very small, such terms as $\delta/r_0$ and $(\delta/r_0)\ln\delta/r_0$ become negligible $(\lim_{x\to 0} x\ln x = 0)$; thus

$$V = u_m - \frac{3}{2}\frac{u_*}{\kappa}$$

or

$$\frac{u_m - V}{u_*} = \frac{3}{2\kappa}$$

In evaluating the constant in Eq. (5.4.9) following the methods of Bakhmeteff,[1] $u = u_w$, the "wall velocity," when $y = \delta$. According to Eq. (5.4.6)

$$\frac{u_w}{u_*} = \frac{u_*\delta}{\nu} = N \tag{5.4.10}$$

from which it is reasoned that $u_*\delta/\nu$ should have a critical value $N$ at which flow changes from laminar to turbulent, since it is a Reynolds number in form. By substituting $u = u_w$ when $y = \delta$ into Eq. (5.4.9) and by using Eq. (5.4.10),

$$\frac{u_w}{u_*} = N = \frac{1}{\kappa}\ln\delta + \text{const} = \frac{1}{\kappa}\ln\frac{N\nu}{u_*} + \text{const}$$

After eliminating the constant,

$$\frac{u}{u_*} = \frac{1}{\kappa}\ln\frac{yu_*}{\nu} + N - \frac{1}{\kappa}\ln N$$

or

$$\frac{u}{u_*} = \frac{1}{\kappa}\ln\frac{yu_*}{\nu} + A \tag{5.4.11}$$

in which $A = N - \dfrac{1}{\kappa}\ln N$ has been found experimentally by plotting $u/u_*$

against $\ln yu_*/\nu$. For flat plates $\kappa = 0.417$, $A = 5.84$, but for smooth wall pipes Nikuradse's[2] experiments yield $\kappa = 0.40$ and $A = 5.5$.

Prandtl has developed a convenient exponential velocity distribution

---

[1] B. A. Bakhmeteff, "The Mechanics of Turbulent Flow," Princeton University Press, Princeton, N.J., 1941.

[2] J. Nikuradse, Gesetzmassigkeiten der turbulenten Strömung in glatten Rohren, *VDI-Forschungsh.*, vol. 356, 1932.

formula for turbulent pipe flow,

$$\frac{u}{u_m} = \left(\frac{y}{r_0}\right)^n \tag{5.4.12}$$

in which $n$ varies with the Reynolds number.   This empirical equation is valid only at some distance from the wall.   For **R** less than 100,000, $n = 1/7$, and for greater values of **R**, $n$ decreases.   The velocity distribution equations, Eqs. (5.4.11) and (5.4.12), both have the fault of a nonzero value of $du/dy$ at the center of the pipe.

**example 5.4**   Find an approximate expression for mixing-length distribution in turbulent flow in a pipe from Prandtl's one-seventh-power law.
   By writing a force balance for steady flow in a round tube (Fig. 5.13),

$$\tau = -\frac{dp}{dl}\frac{r}{2}$$

At the wall

$$\tau_0 = -\frac{dp}{dl}\frac{a}{2}$$

hence

$$\tau = \tau_0\frac{r}{a} = \tau_0\left(1 - \frac{y}{a}\right) = \rho l^2\left(\frac{du}{dy}\right)^2$$

In solving for $l$,

$$l = \frac{u_*\sqrt{1 - y/r_0}}{du/dy}$$

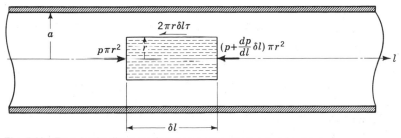

**Fig. 5.13**  Free-body diagram for steady flow through round tube.

From Eq. (5.4.12)

$$\frac{u}{u_m} = \left(\frac{y}{r_0}\right)^{1/7}$$

the approximate velocity gradient is obtained,

$$\frac{du}{dy} = \frac{u_m}{r_0}\frac{1}{7}\left(\frac{y}{r_0}\right)^{-6/7}$$

and

$$\frac{l}{r_0} = \frac{u_*}{u_m}\, 7\left(\frac{y}{r_0}\right)^{6/7}\sqrt{1 - y/r_0}$$

The dimensionless *velocity deficiency*, $(u_m - u)/u_*$, is a function of $y/r_0$ only for large Reynolds numbers (Example 5.3) whether the pipe surface is smooth or rough. From Eq. (5.4.9), by evaluating the constant for $u = u_m$ when $y = r_0$,

$$\frac{u_m - u}{u_*} = \frac{1}{\kappa}\ln\frac{r_0}{y} \tag{5.4.13}$$

For rough pipes, the velocity may be assumed to be $u_w$ at the wall distance $y_w = m\epsilon$, in which $\epsilon$ is a typical height of the roughness projections and $m$ is a form coefficient depending upon the nature of the roughness. By substituting into Eq. (5.4.13), then by eliminating $u_m/u_*$ between the two equations,

$$\frac{u}{u_*} = \frac{1}{\kappa}\ln\frac{y}{\epsilon} + \frac{u_w}{u_*} - \frac{1}{\kappa}\ln m \tag{5.4.14}$$

in which the last two terms on the right-hand side are constant for a given type of roughness,

$$\frac{u}{u_*} = \frac{1}{\kappa}\ln\frac{y}{\epsilon} + B \tag{5.4.15}$$

In Nikuradse's experiments with sand-roughened pipes constant-size sand particles (those passing a given screen and being retained on a slightly finer screen) were glued to the inside pipe walls. If $\epsilon$ represents the diameter of sand grains, experiment shows that $\kappa = 0.40$, $B = 8.48$.

## 5.5  rate processes

The violent interchange of fluid globules in turbulence also tends to transfer any uneven concentration within the fluid, such as salinity, temperature, dye coloring, or sediment concentration.   Studies[1] indicate that the transfer coefficient is roughly proportional to, but probably larger than, the eddy viscosity for turbulent diffusions of concentrations other than momentum.

If $T$ is the temperature, $H$ the heat transfer per unit area per unit time, and $c_p$ the specific heat at constant pressure (Btu per unit of temperature per unit of mass), then

$$H = -c_p\eta\,\frac{\partial T}{\partial y} = -c_p\rho l^2\,\frac{\partial u}{\partial y}\frac{\partial T}{\partial y} \tag{5.5.1}$$

in which $c_p\eta$ is the eddy conductivity.   For transfer of material substances, such as salinity, dye, or sediment, if $C$ is the concentration per unit volume (e.g., pounds of salt per cubic foot, number of particles per cubic foot) and $c$ the rate of transfer per unit area per unit time (e.g., pounds of salt per square foot per second, number of sediment particles per square foot per second), then

$$c = -\epsilon_c\,\frac{\partial C}{\partial y} \tag{5.5.2}$$

and $\epsilon_c$ is proportional to $\epsilon$.

**example 5.5**   A tank of liquid containing fine solid particles of uniform size is agitated so that the kinematic eddy viscosity may be considered constant. If the fall velocity of the particles in still liquid is $v_f$ and the concentration of particles is $C_0$ at $y = y_0$ ($y$ measured from the bottom), find the distribution of solid particles vertically throughout the liquid.

By using Eq. (5.5.2) to determine the rate per second carried upward by turbulence per square foot of area at the level $y$, the amount per second falling across this surface by settling is equated to it for steady conditions. Those particles in the height $v_f$ above the unit area will fall out in a second, i.e., $Cv_f$ particles cross the level downward per second per square foot. From Eq. (5.5.2) $-\epsilon_c\,dC/dy$ particles are carried upward due to the turbulence and the higher concentration below; hence

$$Cv_f = -\epsilon_c\,\frac{dC}{dy}$$

or

$$\frac{dC}{C} = -\frac{v_f}{\epsilon_c}\,dy$$

[1] See footnote 2, p. 250.

After integrating,

$$\ln C = -\frac{v_f}{\epsilon_c} y + \text{const}$$

For $C = C_0$, $y = y_0$,

$$C = C_0 \exp\left[ -\frac{v_f}{\epsilon_c} (y - y_0) \right]$$

## 5.6 boundary-layer concepts

In 1904 Prandtl[1] developed the concept of the boundary layer. It provides an important link between ideal-fluid flow and real-fluid flow. *For fluids having relatively small viscosity, the effect of internal friction in a fluid is appreciable only in a narrow region surrounding the fluid boundaries.* From this hypothesis, the flow outside of the narrow region near the solid boundaries may be considered as ideal flow or potential flow. Relations within the boundary-layer region may be computed from the general equations for viscous fluids, but use of the momentum equation permits the developing of approximate equations for boundary-layer growth and drag. In this section the boundary layer is described and the momentum equation applied to it. Two-dimensional flow along a flat plate is studied by means of the momentum relationships for both the laminar and the turbulent boundary layer. The phenomenon of separation of the boundary layer and formation of the wake is described.

### *description of the boundary layer*

When motion is started in a fluid having very small viscosity, the flow is essentially irrotational[2] in the first instants. Since the fluid at the boundaries has zero velocity relative to the boundaries, there is a steep velocity gradient from the boundary into the flow. This velocity gradient in a real fluid sets up near the boundary shear forces that reduce the flow relative to the boundary. That fluid layer which has had its velocity affected by the boundary shear is called the *boundary layer*. The velocity in the boundary layer approaches the velocity in the main flow asymptotically. The boundary layer is very thin at the upstream end of a streamlined body at rest in

---

[1] L. Prandtl, Über Flussigkeitsbewegung bei sehr kleiner Reibung, *Verhandl. III Intern. Math.-Kongr.*, Heidelberg, 1904.
[2] See Sec 3.3 for definition of irrotational flow.

an otherwise uniform flow.   As this layer moves along the body, the continual action of shear stress tends to slow down additional fluid particles, causing the thickness of the boundary layer to increase with distance from the upstream point.   The fluid in the layer is also subjected to a pressure gradient, determined from the potential flow, that increases the momentum of the layer if the pressure decreases downstream and decreases its momentum if the pressure increases downstream (*adverse* pressure gradient).   The flow outside the boundary layer may also bring momentum into the layer.

For smooth upstream boundaries, the boundary layer starts out as a *laminar boundary layer* in which the fluid particles move in smooth layers. As the thickness of the laminar boundary layer increases, it becomes unstable and finally transforms into a *turbulent boundary layer* in which the fluid particles move in haphazard paths, although their velocity has been reduced by the action of viscosity at the boundary.   When the boundary layer has become turbulent, there is still a very thin layer next to the boundary that has laminar motion.   It is called the *laminar sub-layer*.

Various definitions of boundary-layer thickness $\delta$ have been suggested. The most basic definition refers to the displacement of the main flow due to slowing down of fluid particles in the boundary zone.   This thickness $\delta_1$, called the *displacement thickness*, is expressed by

$$U\delta_1 = \int_0^\delta (U - u)\, dy \tag{5.6.1}$$

in which $\delta$ is that value of $y$ at which $u = U$.   In Fig. 5.14$a$, the line $y = \delta_1$ is drawn so that the shaded areas are equal.   This distance is, in itself, not the distance that is strongly affected by the boundary.   In fact, that region is frequently taken as $3\delta_1$,   Another definition, expressed by Fig. 5.14$b$, is the distance to the point where $u/U = 0.99$.

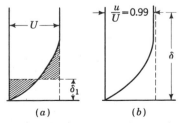

(*a*)                    (*b*)

**Fig. 5.14**  Definitions of boundary-layer thickness.

**Fig. 5.15** Control volume applied to fluid flowing over one side of a flat plate.

*momentum equation applied to the boundary layer*

By following von Kármán's method[1] the principle of momentum may be applied directly to the boundary layer in steady flow along a flat plate. In Fig. 5.15 a control volume is taken enclosing the fluid above the plate, as shown, extending the distance $x$ along the plate. In the $y$-direction it extends a distance $h$ so great that the velocity is undisturbed in the $x$-direction, although some flow occurs along the upper surface, leaving the control volume.

The momentum equation for the $x$-direction is

$$\Sigma F_x = \frac{\partial}{\partial t} \int_{cv} \rho\, u\, d\mathcal{V} + \int_{cs} \rho u \mathbf{v} \cdot d\mathbf{A}$$

It will be applied to the case of incompressible steady flow. The only force acting is due to drag or shear at the plate, since the pressure is constant around the periphery of the control volume. For unit width of plate normal to the paper,

$$-\text{Drag} = \rho \int_0^h u^2\, dy - \rho U^2 h + U\rho \int_0^h (U - u)\, dy$$

The first term on the right-hand side of the equation is the efflux of $x$-momentum from $CD$, and the second term is the $x$-momentum influx through $AB$. The integral in the third term is the net volume influx through $AB$ and $CD$ which, by continuity, must just equal the volume efflux through $BC$. It is multiplied by $U\rho$ to yield $x$-momentum efflux

[1] Th. von Kármán, On Laminar and Turbulent Friction, *Z. Angew. Math. Mech.*, vol. 1, pp. 235–236, 1921.

through $BC$. After combining the integrals,

$$\text{Drag} = \rho \int_0^h u(U - u) \, dy \qquad (5.6.2)$$

The drag $D(x)$ on the plate is in the reverse direction, so that

$$D(x) = \rho \int_0^h u(U - u) \, dy \qquad (5.6.3)$$

The drag on the plate may also be expressed as an integral of the shear stress along the plate,

$$D(x) = \int_0^x \tau_0 \, dx \qquad (5.6.4)$$

By equating the last two expressions, then differentiating with respect to $x$,

$$\tau_0 = \rho \frac{d}{dx} \int_0^h u(U - u) \, dy \qquad (5.6.5)$$

which is the momentum equation for two-dimensional flow along a flat plate.

Calculations of boundary-layer growth, in general, are complex and require advanced mathematical treatment. The parallel-flow cases, laminar or turbulent, along a flat plate may be worked out approximately by use of momentum methods that do not give any detail regarding the velocity distribution—in fact a velocity distribution must be assumed. The results can be shown to agree closely with the more exact approach obtained from general viscous-flow differential equations.

For an assumed distribution, which satisfies the boundary conditions $u = 0$, $y = 0$ and $u = U$, $y = \delta$, the boundary-layer thickness as well as the shear at the boundary can be determined. The velocity distribution is assumed to have the same form at each value of $x$,

$$\frac{u}{U} = F\left(\frac{y}{\delta}\right) = F(\eta) \qquad \eta = \frac{y}{\delta}$$

when $\delta$ is unknown. Prandtl assumed that

$$\frac{u}{U} = F = \frac{3}{2}\eta - \frac{\eta^3}{2} \qquad 0 \le y \le \delta$$

and

$$F = 1 \qquad \delta \le y$$

which satisfy the boundary conditions.   Equation (5.6.5) may be rewritten

$$\tau_0 = \rho U^2 \frac{\partial \delta}{\partial x} \int_0^1 \left(1 - \frac{u}{U}\right)\frac{u}{U}\, d\eta$$

and

$$\tau_0 = \rho U^2 \frac{\partial \delta}{\partial x} \int_0^1 \left(1 - \frac{3}{2}\eta + \frac{\eta^3}{2}\right)\left(\frac{3}{2}\eta - \frac{\eta^3}{2}\right) d\eta = 0.139\rho U^2 \frac{\partial \delta}{\partial x}$$

At the boundary

$$\tau_0 = \mu \frac{\partial u}{\partial y}\Big|_{y=0} = \mu \frac{U}{\delta}\frac{\partial F}{\partial \eta}\Big|_{\eta=0} = \mu \frac{U}{\delta}\frac{\partial}{\partial \eta}\left(\frac{3}{2}\eta - \frac{\eta^3}{2}\right)\Big|_{\eta=0} = \frac{3}{2}\mu\frac{U}{\delta} \qquad (5.6.6)$$

In equating the two expressions for $\tau_0$,

$$\frac{3}{2}\mu\frac{U}{\delta} = 0.139\rho U^2 \frac{\partial \delta}{\partial x}$$

By rearranging,

$$\delta\, d\delta = 10.78 \frac{\mu\, dx}{\rho U}$$

since $\delta$ is a function of $x$ only in this equation.   After integrating,

$$\frac{\delta^2}{2} = 10.78 \frac{\nu}{U} x + \text{const}$$

If $\delta = 0$, for $x = 0$, the constant of integration is zero.   In solving for $\delta/x$,

$$\frac{\delta}{x} = 4.65 \sqrt{\frac{\nu}{Ux}} = \frac{4.65}{\sqrt{\mathbf{R}_x}} \qquad (5.6.7)$$

in which $\mathbf{R}_x = Ux/\nu$ is a Reynolds number based on the distance $x$ from the leading edge of the plate.   This equation for boundary-layer thickness in laminar flow shows that $\delta$ increases as the square root of the distance from the leading edge.

After substituting the value of $\delta$ into Eq. (5.6.6),

$$\tau_0 = 0.322 \sqrt{\frac{\mu\rho U^3}{x}} \qquad (5.6.8)$$

The shear stress varies inversely as the square root of $x$ and directly as the three-halves power of the velocity.   The drag on one side of the plate, of unit width, is

$$\text{Drag} = \int_0^l \tau_0 \, dx = 0.644 \sqrt{\mu\rho U^3 l} \tag{5.6.9}$$

The selecting of other velocity distributions does not radically alter these results.   The exact solution, worked out by Blasius from the general equations of viscous motion, yields the coefficients 0.332 and 0.664 for Eqs. (5.6.8) and (5.6.9), respectively.

The drag can be expressed in terms of a drag coefficient $C_D$ times the stagnation pressure $\rho U^2/2$ and the area of plate $l$ (per unit breadth),

$$\text{Drag} = C_D \frac{\rho U^2}{2} l$$

in which, for the laminar boundary layer,

$$C_D = \frac{1.328}{\sqrt{\mathbf{R}_l}} \tag{5.6.10}$$

and $\mathbf{R}_l = Ul/\nu$.

When the Reynolds number for the plate reaches a value between 500,000 and 1,000,000, the boundary layer becomes turbulent.   Figure 5.16 indicates the growth and transition from laminar to turbulent boundary layer.   The critical Reynolds number depends upon the initial turbulence of the fluid stream, upon the upstream edge of the plate, and upon the plate roughness.

*turbulent boundary layer*

The momentum equation can be used to determine turbulent boundary-layer growth and shear stress along a smooth plate in a manner analogous to the treatment of the laminar boundary layer.   The universal velocity-distribution law for smooth pipes, Eq. (5.4.11), provides the best basis, but

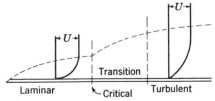

**Fig. 5.16**   Boundary-layer growth.   (The vertical scale is greatly enlarged.)

the calculations are involved. A simpler approach is to use Prandtl's *one-seventh-power* law. It is $u/u_{\max} = (y/r_0)^{1/7}$, in which $y$ is measured from the wall of the pipe and $r_0$ is the pipe radius. Applying it to flat plates produces

$$F = \frac{u}{U} = \left(\frac{y}{\delta}\right)^{1/7} = \eta^{1/7}$$

and

$$\tau_0 = 0.0228\rho U^2 \left(\frac{\nu}{U\delta}\right)^{1/4} \tag{5.6.11}$$

in which the latter expression is the shear stress at the wall of a smooth plate with a turbulent boundary layer. With the same method as that used to calculate the laminar boundary layer,

$$\tau_0 = \rho U^2 \frac{d\delta}{dx} \int_0^1 (1 - \eta^{1/7})\eta^{1/7} \, d\eta = \frac{7}{72} \rho U^2 \frac{d\delta}{dx} \tag{5.6.12}$$

By equating the expressions for shear stress, the differential equation for boundary-layer thickness $\delta$ is obtained,

$$\delta^{1/4} \, d\delta = 0.234 \left(\frac{\nu}{U}\right)^{1/4} dx$$

After integrating, and then by assuming that the boundary layer is turbulent over the whole length of the plate so that the initial conditions $x = 0$, $\delta = 0$ can be used,

$$\delta^{5/4} = 0.292 \left(\frac{\nu}{U}\right)^{1/4} x$$

After solving for $\delta$,

$$\delta = 0.37 \left(\frac{\nu}{U}\right)^{1/5} x^{4/5} = \frac{0.37x}{(Ux/\nu)^{1/5}} = \frac{0.37x}{\mathbf{R}_x^{1/5}} \tag{5.6.13}$$

The thickness increases more rapidly in the turbulent boundary layer. In it the thickness increases as $x^{4/5}$, but in the laminar boundary layer $\delta$ varies as $x^{1/2}$.

To determine the drag on a smooth, flat plate, $\delta$ is eliminated in Eqs. (5.6.11) and (5.6.13), and

$$\tau_0 = 0.029\rho U^2 \left(\frac{\nu}{Ux}\right)^{1/5} \tag{5.6.14}$$

The drag for unit width on one side of the plate is

$$\text{Drag} = \int_0^l \tau_0\, dx - 0.036\rho U^2 l \left(\frac{\nu}{Ul}\right)^{1/5} = \frac{0.036\rho U^2 l}{\mathbf{R}_l^{1/5}} \tag{5.6.15}$$

In terms of the drag coefficient,

$$C_D = 0.072\mathbf{R}_l^{-1/5} \tag{5.6.16}$$

in which $\mathbf{R}_l$ is the Reynolds number based on the length of plate.

The above equations are valid only for the range in which the Blasius resistance equation holds.   For larger Reynolds numbers in smooth-pipe flow, the exponent in the velocity-distribution law is reduced.   For $\mathbf{R} = 400{,}000$, $n = \frac{1}{8}$, and for $\mathbf{R} = 4{,}000{,}000$, $n = \frac{1}{10}$.   The drag law, Eq. (5.6.15), is valid for a range

$$5 \times 10^5 < \mathbf{R}_l < 10^7$$

Experiment shows that the drag is slightly higher than is predicted by Eq. (5.6.16),

$$C_D = 0.074\mathbf{R}_l^{-1/5} \tag{5.6.17}$$

The boundary layer is actually laminar along the upstream part of the plate.   Prandtl[1] has subtracted the laminar portion, producing the equation

$$C_D = 0.074\mathbf{R}_l^{-1/5} - \frac{1700}{\mathbf{R}_l} \qquad 5 \times 10^5 < \mathbf{R}_l < 10^7 \tag{5.6.18}$$

In Fig. 5.17 a log-log plot of $C_D$ vs. $\mathbf{R}_l$ shows the trend of the drag coefficients.   Use of the logarithmic velocity distribution for pipes produces

$$C_D = \frac{0.455}{(\log_{10} \mathbf{R}_l)^{2.58}} \qquad 10^6 < \mathbf{R}_l < 10^9 \tag{5.6.19}$$

in which the constant term has been selected for best agreement with experimental results.

**example 5.6**   A smooth, flat plate 10 ft wide and 100 ft long is towed through still water at 68°F with a speed of 20 ft/sec.   Determine the drag on one side of the plate and the drag on the first 10 ft of the plate.

For the whole plate

$$\mathbf{R}_l = \frac{100 \times 20 \times 1.935}{0.01/479} = 1.85 \times 10^8$$

[1] L. Prandtl, Über den Reibungswiderstand strömender Luft, *Results Aerodynamic Test Inst.*, *Göttingen*, III Lieferung, 1927.

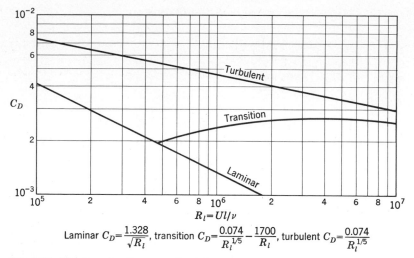

$$\text{Laminar } C_D = \frac{1.328}{\sqrt{R_l}}, \text{ transition } C_D = \frac{0.074}{R_l^{1/5}} - \frac{1700}{R_l}, \text{ turbulent } C_D = \frac{0.074}{R_l^{1/5}}$$

**Fig. 5.17** The drag law for smooth plates.

From Eq. (5.6.19)

$$C_D = \frac{0.455}{[\log_{10}(1.85 \times 10^8)]^{2.58}} = \frac{0.455}{(8.2675)^{2.58}} = 0.00196$$

The drag on one side is

$$\text{Drag} = C_D b l \frac{\rho U^2}{2} = 0.00196 \times 10 \times 100 \times \frac{1.935}{2} \times (20)^2 = 760 \text{ lb}$$

in which $b$ is the plate width. If the critical Reynolds number occurs at $5 \times 10^5$, the length $l_0$ to the transition is

$$\frac{l_0 \times 20 \times 1.935}{0.01/479} = 5 \times 10^5 \qquad l_0 = 0.27 \text{ ft}$$

For the first 10 ft of the plate, $R_l = 1.85 \times 10^7$, $C_D = 0.00274$, and

$$\text{Drag} = 0.00274 \times 10 \times 10 \times \frac{1.935}{2} \times (20)^2 = 106 \text{ lb}$$

Calculation of the turbulent boundary layer over rough plates proceeds in similar fashion, starting with the rough-pipe tests using sand roughnesses. At the upstream end of the flat plate, the flow may be laminar; then, in the turbulent boundary layer where the boundary layer is still thin and the ratio of roughness height to boundary-layer thickness $\epsilon/\delta$ is significant, the region of fully developed roughness occurs, and the drag is proportional to the square of the velocity.    For long plates, this region is followed by a transition region where $\epsilon/\delta$ becomes increasingly smaller, and eventually the plate becomes hydraulically smooth; i.e., the loss would not be reduced by reducing the roughness.    Prandtl and Schlichting[1] have carried through these calculations, which are too complicated for reproduction here.

*separation.    wake*

Along a flat plate the boundary layer continues to grow in the downstream direction, regardless of the length of the plate, when the pressure gradient remains zero.    With the pressure decreasing in the downstream direction, as in a conical reducing section, the boundary layer tends to be reduced in thickness.

For *adverse* pressure gradients, i.e., with pressure increasing in the downstream direction, the boundary layer thickens rapidly.    The adverse gradient plus the boundary shear decrease the momentum in the boundary layer, and if they both act over a sufficient distance, they cause the boundary layer to come to rest.    This phenomenon is called *separation*.    Figure 5.18a illustrates this case.    The boundary streamline must leave the boundary at the separation point, and downstream from this point the adverse pressure gradient causes backflow near the wall.    This region downstream from the streamline that separates from the boundary is known as the *wake*.    The effect of separation is to decrease the net amount of flow work that can be done by a fluid element on the surrounding fluid at the expense of its kinetic energy, with the net result that pressure recovery is incomplete and flow losses (drag) increase.    Figures 5.18b and 5.18c illustrate actual flow cases, the first with a very small adverse pressure gradient, which causes thickening of the boundary layer, and the second with a large diffuser angle, causing separation and backflow near the boundaries.

Streamlined bodies (Fig. 5.19) are designed so that the separation point occurs as far downstream along the body as possible.    If separation can be avoided, the boundary layer remains thin, and the pressure is almost recovered downstream along the body.    The only loss or drag is due to shear stress in the boundary layer, called *skin friction*.    In the wake, the pressure is not recovered and a *pressure drag* results.    Reduction of wake reduces the pressure drag on a body.    In general, the drag is caused by both skin friction and pressure drag.

Flow around a sphere is an excellent example of the effect of separation

[1] Prandtl and H. Schlichting, Das Widerstandsgesetz rauher Platten, *Werft, Reederei, Hafen*, p. 1, 1934.    See also *NACA Tech. Mem.* 1218, part II.

**Fig. 5.18***a* Effect of adverse pressure gradient on boundary layer. Separation.

**Fig. 5.18***b* Boundary-layer growth in a small-angle diffuser. (*From the film Fundamentals of Boundary Layers by the National Committee for Fluid Mechanics Films and the Education Development Center.*)

**Fig. 5.18***c* Boundary-layer separation in a large-angle diffuser. (*From the film Fundamentals of Boundary Layers by the National Committee for Fluid Mechanics Films and the Education Development Center.*)

**Fig. 5.19**  Streamlined body.

on drag.   For very small Reynolds numbers, $VD/\nu < 1$, the flow is everywhere nonturbulent, and the drag is referred to as *deformation drag*. Stokes' law[1] gives the drag force for this case.   For large Reynolds numbers, the flow may be considered potential flow except in the boundary layer and the wake.   The boundary layer forms at the forward stagnation point and is generally laminar.   In the laminar boundary layer, an adverse pressure gradient causes separation more readily than in a turbulent boundary layer, because of the small amount of momentum brought into the laminar layer.   If separation occurs in the laminar boundary layer, the location is farther upstream on the sphere than it is when the boundary layer becomes turbulent first and then separation occurs.

In Fig. 5.20 this is graphically portrayed by the photographs of the two spheres dropped into water at 25 ft/sec.   In $a$, separation occurs in the laminar boundary layer that forms along the smooth surface and causes a very large wake with a resulting large pressure drag.   In $b$, the nose of the sphere, roughened by sand glued to it, induced an early transition to turbulent boundary layer before separation occurred.   The high momentum transfer in the turbulent boundary layer delayed the separation so that the wake is substantially reduced, resulting in a total drag on the sphere less than half that occurring in $a$.

A plot of drag coefficient against Reynolds number (Fig. 5.21) for smooth spheres shows that the shift to turbulent boundary layer (before separation) occurs by itself at a sufficiently high Reynolds number, as evidenced by the sudden drop in drag coefficient.   The exact Reynolds number for the sudden shift depends upon the smoothness of the sphere and upon the turbulence in the fluid stream.   In fact, the sphere is frequently used as a turbulence meter by determining the Reynolds number at which the drag coefficient is 0.30, a point located in the center of the sudden drop (Fig. 5.21).   By use of the hot-wire anemometer, Dryden[2] has correlated the turbulence level of the fluid stream to the Reynolds number for the sphere at $C_D = 0.30$.   The greater the turbulence of the fluid stream, the smaller the Reynolds number for shift in separation point.

In Sec. 7.8, for ideal-fluid flow, equations are developed that permit the velocity and pressure to be found at any point in the fluid for flow around a

[1] See Sec. 5.7.
[2] H. Dryden, Reduction of Turbulence in Wind Tunnels, *NACA Tech. Rept.* 392, 1931.

**Fig. 5.20** Shift in separation point due to induced turbulence. (*a*) 8.5-in. bowling ball, smooth surface, 25 ft/sec entry velocity into water. (*b*) Same except for 4-in.-diameter patch of sand on nose. (*Official U.S. Navy photograph made at Navy Ordnance Test Station, Pasadena Annex.*)

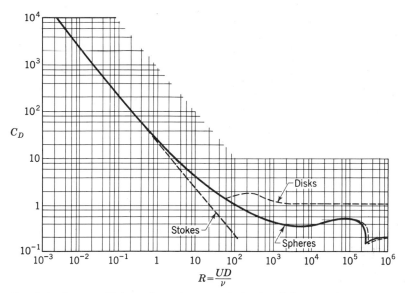

**Fig. 5.21**  Drag coefficients for spheres and circular disks.

sphere.   In ideal-fluid flow, slip is permitted at the boundary; in addition, the boundary condition states that the normal component of the velocity at a boundary is zero in steady flow.   Therefore separation is ruled out of consideration.   In ideal-fluid flow, which is for constant energy, there is no drag on a body and no boundary layer.   A comparison of Figs. 5.20 and 7.23 shows the great contrast between ideal- and real-fluid flow around a bluff body.   The ideal-fluid flow, however, does yield a good representation of velocity and pressure for the upstream portion of the flow, away from the effects of boundary-layer separation and wake formation.

## 5.7  drag on immersed bodies

The principles of potential flow around bodies are developed in Chap. 7, and principles of the boundary layer, separation, and wake in the section preceding this one (Sec. 5.6).   In this section drag is defined, some experimental drag coefficients are listed, the effect of compressibility on drag is discussed, and Stokes' law is presented.   Lift is defined and the lift and drag coefficients for an airfoil are given.

Drag is defined as the force component, parallel to the relative approach velocity, exerted on the body by the moving fluid.   The drag-coefficient

**Fig. 5.22**   Drag coefficients for circular cylinders.

curves for spheres and circular disks are shown in Fig. 5.21.   In Fig. 5.22 the drag coefficient for an infinitely long circular cylinder (two-dimensional case) is plotted against the Reynolds number.   This case also has the sudden shift in separation point as in the case of the sphere.   In each case, the drag coefficient $C_D$ is defined by

$$\text{Drag} = C_D A \, \frac{\rho U^2}{2}$$

in which $A$ is the projected area of the body on a plane normal to the flow.

In Table 5.1 typical drag coefficients are shown for several cylinders. In general, the values given are for the range of Reynolds numbers in which the coefficient changes little with the Reynolds number.

A typical lift and drag curve for an airfoil section is shown in Fig. 5.23. Lift is the fluid-force component on a body at right angles to the relative approach velocity.   The lift coefficient $C_L$ is defined by

$$\text{Lift} = C_L A \, \frac{\rho U^2}{2}$$

in which $A$ refers to the chord length times the wing length for lift and drag for airfoil sections.

*effect of compressibility on drag*

To determine drag in gas flow the effects of compressibility, as expressed by the *Mach* number, are more important than the Reynolds number.

**Table 5.1   Typical drag coefficients for various cylinders in two-dimensional flow** †

| Body shape | | $C_D$ | Reynolds number |
|---|---|---|---|
| Circular cylinder | ○ | 1.2 | $10^4$ to $1.5 \times 10^5$ |
| Elliptical cylinder | ⬭ 2:1 | 0.6 | $4 \times 10^4$ |
| | | 0.46 | $10^5$ |
| | 4:1 | 0.32 | $2.5 \times 10^4$ to $10^5$ |
| | 8:1 | 0.29 | $2.5 \times 10^4$ |
| | | 0.20 | $2 \times 10^5$ |
| Square cylinder | ☐ | 2.0 | $3.5 \times 10^4$ |
| | ◇ | 1.6 | $10^4$ to $10^5$ |
| Triangular cylinders | 120° | 2.0 | $10^4$ |
| | 120° | 1.72 | $10^4$ |
| | 90° | 2.15 | $10^4$ |
| | 90° | 1.60 | $10^4$ |
| | 60° | 2.20 | $10^4$ |
| | 60° | 1.39 | $10^4$ |
| | 30° | 1.8 | $10^5$ |
| | 30° | 1.0 | $10^5$ |
| Semitubular | ) | 2.3 | $4 \times 10^4$ |
| | ( | 1.12 | $4 \times 10^4$ |

† Data from W. F. Lindsey, *NACA Tech. Rept.* 619, 1938.

**Fig. 5.23**  Typical lift and drag coefficients for an airfoil.

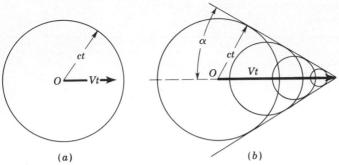

**Fig. 5.24**  Wave propagation produced by a particle moving at $(a)$ subsonic velocity and $(b)$ supersonic velocity.

The Mach number **M** is defined as the ratio of fluid velocity to velocity of sound in the fluid medium.   When flow is at the critical velocity $c$, it has exactly the speed of the sound wave so that small pressure waves cannot travel upstream.   For this condition **M** = 1.   When **M** is greater than unity, the flow is supersonic; and when **M** is less than unity, it is subsonic.

Any small disturbance is propagated with the speed of sound (Sec. 6.2). For example, a disturbance in still air travels outward as a spherical pressure wave.   When the source of the disturbance moves with a velocity less than $c$, as in Fig. 5.24$a$, the wave travels ahead of the disturbing body and gives the fluid a chance to adjust itself to the oncoming body.   By the time the particle has moved a distance $Vt$, the disturbance wave has moved out as far as $r = ct$ from the point $O$.   As the disturbing body moves along, new spherical waves are sent out, but in all subsonic cases they are contained within the initial spherical wave shown.   In supersonic motion of a particle (Fig. 5.24$b$) the body moves faster than the spherical wave emitted from it, yielding a cone-shaped wave front with vertex at the body, as shown. The half angle of cone $\alpha$ is called the *Mach angle*,

$$\alpha = \sin^{-1} \frac{ct}{Vt} = \sin^{-1} \frac{c}{V}$$

The conical pressure front extends out behind the body and is called a *Mach wave* (Sec. 6.4).   There is a sudden small change in velocity and pressure across a Mach wave.

The drag on bodies varies greatly with the Mach number and becomes relatively independent of the Reynolds number when compressibility effects become important.   In Fig. 5.25 the drag coefficients for four projectiles are plotted against the Mach number.

For low Mach numbers, a body should be rounded in front, with a blunt

**Fig. 5.25** Drag coefficients for projectiles as a function of the Mach number. (*From L. Prandtl, "Abriss der Strömungslehre," Friedrich Vieweg und Sohn, Brunswick, Germany, 1935.*)

nose and a long, tapering afterbody for minimum drag.  For high Mach numbers (0.7 and over), the drag rises very rapidly owing to formation of the vortices behind the projectile and to formation of the shock waves; the body should have a tapered nose or thin forward edge.  As the Mach numbers increase, the curves tend to drop and to approach a constant value asymptotically.  This appears to be due to the fact that the reduction of pressure behind the projectile is limited to absolute zero, and hence its contribution to the total drag tends to become constant.  The pointed projectile creates a narrower shock front that tends to reduce the limiting value of the drag coefficient.

*Stokes' law*

The flow of a viscous incompressible fluid around a sphere has been solved by Stokes[1] for values of the Reynolds number $UD/\nu$ below 1.  The derivation is beyond the scope of this treatment; the results, however, are of value in such problems as the settling of dust particles.  Stokes found the drag (force exerted on the sphere by flow of fluid around it) to be

$$\text{Drag} = 6\pi a \mu U$$

[1] G. Stokes, *Trans. Cambridge Phil. Soc.*, vol. 8, 1845; vol. 9, 1851.

in which $a$ is the radius of sphere and $U$ the velocity of sphere relative to the fluid at a great distance. To find the terminal velocity for a sphere dropping through a fluid that is otherwise at rest, the buoyant force plus the drag force must just equal its weight, or

$$\tfrac{4}{3}\pi a^3\gamma + 6\pi a\mu U = \tfrac{4}{3}\pi a^3\gamma_s$$

in which $\gamma$ is the specific weight of liquid and $\gamma_s$ is the specific weight of the sphere. By solving for $U$, the terminal velocity is found to be

$$U = \frac{2}{9}\frac{a^2}{\mu}(\gamma_s - \gamma) \qquad (5.7.1)$$

The straight-line portion of Fig. 5.21 represents Stokes' law.

The drag relations on particles, as given by Stokes' law and by the experimental results of Fig. 5.21, are useful in the design of settling basins for separating small solid particles from fluids. Applications include the separation of coolants from metal chips in machining operations, the desilting of river flow, and sanitary engineering applications to both raw water treatment and sewage treatment.

## 5.8   resistance to turbulent flow in open and closed conduits

In steady turbulent incompressible flow in conduits of constant cross section (steady uniform flow) the wall shear stress varies closely proportional to the square of the velocity,

$$\tau_0 = \lambda\frac{\rho}{2}V^2 \qquad (5.8.1)$$

in which $\lambda$ is a dimensionless coefficient. For open channels and noncircular closed conduits the shear stress is not constant over the surface. In these cases, $\tau_0$ is used as the average wall shear stress. Secondary flows[1] occurring in noncircular conduits act to equalize the wall shear stress.

The momentum equation applied to the control volume (Fig. 5.26) comprising the liquid between sections 1 and 2, under the assumptions made, shows no net efflux of momentum, and hence shows equilibrium of forces on the control volume in the direction of motion

$$(p_1 - p_2)A + \gamma A\,\Delta z = \tau_0 LP$$

in which $\Delta z = L\sin\theta$ and $P$ is the *wetted perimeter* of the conduit, i.e., the

---

[1] Secondary flows, not wholly understood, are transverse components that cause the main central flow to spread out into corners or near walls.

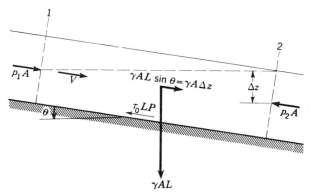

**Fig. 5.26** Axial forces on free body of fluid in a conduit.

portion of the perimeter where the wall is in contact with the fluid (free-liquid surface excluded). The ratio $A/P$ is called the *hydraulic radius R* of the conduit. If $p_1 - p_2 = \Delta p$,

$$\frac{\Delta p + \gamma\, \Delta z}{L} = \frac{\tau_0}{R} = \frac{\lambda \rho V^2}{2R} \tag{5.8.2}$$

or, when divided through by $\gamma$, if $h_f = (\Delta p + \gamma\, \Delta z)/\gamma$ be the losses per unit weight,

$$\frac{h_f}{L} = S = \frac{\lambda}{R} \frac{V^2}{2g}$$

in which $S$ represents the losses per unit weight per unit length. After solving for $V$,

$$V = \sqrt{\frac{2g}{\lambda}}\, \sqrt{RS} = C\,\sqrt{RS} \tag{5.8.3}$$

This is the Chézy formula, in which originally the Chézy coefficient $C$ was thought to be a constant for any size conduit or wall-surface condition. Various formulas for $C$ are now generally used.

For pipes, when $\lambda = f/4$ and $R = D/4$, the Darcy-Weisbach equation is obtained,

$$h_f = f\frac{L}{D}\frac{V^2}{2g} \tag{5.8.4}$$

in which $D$ is the inside pipe diameter. This equation may be applied to open channels in the form

$$V = \sqrt{\frac{8g}{f}} \sqrt{RS} \qquad (5.8.5)$$

with values of $f$ determined from pipe experiments.

## 5.9 steady uniform flow in open channels

For incompressible, steady flow at constant depth in a prismatic open channel, the $Manning$ formula is widely used. It can be obtained from the Chézy formula [Eq. (5.8.3)] by setting

$$C = \frac{1.49}{n} R^{1/6} \qquad (5.9.1)$$

so

$$V = \frac{1.49}{n} R^{2/3}S^{1/2} \qquad (5.9.2)$$

which is the Manning formula. $V$ is the average velocity at a cross section, $R$ the hydraulic radius (Sec. 5.8), and $S$ the losses per unit weight per unit length of channel or the slope of the bottom of the channel. It is also the slope of the water surface, which is parallel to the channel bottom. The coefficient $n$ was thought to be an absolute roughness coefficient, i.e., dependent upon surface roughness only, but actually depends upon the size and shape of channel cross section in some unknown manner. Values of the coefficient $n$, determined by many tests on actual canals, are given in Table 5.2. Equation (5.9.2) must have velocity in feet per second and $R$ in feet for use with the values in Table 5.2.

When Eq. (5.9.2) is multiplied by the cross-sectional area $A$, the Manning formula takes the form

$$Q = \frac{1.49}{n} AR^{2/3}S^{1/2} \qquad (5.9.3)$$

When the cross-sectional area is known, any one of the other quantities can be obtained from Eq. (5.9.3) by direct solution.

**example 5.7** Determine the discharge for a trapezoidal channel (Fig. 5.27) with a bottom width $b = 8$ ft and side slopes 1 on 1. The depth is 6 ft, and

**Table 5.2   Average values of the Manning roughness factor for various boundary materials†**

| Boundary material | Manning $n$ |
|---|---|
| Planed wood | 0.012 |
| Unplaned wood | 0.013 |
| Finished concrete | 0.012 |
| Unfinished concrete | 0.014 |
| Cast iron | 0.015 |
| Brick | 0.016 |
| Riveted steel | 0.018 |
| Corrugated metal | 0.022 |
| Rubble | 0.025 |
| Earth | 0.025 |
| Earth, with stones or weeds | 0.035 |
| Gravel | 0.029 |

† Recent work by the U.S. Bureau of Reclamation and other government agencies indicates that the Manning roughness factor should be increased (say, 10 to 15 per cent) for hydraulic radii greater than about 10 ft. The loss in capacity of large channels is due to the roughening of the surfaces with age, marine and plant growths, deposits, and the addition of bridge piers as the highway system is expanded.

the slope of the bottom is 0.0009.   The channel has a finished concrete lining.

From Table 5.2, $n = 0.012$.   The area is

$$A = 8 \times 6 + 6 \times 6 = 84 \text{ ft}^2$$

and the wetted perimeter is

$$P = 8 + 2 \times 6 \sqrt{2} - 24.96$$

**Fig. 5.27** Notation for trapezoidal cross section.

By substituting into Eq. (5.9.3),

$$Q = \frac{1.49}{0.012} 84 \left(\frac{84}{24.96}\right)^{2/3} (0.0009)^{1/2} = 703 \text{ cfs}$$

Trial solutions are required in some instances when the cross-sectional area is unknown. Expressions for both the hydraulic radius and the area contain the depth in a form that cannot be solved explicitly.

**example 5.8**  What depth is required for 150 cfs flow in a rectangular planed-wood channel 5 ft wide with a bottom slope of 0.002?

If the depth is $y$, $A = 5y$, $P = 5 + 2y$, and $n = 0.012$. By substituting in Eq. (5.9.3),

$$150 = \frac{1.49}{0.012} 5y \left(\frac{5y}{5 + 2y}\right)^{2/3} (0.002)^{1/2}$$

After simplifying,

$$f(y) = y \left(\frac{y}{1 + 0.4y}\right)^{2/3} = 5.4$$

Assume $y = 4$ ft; then $f(y) = 5.332$. Assume $y = 4.05$; then $f(y) = 5.41$. The correct depth then is about 4.05 ft.

More general cases of open-channel flow are considered in Chap. 11.

## 5.10   steady, incompressible flow through simple pipe systems

*Colebrook formula*

A force balance for steady flow (no acceleration) in a pipe (Fig. 5.28) yields

$$\Delta p \, \pi r_0{}^2 = \tau_0 2\pi r_0 \, \Delta L$$

**Fig.  5.28** Equilibrium conditions for steady flow in a pipe.

or simplifying,

$$\tau_0 = \frac{\Delta p}{\Delta L} \frac{r_0}{2} \qquad (5.10.1)$$

which holds for laminar or turbulent flow.   The Darcy-Weisbach equation (5.8.4) may be written

$$\Delta p = \gamma h_f = f \frac{\Delta L}{2r_0} \rho \frac{V^2}{2}$$

After eliminating $\Delta p$ in the two equations and simplifying,

$$\sqrt{\frac{\tau_0}{\rho}} = \sqrt{\frac{f}{8}} V \qquad (5.10.2)$$

which relates wall shear stress, friction factor, and average velocity.   The average velocity $V$ may be obtained from Eq. (5.4.11) by integrating over the cross section.   Substituting for $V$ in Eq. (5.10.2) and simplifying produces the equation for friction factor in smooth-pipe flow,

$$\frac{1}{\sqrt{f}} = A_s + B_s \ln (\mathbf{R} \sqrt{f}) \qquad (5.10.3)$$

With the Nikuradse[1] data for smooth pipes, the equation becomes

$$\frac{1}{\sqrt{f}} = 0.86 \ln (\mathbf{R} \sqrt{f}) - 0.8 \qquad (5.10.4)$$

For rough pipes in the complete turbulence zone,

$$\frac{1}{\sqrt{f}} = F_2 \left( m, \frac{\epsilon'}{D} \right) + B_r \ln \frac{\epsilon}{D} \qquad (5.10.5)$$

in which $F_2$ is, in general, a constant for a given form and spacing of the roughness elements.   For the Nikuradse sand-grain roughness (Fig. 5.31) Eq. (5.10.5) becomes

$$\frac{1}{\sqrt{f}} = 1.14 - 0.86 \ln \frac{\epsilon}{D} \qquad (5.10.6)$$

The roughness height $\epsilon$ for sand-roughened pipes may be used as a measure of the roughness of commercial pipes.   If the value of $f$ is known for a commercial pipe in the fully developed wall turbulence zone, i.e., large Reynolds numbers and the loss proportional to the square of the

---

[1] J. Nikuradse, Gesetzmassigkeiten der turbulenten Strömung in glatten Rohren, *VDI-Forschungsh.*, vol. 356, 1932.

velocity, the value of $\epsilon$ may be computed by Eq. (5.10.6).   In the transition region where $f$ depends upon both $\epsilon/D$ and $\mathbf{R}$, sand-roughened pipes produce different results than commercial pipes.   This is made evident by a graph based on Eqs. (5.10.4) and (5.10.6) with both sand-roughened- and commercial-pipe-test results shown.   By rearranging Eq. (5.10.6)

$$\frac{1}{\sqrt{f}} + 0.86 \ln \frac{\epsilon}{D} = 1.14$$

and by adding 0.86 ln $\epsilon/D$ to each side of Eq. (5.10.4)

$$\frac{1}{\sqrt{f}} + 0.86 \ln \frac{\epsilon}{D} = 0.86 \ln \left( \mathbf{R} \sqrt{f} \frac{\epsilon}{D} \right) - 0.8$$

By selecting $1/\sqrt{f} + 0.86 \ln \epsilon/D$ as ordinate and $\ln (\mathbf{R} \sqrt{f} \epsilon/D)$ as abscissa (Fig. 5.29), smooth-pipe-test results plot as a straight line with slope $+0.86$ and rough-pipe-test results in the complete turbulence zone plot as the horizontal line.   Nikuradse sand-roughness-test results plot along the dashed line in the transition region and commercial-pipe-test results plot along the lower curved line.

The explanation of the difference in shape of the artificial roughness curve of Nikuradse and the commercial roughness curve is that the laminar sub-layer or laminar film covers all the artificial roughness or allows it to protrude uniformly as the film thickness decreases.   With commercial roughness, which varies greatly in uniformity, small portions extend beyond the film first, as the film decreases in thickness with increasing Reynolds

**Fig. 5.29**  Colebrook transition function.

number.  An empirical transition function for commercial pipes for the region between smooth pipes and the complete turbulence zone has been developed by Colebrook,[1]

$$\frac{1}{\sqrt{f}} = -0.86 \ln \left( \frac{\epsilon/D}{3.7} + \frac{2.51}{\mathbf{R}\sqrt{f}} \right) \qquad (5.10.7)$$

which is the basis for the Moody diagram (Fig. 5.32).

*pipe flow*

In steady incompressible flow in a pipe the irreversibilities are expressed in terms of a head loss, or drop in *hydraulic grade line* (Sec. 10.1).  The hydraulic grade line is $p/\gamma$ above the center of the pipe, and if $z$ is the elevation of the center of the pipe, then $z + p/\gamma$ is the elevation of a point on the hydraulic grade line.  The locus of values of $z + p/\gamma$ along the pipeline gives the hydraulic grade line.  Losses, or irreversibilities, cause this line to drop in the direction of flow.  The Darcy-Weisbach equation

$$h_f = f \frac{L}{D} \frac{V^2}{2g} \qquad (5.8.4)$$

is generally adopted for pipe-flow calculations.  $h_f$ is the head loss, or drop in hydraulic grade line, in the pipe length $L$, having an inside diameter $D$ and an average velocity $V$.  $h_f$ has the dimension length and is expressed in terms of foot-pounds per pound or feet.  The friction factor $f$ is a dimensionless factor that is required to make the equation produce the correct value for losses.  All quantities in Eq. (5.8.4) except $f$ may be measured experimentally.  A typical setup is shown in Fig. 5.30.  By measuring the discharge and inside diameter, the average velocity can be computed.

---

[1] C. F. Colebrook, Turbulent Flow in Pipes, with Particular Reference to the Transition Region between the Smooth and Rough Pipe Laws, *J. Inst. Civil Engrs. London*, vol. 11, pp. 133–156, 1938–1939.

**Fig. 5.30**  Experimental arrangement for determination of head loss in a pipe.

The head loss $h_f$ is measured by a differential manometer attached to piezometer openings at sections 1 and 2, distance $L$ apart.

Experimentation shows the following to be true in turbulent flow:

1. The head loss varies directly as the length of the pipe.
2. The head loss varies almost as the square of the velocity.
3. The head loss varies almost inversely as the diameter.
4. The head loss depends upon the surface roughness of the interior pipe wall.
5. The head loss depends upon the fluid properties of density and viscosity.
6. The head loss is independent of the pressure.

The friction factor $f$ must be selected in a manner so that Eq. (5.8.4) correctly yields the head loss; hence, $f$ cannot be a constant but must depend upon velocity $V$, diameter $D$, density $\rho$, viscosity $\mu$, and certain characteristics of the wall roughness that are signified by $\epsilon$, $\epsilon'$, and $m$. These symbols are defined thus: $\epsilon$ is a measure of the *size* of the roughness projections and has the dimensions of a length; $\epsilon'$ is a measure of the *arrangement* or *spacing* of the roughness elements and also has the dimensions of a length; $m$ is a form factor, depending upon the *shape* of the individual roughness elements, and is dimensionless. The term $f$, instead of being a simple constant, turns out to be a factor that depends upon seven quantities,

$$f = f(V,D,\rho,\mu,\epsilon,\epsilon',m) \tag{5.10.8}$$

Since $f$ is a dimensionless factor, it must depend upon the grouping of these quantities into dimensionless parameters. For *smooth* pipe $\epsilon = \epsilon' = m = 0$, leaving $f$ dependent upon the first four quantities. They can be arranged in only one way to make them dimensionless, namely, $VD\rho/\mu$, which is the Reynolds number. For *rough* pipes the terms $\epsilon$, $\epsilon'$ may be made dimensionless by dividing by $D$. Therefore, in general,

$$f = f\left(\frac{VD\rho}{\mu}, \frac{\epsilon}{D}, \frac{\epsilon'}{D}, m\right) \tag{5.10.9}$$

The proof of this relationship is left to experimentation. For smooth pipes a plot of all experimental results shows the functional relationship, subject to a scattering of $\pm 5$ per cent. The plot of friction factor against the Reynolds number on a log-log chart is called a *Stanton diagram*. Blasius[1] was the first to correlate the smooth-pipe experiments in turbulent

[1] H. Blasius, Das Aehnlichkeitsgesetz bei Reibungsvorgängen in Flüssigkeiten, *VDI-Forschungsh.*, vol. 131, 1913.

flow.   He presented the results by an empirical formula that is valid up to about **R** = 100,000.   The Blasius formula is

$$f = \frac{0.316}{\mathbf{R}^{1/4}}$$  (5.10.10)

In rough pipes the term $\epsilon/D$ is called the *relative roughness*.   Nikuradse[1] proved the validity of the relative roughness concept by his tests on sand-roughened pipes.   He used three sizes of pipes and glued sand grains ($\epsilon$ = diameter of the sand grains) of practically constant size to the interior walls so that he had the same values of $\epsilon/D$ for different pipes.   These experiments (Fig. 5.31) show that for one value of $\epsilon/D$ the $f$, **R** curve is smoothly connected regardless of the actual pipe diameter.   These tests did not permit variation of $\epsilon'/D$ or $m$ but proved the validity of the equation

$$f = f\left(\mathbf{R}, \frac{\epsilon}{D}\right)$$

for one type of roughness.

[1] J. Nikuradse, Strömungsgesetze in rauhen Rohren, *VDI-Forschungsh.*, vol. 361, 1933.

**Fig. 5.31**  Nikuradse's sand-roughened-pipe tests.

Because of the extreme complexity of naturally rough surfaces, most of the advances in understanding the basic relationships have been developed around experiments on artificially roughened pipes.   Moody[1] has constructed one of the most convenient charts for determining friction factors in clean, commercial pipes.   This chart, presented in Fig. 5.32, is the basis for pipeflow calculations in this chapter.   The chart is a Stanton diagram that expresses $f$ as a function of relative roughness and the Reynolds number.   The values of absolute roughness of the commercial pipes are determined by experiment in which $f$ and $\mathbf{R}$ are found and substituted into the Colebrook formula, Eq. (5.10.7), which closely represents natural pipe trends.   These are listed in the table in the lower left-hand corner of Fig. 5.32.   The Colebrook formula provides the shape of the $\epsilon/D = \text{const}$ curves in the transition region.

The straight line marked "laminar flow" is the Hagen-Poiseuille equation. Equation (5.2.10$b$),

$$V = \frac{\Delta p \, r_0{}^2}{8\mu L}$$

may be transformed into Eq. (5.8.4) with $\Delta p = \gamma h_f$ and by solving for $h_f$,

$$h_f = \frac{V 8\mu L}{\gamma r_0{}^2} = \frac{64\mu}{\rho D} \frac{L}{D} \frac{V}{2g} = \frac{64}{\rho D V/\mu} \frac{L}{D} \frac{V^2}{2g}$$

or

$$h_f = f \frac{L}{D} \frac{V^2}{2g} = \frac{64}{\mathbf{R}} \frac{L}{D} \frac{V^2}{2g} \tag{5.10.11}$$

from which

$$f = \frac{64}{\mathbf{R}} \tag{5.10.12}$$

This equation, which plots as a straight line with slope $-1$ on a log-log chart, may be used for the solution of laminar-flow problems in pipes.   It applies to all roughnesses, as the head loss in laminar flow is independent of wall roughness.   The Reynolds critical number is about 2000, and the *critical zone*, where the flow may be either laminar or turbulent, is about 2000 to 4000.

It should be noted that the relative-roughness curves $\epsilon/D = 0.001$ and smaller approach the smooth-pipe curve for decreasing Reynolds numbers. This can be explained by the presence of a laminar film at the wall of the pipe that decreases in thickness as the Reynolds number increases.   For

---

[1] L. F. Moody, Friction Factors for Pipe Flow, *Trans. ASME*, November, 1944.

certain ranges of Reynolds numbers in the transition zone, the film completely covers small roughness projections, and the pipe has a friction factor the same as that of a smooth pipe.   For larger Reynolds numbers, projections protrude through the laminar film, and each projection causes extra turbulence that increases the head loss.   For the zone marked "complete turbulence, rough pipes," the film thickness is negligible compared with the height of roughness projections, and each projection contributes fully to the turbulence.   Viscosity does not affect the head loss in this zone, as evidenced by the fact that the friction factor does not change with the Reynolds number.   In this zone the loss follows the $V^2$ law; i.e., it varies directly as the square of the velocity.

Two auxiliary scales are given along the top of the Moody diagram. One is for water at 60°F, and the other is for air at standard atmospheric pressure and 60°F.   Since the kinematic viscosity is constant in each case, the Reynolds number is a function of $VD$.   For these two scales only, $D$ must be expressed in inches.

*simple pipe problems*

The three simple pipe-flow cases that are basic to solutions of the more complex problems are

|  | *Given* | *To find* |
|---|---|---|
| I. | $Q, L, D, \nu, \epsilon$ | $h_f$ |
| II. | $h_f, L, D, \nu, \epsilon$ | $Q$ |
| III. | $h_f, Q, L, \nu, \epsilon$ | $D$ |

In each of these cases the Darcy-Weisbach equation, the continuity equation, and the Moody diagram are used to determine the unknown quantity.

In the first case the Reynolds number and the relative roughness are readily determined from the data given, and $h_f$ is found by determining $f$ from the Moody diagram and substituting into the Darcy-Weisbach equation.

**example 5.9**   Determine the head loss due to the flow of 2000 gpm of oil, $\nu = 0.0001$ ft²/sec, through 1000 ft of 8-in.-diameter cast-iron pipe.

$$V = \frac{2000}{448\pi/9} = 12.8 \text{ ft/sec} \qquad R = 12.8 \times \frac{2}{3} \times \frac{1}{0.0001} = 85{,}500$$

The relative roughness is $\epsilon/D = 0.00085/0.667 = 0.0013$.   From Fig. 5.32, by interpolation, $f = 0.024$; hence

$$h_f = f \frac{L}{D} \frac{V^2}{2g} = 0.024 \times \frac{1000}{\frac{2}{3}} \frac{(12.8)^2}{64.4} = 91.8 \text{ ft-lb/lb}$$

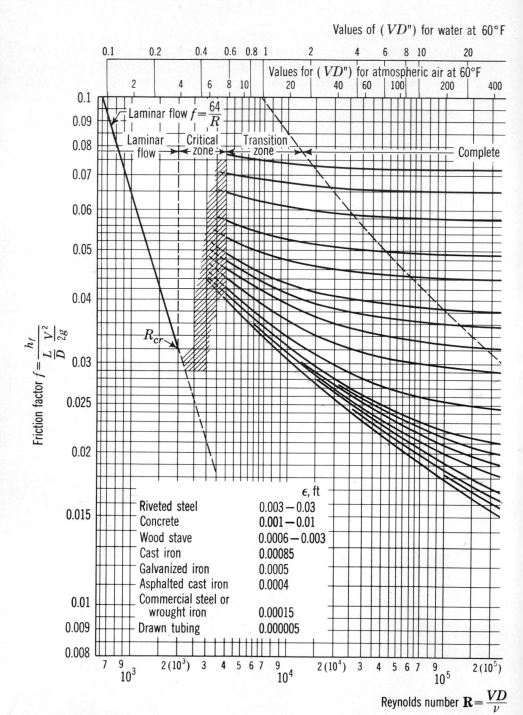

**Fig. 5.32** Moody diagram.

( velocity in ft/sec x diameter in in. )

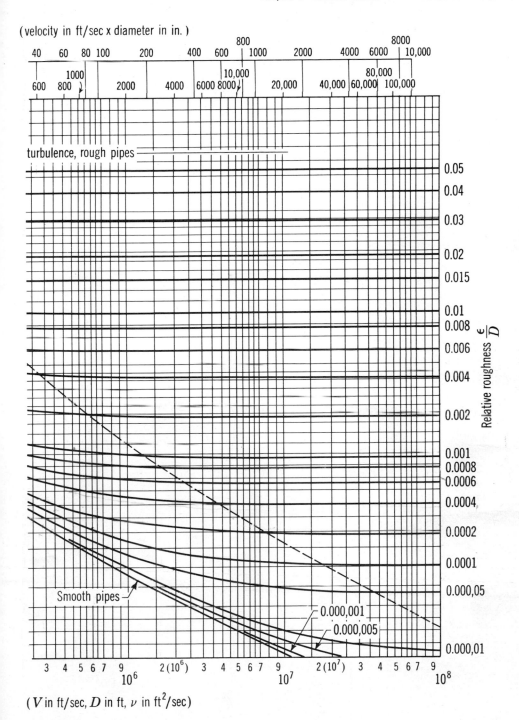

( $V$ in ft/sec, $D$ in ft, $\nu$ in ft$^2$/sec)

In the second case, $V$ and $f$ are unknowns, and the Darcy-Weisbach equation and Moody diagram must be used simultaneously to find their values. Since $\epsilon/D$ is known, a value of $f$ may be assumed by inspection of the Moody diagram. Substitution of this trial $f$ into the Darcy-Weisbach equation produces a trial value of $V$, from which a trial Reynolds number is computed. With the Reynolds number an improved value of $f$ is found from the Moody diagram. When $f$ has been found correct to two significant figures, the corresponding $V$ is the value sought, and $Q$ is determined by multiplying by the area.

**example 5.10**   Water at 60°F flows through a 12-in.-diameter riveted-steel pipe, $\epsilon = 0.01$, with a head loss of 20 ft in 1000 ft. Determine the flow.

The relative roughness is $\epsilon/D = 0.01$, and from Fig. 5.32 a trial $f$ is taken as 0.040. By substituting into Eq. (5.8.4),

$$20 = 0.040 \frac{1000}{1} \frac{V^2}{64.4} \qquad V = 5.67 \text{ ft/sec}$$

and $VD'' = 68$ for use with the scale at the top of Fig. 5.32, which shows $f = 0.038$. With this $f$ in place of 0.040 in the above equation, $V = 5.81$, $VD'' = 69.8$, and $f$ remains 0.038. The discharge is

$$Q = 5.81 \frac{\pi}{4} = 4.56 \text{ cfs} = 2044 \text{ gpm}$$

In the third case, with $D$ unknown, there are three unknowns in Eq. (5.8.4), $f$, $V$, $D$; two in the continuity equation, $V$, $D$; and three in the Reynolds number equation, $V$, $D$, **R**. The relative roughness is also unknown. Using the continuity equation to eliminate the velocity in Eq. (5.8.4) and in the expression for **R** simplifies the problem. Equation (5.8.4) becomes

$$h_f = f \frac{L}{D} \frac{Q^2}{2g(D^2\pi/4)^2}$$

or

$$D^5 = \frac{8LQ^2}{h_f g \pi^2} f = C_1 f \qquad\qquad (5.10.13)$$

in which $C_1$ is the known quantity $8LQ^2/h_f g\pi^2$. As $VD^2 = 4Q/\pi$ from continuity,

$$\mathbf{R} = \frac{VD}{\nu} = \frac{4Q}{\pi\nu}\frac{1}{D} = \frac{C_2}{D} \qquad\qquad (5.10.14)$$

in which $C_2$ is the known quantity $4Q/\pi\nu$. The solution is now effected by the following procedure:

1. Assume a value of $f$.   WATER ~ .02
2. Solve Eq. (5.10.13) for $D$.
3. Solve Eq. (5.10.14) for **R**.
4. Find the relative roughness $\epsilon/D$.
5. With **R** and $\epsilon/D$, look up a new $f$ from Fig. 5.32.
6. Use the new $f$, and repeat the procedure.
7. When the value of $f$ does not change, all equations are satisfied and the problem is solved.

Normally only one or two trials are required. Since standard pipe sizes are usually selected, the next larger size of pipe from that given by the computation is taken. Nominal standard pipe sizes are $\frac{1}{8}$, $\frac{1}{4}$, $\frac{3}{8}$, $\frac{1}{2}$, $\frac{3}{4}$, 1, $1\frac{1}{4}$, $1\frac{1}{2}$, 2, $2\frac{1}{2}$, 3, $3\frac{1}{2}$, 4, 5, 6, 8, 10, 12, 14, 16, 18, 24, and 30 in. The inside diameters are larger than the nominal up to 12 in. Above the 12-in. size the actual inside diameter depends upon the "schedule" of the pipe, and manufacturers' tables should be consulted. Throughout this chapter the nominal size is taken as the actual inside diameter.

**example 5.11**   Determine the size of clean wrought-iron pipe required to convey 4000 gpm oil, $\nu = 0.0001$ ft²/sec, 10,000 ft with a head loss of 75 ft-lb/lb.

The discharge is

$$Q = \frac{4000}{448} = 8.93 \text{ cfs}$$

From Eq. (5.10.13)

$$D^5 = \frac{8 \times 10,000 \times (8.93)^2}{75 \times 32.2 \times \pi^2} f = 267.0f$$

and from Eq. (5.10.14)

$$\mathbf{R} = \frac{4 \times 8.93}{\pi 0.0001} \frac{1}{D} = \frac{113,800}{D}$$

and from Fig. 5.32, $\epsilon = 0.00015$ ft.

If $f = 0.02$, $D = 1.398$ ft, $\mathbf{R} = 81,400$, $\epsilon/D = 0.00011$, and from Fig. 5.32, $f = 0.019$. In repeating the procedure, $D = 1.382$, $\mathbf{R} = 82,300$, $f = 0.019$. Therefore, $D = 1.382 \times 12 = 16.6$ in. If a 75-ft head loss is the maximum allowable, an 18-in. pipe is required.

In each of the cases considered, the loss has been expressed in feet of head or in foot-pounds per pound.   For horizontal pipes, this loss shows up as a gradual reduction in pressure along the line.   For nonhorizontal cases, the energy equation (3.10.1) is applied to the two end sections of the pipe, and the loss term is included; thus

$$\frac{V_1{}^2}{2g} + \frac{p_1}{\gamma} + z_1 = \frac{V_2{}^2}{2g} + \frac{p_2}{\gamma} + z_2 + h_f \qquad (5.10.15)$$

in which the kinetic-energy correction factors have been taken as unity. The upstream section is given the subscript 1 and the downstream section the subscript 2.   The total head at section 1 is equal to the sum of the total head at section 2 and all the head losses between the two sections.

**example 5.12**   In the preceding example, for $D = 16.6$ in., if the specific gravity is 0.85, $p_1 = 40$ psi, $z_1 = 200$ ft, and $z_2 = 50$ ft, determine the pressure at section 2.

In Eq. (5.10.15) $V_1 = V_2$; hence

$$\frac{40}{0.85 \times 0.433} + 200 = \frac{p_2}{0.85 \times 0.433} + 50 + 75$$

and

$$p_2 = 67.6 \text{ psi}$$

*digital computer solution of simple pipe problems*

In solving simple pipe problems by computer, the Colebrook equation (5.10.7) would be used in place of the Moody diagram, which is its graphical representation.   Wood[1] has developed an empirical, explicit, form of the Colebrook equation which closely approximates it for values of **R** $> 10,000$ and $1 \times 10^{-5} < \epsilon/D < 0.04$.   It is (for $k = \epsilon/D$)

$$f = a + b\mathbf{R}^{-c}$$
$$a = 0.094k^{0.225} + 0.53k$$
$$b = 88k^{0.44}$$
$$c = 1.62k^{0.134}$$

The first type, for solution of head loss (HEAD), is direct, as given in Fig. 5.33.   In the programs EPS = $\epsilon$, MU = $\mu$, RHO = $\rho$.   The second type, for solution for discharge, starts with an assumption for $f$, Fig. 5.34.   The value of F (F1) is improved until the criterion (F does not change by 0.0005

[1] Don J. Wood, An Explicit Friction Factor Relationship, *Civil Eng.*, pp. 60, 61, December, 1966.

```
C      SOLUTION OF SIMPLE PIPE PROBLEM TO FIND HEAD LOSS.  DATA GIVEN IN
C      CONSISTENT UNITS.
       REAL K,MU,L
     2 FORMAT('0      EPS=',F8.6,3H D=,F7.4,3H Q=,F7.3,3H L=,F9.2,4H MU=,
      2F9.7,5H RHO=,F7.4,3H G=,F7.3)
     3 FORMAT('0      HEAD=',F10.3,3H R=,F11.1,7H EPS/D=,F8.6,3H F=,F7.4)
       NAMELIST/DATA/EPS,D,Q,L,MU,RHO,G
     1 READ(5,DATA,END=99)
       WRITE(6,2) EPS,D,Q,L,MU,RHO,G
       V=Q/(.7854*D*D)
       R=V*D*RHO/MU
       K=EPS/D
       A=.094*K**.225+.53*K
       B=88.*K**.44
       C=1.62*K**.134
       F=A+B/R**C
       HEAD=F*L*V*V/(2.*G*D)
       WRITE(6,3) HEAD,R,K,F
       GO TO 1
    99 CALL SYSTEM
       END
```

```
EPS=0.000850 D= 1.3330 Q=  6.620 L= 12346.00 MU=0.0000200 RHO= 1.9350 G= 32.200

HEAD=     62.752 R=    611770.2 EPS/D=0.000638 F= 0.0194

EPS=0.005000 D= 2.0000 Q= 12.300 L=  1600.00 MU=0.0013000 RHO= 1.5900 G= 32.200

HEAD=      6.449 R=      9577.2 EPS/D=0.002500 F= 0.0339
```

**Fig. 5.33**  Computer program, data, and results for determination of head loss in a single pipe.

```
C      SOLUTION OF SIMPLE PIPE PROBLEM TO FIND DISCHARGE.
C      DATA IN CONSISTENT UNITS
       REAL K,MU,L
     1 FORMAT('0 ANSWER DOES NOT CONVERGE')
     2 FORMAT('0      EPS=',F8.6,3H D=,F7.4,6H HEAD=,F10.3,3H L=,F9.2,4H M
      2U=,F9.7,5H RHO=,F7.4,5H G=,F7.3,3H F=,F7.4)
     3 FORMAT('0      Q=',F7.3,3H V=,F7.3,3H F=,F7.4,3H R=,F11.1)
       NAMELIST/DATA/EPS,D,HEAD,L,MU,RHO,G,F
     5 READ(5,DATA,END=99)
       WRITE(6,2) EPS,D,HEAD,L,MU,RHO,G,F
       I=0
       K=EPS/D
       A=.094*K**.225+.53*K
       B=88.*K**.44
       C=1.62*K**.134
     6 V=SQRT(2.*G*D*HEAD/(F*L))
       R=V*D*RHO/MU
       F1=A+B/R**C
       IF(ABS(F1-F).LT..0005) GO TO 7
       I=I+1
       IF(I.EQ.8) GO TO 8
       F=F1
       GO TO 6
     7 Q=.7854*D*D*V
       WRITE(6,3) Q,V,F,R
       GO TO 5
     8 WRITE(6,1)
       GO TO 5
    99 CALL SYSTEM
       END
```

```
EPS=0.000500 D= 3.3300 HEAD=   18.000 L=  1650.00 MU=0.0000133 RHO= 1.9200 G= 32.200 F= 0.0200

Q=113.090 V= 12.985 F= 0.0139 R=  6242213.0

EPS=0.006000 D=12.0000 HEAD=   12.000 L=  6850.00 MU=0.0000200 RHO= 1.9350 G= 32.200 F= 0.0200

Q=994.206 V=  8.791 F= 0.0175 R= 10205996.0
```

**Fig. 5.34**  Computer program, data, and results for determination of discharge in a single pipe.

```
C     SOLUTION OF SIMPLE PIPE PROBLEM FOR DIAMETER.  DATA IN CONSISTENT
C     UNITS.
      REAL K,MU,L
    1 FORMAT('0   ANSWER DOES NOT CONVERGE')
    2 FORMAT('0       EPS=',F8.6,6H HEAD=,F10.3,3H Q=,F7.3,3H L=,F9.2,4H M
     2U=,F9.7,5H RHO=,F7.4,3H G=,F7.3,3H F=,F7.4)
    3 FORMAT('0       D=',F7.4,3H F=,F7.4,3H R=,F11.1)
      NAMELIST/DATA/EPS,HEAD,Q,L,MU,RHO,G,F
    5 READ(5,DATA,END=99)
      WRITE(6,2) EPS,HEAD,Q,L,MU,RHO,G,F
      I=0
    6 D=(F*L*Q*Q/(2.*G*HEAD*.7854**2))**.2
      K=EPS/D
      V=Q/(.7854*D*D)
      R=V*D*RHO/MU
      A=.094*K**.225+.53*K
      B=88.*K**.44
      C=1.62*K**.134
      F1=A+B/R**C
      IF(ABS(F1-F).LT..0005) GO TO 7
      I=I+1
      IF(I.EQ.8) GO TO 8
      F=F1
      GO TO 6
    7 WRITE(6,3) D,F,R
      GO TO 5
    8 WRITE(6,1)
      GO TO 5
   99 CALL SYSTEM
      END
```

EPS=0.000850 HEAD=   23.000 Q=  7.500 L=  3200.00 MU=0.0004000 RHO= 1.6900 G= 32.200 F= 0.0200

D= 1.3758 F= 0.0250 R=    29324.4

EPS=0.005000 HEAD=   23.000 Q=  7.500 L=  3200.00 MU=0.0004000 RHO= 1.6900 G= 32.200 F= 0.0200

D= 1.4412 F= 0.0316 R=    27993.6

**Fig. 5.35** Computer program, data, and results for determination of diameter in a single pipe.

in an iteration) is satisfied.   The third type, for determination of diameter, also starts with an assumed value of F, Fig. 5.35.   If the criterion is not met in eight iterations, the program moves to the next set of data.   The programs may be modified to include minor losses, which are discussed in the remaining portion of this section.

*minor losses*

Those losses which occur in pipelines due to bends, elbows, joints, valves, etc., are called *minor losses*.   This is a misnomer, because in many situations they are more important than the losses due to pipe friction considered in the preceding section, but it is the conventional name.   In almost all cases the minor loss is determined by experiment.   However, one important exception is the head loss due to a sudden expansion in a pipeline (Sec. 3.11).

Equation (3.11.22) may also be written

$$h_e = K \frac{V_1^2}{2g} = \left[ 1 - \left( \frac{D_1}{D_2} \right)^2 \right]^2 \frac{V_1^2}{2g} \qquad (5.10.16)$$

in which

$$K = \left[ 1 - \left( \frac{D_1}{D_2} \right)^2 \right]^2 \qquad (5.10.17)$$

From Eq. (5.10.16) it is obvious that the head loss varies as the square of the velocity. This is substantially true for all minor losses in turbulent flow. A convenient method of expressing the minor losses in flow is by means of the coefficient $K$, usually determined by experiment.

If the sudden expansion is from a pipe to a reservoir, $D_1/D_2 = 0$ and the loss becomes $V_1^2/2g$, that is, the complete kinetic energy in the flow is converted into thermal energy.

The head loss $h_c$ due to a sudden contraction in the pipe cross section, illustrated in Fig. 5.36, is subject to the same analysis as the sudden expansion, provided that the amount of contraction of the jet is known. The process of converting pressure head into velocity head is very efficient; hence, the head loss from section 1 to the *vena contracta*[1] is small compared with the loss from section 0 to section 2, where velocity head is being reconverted into pressure head. By applying Eq. (3.11.22) to this expansion the head loss is computed to be

$$h_c = \frac{(V_0 - V_2)^2}{2g}$$

With the continuity equation $V_0 C_c A_2 = V_2 A_2$, in which $C_c$ is the contraction coefficient (i.e., the area of jet at section 0 divided by the area of section 0), the head loss is computed to be

$$h_c = \left( \frac{1}{C_c} - 1 \right)^2 \frac{V_2^2}{2g} \qquad (5.10.18)$$

[1] The *vena contracta* is the section of greatest contraction of the jet.

**Fig. 5.36** Sudden contraction in a pipeline.

The contraction coefficient $C_c$ for water, determined by Weisbach,[1] is presented in the tabulation.

| $A_2/A_1$ | 0.1 | 0.2 | 0.3 | 0.4 | 0.5 | 0.6 | 0.7 | 0.8 | 0.9 | 1.0 |
|-----------|-----|-----|-----|-----|-----|-----|-----|-----|-----|-----|
| $C_c$ | | 0.624 | 0.632 | 0.643 | 0.659 | 0.681 | 0.712 | 0.755 | 0.813 | 0.892 | 1.00 |

The head loss at the entrance to a pipeline from a reservoir is usually taken as $0.5V^2/2g$, if the opening is square-edged. For well-rounded entrances, the loss is between $0.01V^2/2g$ and $0.05V^2/2g$ and may usually be neglected. For re-entrant openings, as with the pipe extending into the reservoir beyond the wall, the loss is taken as $1.0V^2/2g$, for thin pipe walls.

The head loss due to gradual expansions has been investigated experimentally by Gibson,[2] whose results are given in Fig. 5.37.

A summary of representative head loss coefficients $K$ for typical fittings, published by the Crane Company,[3] is given in Table 5.3.

[1] Julius Weisbach, "Die Experimental-Hydraulik," p. 133, J. S. Englehardt, Freiburg, 1855.
[2] A. H. Gibson, The Conversion of Kinetic to Pressure Energy in the Flow of Water through Passages Having Divergent Boundaries, *Engineering*, vol. 93, p. 205, 1912.
[3] Crane Company, Flow of Fluids, *Tech. Paper* 409, May, 1942.

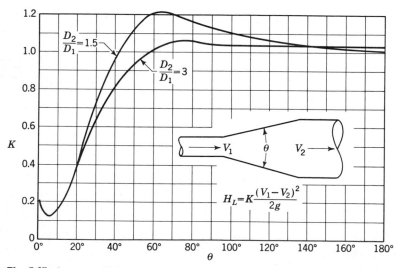

**Fig. 5.37** Loss coefficients for conical expansions.

**Table 5.3   Head loss coefficients $K$
for various fittings**

| Fitting | $K$ |
| --- | --- |
| Globe valve (fully open) | 10.0 |
| Angle valve (fully open) | 5.0 |
| Swing check valve (fully open) | 2.5 |
| Gate valve (fully open) | 0.19 |
| Close return bend | 2.2 |
| Standard tee | 1.8 |
| Standard elbow | 0.9 |
| Medium sweep elbow | 0.75 |
| Long sweep elbow | 0.60 |

Minor losses may be expressed in terms of the equivalent length $L_e$ of pipe that has the same head loss in foot-pounds per pound for the same discharge; thus

$$f \frac{L_e}{D} \frac{V^2}{2g} = K \frac{V^2}{2g}$$

in which $K$ may refer to one minor head loss or to the sum of several losses. After solving for $L_e$,

$$L_e - \frac{KD}{f} \tag{5.10.19}$$

For example, if the minor losses in a 12-in. pipeline add to $K = 20$ and if $f = 0.020$ for the line, then to the actual length of line may be added $20 \times 1/0.020 = 1000$ ft, and this additional or equivalent length causes the same resistance to flow as the minor losses.

**example 5.13**   Find the discharge through the pipeline in Fig. 5.38 for $H = 30$ ft, and determine the head loss $H$ for $Q = 2.0$ cfs.

**Fig. 5.38**  Pipeline with minor losses.

The energy equation applied to points 1 and 2, including all the losses, may be written

$$H + 0 + 0 = \frac{V^2}{2g} + 0 + 0 + \frac{1}{2}\frac{V^2}{2g} + f\frac{340}{\frac{1}{2}}\frac{V^2}{2g} + 2 \times 0.9\frac{V^2}{2g} + 10\frac{V^2}{2g}$$

After simplifying,

$$H = \frac{V^2}{2g}(13.3 + 680f)$$

When the head is given, this problem is solved as the second type of simple pipe problem.   If $f = 0.02$, then

$$30 = \frac{V^2}{2g}(13.3 + 680 \times 0.02)$$

and $V = 8.46$ ft/sec.   $\epsilon/D = 0.00085/0.5 = 0.0017$;   $VD'' = 8.46 \times 6 = 50.7$.   From Fig. 5.32, $f = 0.023$.   By solving again for the velocity, $V = 8.16$ ft/sec, $VD'' = 8.16 \times 6 = 49$, and $f$ does not change.   The discharge is

$$Q = 8.16\frac{\pi}{16} = 1.60 \text{ cfs}$$

For the second part, with $Q$ known, the solution is straightforward,

$$V = \frac{2}{\pi} \times 16 = 10.18 \text{ ft/sec} \qquad VD'' = 61.1 \qquad f = 0.023$$

and

$$H = \frac{(10.18)^2}{64.4}(13.3 + 680 \times 0.023) = 46.5 \text{ ft}$$

With equivalent lengths [Eq. (5.10.19)], the value of $f$ is approximated, say $f = 0.020$.   The sum of minor losses is $K = 13.3$, in which the kinetic energy at 2 is included as a minor loss,

$$L_e = \frac{13.3 \times 0.50}{0.02} = 332 \text{ ft}$$

Hence, the total length of pipe is $332 + 340 = 672$ ft.   The first part of the problem is solved by this method,

$$30 = f\frac{L + L_e}{D}\frac{V^2}{2g} = f\frac{672}{0.50}\frac{V^2}{2g}$$

If $f = 0.02$, $V = 8.47$, $VD'' = 50.8$, $f = 0.023$; then $V = 7.9$, $VD'' = 47.4$, $f = 0.023$, $Q = 1.55$ cfs.   Normally it is not necessary to use the new value of $f$ in Eq. (5.10.19).

Minor losses may be neglected in those situations where they compose only 5 per cent or less of the head losses due to pipe friction.   The friction factor, at best, is subject to about 5 per cent error, and it is meaningless to select values to more than two significant figures.   In general, minor losses may be neglected when, on the average, there is a length of 1000 diameters between each minor loss.

Compressible flow in pipes is treated in Chap. 6.   Complex pipe-flow situations are treated in Chap. 10.

## 5.11  lubrication mechanics

The effect of viscosity on flow and its effects on head losses have been examined in the preceding sections of this chapter.   A laminar-flow case of great practical importance is the hydrodynamic theory of lubrication. Simple aspects of this theory are developed in this section.

Large forces are developed in small clearances when the surfaces are slightly inclined and one is in motion so that fluid is "wedged" into the decreasing space.   The slipper bearing, which operates on this principle, is illustrated In Fig. 5.39.   The journal bearing (Fig. 5.40) develops its force by the same action, except that the surfaces are curved.

The laminar-flow equations may be used to develop the theory of lubrication.   The assumption is made that there is no flow out of the ends of the bearing, normal to the plane of Fig. 5.39.   Starting with Eq. (5.1.4), which relates pressure drop and shear stress, the equation for the force $P$ that the bearing will support is worked out, and the drag on the bearing is computed.

**Fig. 5.39**  Sliding bearing.

**Fig. 5.40** Journal bearing.

Substituting Newton's law of viscosity into Eq. (5.1.4) produces

$$\frac{dp}{dx} = \mu \frac{d^2u}{dy^2} \tag{5.11.1}$$

Since the inclination of the upper portion of the bearing (Fig. 5.39) is very slight, it may be assumed that the velocity distribution is the same as if the plates were parallel and that $p$ is independent of $y$. Integrating Eq. (5.11.1) twice with respect to $y$, with $dp/dx$ constant, produces

$$\frac{dp}{dx} \int dy = \mu \int \frac{d^2u}{dy_z} \, dy + A$$

or

$$\frac{dp}{dx} y = \mu \frac{du}{dy} + A$$

and the second time

$$\frac{dp}{dx} \int y \, dy = \mu \int \frac{du}{dy} \, dy + A \int dy + B$$

or

$$\frac{dp}{dx} \frac{y^2}{2} = \mu u + Ay + B$$

The constants of integration $A$, $B$ are determined from the conditions $u = 0$, $y = b$; $u = U$, $y = 0$. Substituting in turn produces

$$\frac{dp}{dx} \frac{b^2}{2} = Ab + B \qquad \mu U + B = 0$$

Eliminating $A$ and $B$ and solving for $u$ results in

$$u = \frac{y}{2\mu}\frac{dp}{dx}(y - b) + U\left(1 - \frac{y}{b}\right) \tag{5.11.2}$$

The discharge $Q$ must be the same at each cross section.   By integrating over a typical section, again with $dp/dx$ constant,

$$Q = \int_0^b u\,dy = \frac{Ub}{2} - \frac{b^3}{12\mu}\frac{dp}{dx} \tag{5.11.3}$$

Now, since $Q$ cannot vary with $x$, $b$ may be expressed in terms of $x$, $b = b_1 - \alpha x$, in which $\alpha = (b_1 - b_2)/L$, and the equation is integrated with respect to $x$ to determine the pressure distribution.   Solving Eq. (5.11.3) for $dp/dx$ produces

$$\frac{dp}{dx} = \frac{6\mu U}{(b_1 - \alpha x)^2} - \frac{12\mu Q}{(b_1 - \alpha x)^3} \tag{5.11.4}$$

By integrating,

$$\int \frac{dp}{dx}\,dx = 6\mu U \int \frac{dx}{(b_1 - \alpha x)^2} - 12\mu Q \int \frac{dx}{(b_1 - \alpha x)^3} + C$$

or

$$p = \frac{6\mu U}{\alpha(b_1 - \alpha x)} - \frac{6\mu Q}{\alpha(b_1 - \alpha x)^2} + C$$

In this equation $Q$ and $C$ are unknowns.   Since the pressure must be the same, say zero, at the ends of the bearing, namely, $p = 0$, $x = 0$; $p = 0$, $x = L$, the constants may be determined,

$$Q = \frac{Ub_1 b_2}{b_1 + b_2} \qquad C = -\frac{6\mu U}{\alpha(b_1 + b_2)}$$

With these values inserted, the equation for pressure distribution becomes

$$p = \frac{6\mu U x(b - b_2)}{b^2(b_1 + b_2)} \tag{5.11.5}$$

This equation shows that $p$ is positive between $x = 0$ and $x = L$ if $b > b_2$. It is plotted in Fig. 5.39 to show the distribution of pressure throughout the bearing.   With this one-dimensional method of analysis the very slight change in pressure along a vertical line $x = $ const is neglected.

The total force $P$ that the bearing will sustain, per unit width, is

$$P = \int_0^L p \, dx = \frac{6\mu U}{b_1 + b_2} \int_0^L \frac{x(b - b_2) \, dx}{b^2}$$

After substituting the value of $b$ in terms of $x$ and performing the integration,

$$P = \frac{6\mu U L^2}{(b_1 - b_2)^2} \left( \ln \frac{b_1}{b_2} - 2 \frac{b_1 - b_2}{b_1 + b_2} \right) \tag{5.11.6}$$

The drag force $D$ required to move the lower surface at speed $U$ is expressed by

$$D = \int_0^L \tau \Big|_{y=0} dx = - \int_0^L \mu \frac{du}{dy} \Big|_{y=0} dx$$

By evaluating $du/dy$ from Eq. (5.11.2), for $y = 0$,

$$\frac{du}{dy} \Big|_{y=0} = -\frac{b}{2\mu} \frac{dp}{dx} - \frac{U}{b}$$

With this value in the integral, along with the value of $dp/dx$ from Eq. (5.11.4),

$$D = \frac{2\mu U L}{b_1 - b_2} \left( 2 \ln \frac{b_1}{b_2} - 3 \frac{b_1 - b_2}{b_1 + b_2} \right) \tag{5.11.7}$$

The maximum load $P$ is computed with Eq. (5.11.6) when $b_1 = 2.2b_2$. With this ratio,

$$P = 0.16 \frac{\mu U L^2}{b_2{}^2} \qquad D = 0.75 \frac{\mu U L}{b_2} \tag{5.11.8}$$

The ratio of load to drag for optimum load is

$$\frac{P}{D} = 0.21 \frac{L}{b_2} \tag{5.11.9}$$

which can be very large since $b_2$ can be very small.

**example 5.14**   A vertical turbine shaft carries a load of 80,000 lb on a thrust bearing consisting of 16 flat rocker plates, 3 by 9 in., arranged with their long dimensions radial from the shaft and with their centers on a circle of radius 1.5 ft. The shaft turns at 120 rpm; $\mu = 0.002$ lb-sec/ft$^2$. If the plates take the angle for maximum load, neglecting effects of curvature of path and radial lubricant flow, find ($a$) the clearance between rocker plate and fixed plate; ($b$) the torque loss due to the bearing.

($a$)   Since the motion is considered straight-line,

$$U = 1.5 \times \frac{120}{60} 2\pi - 18.85 \text{ ft/sec}$$

$$L = 0.25 \text{ ft}$$

The load is 5000 lb for each plate, which is $5000/0.75 = 6667$ lb for unit width.   By solving for the clearance $b_2$, from Eq. (5.11.8),

$$b_2 = \sqrt{\frac{0.16\mu U L^2}{P}} = 0.4 \times 0.25 \sqrt{\frac{0.002 \times 18.85}{6667}} = 2.38 \times 10^{-4}$$

$$= 0.0029 \text{ in.}$$

($b$)   The drag due to one rocker plate is, per foot of width,

$$D = 0.75 \frac{\mu U L}{b_2} = \frac{0.75 \times 0.002 \times 18.85 \times 0.25}{2.38 \times 10^{-4}} = 29.6 \text{ lb}$$

For a 9-in. plate, $D = 29.6 \times 0.75 = 22.2$ lb.   The torque loss due to the 16 rocker plates is

$$16 \times 22.2 \times 1.5 = 533 \text{ ft-lb}$$

Another form of lubrication, called *hydrostatic lubrication*,[1] has many important applications.   It involves the continuous high-pressure pumping of oil under a step bearing, as illustrated in Fig. 5.41.   The load may be lifted by the lubrication before rotation starts, which greatly reduces starting friction.

[1] For further information on hydrostatic lubrication see D. D. Fuller, Lubrication Mechanics, in "Handbook of Fluid Dynamics," ed. by V. L. Streeter, pp. **22**–21 to **22**–30, McGraw-Hill Book Company, New York, 1961.

**Fig. 5.41** Hydrostatic lubrication by high-pressure pumping of oil.

## problems

**5.1**  Determine the formulas for shear stress on each plate and for the velocity distribution for flow in Fig. 5.1 when an adverse pressure gradient exists such that $Q = 0$.

**5.2**  In Fig. 5.1, with $U$ positive as shown, find the expression for $d(p + \gamma h)/dl$ such that the shear is zero at the fixed plate.   What is the discharge for this case?

**5.3**  In Fig. 5.42a, $U = 2$ ft/sec.   Find the rate at which oil is carried into the pressure chamber by the piston and the shear force and total force $F$ acting.

**5.4**  Determine the force on the piston of Fig. 5.42a due to shear and the leakage from the pressure chamber for $U = 0$.

**5.5**  Find $F$ and $U$ in Fig. 5.42a such that no oil is lost through the clearance from the pressure chamber.

**5.6**  Derive an expression for the flow past a fixed cross section of Fig. 5.42b for laminar flow between the two moving plates.

**5.7**  In Fig. 5.42b, for $p_1 = p_2 = 10$ psi, $U = 2V = 8$ ft/sec, $a = 0.005$ ft, $\mu = 0.5$ poise, find the shear stress at each plate.

**5.8**  Compute the kinetic-energy and momentum correction factors for laminar flow between fixed parallel plates.

**5.9**  Determine the formula for angle $\theta$ for fixed parallel plates so that laminar flow at constant pressure takes place.

**5.10**   With a free body, as in Fig. 5.43, for uniform flow of a thin lamina of liquid down an inclined plane, show that the velocity distribution is

$$u = \frac{\gamma}{2\mu} (b^2 - s^2) \sin \theta$$

and that the discharge per unit width is

$$Q = \frac{\gamma}{3\mu} b^3 \sin \theta$$

(a)

(b)

**Fig. 5.42**

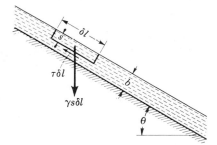

**Fig. 5.43**

**5.11**  Derive the velocity distribution of Prob. 5.10 by inserting into the appropriate equation prior to Eq. (5.1.2) the condition that the shear at the free surface must be zero.

**5.12**  In Fig. 5.44, $p_1 = 6$ psi, $p_2 = 8$ psi, $l = 4$ ft, $a = 0.006$ ft, $\theta = 30°$, $U = 3$ ft/sec, $\gamma = 50$ lb/ft³, and $\mu = 0.8$ poise.   Determine the tangential force per square foot exerted on the upper plate and its direction.

**5.13**  For $\theta = 90°$ in Fig. 5.44, what speed $U$ is required for no discharge? $\gamma = 55$ lb/ft³, $a = 0.01$ ft, $p_1 = p_2$, and $\mu = 0.004$ lb-sec/ft².

**5.14**  The belt conveyor (Fig. 5.45) is of sufficient length that the velocity on the free-liquid surface is zero.   By considering only the work done by the belt on the fluid in shear, how efficient is this device in transferring energy to the fluid?

**5.15**  What is the velocity distribution of the fluid on the belt and the volume rate of fluid being transported in Prob. 5.14?

**5.16**  What is the time rate of momentum and kinetic energy passing through a cross section that is normal to the flow if in Eq. (5.1.3) $Q = 0$?

**Fig. 5.44**

**Fig. 5.45**

**5.17**  A film of fluid 0.005 ft thick flows down a fixed vertical surface with a surface velocity of 2 ft/sec.   Determine the fluid viscosity.   $\gamma = 55$ lb/ft³.

**5.18**  Determine the momentum correction factor for laminar flow in a round tube.

**5.19**  Water at standard conditions is flowing laminarly in a tube of 0.05 in. diameter.   This tube expands to a diameter of 0.1 in., and the flow is again described by Eq. (5.2.6) some distance downstream of the expansion. Determine the force on the tube which results from the difference in the momentum flux in the two tubes.

**5.20**  At what distance $r$ from the center of a tube of radius $r_0$ does the average velocity occur in laminar flow?

**5.21**  Determine the maximum wall shear stress for laminar flow in a tube of diameter $D$ with fluid properties $\mu$ and $\rho$ given.

**5.22**  Show that laminar flow between parallel plates may be used in place of flow through an annulus for 1 per cent accuracy if the clearance is no more than 4 per cent of the inner radius.

**5.23**  What are the losses per pound per foot of tubing for flow of mercury at 100°F through 0.002 ft diameter at a Reynolds number of 1800?

**5.24**  Determine the shear stress at the wall of a $\frac{1}{16}$-in.-diameter tube when water at 80°F flows through it with a velocity of 1 ft/sec.

**5.25**  Determine the pressure drop per 100 ft of $\frac{1}{8}$-in. ID tubing for flow of liquid, $\mu = 60$ centipoises, sp gr $= 0.83$, at a Reynolds number of 100.

**5.26**  Glycerin at 80°F flows through a $\frac{3}{8}$-in.-diameter pipe with a pressure drop of 5 psi/ft.   Find the discharge and the Reynolds number.

**5.27**  Calculate the diameter of vertical pipe needed for flow of liquid at a Reynolds number of 1800 when the pressure remains constant.   $\nu = 1.5 \times 10^{-5}$ ft²/sec.

**5.28**  Calculate the discharge of the system in Fig. 5.46, neglecting all losses except through the pipe.

**Fig. 5.46**

**5.29**   In Fig. 5.47, $H = 30$ ft, $L = 60$ ft, $\theta = 30°$, $D = \frac{3}{8}$ in., $\gamma = 64$ lb/ft³, and $\mu = 0.001736$ lb-sec/ft². Find the head loss per unit length of pipe and the discharge in gallons per minute.

**5.30**   In Fig. 5.47 and Prob. 5.29, find $H$ if the velocity is 10 ft/sec.

**5.31**   Oil, sp gr 0.85, $\mu = 0.50$ poise, flows through an annulus $a = 0.60$ in., $b = 0.30$ in.   When the shear stress at the outer wall is 0.25 lb/ft², calculate ($a$) the pressure drop per foot for a horizontal system, ($b$) the discharge in gallons per hour, and ($c$) the axial force exerted on the inner tube per foot of length.

**5.32**   What is the Reynolds number of flow of 4500 gpm oil, sp gr 0.86, $\mu = 0.27$ poise, through an 18-in.-diameter pipe?

**5.33**   Calculate the flow of crude oil, sp gr 0.86, at 80°F in a $\frac{3}{8}$-in. diameter tube to yield a Reynolds number of 1200.

**5.34**   Determine the velocity of kerosene at 90°F in a 3-in. pipe to be dynamically similar to the flow of 6000 cfm air at 20 psia and 60°F through a 30-in. duct.

**Fig. 5.47**

**5.35** What is the Reynolds number for a sphere 0.004 ft in diameter falling through water at 80°F at 0.5 ft/sec?

**5.36** Show that the power input for laminar flow in a round tube is $Q\Delta p$ by integration of Eq. (5.1.7).

**5.37** By use of the one-seventh-power law of velocity distribution $u/u_{max} = (y/r_0)^{1/7}$, determine the mixing-length distribution $l/r_0$ in terms of $y/r_0$ from Eq. (5.4.4).

**5.38** A fluid is agitated so that the kinematic eddy viscosity increases linearly from $y = 0$ at the bottom of the tank to 2.0 ft$^2$/sec at $y = 2$ ft. For uniform particles with fall velocities of 1 ft/sec in still fluid, find the concentration at $y = 1$ if it is 200/ft$^3$ at $y = 2$.

**5.39** Plot a curve of $\epsilon/u_*r_0$ as a function of $y/r_0$ using Eq. (5.4.9) for velocity distribution in a pipe.

**5.40** Find the value of $y/r_0$ in a pipe where the velocity equals the average velocity for turbulent flow.

**5.41** Plot the velocity profiles for Prandtl's exponential velocity formula for values of $n$ of $\frac{1}{7}$, $\frac{1}{8}$, and $\frac{1}{9}$.

**5.42** Estimate the skin-friction drag on an airship 300 ft long, average diameter 60 ft, with velocity of 80 mph traveling through air at 13 psia and 80°F.

**5.43** The velocity distribution in a boundary layer is given by $u/U = 3(y/\delta) - 2(y/\delta)^2$. Show that the displacement thickness of the boundary layer is $\delta_1 = \delta/6$.

**5.44** Using the velocity distribution $u/U = \sin \pi y/2\delta$, determine the equation for growth of the laminar boundary layer and for shear stress along a smooth, flat plate in two-dimensional flow.

**5.45** Compare the drag coefficients that are obtained with the velocity distributions given in Probs. 5.43 and 5.44.

**5.46** Work out the equations for growth of the turbulent boundary layer, based on the exponential law $u/U = (y/\delta)^{1/9}$ and $f = 0.185/\mathbf{R}^{1/5}$. ($\tau_0 = \rho f V^2/8$.)

**5.47** Air at 70°F, 14.7 psia, flows along a smooth plate with a velocity of 100 mph. How long does the plate have to be to obtain a boundary-layer thickness of $\frac{1}{4}$ in.?

**5.48** The walls of a wind tunnel are sometimes made divergent to offset the effect of the boundary layer in reducing the portion of the cross section in which the flow is of constant speed. At what angle must plane walls be set so that the displacement thickness does not encroach upon the tunnel's constant-speed cross section at distances greater than 0.8 ft from the leading edge of the wall? Use the data of Prob. 5.47.

**5.49** What is the terminal velocity of a 2-in.-diameter metal ball, sp gr 3.5, dropped in oil, sp gr 0.80, $\mu = 1$ poise? What would be the terminal velocity for the same size ball but with a 7.0 sp gr? How do these results agree with the experiments attributed to Galileo at the Leaning Tower of Pisa?

**5.50** At what speed must a 5-in. sphere travel through water at 50°F to have a drag of 1 lb?

**5.51** A spherical balloon contains helium and ascends through air at 14 psia, 40°F. Balloon and pay load weigh 300 lb. What diameter permits ascension at 10 ft/sec? $C_D = 0.21$. If the balloon is tethered to the ground in a 60-mph wind, what is the angle of inclination of the retaining cable?

**5.52** How many 100-ft-diameter parachutes ($C_D = 1.2$) should be used to drop a bulldozer weighing 10,000 lb at a terminal speed of 32 ft/sec through air at 14.5 psia, 70°F?

**5.53** An object weighing 300 lb is attached to a circular disk and dropped from a plane. What diameter should the disk be to have the object strike the ground at 72 ft/sec? The disk is attached so that it is normal to direction of motion. $p = 14.7$ psia; $t = 70°F$.

**5.54** A circular disk 12 ft in diameter is held normal to a 60-mph air stream ($\rho = 0.0024$ slug/ft³). What force is required to hold it at rest?

**5.55** Discuss the origin of the drag on a disk when its plane is parallel to the flow and when it is normal to it.

**5.56** A semitubular cylinder of 6-in. radius with concave side upstream is submerged in water flowing 2 ft/sec. Calculate the drag for a cylinder 24 ft long.

**5.57** A projectile of the form of ($a$), Fig. 5.25, is 108 mm in diameter and travels at 3000 ft/sec through air. $\rho = 0.002$ slug/ft³; $c = 1000$ ft/sec. What is its drag?

**5.58** On the basis of the discussion of the Mach angle explain why a supersonic airplane is often seen before it is heard.

**5.59** If an airplane 1 mile above the earth passes over an observer and the observer does not hear the plane until it has traveled 1.6 miles farther, what is its speed? Sound velocity is 1080 ft/sec. What is its Mach angle?

**5.60** Give some reason for the discontinuity in the curves of Fig. 5.23 at the angle of attack of 22°.

**5.61** What is the ratio of lift to drag for the airfoil section of Fig. 5.23 for an angle of attack of 2°?

**5.62** Determine the settling velocity of small metal spheres, sp gr 4.5, 0.004 in. diameter, in crude oil at 80°F.

**5.63**  A spherical dust particle at an altitude of 50 miles is radioactive as a result of an atomic explosion.   Determine the time it will take to settle to earth if it falls in accordance with Stokes' law.   Its size and sp gr are 25 microns and 2.5.   Neglect wind effects.   1 micron = $10^{-6}$ meter.   Use isothermal atmosphere at 0°F.

**5.64**  How large a spherical particle of dust, sp gr 2.5, will settle in atmospheric air at 70°F in obedience to Stokes' law?   What is the settling velocity?

**5.65**  The Chézy coefficient is 127 for flow in a rectangular channel 6 ft wide, 2 ft deep, with bottom slope of 0.0016.   What is the discharge?

**5.66**  A rectangular channel 4 ft wide, Chézy $C = 60$, $S = 0.0064$, carries 40 cfs.   Determine the velocity.

**5.67**  What is the value of the Manning roughness factor $n$ in Prob. 5.66?

**5.68**  A rectangular, brick-lined channel 6 ft wide and 5 ft deep carries 210 cfs.   What slope is required for the channel?

**5.69**  The channel cross section shown in Fig. 5.48 is made of unplaned wood and has a slope of 0.0009.   What is the discharge?

**5.70**  A trapezoidal, unfinished concrete channel carries water at a depth of 6 ft.   Its bottom width is 8 ft and side slope 1 horizontal to $1\frac{1}{2}$ vertical.   For a bottom slope of 0.004 what is the discharge?

**5.71**  A trapezoidal channel with bottom slope 0.003, bottom width of 4 ft, and side slopes 2 horizontal to 1 vertical carries 220 cfs at a depth of 4 ft.   What is the Manning roughness factor?

**5.72**  A trapezoidal earth canal, bottom width 8 ft and side slope 2 on 1 (2 horizontal to 1 vertical), is to be constructed to carry 280 cfs.   The best velocity for nonscouring is 2.8 ft/sec with this material.   What is the bottom slope required?

**5.73**  What diameter is required of a semicircular corrugated-metal channel to carry 50 cfs when its slope is 0.01?

**5.74**  A semicircular corrugated-metal channel 10 ft in diameter has a bottom slope of 0.004.   What is its capacity when flowing full?

**Fig. 5.48**

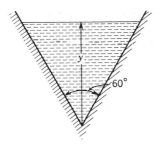

**Fig. 5.49**

**5.75**   Calculate the depth of flow of 2000 cfs in a gravel trapezoidal channel with bottom width of 12 ft, side slopes of 3 horizontal to 1 vertical, and bottom slope of 0.001.

**5.76**   What is the velocity of flow of 260 cfs in a rectangular channel 12 ft wide?   $S = 0.0049$; $n = 0.016$.

**5.77**   A trapezoidal channel, brick-lined, is to be constructed to carry 1200 cfs 5 miles with a head loss of 12 ft.   The bottom width is 16 ft, the side slopes 1 on 1.   What is the velocity?

**5.78**   How does the discharge vary with depth in Fig. 5.49?

**5.79**   How does the velocity vary with depth in Fig. 5.49?

**5.80**   Determine the depth of flow in Fig. 5.49 for discharge of 12 cfs.   It is made of riveted steel with bottom slope 0.02.

**5.81**   Determine the depth $y$ (Fig. 5.50) for maximum velocity for given $n$ and $S$.

**5.82**   Determine the depth $y$ (Fig. 5.50) for maximum discharge for given $n$ and $S$.

**5.83**   A test on a 12-in.-diameter pipe with water showed a gage difference of 13 in. on a mercury-water manometer connected to two piezometer rings 400 ft apart.   The flow was 8.24 cfs.   What is the friction factor?

**Fig. 5.50**

**5.84**  By using the Blasius equation for determination of friction factor, determine the horsepower per mile required to pump 3.0 cfs liquid, $\nu = 3.3 \times 10^{-4}$ ft$^2$/sec, $\gamma = 55$ lb/ft$^3$, through an 18-in. pipeline.

**5.85**  Determine the head loss per 1000 ft required to maintain a velocity of 14 ft/sec in a 0.50-in.-diameter pipe.  $\nu = 4 \times 10^{-4}$ ft$^2$/sec.

**5.86**  Fluid flows through a $\frac{1}{2}$-in.-diameter tube at a Reynolds number of 1800.  The head loss is 30 ft in 100 ft of tubing.  Calculate the discharge in gallons per minute.

**5.87**  What size galvanized-iron pipe is needed to be "hydraulically smooth" at $\mathbf{R} = 3.5 \times 10^5$?  (A pipe is said to be hydraulically smooth when it has the same losses as a smoother pipe under the same conditions.)

**5.88**  Above what Reynolds number is the flow through a 10-ft-diameter riveted steel pipe, $\epsilon = 0.01$, independent of the viscosity of the fluid?

**5.89**  Determine the absolute roughness of a 1-ft-diameter pipe that has a friction factor $f = 0.03$ for $\mathbf{R} = 1,000,000$.

**5.90**  What diameter clean galvanized-iron pipe has the same friction factor for $\mathbf{R} = 100,000$ as a 12-in.-diameter cast-iron pipe?

**5.91**  Under what conditions do the losses in a pipe vary as some power of the velocity greater than the second?

**5.92**  Why does the friction factor increase as the velocity decreases in laminar flow in a pipe?

**5.93**  Look up the friction factor for atmospheric air at 60°F traveling 60 ft/sec through a 3-ft-diameter galvanized pipe.

**5.94**  Water at 70°F is to be pumped through 1200 ft of 8-in.-diameter wrought-iron pipe at the rate of 800 gpm.  Compute the head loss and horsepower required.

**5.95**  16,000 ft$^3$/min atmospheric air at 90° F is conveyed 1000 ft through a 4-ft-diameter wrought-iron pipe.  What is the head loss in inches of water?

**5.96**  What horsepower motor for a fan must be purchased to circulate standard air in a wind tunnel at 300 mph?  The tunnel is a closed loop, 200 ft long, and it can be assumed to have a constant circular cross section with a 6-ft diameter.  Assume smooth pipe.

**5.97**  Must there be a provision made to cool the air at some section of the tunnel described in Prob. 5.96?  To what extent?

**5.98**  2.0 cfs oil, $\mu = 0.16$ poise, $\gamma = 54$ lb/ft$^3$, is pumped through a 12-in. pipeline of cast iron.  If each pump produces 80 psi, how far apart may they be placed?

**5.99**  A 2.5-in.-diameter smooth pipe 500 ft long conveys 150 gpm water at 80°F from a water main, $p = 100$ psi, to the top of a building 85 ft above the main.  What pressure can be maintained at the top of the building?

240 ft

260 ft

2-in.-diam
wrought iron

**Fig. 5.51**

**5.100**  For water at 150°F calculate the discharge for the pipe of Fig. 5.51.

**5.101**  In Fig. 5.51, how much power would be required to pump 160 gpm from a reservoir at the bottom of the pipe to the reservoir shown?

**5.102**  A $\frac{1}{2}$-in.-diameter commercial steel pipe 40 ft long is used to drain an oil tank.  Determine the discharge when the oil level in the tank is 6 ft above the exit end of the pipe.  $\mu = 0.10$ poise; $\gamma = 50$ lb/ft$^3$.

**5.103**  Two liquid reservoirs are connected by 200 ft of 2-in.-diameter smooth tubing.  What is the flow rate when the difference in elevation is 50 ft?  $\nu - 0.001$ ft$^2$/sec.

**5.104**  For a head loss of 3 in. water in a length of 600 ft for flow of atmospheric air at 60°F through a 4-ft-diameter duct, $\epsilon = 0.003$ ft, calculate the flow in a cubic feet per minute.

**5.105**  A gas of molecular weight 37 flows through a 24-in.-diameter galvanized duct at 90 psia and 100°F.  The head loss per 100 ft of duct is 2 in. water.  What is the flow in slugs per hour?  $\mu = 1.94 \times 10^{-4}$ poise.

**5.106**  What is the horsepower per mile required for a 70-per-cent-efficient blower to maintain the flow of Prob. 5.105?

**5.107**  100 lb$_m$/min air is required to ventilate a mine.  It is admitted through 2000 ft of 12-in.-diameter galvanized pipe.  Neglecting minor losses, what head in inches of water does a blower have to produce to furnish this flow?  $p = 14$ psia; $t = 90$°F.

**5.108**  In Fig. 5.47 $H = 60$ ft, $L = 500$ ft, $D = 2$ in., $\gamma = 55$ lb/ft$^3$, $\mu = 0.04$ poise, $\epsilon = 0.003$ ft.  Find the pounds per second flowing.

**5.109**  In a process 10,000 lb/hr of distilled water at 70°F is conducted through a smooth tube between two reservoirs having a distance between them of 30 ft and a difference in elevation of 4 ft.  What size tubing is needed?

**5.110**   What size of new cast-iron pipe is needed to transport 10 cfs water at 80°F 1 mile with head loss of 6 ft?

**5.111**   Two types of steel plate, having surface roughnesses of $\epsilon_1 = 0.0003$ ft and $\epsilon_2 = 0.0001$ ft, have a cost differential of 10 per cent more for the smoother plate.   With an allowable stress in each of 10,000 psi, which plate should be selected to convey 100 cfs water at 200 psi with a head loss of 6 ft/mile?   $D_1 = 4.758$ ft.   $D_2 = 4.842$ ft.

**5.112**   An old pipe 72 in. in diameter has a roughness of $\epsilon = 0.1$.   A $\frac{1}{2}$-in.-thick lining would reduce the roughness to $\epsilon = 0.0004$.   How much in pumping costs would be saved per year per 1000 ft of pipe for water at 70°F with velocity of 8 ft/sec?   The pumps and motors are 80 per cent efficient and power costs 1 cent per kilowatthour.   $15,000

**5.113**   Calculate the diameter of new wood-stave pipe in excellent condition needed to convey 300 cfs water at 60°F with a head loss of 1 ft per 1000 ft of pipe.

**5.114**   Two oil reservoirs with difference in elevation of 15 ft are connected by 1000 ft of commercial steel pipe.   What size must the pipe be to convey 1000 gpm?   $\mu = 0.001$ slug/ft-sec; $\gamma = 55$ lb/ft³.

**5.115**   200 cfs air, $p = 16$ psia, $t = 70°F$, is to be delivered to a mine with a head loss of 3 in. water per 1000 ft.   What size galvanized pipe is needed?

**5.116**   Compute the losses in foot-pounds per pound due to flow of 900 cfm air, $p = 14.7$ psia, $t = 70°F$, through a sudden expansion from 12- to 36-in. pipe.   How much head would be saved by using a 10° conical diffuser?

**5.117**   Calculate the value of $H$ in Fig. 5.52 for 6 cfs water at 60°F through commercial steel pipe.   Include minor losses.

**5.118**   In Prob. 5.28 what would be the discharge if a globe valve were inserted into the line?   Assume a smooth pipe and a well-rounded inlet.

**5.119**   In Fig. 5.52 for $H = 10$ ft, calculate the discharge of oil, $\gamma = 55$ lb/ft³, $\mu = 0.07$ poise, through smooth pipe.   Include minor losses.

**5.120**   If a valve is placed in the line in Prob. 5.119 and adjusted to reduce the discharge by one-half, what is $K$ for the valve and what is its equivalent length of pipe at this setting?

**Fig. 5.52**

**Fig. 5.53**

**5.121** A water line connecting two reservoirs at 70°F has 5000 ft of 24-in.-diameter steel pipe, three standard elbows, a globe valve, and a re-entrant pipe entrance. What is the difference in reservoir elevations for 20 cfs?

**5.122** Determine the discharge in Prob. 5.121 if the difference in elevation is 40 ft.

**5.123** Compute the losses in horsepower due to flow of 100 cfs water through a sudden contraction from 6- to 4-ft-diameter pipe.

**5.124** What is the equivalent length of 2-in.-diameter pipe, $f = 0.022$, for (a) a re-entrant pipe entrance, (b) a sudden expansion from 2 to 4 in. diameter, (c) a globe valve and a standard tee?

**5.125** Find $H$ in Fig. 5.53 for 200-gpm oil flow, $\mu = 0.1$ poise, $\gamma = 60$ lb/ft³, for the angle valve wide open.

**5.126** Find $K$ for the angle valve in Prob. 5.125 for flow of 80 gpm at the same $H$.

**5.127** What is the discharge through the system of Fig. 5.53 for water at 80°F when $H = 20$ ft?

**5.128** Compare the smooth-pipe curve on the Moody diagram with Eq. (5.10.4) for $\mathbf{R} = 10^5$, $10^6$, $10^7$.

**5.129** Check the location of line $\epsilon/D = 0.0002$ on the Moody diagram with Eq. (5.10.7).

**5.130** In Eq. (5.10.7) show that when $\epsilon = 0$, it reduces to Eq. (5.10.4) and that, when $\mathbf{R}$ is very large, it reduces to Eq. (5.10.6).

**Fig. 5.54**

**5.131** In Fig. 5.54 the rocker plate has a width of 1 ft. Calculate (*a*) the load the bearing will sustain, (*b*) the drag on the bearing. Assume no flow normal to the paper.

**5.132** Find the maximum pressure in the fluid of Prob. 5.131, and determine its location.

**5.133** Determine the pressure center for the rocker plate of Prob. 5.131.

**5.134** Show that a shaft concentric with a bearing can sustain no load.

**5.135** The shear stress in a fluid flowing between two fixed parallel plates

(*a*) is constant over the cross section
(*b*) is zero at the plates and increases linearly to the mid-point
(*c*) varies parabolically across the section
(*d*) is zero at the midplane and varies linearly with distance from the midplane
(*e*) is none of these answers

**5.136** The velocity distribution for flow between two fixed parallel plates

(*a*) is constant over the cross section
(*b*) is zero at the plates and increases linearly to the midplane
(*c*) varies parabolically across the section
(*d*) varies as the three-halves power of the distance from the mid-point
(*e*) is none of these answers

**5.137** The discharge between two parallel plates, distance $a$ apart, when one has the velocity $U$ and the shear stress is zero at the fixed plate, is

(*a*) $Ua/3$    (*b*) $Ua/2$    (*c*) $2Ua/3$    (*d*) $Ua$    (*e*) none of these answers

**5.138** Fluid is in laminar motion between two parallel plates, with one plate in motion, and is under the action of a pressure gradient so that the discharge through any fixed cross section is zero. The minimum velocity occurs at a point which is distant from the fixed plate

(*a*) $a/6$    (*b*) $a/3$    (*c*) $a/2$    (*d*) $2a/3$    (*e*) none of these answers

**5.139** In Prob. 5.138 the value of the minimum velocity is

(*a*) $-3U/4$    (*b*) $-2U/3$    (*c*) $-U/2$    (*d*) $-U/3$    (*e*) $-U/6$

**5.140** The relation between pressure and shear stress in one-dimensional laminar flow in the $x$-direction is given by

(*a*) $dp/dx = \mu\, d\tau/dy$    (*b*) $dp/dy = d\tau/dx$    (*c*) $dp/dy = \mu\, d\tau/dx$
(*d*) $dp/dx = d\tau/dy$    (*e*) none of these answers

**5.141**  The expression for power input per unit volume to a fluid in one-dimensional laminar motion in the $x$-direction is

(a) $\tau\,du/dy$  (b) $\tau/\mu^2$  (c) $\mu\,du/dy$  (d) $\tau(du/dy)^2$  (e) **none** of these answers

**5.142**  When liquid is in laminar motion at constant depth and flowing down an inclined plate ($y$ measured normal to surface),

(a) the shear is zero throughout the liquid
(b) $d\tau/dy = 0$ at the plate
(c) $\tau = 0$ at the surface of the liquid
(d) the velocity is constant throughout the liquid
(e) there are no losses

**5.143**  The shear stress in a fluid flowing in a round pipe

(a) is constant over the cross section
(b) is zero at the wall and increases linearly to the center
(c) varies parabolically across the section
(d) is zero at the center and varies linearly with the radius
(e) is none of these answers

**5.144**  When the pressure drop in a 24-in.-diameter pipeline is 10 psi in 100 ft, the wall shear stress in pounds per square foot is

(a) 0   (b) 7.2   (c) 14.4   (d) 720   (e) none of these answers

**5.145**  In laminar flow through a round tube the discharge varies

(a) linearly as the viscosity
(b) as the square of the radius
(c) inversely as the pressure drop
(d) inversely as the viscosity
(e) as the cube of the diameter

**5.146**  When a tube is inclined, the term $-dp/dl$ is replaced by

(a) $-dz/dl$   (b) $-\gamma\,dz/dl$   (c) $-d(p+z)/dl$
(d) $-d(p+\rho z)/dl$   (e) $-d(p+\gamma z)/dl$

**5.147**  The upper critical Reynolds number is

(a) important from a design viewpoint
(b) the number at which turbulent flow changes to laminar flow
(c) about 2000
(d) not more than 2000
(e) of no practical importance in pipe-flow problems

**5.148**   The Reynolds number for pipe flow is given by

(a) $VD/\nu$      (b) $VD\mu/\rho$      (c) $VD\rho/\nu$      (d) $VD/\mu$      (e) none of these answers

**5.149**   The lower critical Reynolds number has the value

(a) 200      (b) 1200      (c) 12,000      (d) 40,000      (e) none of these answers

**5.150**   The Reynolds number for a 1.0-in.-diameter sphere moving 10 ft/sec through oil, sp gr 0.90, $\mu = 0.002$ lb-sec/ft², is

(a) 375      (b) 725      (c) 806      (d) 8700      (e) none of these answers

**5.151**   The Reynolds number for 10 cfs discharge of water at 68°F through a 12-in.-diameter pipe is

(a) 2460      (b) 980,000      (c) 1,178,000      (d) 14,120,000      (e) none of these answers

**5.152**   The Prandtl mixing length is

(a) independent of radial distance from pipe axis
(b) independent of the shear stress
(c) zero at the pipe wall
(d) a universal constant
(e) useful for computing laminar-flow problems

**5.153**   In a fluid stream of low viscosity

(a) the effect of viscosity does not appreciably increase the drag on a body
(b) the potential theory yields the drag force on a body
(c) the effect of viscosity is limited to a narrow region surrounding a body
(d) the deformation drag on a body always predominates
(e) the potential theory contributes nothing of value regarding flow around bodies

**5.154**   The lift on a body immersed in a fluid stream is

(a) due to buoyant force
(b) always in the opposite direction to gravity
(c) the resultant fluid force on the body
(d) the dynamic fluid-force component exerted on the body normal to the approach velocity
(e) the dynamic fluid-force component exerted on the body parallel to the approach velocity

**5.155**  The displacement thickness of the boundary layer is

($a$)  the distance from the boundary affected by boundary shear
($b$)  one-half the actual thickness of the boundary layer
($c$)  the distance to the point where $u/U = 0.99$
($d$)  the distance the main flow is shifted
($e$)  none of these answers

**5.156**  The shear stress at the boundary of a flat plate is

($a$) $\partial p/\partial x$    ($b$) $\mu\, \partial u/\partial y\, |_{y=0}$    ($c$) $\rho\, \partial u/\partial y\, |_{y=0}$
($d$) $\mu\, \partial u/\partial y\, |_{y=\delta}$    ($e$) none of these answers

**5.157**  Which of the following velocity distributions $u/U$ satisfies the boundary conditions for flow along a flat plate?  $\eta = y/\delta$.

($a$) $e^{\eta}$    ($b$) $\cos \pi\eta/2$    ($c$) $\eta - \eta^2$    ($d$) $2\eta - \eta^3$    ($e$) none of
these answers

**5.158**  The drag coefficient for a flat plate is ($D$ = drag)

($a$) $2D/\rho U^2 l$    ($b$) $\rho U l/D$    ($c$) $\rho U l/2D$    ($d$) $\rho U^2 l/2D$
($e$) none of these answers

**5.159**  The average velocity divided by the maximum velocity, as given by the one-seventh-power law, is

($a$) $\frac{49}{120}$    ($b$) $\frac{1}{2}$    ($c$) $\frac{6}{7}$    ($d$) $\frac{08}{120}$    ($e$) none of these answers

**5.160**  The laminar-boundary-layer thickness varies as

($a$) $1/x^{1/2}$    ($b$) $x^{1/7}$    ($c$) $x^{1/2}$    ($d$) $x^{6/7}$    ($e$) none of these
answers

**5.161**  The turbulent-boundary-layer thickness varies as

($a$) $1/x^{1/5}$    ($b$) $x^{1/5}$    ($c$) $x^{1/2}$    ($d$) $x^{4/5}$    ($e$) none of these
answers

**5.162**  In flow along a rough plate, the order of flow type from upstream to downstream is

($a$)  laminar, fully developed wall roughness, transition region, hydraulically smooth
($b$)  laminar, transition region, hydraulically smooth, fully developed wall roughness
($c$)  laminar, hydraulically smooth, transition region, fully developed wall roughness
($d$)  laminar, hydraulically smooth, fully developed wall roughness, transition region
($e$)  laminar, fully developed wall roughness, hydraulically smooth, transition region

**5.163**   Separation is caused by

(*a*)  reduction of pressure to vapor pressure
(*b*)  reduction of pressure gradient to zero
(*c*)  an adverse pressure gradient
(*d*)  the boundary-layer thickness reducing to zero
(*e*)  none of these answers

**5.164**   Separation occurs when

(*a*)  the cross section of a channel is reduced
(*b*)  the boundary layer comes to rest
(*c*)  the velocity of sound is reached
(*d*)  the pressure reaches a minimum
(*e*)  a valve is closed

**5.165**   The wake

(*a*)  is a region of high pressure
(*b*)  is the principal cause of skin friction
(*c*)  always occurs when deformation drag predominates
(*d*)  always occurs after a separation point
(*e*)  is none of these answers

**5.166**   Pressure drag results from

(*a*)  skin friction
(*b*)  deformation drag
(*c*)  breakdown of potential flow near the forward stagnation point
(*d*)  occurrence of a wake
(*e*)  none of these answers

**5.167**   A body with a rounded nose and long, tapering tail is usually best suited for

(*a*)  laminar flow
(*b*)  turbulent subsonic flow
(*c*)  supersonic flow
(*d*)  flow at speed of sound
(*e*)  none of these answers

**5.168**   A sudden change in position of the separation point in flow around a sphere occurs at a Reynolds number of about

(*a*) 1      (*b*) 300      (*c*) 30,000      (*d*) 3,000,000      (*e*) none of these answers

**5.169**  The effect of compressibility on the drag force is to

($a$)  increase it greatly near the speed of sound
($b$)  decrease it near the speed of sound
($c$)  cause it asymptotically to approach a constant value for large Mach numbers
($d$)  cause it to increase more rapidly than the square of the speed at high Mach numbers
($e$)  reduce it throughout the whole flow range

**5.170**  The terminal velocity of a small sphere settling in a viscous fluid varies as the

($a$)  first power of its diameter
($b$)  inverse of the fluid viscosity
($c$)  inverse square of the diameter
($d$)  inverse of the diameter
($e$)  square of the difference in specific weights of solid and fluid

**5.171**  The losses in open-channel flow generally vary as the

($a$)  first power of the roughness
($b$)  inverse of the roughness
($c$)  square of the velocity
($d$)  inverse square of the hydraulic radius
($e$)  velocity

**5.172**  The most simple form of open-channel-flow computation is

($a$)  steady uniform
($b$)  steady nonuniform
($c$)  unsteady uniform
($d$)  unsteady nonuniform
($e$)  gradually varied

**5.173**  In an open channel of great width the hydraulic radius equals

($a$) $y/3$      ($b$) $y/2$      ($c$) $2y/3$      ($d$) $y$      ($e$) none of these answers

**5.174**  The Manning roughness coefficient for finished concrete is

($a$) 0.002      ($b$) 0.020      ($c$) 0.20      ($d$) dependent upon hydraulic radius      ($e$) none of these answers

**5.175**  In turbulent flow a rough pipe has the same friction factor as a smooth pipe

($a$)  in the zone of complete turbulence, rough pipes
($b$)  when the friction factor is independent of the Reynolds number

(c) when the roughness projections are much smaller than the thickness of the boundary layer

(d) everywhere in the transition zone

(e) when the friction factor is constant

**5.176** The friction factor in turbulent flow in smooth pipes depends upon the following:

(a) $V, D, \rho, L, \mu$      (b) $Q, L, \mu, \rho$      (c) $V, D, \rho, p, \mu$
(d) $V, D, \mu, \rho$      (e) $p, L, D, Q, V$

**5.177** In a *given* rough pipe, the losses depend upon

(a) $f, V$      (b) $\mu, \rho$      (c) **R**      (d) $Q$ only      (e) none of these answers

**5.178** In the complete-turbulence zone, rough pipes,

(a) rough and smooth pipes have the same friction factor
(b) the laminar film covers the roughness projections
(c) the friction factor depends upon Reynolds number only
(d) the head loss varies as the square of the velocity
(e) the friction factor is independent of the relative roughness

**5.179** The friction factor for flow of water at 60°F through a 2-ft-diameter cast-iron pipe with a velocity of 5 ft/sec is

(a) 0.013      (b) 0.017      (c) 0.019      (d) 0.021      (e) none of these answers

**5.180** The procedure to follow in solving for losses when $Q, L, D, \nu,$ and $\epsilon$ are given is to

(a) assume an $f$, look up **R** on Moody diagram, etc.
(b) assume an $h_f$, solve for $f$, check against **R** on Moody diagram
(c) assume an $f$, solve for $h_f$, compute **R**, etc.
(d) compute **R**, look up $f$ for $\epsilon/D$, solve for $h_f$
(e) assume an **R**, compute $V$, look up $f$, solve for $h_f$

**5.181** The procedure to follow in solving for discharge when $h_f, L, D, \nu,$ and $\epsilon$ are given is to

(a) assume an $f$, compute $V$, **R**, $\epsilon/D$, look up $f$, and repeat if necessary
(b) assume an **R**, compute $f$, check $\epsilon/D$, etc.
(c) assume a $V$, compute **R**, look up $f$, compute $V$ again, etc.
(d) solve Darcy-Weisbach for $V$, compute $Q$
(e) assume a $Q$, compute $V$, **R**, look up $f$, etc.

**5.182**   The procedure to follow in solving for pipe diameter when $h_f$, $Q$, $L$, $\nu$, and $\epsilon$ are given is to

(a)   assume a $D$, compute $V$, **R**, $\epsilon/D$, look up $f$, and repeat
(b)   compute $V$ from continuity, assume an $f$, solve for $D$
(c)   eliminate $V$ in **R** and Darcy-Weisbach, using continuity, assume an $f$, solve for $D$, **R**, look up $f$, and repeat
(d)   assume an **R** and an $\epsilon/D$, look up $f$, solve Darcy-Weisbach for $V^2/D$, and solve simultaneously with continuity for $V$ and $D$, compute new **R**, etc.
(e)   assume a $V$, solve for $D$, **R**, $\epsilon/D$, look up $f$, and repeat

**5.183**   The losses due to a sudden contraction are given by

(a) $\left(\dfrac{1}{C_c^2} - 1\right)\dfrac{V_2^2}{2g}$     (b) $(1 - C_c^2)\dfrac{V_2^2}{2g}$     (c) $\left(\dfrac{1}{C_c} - 1\right)^2\dfrac{V_2^2}{2g}$

(d) $(C_c - 1)^2\dfrac{V_2^2}{2g}$     (e) none of these answers

**5.184**   The losses at the exit of a submerged pipe in a reservoir are

(a) negligible     (b) $0.05(V^2/2g)$     (c) $0.5(V^2/2g)$     (d) $V^2/2g$
(e) none of these answers

**5.185**   Minor losses usually may be neglected when

(a)   there are 100 ft of pipe between special fittings
(b)   their loss is 5 per cent or less of the friction loss
(c)   there are 500 diameters of pipe between minor losses
(d)   there are no globe valves in the line
(e)   rough pipe is used

**5.186**   The length of pipe ($f = 0.025$) in diameters, equivalent to a globe valve, is

(a) 40     (b) 200     (c) 300     (d) 400     (e) not determinable; insufficient data

**5.187**   The hydraulic radius is given by

(a)   wetted perimeter divided by area
(b)   area divided by square of wetted perimeter
(c)   square root of area
(d)   area divided by wetted perimeter
(e)   none of these answers

**5.188**   The hydraulic radius of a 6- by 12-in. cross section is, in feet,

(a) $\frac{1}{3}$     (b) $\frac{1}{2}$     (c) $\frac{2}{3}$     (d) $\frac{3}{4}$     (e) none of these answers

**5.189** In the theory of lubrication the assumption is made that

(a) the velocity distribution is the same at all cross sections

(b) the velocity distribution at any section is the same as if the plates were parallel

(c) the pressure variation along the bearing is the same as if the plates were parallel

(d) the shear stress varies linearly between the two surfaces

(e) the velocity varies linearly between the two surfaces

**5.190** A 4-in.-diameter shaft rotates at 240 rpm in a bearing with a radial clearance of 0.006 in. The shear stress in an oil film, $\mu = 0.1$ poise, is, in pounds per square foot,

(a) 0.15    (b) 1.75    (c) 3.50    (d) 16.70    (e) none of these answers

# 6
# compressible flow

In Chap. 5, viscous incompressible-fluid-flow situations were mainly considered. In this chapter on compressible flow, one new variable enters, the density, and one extra equation is available, the equation of state, which relates pressure and density. The other equations—continuity, momentum, and the first and second laws of thermodynamics—are also needed in the analysis of compressible-fluid-flow situations. In this chapter topics In steady one-dimensional flow of a perfect gas are discussed. The one-dimensional approach is limited to those applications in which the velocity and density may be considered constant over any cross section. When density changes are gradual and do not change by more than a few per cent, the flow may be treated as incompressible with the use of an average density.

The following topics are discussed in this chapter: perfect-gas relationships, speed of a sound wave, Mach number, isentropic flow, shock waves, Fanno and Rayleigh lines, adiabatic flow, flow with heat transfer, isothermal flow, and the analogy between shock waves and open channel waves.

## 6.1 perfect-gas relationships

In Sec. 1.6 [Eq. (1.6.2)] a perfect gas is defined as a fluid that has constant specific heats and that follows the law

$$p = \rho RT \qquad (6.1.1)$$

in which $p$ and $T$ are the absolute pressure and absolute temperature, respectively, $\rho$ is the density, and $R$ the gas constant. In this section specific heats are defined, the specific heat ratio is introduced and related to specific heats and the gas constant, internal energy and enthalpy are related to temperature, entropy relations are established, and the isentropic and reversible polytropic processes are introduced.

In general, the specific heat $c_v$ at constant volume is defined by

$$c_v = \left(\frac{\partial u}{\partial T}\right)_v \tag{6.1.2}$$

in which $u$ is the internal energy per unit mass. In words, $c_v$ is the amount of internal energy increase required by a unit mass of gas to increase its temperature by one degree when its volume is held constant. In thermodynamic theory it is proved that $u$ is a function only of temperature for a perfect gas.

The specific heat $c_p$ at constant pressure is defined by

$$c_p = \left(\frac{\partial h}{\partial T}\right)_p \tag{6.1.3}$$

in which $h$ is the enthalpy per unit mass given by $h = u + p/\rho$. Since $p/\rho$ is equal to $RT$ and $u$ is a function only of temperature for a perfect gas, $h$ depends only on temperature. Many of the common gases, such as water vapor, hydrogen, oxygen, carbon monoxide, and air, have a fairly small change in specific heats over the temperature range 500 to 1000°R, and an intermediate value is taken for their use as perfect gases. Table C.2 of Appendix C lists some common gases with values of specific heats at 80°F.

For perfect gases Eq. (6.1.2) becomes

$$du = c_v \, dT \tag{6.1.4}$$

and Eq. (6.1.3) becomes

$$dh = c_p \, dT \tag{6.1.5}$$

Then, from

$$h = u + \frac{p}{\rho} = u + RT$$

differentiating,

$$dh = du + R \, dT$$

and by substitution of Eqs. (6.1.4) and (6.1.5),

$$c_p = c_v + R \tag{6.1.6}$$

which is valid for any gas obeying Eq. (6.1.1) (even when $c_p$ and $c_v$ are changing with temperature).  If $c_p$ and $c_v$ are given in heat units per unit mass (i.e., Btu per pound mass per degree Rankine or Btu per slug per degree Rankine), then $R$ must be in heat units also (i.e., Btu per pound mass per degree Rankine or Btu per slug per degree Rankine).  The conversion factor is 1 Btu = 778 ft-lb if it is desired to express units in the foot-pound-second system.

The *specific-heat ratio* $k$ is defined as the ratio

$$k = \frac{c_p}{c_v} \qquad (6.1.7)$$

By solving with Eq. (6.1.6),

$$c_p = \frac{k}{k-1} R \qquad c_v = \frac{R}{k-1} \qquad (6.1.8)$$

*entropy relationships*

The first law of thermodynamics for a system states that the heat added to a system is equal to the work done by the system plus its increase in internal energy [Eq. (3.7.4)].  In terms of the entropy $s$ the equation takes the form

$$T \, ds = du + p \, d\,\frac{1}{\rho} \qquad (3.7.6)$$

which is a relationship among thermodynamic properties and must hold for all pure substances.

The internal energy change for a perfect gas is

$$u_2 - u_1 = c_v(T_2 - T_1) \qquad (6.1.9)$$

and the enthalpy change is

$$h_2 - h_1 = c_p(T_2 - T_1) \qquad (6.1.10)$$

The change in entropy

$$ds = \frac{du}{T} + \frac{p}{T} d\,\frac{1}{\rho} = c_v \frac{dT}{T} + R\rho \, d\,\frac{1}{\rho} \qquad (6.1.11)$$

may be obtained from Eqs. (6.1.4) and (6.1.1).  After integrating,

$$s_2 - s_1 = c_v \ln \frac{T_2}{T_1} + R \ln \frac{\rho_1}{\rho_2} \qquad (6.1.12)$$

By use of Eqs. (6.1.8) and (6.1.1), Eq. (6.1.12) becomes

$$s_2 - s_1 = c_v \ln \left[ \frac{T_2}{T_1} \left( \frac{\rho_1}{\rho_2} \right)^{k-1} \right] \tag{6.1.13}$$

or

$$s_2 - s_1 = c_v \ln \left[ \frac{p_2}{p_1} \left( \frac{\rho_1}{\rho_2} \right)^{k} \right] \tag{6.1.14}$$

and

$$s_2 - s_1 = c_v \ln \left[ \left( \frac{T_2}{T_1} \right)^{k} \left( \frac{p_2}{p_1} \right)^{1-k} \right] \tag{6.1.15}$$

These equations are forms of the second law of thermodynamics.

If the process is reversible, $ds = dq_H/dT$, or $T\, ds = dq_H$; further, if the process should also be adiabatic, $dq_H = 0$. Thus $ds = 0$ for a reversible, adiabatic process, or $s$ = const; the *reversible*, *adiabatic* process is therefore *isentropic*. Then, from Eq. (6.1.14) for $s_2 = s_1$,

$$\frac{p_1}{\rho_1{}^k} = \frac{p_2}{\rho_2{}^k} \tag{6.1.16}$$

Equation (6.1.16) combined with the general gas law yields

$$\frac{T_2}{T_1} = \left( \frac{p_2}{p_1} \right)^{(k-1)/k} = \left( \frac{\rho_2}{\rho_1} \right)^{k-1} \tag{6.1.17}$$

The enthalpy change for an isentropic process is

$$h_2 - h_1 = c_p(T_2 - T_1) = c_p T_1 \left( \frac{T_2}{T_1} - 1 \right) = c_p T_1 \left[ \left( \frac{p_2}{p_1} \right)^{(k-1)/k} - 1 \right] \tag{6.1.18}$$

The *polytropic* process is defined by

$$\frac{p}{\rho^n} = \text{const} \tag{6.1.19}$$

and is an approximation to certain actual processes in which $p$ would plot substantially as a straight line against $\rho$ on log-log paper. This relationship is frequently used to calculate the work when the polytropic process is reversible, by substitution into the relation $w = \int p\, dv$. Heat transfer occurs in a reversible polytropic process except when $n = k$, the isentropic case.

**example 6.1**   Express $R$ in Btu per slug per degree Rankine for helium.
A conversion from 1 ft-lb/lb$_m$ °R to Btu per slug per degree Rankine is
made first.   Since 1 Btu − 778 ft-lb and 1 slug = 32.17 lb$_m$,

$$1 \text{ ft-lb/lb}_m\ °R = 1 \frac{\text{Btu}}{778} \frac{32.17}{\text{slug }°R} = 0.0414 \text{ Btu/slug }°R$$

Then, for helium, from Table C.2,

$$R = 386 \text{ ft-lb/lb}_m\ °R = 386 \times 0.0414 \text{ Btu/slug }°R = 16.0 \text{ Btu/slug }°R$$

**example 6.2**   Compute the value of $R$ from the values of $k$ and $c_p$ for air
and check in Table C.2.
From Eq. (6.1.8)

$$R = \frac{k-1}{k} c_p = \frac{1.40 - 1.0}{1.40} \times 0.240 = 0.0686 \text{ Btu/lb}_m\ °R$$

By converting from Btu to foot-pounds,

$$R = 0.0686 \times 778 = 53.3 \text{ ft-lb/lb}_m\ °R$$

which checks with the value in Table C.2.

**example 6.3**   Compute the enthalpy change in 7.0 lb$_m$ of oxygen when the
initial conditions are $p_1 = 20$ psia, $t_1 = 50°F$ and the final conditions are
$p_2 = 80$ psia, $t_2 - 200°F$.
Enthalpy is a function of temperature only.   By use of Eq. (6.1.10), the
enthalpy change per pound mass is

$$c_p(T_2 - T_1) = 0.219(200 - 50) = 32.9 \text{ Btu/lb}_m$$

and the enthalpy change for 7.0 lb$_m$ is

$$H_2 - H_1 = 7.0 \times 32.9 = 230.3 \text{ Btu}$$

**example 6.4**   Determine the entropy change in 4.0 slugs of water vapor
when the initial conditions are $p_1 = 6$ psia, $t_1 = 110°F$ and the final conditions are $p_2 = 40$ psia and $t_2 = 38°F$.
From Eq. (6.1.15) and Table C.2

$$s_2 - s_1 = 0.335 \ln\left[\left(\frac{460 + 38}{460 + 110}\right)^{1.33}\left(\frac{40}{6}\right)^{-0.33}\right] = -0.271 \text{ Btu/lb}_m\ °R$$

or

$$S_2 - S_1 = -0.271 \times 4.0 \times 32.17 = -34.9 \text{ Btu/}°R$$

**example 6.5** A cylinder containing 3.5 $lb_m$ nitrogen at 20 psia and 40°F is compressed isentropically to 45 psia. Find the final temperature and the work required.

From the principle of conservation of energy, the work done on the gas must equal its increase in internal energy, since there is no heat transfer in an isentropic process; i.e.,

$$u_2 - u_1 = c_v(T_2 - T_1) = \text{work}$$

By Eq. (6.1.17)

$$T_2 = T_1 \left(\frac{p_2}{p_1}\right)^{(k-1)/k} = (460 + 40) \left(\frac{45}{20}\right)^{(1.4-1)/1.4} = 630°\text{R}$$

and

$$\text{Work} = 0.177(630 - 500) \times 3.5 = 80.6 \text{ Btu}$$

**example 6.6** 3.0 slugs of air are involved in a reversible polytropic process in which the initial conditions $p_1 = 12$ psia, $t_1 = 60°$F change to $p_2 = 20$ psia, and volume $\mathcal{U} = 1011$ ft$^3$. Determine (*a*) the formula for the process, (*b*) the work done on the air, (*c*) the amount of heat transfer, and (*d*) the entropy change.

$$(a) \quad \rho_1 = \frac{p_1}{RT_1} = \frac{12 \times 144}{53.3 \times 32.17(460 + 520)} = 0.00194 \text{ slug/ft}^3$$

$R$ was converted to foot-pounds per slug per degree Rankine by multiplying by 32.17. Also

$$\rho_2 = \frac{3}{1011} = 0.002965 \text{ slug/ft}^3$$

From Eq. (6.1.19)

$$\frac{p_1}{\rho_1{}^n} = \frac{p_2}{\rho_2{}^n}$$

$$n = \frac{\ln (p_2/p_1)}{\ln (\rho_2/\rho_1)} = \frac{\ln \frac{20}{12}}{\ln (0.002965/0.00194)} = 1.20$$

hence

$$\frac{p}{\rho^{1.2}} = \text{const}$$

describes the polytropic process.

(b)  Work of expansion is

$$W = \int_{\mathcal{V}_1}^{\mathcal{V}_2} p \, d\mathcal{V}$$

This is the work done by the gas on its surroundings.  Since

$$p_1 \mathcal{V}_1{}^n = p_2 \mathcal{V}_2{}^n = p \mathcal{V}^n$$

by substituting into the integral,

$$W = p_1 \mathcal{V}_1{}^n \int_{\mathcal{V}_1}^{\mathcal{V}_2} \frac{d\mathcal{V}}{\mathcal{V}^n} = \frac{p_2 \mathcal{V}_2 - p_1 \mathcal{V}_1}{1 - n} = \frac{mR}{1 - n}(T_2 - T_1)$$

if $m$ is the mass of gas.  $\mathcal{V}_2 = 1011 \text{ ft}^3$ and

$$\mathcal{V}_1 = \mathcal{V}_2 \left(\frac{p_2}{p_1}\right)^{1/n} = 1011 \left(\frac{20}{12}\right)^{1/1.2} = 1548 \text{ ft}^3$$

Then

$$W = \frac{20 \times 144 \times 1011 - 12 \times 144 \times 1548}{1 - 1.2} = -1{,}183{,}000 \text{ ft-lb}$$

Hence the work done on the gas is 1,183,000 ft-lb.

(c)  From the first law of thermodynamics the heat added minus the work done by the gas must equal the increase in internal energy; i.e.,

$$Q_H - W = U_2 - U_1 = c_v m(T_2 - T_1)$$

First

$$T_2 = \frac{p_2}{\rho_2 R} = \frac{20 \times 144}{0.002965 \times 53.3 \times 32.17} = 566°R$$

Then

$$Q_H = -\frac{1{,}183{,}000}{778} + 0.171 \times 32.17 \times 3(566 - 520)$$

$$= -760 \text{ Btu}$$

760 Btu were transferred from the mass of air.

(d)  From Eq. (6.1.14) the entropy change is computed:

$$s_2 - s_1 = 0.171 \ln \left[\frac{20}{12}\left(\frac{0.00194}{0.002965}\right)^{1.4}\right] = -0.01441 \text{ Btu/lb}_m \text{ °R}$$

and

$$S_2 - S_1 = -0.01441 \times 3 \times 32.17 = -1.392 \text{ Btu/°R}$$

A rough check on the heat transfer may be made by using Eq. (3.7.5), by using an average temperature $T = (520 + 566)/2 = 543$, and by remembering that the losses are zero in a reversible process.

$$Q_H = T(S_2 - S_1) = 543 \times (-1.392) = -756 \text{ Btu}$$

## 6.2   speed of a sound wave.   Mach number

The speed of a small disturbance in a conduit may be determined by application of the momentum equation and the continuity equation.   The question is first raised as to whether a *stationary* small change in velocity, pressure, and density can occur in a channel.   By referring to Fig. 6.1, the continuity equation can be written

$$\rho V A = (\rho + d\rho)(V + dV)A$$

in which $A$ is the cross-sectional area of channel.   The equation can be reduced to

$$\rho \, dV + V \, d\rho = 0$$

When the momentum equation [Eq. (3.11.2)] is applied to the control volume within the dotted lines,

$$pA - (p + dp)A = \rho V A(V + dV - V)$$

or

$$dp = -\rho V \, dV$$

If $\rho \, dV$ is eliminated between the two equations,

$$V^2 = \frac{dp}{d\rho} \tag{6.2.1}$$

**Fig. 6.1** Steady flow in prismatic channel with sudden small change in velocity, pressure, and density.

Hence, a small disturbance or sudden change in conditions in steady flow can occur only when the particular velocity $V = \sqrt{dp/d\rho}$ exists in the conduit.   Now this problem can be converted to the unsteady flow of a small disturbance through still fluid by superposing on the whole system and its surroundings the velocity $V$ to the left, since this in no way affects the dynamics of the system.   This is called the speed of sound $c$ in the medium.   The disturbance from a point source would cause a spherical wave to emanate, but at some distance from the source the wave front would be essentially linear or one-dimensional.   Large disturbances may travel faster than the speed of sound, e.g., a bomb explosion.   The equation for speed of sound

$$c = \sqrt{\frac{dp}{d\rho}} \qquad\qquad\qquad (6.2.2)$$

may be expressed in several useful forms.   The bulk modulus of elasticity can be introduced:

$$K = -\frac{dp}{d\upsilon/\upsilon}$$

in which $\upsilon$ is the volume of fluid subjected to the pressure change $dp$. Since

$$\frac{d\upsilon}{\upsilon} = \frac{dv_s}{v_s} = -\frac{d\rho}{\rho}$$

$K$ may be expressed as

$$K = \frac{\rho\,dp}{d\rho}$$

Then, from Eq. (6.2.2),

$$c = \sqrt{\frac{K}{\rho}} \qquad\qquad\qquad (6.2.3)$$

This equation applies to liquids as well as gases.

**example 6.7**   Carbon tetrachloride has a bulk modulus of elasticity of 163,000 psi and a density of 3.09 slugs/ft³.   What is the speed of sound in the medium?

$$c = \sqrt{\frac{K}{\rho}} = \sqrt{163{,}000 \times \frac{144}{3.09}} = 2758 \text{ ft/sec}$$

Since the pressure and temperature changes due to passage of a sound wave are extremely small, the process is almost reversible.    Also, the relatively rapid process of passage of the wave, together with the minute temperature changes, makes the process almost adiabatic.    In the limit, the process may be considered to be isentropic,

$$p\rho^{-k} = \text{const} \qquad \frac{dp}{d\rho} = \frac{kp}{\rho}$$

and

$$c = \sqrt{\frac{kp}{\rho}} \qquad\qquad (6.2.4)$$

or, from the perfect-gas law $p = \rho RT$,

$$c = \sqrt{kRT} \qquad\qquad (6.2.5)$$

which shows that the speed of sound in a perfect gas is a function of its absolute temperature only.    In flow of gas through a conduit, the speed of sound generally changes from section to section as the temperature is changed by density changes and friction effects.    In isothermal flow the speed of sound remains constant.

The Mach number has been defined as the ratio of velocity of a fluid to the local velocity of sound in the medium,

$$\mathbf{M} = \frac{V}{c} \qquad\qquad (6.2.6)$$

Squaring the Mach number produces $V^2/c^2$, which may be interpreted as the ratio of kinetic energy of the fluid to its thermal energy, since kinetic energy is proportional to $V^2$ and thermal energy is proportional to $T$.    The Mach number is a measure of the importance of compressibility.    In an incompressible fluid $K$ is infinite and $\mathbf{M} = 0$.    For perfect gases

$$K = kp \qquad\qquad (6.2.7)$$

when the compression is isentropic.

**example 6.8**    What is the speed of sound in dry air at sea level when $t = 68°F$, and in the stratosphere when $t = -67°F$?
    At sea level, from Eq. (6.2.5),

$$c = \sqrt{1.4 \times 32.2 \times 53.3(460 + 68)} = 1125 \text{ ft/sec}$$

and in the stratosphere

$$c = \sqrt{1.4 \times 32.2 \times 53.3(460 - 67)} = 972 \text{ ft/sec}$$

## 6.3   isentropic flow

Frictionless adiabatic, or isentropic, flow is an ideal that cannot be reached in the flow of real gases.   It is approached, however, in flow through transitions, nozzles, and venturi meters where friction effects are minor, owing to the short distances traveled, and heat transfer is minor because the changes that a particle undergoes are slow enough to keep the velocity and temperature gradients small.[1]   The performance of fluid machines is frequently compared with the performance assuming the flow were isentropic.   In this section one-dimensional steady flow of a perfect gas through converging and converging-diverging ducts is studied.

Some very general results may be obtained by use of Euler's equation (3.5.4), neglecting elevation changes,

$$V\,dV + \frac{dp}{\rho} = 0 \tag{6.3.1}$$

and the continuity equation

$$\rho A V = \text{const} \tag{6.3.2}$$

By differentiating $\rho A V$, then dividing through by $\rho A V$,

$$\frac{d\rho}{\rho} + \frac{dV}{V} + \frac{dA}{A} = 0 \tag{6.3.3}$$

From Eq. (6.2.2) $dp$ may be obtained and substituted into Eq. (6.3.1), yielding

$$V\,dV + c^2 \frac{d\rho}{\rho} = 0 \tag{6.3.4}$$

By eliminating $d\rho/\rho$ in the last two equations and rearranging,

$$\frac{dA}{dV} = \frac{A}{V}\left(\frac{V^2}{c^2} - 1\right) = \frac{A}{V}(\mathbf{M}^2 - 1) \tag{6.3.5}$$

The assumptions underlying this equation are that the flow is steady and frictionless.   No restrictions as to heat transfer have been imposed. Equation (6.3.5) shows that for subsonic flow (**M** < 1), $dA/dV$ is always negative; i.e., the channel area must decrease for increasing velocity.   As $dA/dV$ is zero for **M** = 1 only, the velocity keeps increasing until the minimum section or throat is reached, and that is the only section at which sonic flow may occur.   Also, for Mach numbers greater than unity (super-

---

[1] H. W. Liepmann and A. Roshko, "Elements of Gas Dynamics," p. 51, John Wiley & Sons, Inc., New York, 1957.

sonic flow) $dA/dV$ is positive and the area must increase for an increase in velocity. Hence to obtain supersonic steady flow from a fluid at rest in a reservoir, it must first pass through a converging duct and than a diverging duct.

When the analysis is restricted to isentropic flow, Eq. (6.1.16) may be written

$$p = p_1 \rho_1^{-k} \rho^k \tag{6.3.6}$$

After differentiating and substituting for $dp$ in Eq. (6.3.1),

$$V \, dV + k \frac{p_1}{\rho_1^k} \rho^{k-2} \, d\rho = 0$$

Integration yields

$$\frac{V^2}{2} + \frac{k}{k-1} \frac{p_1}{\rho_1^k} \rho^{k-1} = \text{const}$$

or

$$\frac{V_1^2}{2} + \frac{k}{k-1} \frac{p_1}{\rho_1} = \frac{V_2^2}{2} + \frac{k}{k-1} \frac{p_2}{\rho_2} \tag{6.3.7}$$

This equation is useful when expressed in terms of temperature; from $p = \rho RT$

$$\frac{V_1^2}{2} + \frac{k}{k-1} RT_1 = \frac{V_2^2}{2} + \frac{k}{k-1} RT_2 \tag{6.3.8}$$

For adiabatic flow from a reservoir where conditions are given by $p_0$, $\rho_0$, $T_0$, at any other section

$$\frac{V^2}{2} = \frac{kR}{k-1} (T_0 - T) \tag{6.3.9}$$

In terms of the local Mach number $V/c$, with $c^2 = kRT$,

$$\mathbf{M}^2 = \frac{V^2}{c^2} = \frac{2kR(T_0 - T)}{(k-1)kRT} = \frac{2}{k-1} \left( \frac{T_0}{T} - 1 \right)$$

or

$$\frac{T_0}{T} = 1 + \frac{k-1}{2} \mathbf{M}^2 \tag{6.3.10}$$

From Eqs. (6.3.10) and (6.1.17), which now restrict the following equations to isentropic flow,

$$\frac{p_0}{p} = \left(1 + \frac{k-1}{2}\mathbf{M}^2\right)^{k/(k-1)} \tag{6.3.11}$$

and

$$\frac{\rho_0}{\rho} = \left(1 + \frac{k-1}{2}\mathbf{M}^2\right)^{1/(k-1)} \tag{6.3.12}$$

Flow conditions are termed critical at the throat section when the velocity there is sonic. Sonic conditions are marked with an asterisk. $\mathbf{M} = 1$; $c^* = V^* = \sqrt{kRT^*}$. By applying Eqs. (6.3.10) to (6.3.12) to the throat section for critical conditions (for $k = 1.4$ in the numerical portion),

$$\frac{T^*}{T_0} = \frac{2}{k+1} = 0.833 \qquad\qquad k = 1.40 \tag{6.3.13}$$

$$\frac{p^*}{p_0} = \left(\frac{2}{k+1}\right)^{k/(k-1)} = 0.528 \quad k = 1.40 \tag{6.3.14}$$

$$\frac{\rho^*}{\rho_0} = \left(\frac{2}{k+1}\right)^{1/(k-1)} = 0.634 \quad k = 1.40 \tag{6.3.15}$$

These relations show that for air flow, the absolute temperature drops about 17 per cent from reservoir to throat, the critical pressure is 52.8 per cent of the reservoir pressure, and the density is reduced by about 37 per cent.

The variation of area with the Mach number for the critical case is obtained by use of the continuity equation and Eqs. (6.3.10) to (6.3.15). First

$$\rho A V = \rho^* A^* V^* \tag{6.3.16}$$

in which $A^*$ is the minimum, or throat, area. Then

$$\frac{A}{A^*} = \frac{\rho^*}{\rho}\frac{V^*}{V} \tag{6.3.17}$$

Now, $V^* = c^* = \sqrt{kRT^*}$, and $V = c\mathbf{M} = \mathbf{M}\sqrt{kRT}$, so that

$$\frac{V^*}{V} = \frac{1}{\mathbf{M}}\sqrt{\frac{T^*}{T}} = \frac{1}{\mathbf{M}}\sqrt{\frac{T^*}{T_0}}\sqrt{\frac{T_0}{T}} = \frac{1}{\mathbf{M}}\left\{\frac{1 + [(k-1)/2]\mathbf{M}^2}{(k+1)/2}\right\}^{1/2} \tag{6.3.18}$$

by use of Eqs. (6.3.13) and (6.3.10).   In a similar manner

$$\frac{\rho^*}{\rho} = \frac{\rho^*}{\rho_0}\frac{\rho_0}{\rho} = \left\{ \frac{1 + [(k-1)/2]\mathbf{M}^2}{(k+1)/2} \right\}^{1/(k-1)} \tag{6.3.19}$$

By substituting the last two equations into Eq. (6.3.17),

$$\frac{A}{A^*} = \frac{1}{\mathbf{M}} \left\{ \frac{1 + [(k-1)/2]\mathbf{M}^2}{(k+1)/2} \right\}^{(k+1)/2(k-1)} \tag{6.3.20}$$

which yields the variation of area of duct in terms of Mach number.   $A/A^*$ is never less than unity, and for any value greater than unity there will be two values of Mach number, one less than and one greater than unity. For gases with $k = 1.40$, Eq. (6.3.20) reduces to

$$\frac{A}{A^*} = \frac{1}{\mathbf{M}} \left( \frac{5 + \mathbf{M}^2}{6} \right)^3 \qquad k = 1.40 \tag{6.3.21}$$

The maximum mass flow rate $\dot{m}_{\max}$ can be expressed in terms of the throat area and reservoir conditions:

$$\dot{m}_{\max} = \rho^* A^* V^* = \rho_0 \left( \frac{2}{k+1} \right)^{1/(k-1)} A^* \sqrt{\frac{kR2T_0}{k+1}}$$

by use of Eqs. (6.3.15) and (6.3.13).   By replacing $\rho_0$ by $p_0/RT_0$,

$$\dot{m}_{\max} = \frac{A^* p_0}{\sqrt{T_0}} \sqrt{\frac{k}{R} \left( \frac{2}{k+1} \right)^{(k+1)/(k-1)}} \tag{6.3.22}$$

For $k = 1.40$ this reduces to

$$\dot{m}_{\max} = 0.686 \frac{A^* p_0}{\sqrt{RT_0}} \tag{6.3.23}$$

For $\dot{m}_{\max}$ in slugs per second, with air, $R = 53.3 \times 32.2$ ft-lb/slug °R, $A^*$ is in square feet, $p_0$ in pounds per square foot absolute, and $T_0$ in degrees Rankine.   Equation (6.3.23) shows that the mass flow rate varies linearly as $A^*$ and $p_0$ and varies inversely as the square root of the absolute temperature.

For subsonic flow throughout a converging-diverging duct, the velocity at the throat must be less than sonic velocity, or $\mathbf{M}_t < 1$ with subscript $t$ indicating the throat section.   The mass rate of flow $\dot{m}$ is obtained from

$$\dot{m} = \rho V A = A \sqrt{2p_0\rho_0 \frac{k}{k-1} \left( \frac{p}{p_0} \right)^{2/k} \left[ 1 - \left( \frac{p}{p_0} \right)^{(k-1)/k} \right]} \tag{6.3.24}$$

which is derived from Eqs. (6.3.9) and (6.3.6) and the perfect-gas law.   This equation holds for any section and is applicable as long as the velocity at the throat is subsonic.   It may be applied to the throat section, and for this section, from Eq. (6.3.14),

$$\frac{p_t}{p_0} \geq \left(\frac{2}{k-1}\right)^{k/(k-1)}$$

$p_t$ is the throat pressure.   When the equals sign is used in the expression, Eq. (6.3.24) reduces to Eq. (6.3.22).

For maximum mass flow rate, the flow downstream from the throat may be either supersonic or subsonic, depending upon the downstream pressure.   After substituting Eq. (6.3.22) for $\dot{m}$ in Eq. (6.3.24) and simplifying,

$$\left(\frac{p}{p_0}\right)^{2/k}\left[1 - \left(\frac{p}{p_0}\right)^{(k-1)/k}\right] = \frac{k-1}{2}\left(\frac{2}{k+1}\right)^{(k+1)/(k-1)}\left(\frac{A^*}{A}\right)^2 \qquad (6.3.25)$$

$A$ may be taken as the outlet area and $p$ as the outlet pressure.   For a given $A^*/A$ (less than unity) there will be two values of $p/p_0$ between zero and unity, the upper value for subsonic flow through the diverging duct and the lower value for supersonic flow through the diverging duct.   For all other pressure ratios less than the upper value complete isentropic flow is impossible and shock waves form in or just downstream from the diverging duct.   They are briefly discussed in the following section.

**example 6.9**   A preliminary design of a wind-tunnel duct to produce Mach number 3.0 at the exit is desired.   The mass flow rate is 2.0 $lb_m$/sec at $p_0 = 12.0$ psia, $t_0 = 80°F$.   Determine: ($a$) the throat area, ($b$) the outlet area, and ($c$) the velocity, pressure, temperature, and density at the outlet.

($a$)   The throat area is determined from Eq. (6.3.23):

$$A^* = \frac{\dot{m}_{max}\sqrt{RT_0}}{0.686 p_0} = \frac{2.0}{32.17} \times \frac{\sqrt{53.3 \times 32.17(460 + 80)}}{0.686 \times 12 \times 144} = 0.0504 \text{ ft}^2$$

($b$)   The area of outlet may be determined from Eq. (6.3.21):

$$A = \frac{A^*}{\mathbf{M}}\left(\frac{5 + \mathbf{M}^2}{6}\right)^3 = \frac{0.0504}{3}\left(\frac{5 + 3^2}{6}\right)^3 = 0.2137 \text{ ft}^2$$

($c$)   From Eq. (6.3.11)

$$p = \frac{p_0}{[1 + (k-1)\mathbf{M}^2/2]^{k/(k-1)}} = \frac{12}{[1 + (1.4 - 1)3^2/2]^{1.4/(1.4-1)}} = 0.326 \text{ psia}$$

From Eq. (6.3.12)

$$\rho = \frac{\rho_0}{[1 + (k-1)\mathbf{M}^2/2]^{1/(k-1)}} = \frac{\rho_0}{RT_0[1 + (k-1)\mathbf{M}^2/2]^{1/(k-1)}}$$

$$= \frac{12 \times 144}{53.3 \times 32.2 \times 540(1 + 0.2 \times 3^2)^{2.5}} = 0.000142 \text{ slug/ft}^3$$

From Eq. (6.3.10)

$$T = \frac{T_0}{1 + (k-1)\mathbf{M}^2/2} = \frac{540}{1 + 0.2 \times 3^2} = 192.7°\text{R}$$

The velocity is

$$V = c\mathbf{M} = \sqrt{kRT}\ 3 = 3\sqrt{1.4 \times 53.3 \times 32.17 \times 192.7} = 2040 \text{ ft/sec}$$

**example 6.10**   A converging-diverging air duct has a throat cross section of 0.40 ft² and an exit cross section of 1.0 ft². Reservoir pressure is 30 psia, and temperature is 60°F. Determine the range of Mach numbers and the pressure range at the exit for isentropic flow. Find the maximum flow rate.

Equation (6.3.21),

$$\frac{A}{A^*} = 2.5 = \frac{1}{\mathbf{M}}\left(\frac{5 + \mathbf{M}^2}{6}\right)^3$$

when solved by trial yields $\mathbf{M} = 2.44$ and $0.24$. Each of these values of Mach number at the exit is for critical conditions; hence the Mach number range for isentropic flow is 0 to 0.24 and the one value 2.44.

From Eq. (6.3.11)

$$\frac{p_0}{p} = (1 + 0.2\mathbf{M}^2)^{3.5}$$

For $\mathbf{M} = 2.44$, $p = 30/15.55 = 1.929$ psia, and for $\mathbf{M} = 0.24$, $p = 30/1.041 = 28.8$ psia. The downstream pressure range is then from 28.8 to 30 psia, and the isolated point 1.929 psia.

The maximum mass flow rate is determined from Eq. (6.3.23):

$$\dot{m}_{max} = \frac{0.686 \times 0.40 \times 30 \times 144}{\sqrt{53.3 \times 32.17(460 + 60)}} = 1.26 \text{ slug/sec} = 40.6 \text{ lb}_m/\text{sec}$$

**example 6.11** A converging-diverging duct in an air line downstream from a reservoir has a 2.0-in.-diameter throat. Determine the mass rate of flow when $p_0 = 120$ psia, $t_0 = 90°F$, and $p_1 = 80$ psia.

$$\rho_0 = \frac{p_0}{RT_0} = \frac{120 \times 144}{53.3 \times 32.17(460 + 90)} = 0.0183 \text{ slug/ft}^3$$

From Eq. (6.3.24)

$$\dot{m} = \frac{\pi}{144} \sqrt{2 \times 120 \times 144 \times 0.0183 \frac{1.4}{1.4 - 1}\left(\frac{80}{120}\right)^{2/1.4}\left[1 - \left(\frac{80}{120}\right)^{0.4/1.4}\right]}$$

$$= 0.254 \text{ slug/sec}$$

Tables which greatly simplify isentropic-flow calculations are available in the books by Cambel and Jennings and by Keenan and Kaye, listed at the end of the chapter. An abbreviated table is given in Appendix C.3.

## 6.4 shock waves

In one-dimensional flow the only type of shock wave that can occur is a normal compression shock wave, as illustrated in Fig. 6.2. For a complete discussion of converging-diverging flow for all downstream pressure ranges,[1] oblique shock waves must be taken into account as they occur at

[1] H. W. Liepmann and A. Roshko, "Elements of Gas Dynamics," John Wiley & Sons, Inc., New York, 1957.

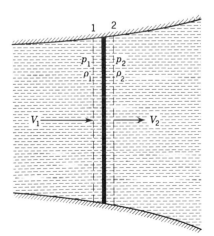

**Fig. 6.2** Normal compression shock wave.

the exit.   In the preceding section isentropic flow was shown to occur throughout a converging-diverging tube for a range of downstream pressures in which the flow was subsonic throughout and for one downstream pressure for supersonic flow through the diffuser (diverging portion).   In this section the normal shock wave in a diffuser is studied, with isentropic flow throughout the tube, except for the shock-wave surface.   The shock wave occurs in supersonic flow and reduces the flow to subsonic flow, as proved in the following section.   It has very little thickness, of the order of the molecular mean free path of the gas.   The controlling equations for adiabatic flow are (Fig. 6.2)

Continuity:

$$G = \frac{\dot{m}}{A} = \rho_1 V_1 = \rho_2 V_2 \tag{6.4.1}$$

Energy:

$$\frac{V_1^2}{2} + h_1 = \frac{V_2^2}{2} + h_2 = h_0 = \frac{V^2}{2} + \frac{k}{k-1}\frac{p}{\rho} \tag{6.4.2}$$

which are obtained from Eq. (3.7.1) for no change in elevation, no heat transfer, and no work done.   $h = u + p/\rho = c_p T$ is the enthalpy, and $h_0$ is the value of stagnation enthalpy, i.e., its value in the reservoir or where the fluid is at rest.   Equation (6.4.2) holds for real fluids and is valid both upstream and downstream from a shock wave.   The momentum equation (3.11.2) for a control volume between sections 1 and 2 becomes

$$(p_1 - p_2)A = \rho_2 A V_2^2 - \rho_1 A V_1^2$$

or

$$p_1 + \rho_1 V_1^2 = p_2 + \rho_2 V_2^2 \tag{6.4.3}$$

For given upstream conditions $h_1$, $p_1$, $V_1$, $\rho_1$, the three equations are to be solved for $p_2$, $\rho_2$, $V_2$.   The equation of state for a perfect gas is also available for use, $p = \rho RT$.   The value of $p_2$ is

$$p_2 = \frac{1}{k+1}[2\rho_1 V_1^2 - (k-1)p_1] \tag{6.4.4}$$

Once $p_2$ is determined by combination of the continuity and momentum equations

$$p_1 + \rho_1 V_1^2 = p_2 + \rho_1 V_1 V_2 \tag{6.4.5}$$

$V_2$ is readily obtained.   Finally $\rho_2$ is obtained from the continuity equation.

For given upstream conditions, with $\mathbf{M}_1 > 1$, the values of $p_2$, $V_2$, $\rho_2$, and $\mathbf{M}_2 = V_2/\sqrt{kp_2/\rho_2}$ exist and $\mathbf{M}_2 < 1$.   By eliminating $V_1$ and $V_2$ among Eqs. (6.4.1), (6.4.2), and (6.4.3) the Rankine-Hugoniot equations are obtained:

$$\frac{p_2}{p_1} = \frac{[(k+1)/(k-1)](\rho_2/\rho_1) - 1}{[(k+1)/(k-1)] - \rho_2/\rho_1} \tag{6.4.6}$$

and

$$\frac{\rho_2}{\rho_1} = \frac{1 + [(k+1)/(k-1)]p_2/p_1}{[(k+1)/(k-1)] + p_2/p_1} = \frac{V_1}{V_2} \tag{6.4.7}$$

These equations, relating conditions on either side of the shock wave, take the place of the isentropic relation, Eq. (6.1.16), $p\rho^{-k} = \text{const.}$
From Eq. (6.4.2), the energy equation,

$$\frac{V^2}{2} + \frac{k}{k-1}\frac{p}{\rho} = \frac{c^{*2}}{2} + \frac{c^{*2}}{k-1} = \frac{k+1}{k-1}\frac{c^{*2}}{2} \tag{6.4.8}$$

since the equation holds for all points in adiabatic flow without change in elevation, and $c^* = \sqrt{kp^*/\rho^*}$ is the velocity of sound.   After dividing Eq. (6.4.3) by Eq. (6.4.1),

$$V_1 - V_2 = \frac{p_2}{\rho_2 V_2} - \frac{p_1}{\rho_1 V_1}$$

and by eliminating $p_2/\rho_2$ and $p_1/\rho_1$ by use of Eq. (6.4.8),

$$V_1 - V_2 = (V_1 - V_2)\left[\frac{c^{*2}(k+1)}{2kV_1V_2} + \frac{k-1}{2k}\right] \tag{6.4.9}$$

which is satisfied by $V_1 = V_2$ (no shock wave) or by

$$V_1 V_2 = c^{*2} \tag{6.4.10}$$

It may be written

$$\frac{V_1}{c^*} \cdot \frac{V_2}{c^*} = 1 \tag{6.4.11}$$

When $V_1$ is greater than $c^*$, the upstream Mach number is greater than unity and $V_2$ is less than $c^*$, and so the final Mach number is less than unity, and vice versa.   It is shown in the following section that the process can occur only from supersonic upstream to subsonic downstream.
By use of Eq. (6.1.14), together with Eqs. (6.4.4), (6.4.6), and (6.4.7), an expression for change of entropy across a normal shock wave may be

obtained in terms of $M_1$ and $k$. From Eq. (6.4.4)

$$\frac{p_2}{p_1} = \frac{1}{k+1}\left[\frac{2k\rho_1 V_1^2}{kp_1} - (k-1)\right] \tag{6.4.12}$$

Since $c_1^2 = kp_1/\rho_1$ and $M_1 = V_1/c_1$, from Eq. (6.4.12),

$$\frac{p_2}{p_1} = \frac{2kM_1^2 - (k-1)}{k+1} \tag{6.4.13}$$

Placing this value of $p_2/p_1$ in Eq. (6.4.7) yields

$$\frac{\rho_2}{\rho_1} = \frac{M_1^2(k+1)}{2 + M_1^2(k-1)}$$

Now, after substituting these pressure and density ratios into Eq. (6.1.14),

$$s_2 - s_1 = c_v \ln\left\{\frac{2kM_1^2 - k + 1}{k+1}\left[\frac{2 + M_1^2(k-1)}{M_1^2(k+1)}\right]^k\right\} \tag{6.4.14}$$

By substitution of $M_1 > 1$ into this equation for the appropriate value of $k$, the entropy may be shown to increase across the shock wave, showing that the normal shock may proceed from supersonic flow upstream to subsonic flow downstream. Substitution of values of $M_1 < 1$ into Eq. (6.4.14) has no meaning, since Eq. (6.4.13) yields a negative value of the ratio $p_2/p_1$.

In the next section the shock wave is examined further by introduction of Fanno and Rayleigh lines. Appendix C.4 is useful in solving normal-shock problems.

**example 6.12** If a normal shock wave occurs in the flow of helium, $p_1 = 1$ psia, $t_1 = 40°F$, $V_1 = 4500$ ft/sec, find $p_2$, $\rho_2$, $V_2$, and $t_2$.
From Table C.2, $R = 386$, $k = 1.66$, and

$$\rho_1 = \frac{p_1}{RT_1} = \frac{1 \times 144}{386 \times 32.17(460 + 40)} = 0.0000232 \text{ slug/ft}^3$$

From Eq. (6.4.4)

$$p_2 = \frac{1}{1.66 + 1}[2 \times 0.0000232 \times (4500)^2 - (1.66 - 1) \times 144 \times 1]$$

$$= 317 \text{ lb/ft}^2 \text{ abs}$$

From Eq. (6.4.5)

$$V_2 = V_1 - \frac{p_2 - p_1}{\rho_1 V_1} = 4500 - \frac{317 - 144}{4500 \times 0.0000232} = 2840 \text{ ft/sec}$$

From Eq. (6.4.1)

$$\rho_2 = \rho_1 \frac{V_1}{V_2} = \frac{0.000746}{32.2} \times \frac{4500}{2840} = 0.0000367 \text{ slug/ft}^3$$

and

$$t_2 = T_2 - 460 = \frac{p_2}{\rho_2 R} - 460 = \frac{317}{0.0000367 \times 32.2 \times 386} - 460 = 235°F$$

## 6.5   Fanno and Rayleigh lines

To examine more closely the nature of the flow change in the short distance across a shock wave, where the area may be considered constant, the continuity and energy equations are combined for steady, frictional, adiabatic flow.   By considering upstream conditions fixed, that is, $p_1$, $V_1$, $\rho_1$, a plot may be made of all possible conditions at section 2, Fig. 6.2.   The lines on such a plot for constant mass flow $G$ per unit area are called *Fanno lines*.   The most revealing plot is that of enthalpy against entropy, i.e., an *hs* diagram.

The entropy equation for a perfect gas, Eq. (6.1.14), is

$$s - s_1 = c_v \ln \left[ \frac{p}{p_1} \left( \frac{\rho_1}{\rho} \right)^k \right] \tag{6.5.1}$$

The energy equation for adiabatic flow with no change in elevation, from Eq. (6.4.2), is

$$h_0 = h + \frac{V^2}{2} \tag{6.5.2}$$

and the continuity equation for no change in area, from Eq. (6.4.1), is

$$G = \rho V \tag{6.5.3}$$

The equation of state, linking $h$, $p$, and $\rho$, is

$$h = c_p T = \frac{c_p p}{R \rho} \tag{6.5.4}$$

By eliminating $p$, $\rho$, and $V$ from the four equations,

$$s = s_1 + c_v \ln \left[ \frac{\rho_1{}^k}{p_1} \frac{R}{c_p} \left( \frac{\sqrt{2}}{G} \right)^{k-1} \right] + c_v \ln \left[ h(h_0 - h)^{(k-1)/2} \right] \tag{6.5.5}$$

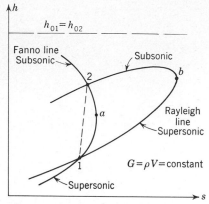

**Fig. 6.3** Fanno and Rayleigh lines.

which is shown on Fig. 6.3 (not to scale).   To find the conditions for maximum entropy, Eq. (6.5.5) is differentiated with respect to $h$ and $ds/dh$ set equal to zero.   By indicating by subscript $a$ values at the maximum entropy point,

$$\frac{ds}{dh} = 0 = \frac{1}{h_a} - \frac{k-1}{2}\frac{1}{h_0 - h_a}$$

or

$$h_a = \frac{2}{k+1}h_0$$

After substituting this into Eq. (6.5.2) to find $V_a$,

$$h_0 = \frac{k+1}{2}h_a = h_a + \frac{V_a{}^2}{2}$$

and

$$V_a{}^2 = (k-1)h_a = (k-1)c_p T_a = (k-1)\frac{kR}{k-1}T_a = kRT_a = c_a{}^2$$

$$(6.5.6)$$

Hence the maximum entropy at point $a$ is for **M** $= 1$, or sonic conditions. For $h > h_a$ the flow is subsonic, and for $h < h_a$ the flow is supersonic. The two conditions, before and after the shock, must lie on the proper Fanno line for the area at which the shock wave occurs.   The momentum equation was not used to determine the Fanno line, and so the complete solution is not determined yet.

*Rayleigh line*

Conditions before and after the shock must also satisfy the momentum and continuity equations. Assuming constant upstream conditions and constant area, Eqs. (6.5.1), (6.5.3), (6.5.4), and (6.4.1) are used to determine the *Rayleigh line*. Eliminating $V$ in the continuity and momentum equations,

$$p + \frac{G^2}{\rho} = \text{const} = B \tag{6.5.7}$$

Next, by eliminating $p$ from this equation and the entropy equation,

$$s = s_1 + c_v \ln \frac{\rho_1^k}{p_1} + c_v \ln \frac{B - G^2/\rho}{\rho^k} \tag{6.5.8}$$

Enthalpy may be expressed as a function of $\rho$ and upstream conditions, from Eq. (6.5.7):

$$h = c_p T = c_p \frac{p}{R\rho} = \frac{c_p}{R} \frac{1}{\rho}\left(B - \frac{G^2}{\rho}\right) \tag{6.5.9}$$

The last two equations determine $s$ and $h$ in terms of the parameter $\rho$ and plot on the $hs$ diagram as indicated in Fig. 6.3. This is a *Rayleigh line*. The value of maximum entropy is found by taking $ds/d\rho$ and $dh/d\rho$ from the equations, then by division and equating to zero, using subscript $b$ for maximum point:

$$\frac{ds}{dh} = \frac{c_v}{c_p} R\rho_b \frac{G^2/[\rho_b(B - G^2/\rho_b)] - k}{2G^2/\rho_b - B} = 0$$

To satisfy this equation, the numerator must be zero and the denominator not zero. The numerator set equal to zero yields

$$k = \frac{G^2}{\rho_b(B - G^2/\rho_b)} = \frac{\rho_b^2 V_b^2}{\rho_b p_b}$$

or

$$V_b^2 = \frac{k p_b}{\rho_b} = c_b^2$$

that is, **M** = 1. For this value the denominator is not zero. Again, as with the Fanno line, sonic conditions occur at the point of maximum entropy. Since the flow conditions must be on both curves, just before and just after the shock wave, it must suddenly change from one point of intersection to the other. The entropy cannot decrease, as no heat is being transferred from the flow, so that the upstream point must be the intersection with least entropy. In all gases investigated the intersection in the subsonic flow has the greater entropy. Thus the shock occurs from supersonic to subsonic.

The Fanno and Rayleigh lines are of value in analyzing flow in constant-area ducts. These are treated in Secs. 6.6 and 6.7.

### *converging-diverging nozzle flow*

Following the presentation of Liepmann and Roshko (see references at end of chapter), the various flow situations for converging-diverging nozzles are investigated. Equation (6.3.20) gives the relation between area ratio and Mach number for isentropic flow throughout the nozzle. By use of Eq. (6.3.11) the area ratio is obtained as a function of pressure ratio

$$\frac{A^*}{A} = \frac{\rho V}{\rho^* V^*} = \frac{[1 - (p/p_0)^{(k-1)/k}]^{1/2}(p/p_0)^{1/k}}{[(k-1)/2]^{1/2}[2/(k+1)]^{(k+1)/2(k-1)}} \tag{6.5.10}$$

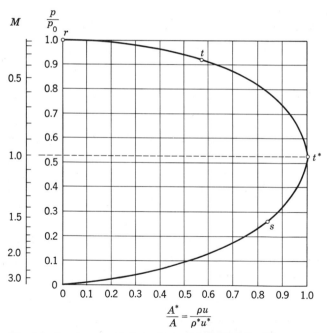

**Fig. 6.4** Isentropic relations for a converging-diverging nozzle. *(By permission, from "Elements of Gas Dynamics," by H. W. Liepmann and A. Roshko, John Wiley & Sons, Inc., New York, 1957.)*

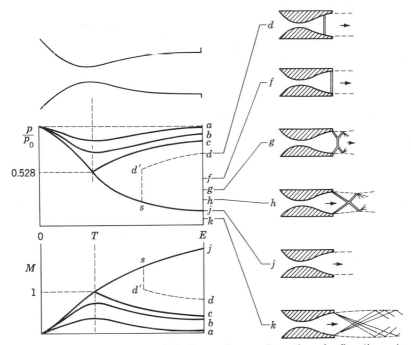

**Fig. 6.5** Various pressure and Mach number configurations for flow through a nozzle. *(By permission, from "Elements of Gas Dynamics," by H. W. Liepmann and A. Roshko, John Wiley & Sons, Inc., New York, 1957.)*

Figure 6.4 is a plot of area ratio vs. pressure ratio and **M**, good only for isentropic flow.

By use of the area ratios the distribution of pressure and Mach number along a given converging-diverging nozzle may now be plotted.   Figure 6.5 illustrates the various flow conditions that may occur.   If the downstream pressure is $p_c$ or greater, isentropic subsonic flow occurs throughout the tube.   If the pressure is at $j$, isentropic flow occurs throughout, with subsonic flow to the throat, sonic flow at the throat, and supersonic flow downstream.   For downstream pressure between $c$ and $f$, a shock wave occurs within the nozzle, as shown for $p_d$.   For pressure at $p_f$ a normal shock wave occurs at the exit, and for pressures between $p_f$ and $p_j$ oblique shock waves at the exit develop.

## 6.6   adiabatic flow with friction in conduits

Gas flow through a pipe or constant-area duct is analyzed in this section subject to the following assumptions:

1. Perfect gas (constant specific heats).
2. Steady, one-dimensional flow.
3. Adiabatic flow (no heat transfer through walls).
4. Constant friction factor over length of conduit.
5. Effective conduit diameter $D$ is four times hydraulic radius (cross-sectioned area divided by perimeter).
6. Elevation changes are unimportant as compared with friction effects.
7. No work added to or extracted from the flow.

The controlling equations are continuity, energy, momentum, and the equation of state. The Fanno line, developed in Sec. 6.5 and shown in Fig. 6.3, was for constant area and used the continuity and energy equations; hence, it applies to adiabatic flow in a duct of constant area. A particle of gas at the upstream end of the duct may be represented by a point on the appropriate Fanno line for proper stagnation enthalpy $h_0$ and mass flow rate $G$ per unit area. As the particle moves downstream, its properties change, owing to friction or irreversibilities such that the entropy always increases in adiabatic flow. Thus the point representing these properties moves along the Fanno line toward the maximum $s$ point, where **M** = 1. If the duct is fed by a converging-diverging nozzle, the flow may originally be supersonic; the velocity must then decrease downstream. If the flow is subsonic at the upstream end, the velocity must increase in the downstream direction.

For exactly one length of pipe, depending upon upstream conditions, the flow is just sonic (**M** = 1) at the downstream end. For shorter lengths of pipe, the flow will not have reached sonic conditions at the outlet, but for longer lengths of pipe, there must be shock waves (and possibly *choking*) if supersonic and *choking* effects if subsonic. By *choking*, one means that the mass flow rate specified cannot take place in this situation and less

**Table 6.1**

| Property | Subsonic flow | Supersonic flow |
|---|---|---|
| Velocity $V$ | Increases | Decreases |
| Mach number **M** | Increases | Decreases |
| Pressure $p$ | Decreases | Increases |
| Temperature $T$ | Decreases | Increases |
| Density $\rho$ | Decreases | Increases |
| Stagnation enthalpy | Constant | Constant |
| Entropy | Increases | Increases |

flow will occur.  Table 6.1 indicates the trends in properties of a gas in adiabatic flow through a constant-area duct, as can be shown from the equations in this section.

The gas cannot change gradually from subsonic to supersonic or vice versa in a constant-area duct.

The momentum equation must now include the effects of wall shear stress and is conveniently written for a segment of duct of length $\delta x$ (Fig. 6.6):

$$pA - \left(p + \frac{dp}{dx}\,\delta x\right)A - \tau_0\pi D\,\delta x = \rho VA\left(V + \frac{dV}{dx}\,\delta x - V\right)$$

Upon simplification,

$$dp + \frac{4\tau_0}{D}\,dx + \rho V\,dV = 0 \tag{6.6.1}$$

By use of Eq. (5.10.2), $\tau_0 = \rho f V^2/8$, in which $f$ is the Darcy-Weisbach friction factor,

$$dp + \frac{f\rho V^2}{2D}\,dx + \rho V\,dV = 0 \tag{6.6.2}$$

For constant $f$, or average value over the length of reach, this equation may be transformed into an equation for $x$ as a function of Mach number. By dividing Eq. (6.6.2) by $p$,

$$\frac{dp}{p} + \frac{f}{2D}\frac{\rho V^2}{p}\,dx + \frac{\rho V}{p}\,dV = 0 \tag{6.6.3}$$

each term is now developed in terms of **M**.  By definition $V/c =$ **M**,

$$V^2 = \mathbf{M}^2\frac{kp}{\rho} \tag{6.6.4}$$

**Fig. 6.6** Notation for application of momentum equation.

or

$$\frac{\rho V^2}{p} = k\mathbf{M}^2 \tag{6.6.5}$$

for the middle term of the momentum equation. By rearranging Eq. (6.6.4),

$$\frac{\rho V}{p} dV = k\mathbf{M}^2 \frac{dV}{V} \tag{6.6.6}$$

Now to express $dV/V$ in terms of **M**, from the energy equation,

$$h_0 = h + \frac{V^2}{2} = c_p T + \frac{V^2}{2} \tag{6.6.7}$$

Differentiating,

$$c_p\, dT + V\, dV = 0 \tag{6.6.8}$$

By dividing through by $V^2 = \mathbf{M}^2 kRT$,

$$\frac{c_p}{R} \frac{1}{k\mathbf{M}^2} \frac{dT}{T} + \frac{dV}{V} = 0$$

Since $c_p/R = k/(k-1)$,

$$\frac{dT}{T} = -\mathbf{M}^2(k-1) \frac{dV}{V} \tag{6.6.9}$$

Differentiating $V^2 = \mathbf{M}^2 kRT$ and dividing by the equation,

$$2\frac{dV}{V} = 2\frac{d\mathbf{M}}{\mathbf{M}} + \frac{dT}{T} \tag{6.6.10}$$

Eliminating $dT/T$ in Eqs. (6.6.9) and (6.6.10) and simplifying,

$$\frac{dV}{V} = \frac{d\mathbf{M}/\mathbf{M}}{[(k-1)/2]\mathbf{M}^2 + 1} \tag{6.6.11}$$

which permits elimination of $dV/V$ from Eq. (6.6.6), yielding

$$\frac{\rho V}{p} dV = \frac{k\mathbf{M}\, d\mathbf{M}}{[(k-1)/2]\mathbf{M}^2 + 1} \tag{6.6.12}$$

And finally, to express $dp/p$ in terms of **M**, from $p = \rho RT$ and $G = \rho V$,

$$pV = GRT \tag{6.6.13}$$

By differentiation

$$\frac{dp}{p} = \frac{dT}{T} - \frac{dV}{V}$$

Equations (6.6.9) and (6.6.11) are used to eliminate $dT/T$ and $dV/V$:

$$\frac{dp}{p} = -\frac{(k-1)\mathbf{M}^2 + 1}{[(k-1)/2]\mathbf{M}^2 + 1}\frac{d\mathbf{M}}{\mathbf{M}} \tag{6.6.14}$$

Equations (6.6.5), (6.6.12), and (6.6.14) are now substituted into the momentum equation (6.6.3). After rearranging,

$$\frac{f}{D}dx = \frac{2(1 - \mathbf{M}^2)}{k\mathbf{M}^3\{[(k-1)/2]\mathbf{M}^2 - 1\}}d\mathbf{M}$$

$$= \frac{2}{k}\frac{d\mathbf{M}}{\mathbf{M}^3} - \frac{k+1}{k}\frac{d\mathbf{M}}{\mathbf{M}\{[(k-1)/2]\mathbf{M}^2 + 1\}} \tag{6.6.15}$$

which may be integrated directly. By using the limits $x = 0$, $\mathbf{M} = \mathbf{M}_0$, $x = l$, $\mathbf{M} = \mathbf{M}$,

$$\frac{fl}{D} = -\frac{1}{k\mathbf{M}^2}\Bigg]_{\mathbf{M}_0}^{\mathbf{M}} - \frac{k+1}{2k}\ln\frac{\mathbf{M}^2}{[(k-1)/2]\mathbf{M}^2 + 1}\Bigg]_{\mathbf{M}_0}^{\mathbf{M}} \tag{6.6.16}$$

$$= \frac{1}{k}\left(\frac{1}{\mathbf{M}_0^2} - \frac{1}{\mathbf{M}^2}\right) + \frac{k+1}{2k}\ln\left[\left(\frac{\mathbf{M}_0}{\mathbf{M}}\right)^2\frac{(k-1)\mathbf{M}^2 + 2}{(k-1)\mathbf{M}_0^2 + 2}\right] \tag{6.6.17}$$

For $k = 1.4$, this reduces to

$$\frac{fl}{D} = \frac{5}{7}\left(\frac{1}{\mathbf{M}_0^2} - \frac{1}{\mathbf{M}^2}\right) + \frac{6}{7}\ln\left[\left(\frac{\mathbf{M}_0}{\mathbf{M}}\right)^2\frac{\mathbf{M}^2 + 5}{\mathbf{M}_0^2 + 5}\right] \qquad k = 1.4 \tag{6.6.18}$$

If $\mathbf{M}_0$ is greater than 1, then $\mathbf{M}$ cannot be less than 1, and if $\mathbf{M}_0$ is less than 1, then $\mathbf{M}$ cannot be greater than 1. For the limiting condition $\mathbf{M} = 1$ and $k = 1.4$,

$$\frac{fL_{\max}}{D} = \frac{5}{7}\left(\frac{1}{\mathbf{M}_0^2} - 1\right) + \frac{6}{7}\ln\frac{6\mathbf{M}_0^2}{\mathbf{M}_0^2 + 5} \qquad k = 1.4 \tag{6.6.19}$$

Experiments by Keenan and Neumann[1] show apparent friction factors for supersonic flow of about half the value for subsonic flow.

**example 6.13** Determine the maximum length of 2.0-in. ID pipe, $f = 0.02$ for flow of air, when the Mach number at the entrance to the pipe is 0.30.

[1] J. H. Keenan and E. P. Neumann, Measurements of Friction in a Pipe for Subsonic and Supersonic Flow of Air, *J. Appl. Mech.*, vol. 13, no. 2, p. A-91, 1946.

From Eq. (6.6.19)

$$\frac{0.02}{\frac{2}{12}} L_{\max} = \frac{5}{7}\left[\frac{1}{(0.3)^2} - 1\right] + \frac{6}{7}\ln\frac{6\times(0.30)^2}{(0.30)^2 + 5}$$

from which $L_{\max} = 44.17$ ft.

The pressure, velocity, and temperature may also be expressed in integral form in terms of the Mach number. To simplify the equations that follow they will be integrated from upstream conditions to conditions at $\mathbf{M} = 1$, indicated by $p^*$, $V^*$, and $T^*$. From Eq. (6.6.14)

$$\frac{p^*}{p_0} = \mathbf{M}_0 \sqrt{\frac{(k-1)\mathbf{M}_0{}^2 + 2}{k+1}} \tag{6.6.20}$$

From Eq. (6.6.11)

$$\frac{V^*}{V_0} = \frac{1}{\mathbf{M}_0}\sqrt{\frac{(k-1)\mathbf{M}_0{}^2 + 2}{k+1}} \tag{6.6.21}$$

From Eqs. (6.6.9) and (6.6.11)

$$\frac{dT}{T} = -(k-1)\frac{\mathbf{M}\,d\mathbf{M}}{[(k-1)/2]\mathbf{M}^2 + 1}$$

which, when integrated, yields

$$\frac{T^*}{T_0} = \frac{(k-1)\mathbf{M}_0{}^2 + 2}{k+1} \tag{6.6.22}$$

**example 6.14**  A 4.0-in. ID pipe, $f = 0.010$, has air at 14.7 psia and at $t = 60°F$ flowing at the upstream end with Mach number 3.0. Determine $L_{\max}$, $p^*$, $V^*$, $T^*$, and values of $p$, $V$, $T$, and $L$ at $\mathbf{M} = 2.0$
From Eq. (6.6.19)

$$\frac{0.01}{0.333} L_{\max} = \frac{5}{7}\left(\frac{1}{9} - 1\right) + \frac{6}{7}\ln\frac{6\times 3^2}{3^2 + 5}$$

from which $L_{\max} = 17.33$ ft. If the flow originated at $\mathbf{M} = 2$, the length $L_{\max}$ is given by the same equation:

$$\frac{0.01}{0.333} L_{\max} = \frac{5}{7}\left(\frac{1}{4} - 1\right) + \frac{6}{7}\ln\frac{6\times 2^2}{2^2 + 5}$$

from which $L_{\max} = 10.14$ ft.
Hence the length from the upstream section at $\mathbf{M} = 3$ to the section where $\mathbf{M} = 2$ is $17.33 - 10.14 = 7.19$ ft.

The velocity at the entrance is

$$V = \sqrt{kRT}\, \mathbf{M} = \sqrt{1.4 \times 53.3 \times 32.17(460 + 60)} \times 3 = 3354 \text{ ft/sec}$$

From Eqs. (6.6.20) to (6.6.22)

$$\frac{p^*}{14.7} = 3\sqrt{\frac{0.4 \times 3^2 + 2}{2.4}} = 4.581$$

$$\frac{V^*}{3354} = \frac{1}{3}\sqrt{\frac{0.4 \times 3^2 + 2}{2.4}} = 0.509$$

$$\frac{T^*}{520} = \frac{0.4 \times 3^2 + 2}{2.4} = \frac{7}{3}$$

So $p^* = 67.4$ psia, $V^* = 1707$ ft/sec, $T^* = 1213°R$.   For $\mathbf{M} = 2$ the same equations are now solved for $p_0'$, $V_0'$, and $T_0'$:

$$\frac{67.4}{p_0'} = 2\sqrt{\frac{0.4 \times 2^2 + 2}{2.4}} = 2.45$$

$$\frac{1707}{V_0'} = \frac{1}{2}\sqrt{\frac{0.4 \times 2^2 + 2}{2.4}} = 0.6125$$

$$\frac{1213}{T_0'} = \frac{0.4 \times 2^2 + 2}{2.4} = \frac{3}{2}$$

So $p_0' = 27.5$ psia, $V_0' = 2790$ ft/sec, and $T_0' = 809°R$.

### 6.7   frictionless flow through ducts with heat transfer

The steady flow of a perfect gas (with constant specific heats) through a constant-area duct is considered in this section.   Friction is neglected, and no work is done on or by the flow.
The appropriate equations for analysis of this case are
Continuity:

$$G = \frac{\dot{m}}{A} = \rho V \tag{6.7.1}$$

Momentum:

$$p + \rho V^2 = \text{const} \tag{6.7.2}$$

Energy:

$$q_H = h_2 - h_1 + \frac{V_2{}^2 - V_1{}^2}{2} = c_p(T_2 - T_1) + \frac{V_2{}^2 - V_1{}^2}{2}$$

$$= c_p(T_{02} - T_{01}) \tag{6.7.3}$$

$T_{01}$ and $T_{02}$ are the isentropic stagnation temperatures, i.e., the temperature produced at a section by bringing the flow isentropically to rest.

The Rayleigh line, obtained from the solution of momentum and continuity for a constant cross section by neglecting friction, is very helpful in examining the flow. First, by eliminating $V$ in Eqs. (6.7.1) and (6.7.2),

$$p + \frac{G^2}{\rho} = \text{const} \tag{6.7.4}$$

which is Eq. (6.5.7). Equations (6.5.8) and (6.5.9) express the entropy $s$ and enthalpy $h$ in terms of the parameter $\rho$ for the assumptions of this section, as in Fig. 6.7.

Since, by Eq. (3.7.6), for no losses, entropy can increase only when heat is added, the properties of the gas must change as indicated in Fig. 6.7, moving toward the maximum entropy point as heat is added. At the maximum $s$ point there is no change in entropy for a small change in $h$, and isentropic conditions apply to the point. The speed of sound under isentropic conditions is given by $c = \sqrt{dp/d\rho}$ as given by Eq. (6.2.2). From Eq. (6.7.4), by differentiation,

$$\frac{dp}{d\rho} = \frac{G^2}{\rho^2} = V^2$$

using Eq. (6.7.1). Hence at the maximum $s$ point of the Rayleigh line, $V = \sqrt{dp/d\rho}$ also and $\mathbf{M} = 1$, or sonic conditions, prevail. The addition of heat to supersonic flow causes the Mach number of the flow to decrease toward $\mathbf{M} = 1$, and if just the proper amount of heat is added, $\mathbf{M}$ becomes 1. If more heat is added, choking results and conditions at the upstream end are altered to reduce the mass rate of flow. The addition of heat to

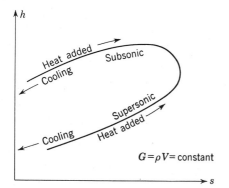

**Fig. 6.7**  Rayleigh line.

subsonic flow causes an increase in the Mach number toward $\mathbf{M} = 1$, and again, too much heat transfer causes choking with an upstream adjustment of mass flow rate to a smaller value.

From Eq. (6.7.3) it is noted that the increase in isentropic stagnation pressure is a measure of the heat added.   From $V^2 = \mathbf{M}^2 kRT$, $p = \rho RT$, and continuity,

$$pV = GRT$$

and

$$\rho V^2 = kp\mathbf{M}^2$$

Now, from the momentum equation,

$$p_1 + kp_1\mathbf{M}_1^2 = p_2 + kp_2\mathbf{M}_2^2$$

and

$$\frac{p_1}{p_2} = \frac{1 + k\mathbf{M}_2^2}{1 + k\mathbf{M}_1^2} \tag{6.7.5}$$

By writing this equation for the limiting case $p_2 = p^*$ when $\mathbf{M}_2 = 1$,

$$\frac{p}{p^*} = \frac{1 + k}{1 + k\mathbf{M}^2} \tag{6.7.6}$$

with $p$ the pressure at any point in the duct where $\mathbf{M}$ is the corresponding Mach number.   For the subsonic case, with $\mathbf{M}$ increasing to the right (Fig. 6.7), $p$ must decrease, and for the supersonic case, as $\mathbf{M}$ decreases toward the right, $p$ must increase.

To develop the other pertinent relations, the energy equation (6.7.3) is used,

$$c_p T_0 = \frac{kR}{k-1} T_0 = \frac{kR}{k-1} T + \frac{V^2}{2}$$

in which $T_0$ is the isentropic stagnation temperature and $T$ the free stream temperature at the same section.   By applying this to section 1, after dividing through by $kRT_1/(k-1)$,

$$\frac{T_{01}}{T_1} = 1 + (k-1)\frac{\mathbf{M}_1^2}{2} \tag{6.7.7}$$

and for section 2

$$\frac{T_{02}}{T_2} = 1 + (k-1)\frac{\mathbf{M}_2^2}{2} \tag{6.7.8}$$

Dividing Eq. (6.7.7) by Eq. (6.7.8),

$$\frac{T_{01}}{T_{02}} = \frac{T_1}{T_2}\frac{2 + (k-1)\mathbf{M}_1{}^2}{2 + (k-1)\mathbf{M}_2{}^2} \tag{6.7.9}$$

The ratio $T_1/T_2$ is determined in terms of the Mach numbers as follows:
From the perfect-gas law, $p_1 = \rho_1 R T_1$, $p_2 = \rho_2 R T_2$,

$$\frac{T_1}{T_2} = \frac{p_1}{p_2}\frac{\rho_2}{\rho_1} \tag{6.7.10}$$

From continuity $\rho_2/\rho_1 = V_1/V_2$, and by definition,

$$\mathbf{M}_1 = \frac{V_1}{\sqrt{kRT_1}} \qquad \mathbf{M}_2 = \frac{V_2}{\sqrt{kRT_2}}$$

so

$$\frac{V_1}{V_2} = \frac{\mathbf{M}_1}{\mathbf{M}_2}\sqrt{\frac{T_1}{T_2}}$$

and

$$\frac{\rho_2}{\rho_1} = \frac{\mathbf{M}_1}{\mathbf{M}_2}\sqrt{\frac{T_1}{T_2}} \tag{6.7.11}$$

Now, by substituting Eqs. (6.7.5) and (6.7.11) into Eq. (6.7.10) and simplifying,

$$\frac{T_1}{T_2} = \left(\frac{\mathbf{M}_1}{\mathbf{M}_2}\frac{1 + k\mathbf{M}_2{}^2}{1 + k\mathbf{M}_1{}^2}\right)^2 \tag{6.7.12}$$

With this equation substituted into Eq. (6.7.9),

$$\frac{T_{01}}{T_{02}} = \left(\frac{\mathbf{M}_1}{\mathbf{M}_2}\frac{1 + k\mathbf{M}_2{}^2}{1 + k\mathbf{M}_1{}^2}\right)^2\frac{2 + (k-1)\mathbf{M}_1{}^2}{2 + (k-1)\mathbf{M}_2{}^2} \tag{6.7.13}$$

By applying this equation to the downstream section where $T_{02} = T_0^*$ and
$\mathbf{M}_2 = 1$, by dropping the subscripts for the upstream section,

$$\frac{T_0}{T_0^*} = \frac{\mathbf{M}^2(k+1)[2 + (k-1)\mathbf{M}^2]}{(1 + k\mathbf{M}^2)^2} \tag{6.7.14}$$

All the necessary equations for determination of frictionless flow with
heat transfer in a constant-area duct are now available.  Heat transfer per
unit mass is given by $q_H = c_p(T_0^* - T_0)$ for $\mathbf{M} = 1$ at the exit.  Use of the
equations is illustrated in the following example.

**example 6.15**  Air at $V_1 = 300$ ft/sec, $p = 40$ psia, $t = 60°F$ flows into a
4.0-in.-diameter duct.  How much heat transfer per unit mass is needed

for sonic conditions at the exit?    Determine pressure, temperature, and velocity at the exit and at the section where $\mathbf{M} = 0.70$.

$$\mathbf{M}_1 = \frac{V_1}{\sqrt{kRT_1}} = \frac{300}{\sqrt{1.4 \times 53.3 \times 32.17(460 + 60)}} = 0.268$$

The isentropic stagnation temperature at the entrance, from Eq. (6.7.7), is

$$T_{01} = T_1\left(1 + \frac{k-1}{2}\mathbf{M}_1^2\right) = 520[1 + 0.2 \times (0.268)^2] = 527°R$$

The isentropic stagnation temperature at the exit, from Eq. (6.7.14), is

$$T_0^* = \frac{T_0(1 + k\mathbf{M}^2)^2}{(k+1)\mathbf{M}_2[2 + (k-1)\mathbf{M}^2]} = \frac{527[1 + 1.4 \times (0.268)^2]^2}{2.4 \times (0.268)^2[2 + 0.4 \times (0.268)^2]}$$

$$= 1827°R$$

The heat transfer per slug of air flowing is

$$q_H = c_p(T_0^* - T_{01}) = 0.24 \times 32.17(1827 - 527) = 10,050 \text{ Btu/slug}$$

The pressure at the exit, Eq. (6.7.6), is

$$p^* = p\frac{1 + k\mathbf{M}^2}{k+1} = \frac{40}{2.4}[1 + 1.4 \times (0.268)^2] = 18.35 \text{ psia}$$

and the temperature, from Eq. (6.7.12),

$$T^* = T\left[\frac{1 + k\mathbf{M}^2}{(k+1)\mathbf{M}}\right]^2 = 520\left[\frac{1 + 1.4 \times (0.268)^2}{2.4 \times 0.268}\right]^2 = 1520°R$$

At the exit,

$$V^* = c^* = \sqrt{kRT^*} = \sqrt{1.4 \times 53.3 \times 32.17 \times 1520} = 1910 \text{ ft/sec}$$

At the section where $\mathbf{M} = 0.7$, from Eq. (6.7.6),

$$p = p^*\frac{k+1}{1 + k\mathbf{M}^2} = \frac{18.35 \times 2.4}{1 + 1.4 \times (0.7)^2} = 26.1 \text{ psia}$$

From Eq. (6.7.12)

$$T = T^*\left[\frac{(k+1)\mathbf{M}}{1 + k\mathbf{M}^2}\right]^2 = 1520\left[\frac{2.4 \times 0.7}{1 + 1.4 \times (0.7)^2}\right]^2 = 1507°R$$

and

$$V = \mathbf{M}\sqrt{kRT} = 0.7\sqrt{1.4 \times 53.3 \times 32.17 \times 1507} = 1332 \text{ ft/sec}$$

**Table 6.2   Trends in flow properties**

| Property | Heating | | Cooling | |
|---|---|---|---|---|
| | **M** $> 1$ | **M** $< 1$ | **M** $> 1$ | **M** $< 1$ |
| Pressure $p$ | Increases | Decreases | Decreases | Increases |
| Velocity $V$ | Decreases | Increases | Increases | Decreases |
| Isentropic stagnation temperature $T_0$ | Increases | Increases | Decreases | Decreases |
| Density $\rho$ | Increases | Decreases | Decreases | Increases |
| Temperature $T$ | Increases | Increases for **M** $< 1/\sqrt{k}$ Decreases for **M** $> 1/\sqrt{k}$ | Decreases | Decreases for **M** $< 1/\sqrt{k}$ Increases for **M** $> 1/\sqrt{k}$ |

The trends in flow properties are shown in Table 6.2.

For curves and tables tabulating the various equations, consult the books by Cambel and Jennings, Keenan and Kaye, and Shapiro, listed in the references at the end of this chapter.

## 6.8   steady isothermal flow in long pipelines

In the analysis of isothermal flow of a perfect gas through long ducts, neither the Fanno nor Rayleigh lines are applicable, since the Fanno line applies to adiabatic flow and the Rayleigh line to frictionless flow.   An analysis somewhat similar to those of the previous two sections is carried out to show the trend in properties with Mach number.

The appropriate equations are
Momentum [Eq. (6.6.3)]:

$$\frac{dp}{p} + \frac{f}{2D} \frac{\rho V^2}{p} \, dx + \frac{\rho V}{p} \, dV = 0 \tag{6.8.1}$$

Equation of state:

$$\frac{p}{\rho} = \text{const} \qquad \frac{dp}{p} = \frac{d\rho}{\rho} \tag{6.8.2}$$

Continuity:

$$\rho V = \text{const} \qquad \frac{d\rho}{\rho} = -\frac{dV}{V} \tag{6.8.3}$$

Energy [Eq. (6.7.7)]:

$$T_0 = T \left[ 1 + \frac{(k-1)}{2} \mathbf{M}^2 \right] \tag{6.8.4}$$

in which $T_0$ is the isentropic stagnation temperature at the section where the free-stream static temperature is $T$ and the Mach number is $\mathbf{M}$. Stagnation pressure [Eq. (6.3.11)]:

$$p_0 = p \left( 1 + \frac{k-1}{2} \mathbf{M}^2 \right)^{k/(k-1)} \tag{6.8.5}$$

in which $p_0$ is the pressure (at the section of $p$ and $\mathbf{M}$) obtained by reducing the velocity to zero isentropically.

From definitions and use of the above equations,

$$V = c\mathbf{M} = \sqrt{kRT}\,\mathbf{M} \qquad \frac{dV}{V} = \frac{d\mathbf{M}}{\mathbf{M}} = \frac{d\mathbf{M}^2}{2\mathbf{M}^2}$$

$$\frac{\rho V}{p}\,dV = \frac{V\,dV}{RT} = \frac{c^2}{RT}\,\mathbf{M}\,d\mathbf{M} = k\mathbf{M}\,d\mathbf{M}$$

$$\frac{\rho V^2}{p} = \frac{c^2 \mathbf{M}^2}{RT} = k\mathbf{M}^2$$

By substituting into the momentum equation, using the relations,

$$\frac{dp}{p} = \frac{d\rho}{\rho} = -\frac{dV}{V} = -\frac{1}{2}\frac{d\mathbf{M}^2}{\mathbf{M}^2} = -\frac{k\mathbf{M}^2}{1 - k\mathbf{M}^2}\frac{f\,dx}{2D} \tag{6.8.6}$$

The differential $dx$ is positive in the downstream direction, and so one may conclude that the trends in properties vary depending upon whether $\mathbf{M}$ is less than $1/\sqrt{k}$ or greater than $1/\sqrt{k}$. For $\mathbf{M} < 1/\sqrt{k}$, the pressure and density decrease and velocity and Mach number increase, with the opposite trends for $\mathbf{M} > 1/\sqrt{k}$; hence, the Mach number always approaches $1/\sqrt{k}$, in place of unity for adiabatic flow in pipelines.

To determine the direction of heat transfer, by differentiation of Eq. (6.8.4) and then division by it, remembering that $T$ is constant,

$$\frac{dT_0}{T_0} - \frac{k-1}{2 + (k-1)\mathbf{M}^2}\,d\mathbf{M}^2 \tag{6.8.7}$$

By eliminating $d\mathbf{M}^2$ in this equation and Eq. (6.8.6),

$$\frac{dT_0}{T_0} = \frac{k(k-1)\mathbf{M}^4}{(1 - k\mathbf{M}^2)[2 + (k-1)\mathbf{M}^2]}\frac{f\,dx}{D} \tag{6.8.8}$$

**Table 6.3   Trends in fluid properties for isothermal flow**

| Property | $M < 1/\sqrt{k}$ subsonic | $M > 1/\sqrt{k}$ subsonic or supersonic |
|---|---|---|
| Pressure $p$ | Decreases | Increases |
| Density $\rho$ | Decreases | Increases |
| Velocity $V$ | Increases | Decreases |
| Mach number $\mathbf{M}$ | Increases | Decreases |
| Stagnation temperature $T_0$ | Increases | Decreases |
| Stagnation pressure $p_0$ | Decreases | Increases for $\mathbf{M} < \sqrt{2/(k+1)}$ |
| | | Decreases for $\mathbf{M} > \sqrt{2/(k+1)}$ |

which shows that the isentropic stagnation temperature increases for $\mathbf{M} < 1/\sqrt{k}$, indicating that heat is transferred to the fluid. For $M > 1/\sqrt{k}$ heat transfer is from the fluid.

From Eqs. (6.8.5) and (6.8.6)

$$\frac{dp_0}{p_0} = \frac{2 - (k+1)\mathbf{M}^2}{2 + (k-1)\mathbf{M}^2} \frac{k\mathbf{M}^2}{k\mathbf{M}^2 - 1} \frac{f\,dx}{2D} \tag{6.8.9}$$

Table 6.3 shows the trends of fluid properties.

By integration of the various Eqs. (6.8.6) in terms of $\mathbf{M}$, the change with Mach number is found. The last two terms yield

$$\frac{f}{D} \int_0^{L_{\max}} dx = \frac{1}{k} \int_M^{1/\sqrt{k}} \frac{(1 - k\mathbf{M}^2)}{\mathbf{M}^4}\,d\mathbf{M}^2$$

or

$$\frac{f}{D} L_{\max} = \frac{1 - k\mathbf{M}^2}{k\mathbf{M}^2} + \ln\,(k\mathbf{M}^2) \tag{6.8.10}$$

in which $L_{\max}$, as before, represents the maximum length of duct. For greater lengths choking occurs and the mass rate is decreased. To find the pressure change,

$$\int_p^{p^{*t}} \frac{dp}{p} = -\frac{1}{2} \int_M^{1/\sqrt{k}} \frac{d\mathbf{M}^2}{\mathbf{M}^2}$$

and

$$\frac{p^{*t}}{p} = \sqrt{k}\,\mathbf{M} \tag{6.8.11}$$

The superscript $^{*t}$ indicates conditions at $\mathbf{M} = 1/\sqrt{k}$, and $\mathbf{M}$ and $p$ represent values at any upstream section.

**example 6.16**  Helium enters a 4.0-in. ID pipe from a converging-diverging nozzle at $\mathbf{M} = 1.30$, $p = 2.0$ psia, $T = 400°R$. Determine for isothermal flow: ($a$) the maximum length of pipe for no choking, ($b$) the downstream conditions, and ($c$) the length from the exit to the section where $\mathbf{M} = 1.0$. $f = 0.006$.

($a$)  From Eq. (6.8.10) for $k = 1.66$

$$\frac{0.006 L_{\max}}{\frac{4}{12}} = \frac{1 - 1.66 \times (1.3)^2}{1.66 \times (1.3)^2} + \ln [1.66 \times (1.3)^2]$$

from which $L_{\max} = 21.54$ ft.

($b$)  From Eq. (6.8.11)

$$p^{*1} = p \sqrt{k} \ \mathbf{M} = 2.0 \sqrt{1.66} \ 1.3 = 3.35 \text{ psia}$$

The Mach number at the exit is $1/\sqrt{1.66} = 0.756$.  From Eqs. (6.8.6)

$$\int_V^{V^{*t}} \frac{dV}{V} = \frac{1}{2} \int_{\mathbf{M}}^{1/\sqrt{k}} \frac{d\mathbf{M}^2}{\mathbf{M}^2}$$

or

$$\frac{V^{*t}}{V} = \frac{1}{\sqrt{k} \ \mathbf{M}}$$

At the upstream section

$$V = \mathbf{M} \sqrt{kRT} = 1.3 \sqrt{1.66 \times 386 \times 32.17 \times 400} = 3740 \text{ ft/sec}$$

and

$$V^{*t} = \frac{V}{\sqrt{k} \ \mathbf{M}} = \frac{3740}{\sqrt{1.66} \ 1.3} = 2072 \text{ ft/sec}$$

($c$)  From Eq. (6.8.10) for $\mathbf{M} = 1$,

$$\frac{0.006}{\frac{4}{12}} L'_{\max} = \frac{1 - 1.66}{1.66} + \ln 1.66$$

or $L'_{\max} = 6.0$ ft.  $\mathbf{M} = 1$ occurs 6.0 ft from the exit.

## 6.9  analogy of shock waves to open-channel waves

Both the oblique and normal shock waves in a gas have their counterpart in open-channel flow.  An elementary surface wave has a speed in still liquid of $\sqrt{gy}$, in which $y$ is the depth in a wide, open channel.   When flow in the channel is such that $V = V_c = \sqrt{gy}$, the Froude number is unity and flow is said to be *critical;* i.e., a small disturbance cannot be propagated upstream.   This is analogous to sonic flow at the throat of a tube, with Mach number unity.   For liquid velocities greater than $V_c = \sqrt{gy}$ the Froude number is greater than unity and the velocity is supercritical, analogous to supersonic gas flow.   Changes in depth are analogous to changes in density in gas flow.

The continuity equation in an open channel of constant width is

$$Vy = \text{const}$$

and the continuity equation for compressible flow in a tube of constant cross section is

$$V\rho = \text{const}$$

Compressible fluid density $\rho$ and open-channel depth $y$ are analogous.

The same analogy is also present in the energy equation.   The energy equation for a horizontal open channel of constant width, neglecting friction, is

$$\frac{V^2}{2g} + y = \text{const}$$

After differentiating,

$$V\,dV + g\,dy = 0$$

By substitution from $V_c = \sqrt{gy}$ to eliminate $g$,

$$V\,dV + V_c{}^2\frac{dy}{y} = 0$$

which is to be compared with the energy equation for compressible flow [Eq. (6.3.4)]

$$V\,dV + c^2\frac{d\rho}{\rho} = 0$$

The two critical velocities $V_c$ and $c$ are analogous, and, hence, $y$ and $\rho$ are analogous.

By applying the momentum equation to a small depth change in horizontal open-channel flow, and to a sudden density change in compressible flow, the density and the open-channel depth can again be shown to be analogous.   In effect, the analogy is between the Froude number and the Mach number.

Analogous to the normal shock wave is the hydraulic jump, which causes a sudden change in velocity and depth, and a change in Froude number from greater than unity to less than unity.   Analogous to the oblique shock and rarefaction waves in gas flow are oblique liquid waves produced in a channel by changes in the direction of the channel walls, or by changes in floor elevation.

A body placed in an open channel with flow at Froude number greater than unity causes waves on the surface that are analogous to shock and rarefaction waves on a similar (two-dimensional) body in a supersonic wind tunnel.   Changes to greater depth are analogous to compression shock, and changes to lesser depth to rarefaction waves.   Shallow water tanks, called ripple tanks, have been used to study supersonic flow situations.

## problems

**6.1**   Three pounds mass of a perfect gas, molecular weight 36, had its temperature increased 3.2°F when 2000 ft-lb of work was done on it in an insulated constant-volume chamber.   Determine $c_v$ and $c_p$.

**6.2**   A gas of molecular weight 48 has a $c_p = 0.372$.   What is $c_v$ for this gas?

**6.3**   Calculate the specific heat ratio $k$ for Probs. 6.1 and 6.2.

**6.4**   The enthalpy of a gas is increased by 0.4 Btu/lb$_m$ °R when heat is added at constant pressure, and the internal energy is increased by 0.3 Btu/lb$_m$ °R when the volume is maintained constant and heat is added. Calculate the molecular weight.

**6.5**   Calculate the enthalpy change of 3 lb$_m$ carbon monoxide from $p_1 = 30$ psia, $T_1 = 40$°F to $p_2 = 60$ psia, $T_2 = 340$°F.

**6.6**   Calculate the entropy change in Prob. 6.5.

**6.7**   From Eq. (6.1.13) and the perfect-gas law, derive the equation of state for isentropic flow.

**6.8**   Compute the enthalpy change per slug for helium from $T_1 = 0$°F, $p_1 = 15$ psia to $T_2 = 100$°F in an isentropic process.

**6.9**   In an isentropic process 3 lb$_m$ oxygen with a volume of 4.5 ft$^3$ at 60°F has its absolute pressure doubled.   What is the final temperature?

**6.10**   Work out the expression for density change with temperature for a reversible polytropic process.

**6.11**   Hydrogen at 40 psia, 30°F, has its temperature increased to 120°F by a reversible polytropic process with $n = 1.20$.   Calculate the final pressure.

**6.12**   A gas has a density decrease of 10 per cent in a reversible polytropic process when the temperature decreases from 115 to 40°F.   Compute the exponent $n$ for the process.

**6.13**   A projectile moves through water at 80°F at 3000 ft/sec.   What is its Mach number?

**6.14**   If an airplane travels at 800 mph at sea level, $p = 14.7$ psia, $t = 68°F$, and at the same speed in the stratosphere where $t = -67°F$, how much greater is the Mach number in the latter case?

**6.15**   What is the speed of sound through hydrogen at 80°F?

**6.16**   Derive the equation for speed of a small liquid wave in an open channel by using the methods of Sec. 6.2 for determination of speed of sound (Fig. 6.8).

**6.17**   By using the energy equation

$$V \, dV + \frac{dp}{\rho} + d \text{ (losses)} = 0$$

the continuity equation $\rho V = \text{const}$, and $c = \sqrt{dp/d\rho}$, show that for sub-sonic flow in a pipe the velocity must increase in the downstream direction.

**6.18**   Isentropic flow of air occurs at a section of a pipe where $p = 40$ psia, $t = 90°F$, and $V = 537$ ft/sec.   An object is immersed in the flow which brings the velocity to zero.   What are the temperature and pressure at the stagnation point?

**6.19**   What is the Mach number for the flow of Prob. 6.18?

**6.20**   How do the temperature and pressure at the stagnation point in isentropic flow compare with reservoir conditions?

**6.21**   Air flows from a reservoir at 160°F, 100 psia.   Assuming isentropic flow, calculate the velocity, temperature, pressure, and density at a section where **M** $= 0.60$.

**6.22**   Oxygen flows from a reservoir where $p_0 = 100$ psia, $t_0 = 60°F$, to a 6-in.-diameter section where the velocity is 600 ft/sec.   Calculate the mass rate of flow (isentropic) and the Mach number, pressure, and temperature at the 6-in. section.

**Fig. 6.8**

**6.23**   Helium discharges from a $\frac{1}{2}$-in.-diameter converging nozzle at its maximum rate for reservoir conditions of $p = 60$ psia, $t = 80°F$.   What restrictions are placed on the downstream pressure?   Calculate the mass flow rate and velocity of the gas at the nozzle.

**6.24**   Air in a reservoir at 350 psia, $t = 290°F$, flows through a 2-in.-diameter throat in a converging-diverging nozzle.   For **M** = 1 at the throat, calculate $p$, $\rho$, and $T$ there.

**6.25**   What must be the velocity, pressure, density, temperature, and diameter at a cross section of the nozzle of Prob. 6.24 where **M** = 2.4?

**6.26**   Nitrogen in sonic flow at a 1-in.-diameter throat section has a pressure of 8 psia, $t = 0°F$.   Determine the mass flow rate.

**6.27**   What is the Mach number for Prob. 6.26 at a $1\frac{1}{2}$-in.-diameter section in supersonic and in subsonic flow?

**6.28**   What diameter throat section is needed for critical flow of 0.5 lb$_m$/sec carbon monoxide from a reservoir where $p = 300$ psia, $t = 100°F$?

**6.29**   A supersonic nozzle is to be designed for air flow with **M** = 3 at the exit section, which is 8 in. in diameter and has a pressure of 1 psia and temperature of $-120°F$.   Calculate the throat area and reservoir conditions.

**6.30**   In Prob. 6.29 calculate the diameter of cross section for **M** = 1.5, 2.0, and 2.5.

**6.31**   For reservoir conditions of $p_0 = 150$ psia, $t_0 = 120°F$, air flows through a converging diverging tube with a 3.0-in.-diameter throat with a maximum Mach number of 0.80.   Determine the mass rate of flow and the diameter, pressure, velocity, and temperature at the exit where **M** = 0.50.

**6.32**   Calculate the exit velocity and the mass rate of flow of nitrogen from a reservoir where $p = 60$ psia, $t = 80°F$, through a converging nozzle of 2 in. diameter discharging to atmosphere.

**6.33**   Reduce Eq. (6.3.25) to its form for air flow.   Plot $p/p_0$ vs. $A*/A$ for the range of $p/p_0$ from 0.98 to 0.02.

**6.34**   By utilizing the plot of Prob. 6.33, find the two pressure ratios for $A*/A = 0.50$.

**6.35**   In a converging-diverging duct in supersonic flow of hydrogen, the throat diameter is 2.0 in.   Determine the pressure ratios $p/p_0$ in the converging and diverging ducts where the diameter is 2.25 in.

**6.36**   A shock wave occurs in a duct carrying air where the upstream Mach number is 2.0 and upstream temperature and pressure are 60°F and 3 psia. Calculate the Mach number, pressure, temperature, and velocity after the shock wave.

**6.37**   Show that entropy has increased across the shock wave of Prob. 6.36.

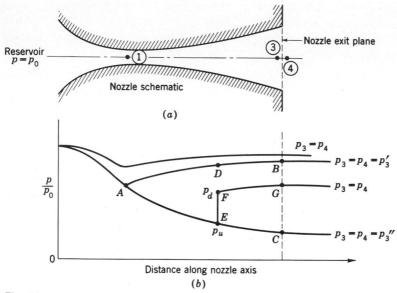

**Fig. 6.9**

**6.38**   Conditions immediately before a normal shock wave in air flow are $p_u = 6$ psia, $t_u = 100°F$, $V_u = 1800$ ft/sec.   Find $\mathbf{M}_u$, $\mathbf{M}_d$, $p_d$, and $t_d$, where the subscript $d$ refers to conditions just downstream from the shock wave.

**6.39**   For $A = 0.16$ ft² in Prob. 6.38, calculate the entropy increase across the shock wave in Btu per second per degree Rankine.

**6.40**   From Eqs. (6.3.1), (6.3.4), and (6.3.5) deduce that at the throat of a convergent-divergent (De Laval) nozzle, point 1 of Fig. 6.9a, $dp = 0$, $d\rho = 0$ for $\mathbf{M} \neq 1$ (cf. Fig. 6.9b).   Are these differentials zero for $\mathbf{M} = 1$?   Explain.

**6.41**   From Eqs. (6.3.1), (6.3.4), and (6.3.5) justify the slopes of the curves shown in Fig. 6.9b.   Do not consider $EFG$.

**6.42**   For the nozzle described below, plot curves $ADB$ and $AEC$ (Fig. 6.9b).  (*Suggestions:* Determine only one intermediate point.   Use section VI.)  The reservoir has air at 50 psia and 100°F when sonic conditions are obtained at the throat.

| Section | I | II | III | IV | V | VI | VII | VIII | IX | X exit |
|---|---|---|---|---|---|---|---|---|---|---|
| Distance downstream from throat, in. | 0.5 | 1.0 | 1.5 | 2.0 | 2.5 | 3.0 | 3.5 | 4.0 | 4.5 | 5.0 |
| $A/A^*$ ($A^* = 0.0313$ ft²) | 1.030 | 1.050 | 1.100 | 1.133 | 1.168 | 1.200 | 1.239 | 1.269 | 1.310 | 1.345 |

**6.43**  Using the data from Prob. 6.42 determine $p_3/p_0$ when a normal shock wave occurs at section VI.

**6.44**  Could a flow discontinuity occur at section VI of Prob. 6.42 so that the flow path would be described by $ADFG$ of Fig. 6.9$b$?  (*Hint:* Determine the entropy changes.)

**6.45**  What is $p_3/p_0$ when a normal shock wave occurs just inside the nozzle exit?  (*Hint:* $p_d = p_4$ and $p_u$ is $p_3$ for isentropic flow up to section VI of Prob. 6.42.)

**6.46**  Suggest what might occur just outside the nozzle if there is a receiver pressure $p_4$ which is above that for which the gas flows isentropically throughout the nozzle into the receiver, point $C$ of Fig. 6.9$b$, but below that for which a normal shock is possible at the nozzle exit (cf. Prob. 6.45).

**6.47**  Speculate on what occurs within and without the nozzle if the receiver pressure is below that corresponding to point $C$ of Fig. 6.9$b$.

**6.48**  Show, from the equations of Sec. 6.6, that temperature, pressure, and density decrease in real, adiabatic duct flow for subsonic conditions and increase for supersonic conditions.

**6.49**  What length of 4-in.-diameter insulated duct, $f = 0.012$, is needed when oxygen enters at **M** = 3.0 and leaves at **M** = 2.0?

**6.50**  Air enters an insulated pipe at **M** = 0.4 and leaves at **M** = 0.6. What portion of the duct length is required for the flow to occur at **M** = 0.5?

**6.51**  Determine the maximum length, without choking, for the adiabatic flow of air in a 4-in.-diameter duct, $f = 0.025$, when upstream conditions are $t = 120°F$, $V = 650$ ft/sec, $p = 30$ psia.  What are the pressure and temperature at the exit?

**6.52**  What minimum size insulated duct is required to transport 2 lb$_m$/sec nitrogen 1000 ft?  The upstream temperature is 80°F, and the velocity there is 200 ft/sec.  $f = 0.020$.

**6.53**  Find the upstream and downstream pressures in Prob. 6.52.

**6.54**  What is the maximum mass rate of flow of air from a reservoir, $t = 60°F$, through 19.15 ft of insulated 1-in.-diameter pipe, $f = 0.020$, discharging to atmosphere?  $p = 14.7$ psia.

**6.55**  In frictionless oxygen flow through a duct the following conditions prevail at inlet and outlet: $V_1 = 300$ ft/sec; $t_1 = 80°F$; **M**$_2$ = 0.4.  Find the heat added per slug and the pressure ratio $p_1/p_2$.

**6.56**  In frictionless air flow through a 4-in.-diameter duct 0.3 lb$_m$/sec enters at $t = 30°F$, $p = 10$ psia.  How much heat, in Btu per pound mass, can be added without choking the flow?

**6.57**  Frictionless flow through a duct with heat transfer causes the Mach number to decrease from 2 to 1.75.  $k = 1.4$.  Determine the temperature, velocity, pressure, and density ratios.

**6.58** In Prob. 6.57 the duct is 2 in. square, $p_1 = 15$ psia, and $V_1 = 2000$ ft/sec. Calculate the mass rate of flow for air flowing.

**6.59** How much heat must be transferred per pound mass to cause the Mach number to increase from 2 to 2.8 in a frictionless duct carrying air? $V_1 = 1500$ ft/sec.

**6.60** Oxygen at $V_1 = 1600$ ft/sec, $p = 12$ psia, $t = 20°F$ flows in a 2-in.-diameter frictionless duct. How much heat transfer per pound mass is needed for sonic conditions at the exit?

**6.61** Prove the density, pressure, and velocity trends given in Sec. 6.8 in the table of trends in flow properties.

**6.62** Apply the first law of thermodynamics, Eq. (3.7.1), to isothermal flow of a perfect gas in a horizontal pipeline, and develop an expression for the heat added per slug flowing.

**6.63** Air is flowing at constant temperature through a 3-in.-diameter horizontal pipe, $f = 0.02$. At the entrance $V_1 = 300$ ft/sec, $t = 120°F$, $p_1 = 30$ psia. What is the maximum pipe length for this flow, and how much heat is transferred to the air per pound mass?

**6.64** Air at 60°F flows through a 1-in.-diameter pipe at constant temperature. At the entrance $V_1 = 200$ ft/sec, and at the exit $V_2 = 300$ ft/sec. $f = 0.016$. What is the length of the pipe?

**6.65** If the pressure at the entrance of the pipe of Prob. 6.64 is 20 psia, what is the pressure at the exit and what is the heat transfer to the pipe per second?

**6.66** Hydrogen enters a pipe from a converging nozzle at **M** $= 1$, $p = 2$ psia, $t = 0°F$. Determine for isothermal flow the maximum length of pipe, in diameters, and the pressure change over this length. $f = 0.010$.

**6.67** Oxygen flows at constant temperature of 68°F from a pressure tank, $p = 1900$ psia, through 10 ft of 0.01-ft ID tubing to another tank where $p = 1600$ psia. $f = 0.010$. Determine the mass rate of flow.

**6.68** In isothermal flow of nitrogen at 80°F, 2 $lb_m$/sec is to be transferred 100 ft from a tank where $p = 200$ psia to a tank where $p = 160$ psia. What is the minimum size tubing, $f = 0.016$, that is needed?

**6.69** Specific heat at constant volume is defined by

(a) $kc_p$   (b) $\left(\dfrac{\partial u}{\partial T}\right)_p$   (c) $\left(\dfrac{\partial T}{\partial u}\right)_v$   (d) $\left(\dfrac{\partial u}{\partial T}\right)_v$   (e) none of these answers

**6.70** Specific heat at constant pressure, for a perfect gas, is *not* given by

(a) $kc_v$   (b) $(\partial h/\partial T)_p$   (c) $(h_2 - h_1)/(T_2 - T_1)$
(d) $[\Delta u + \Delta(p/\rho)]/\Delta t$   (e) any of these answers

**6.71** For a perfect gas, the enthalpy

(a) always increases owing to losses
(b) depends upon the pressure only
(c) depends upon the temperature only
(d) may increase while the internal energy decreases
(e) satisfies none of these answers

**6.72** The following classes of substances may be considered perfect gases:

(a) ideal fluids
(b) saturated steam, water vapor, and air
(c) fluids with a constant bulk modulus of elasticity
(d) water vapor, hydrogen, and nitrogen at low pressure
(e) none of these answers

**6.73** $c_p$ and $c_v$ are related by

(a) $k = c_p/c_v$     (b) $k = c_p c_v$     (c) $k = c_v/c_p$     (d) $c_p = c_v{}^k$
(e) none of these answers

**6.74** If $c_p = 0.30$ Btu/lb$_m$ °R and $k = 1.66$, in foot-pounds per slug per degree Fahrenheit, $c_v$ equals

(a) 0.582     (b) 1452     (c) 4520     (d) 7500     (e) none of these
answers

**6.75** If $c_p = 0.30$ Btu/lb$_m$ °R and $k = 1.33$, the gas constant in Btu per pound mass per degree Rankine is

(a) 0.075     (b) 0.099     (c) 0.399     (d) 0.699     (e) none of these
answers

**6.76** $R = 62$ ft-lb/lb$_m$ °R and $c_p = 0.279$ Btu/lb$_m$ °F. The isentropic exponent $k$ is

(a) 1.2     (b) 1.33     (c) 1.66     (d) 1.89     (e) none of these
answers

**6.77** The specific heat ratio is given by

(a) $\dfrac{1}{1 - R/c_p}$     (b) $1 + \dfrac{c_v}{R}$     (c) $\dfrac{c_p}{c_v} + R$     (d) $\dfrac{1}{1 - c_v/R}$

(e) none of these answers

**6.78** The entropy change for a perfect gas is

(a) always positive
(b) a function of temperature only
(c) $(\Delta q_H/T)_{\text{rev}}$
(d) a thermodynamic property depending upon temperature and pressure
(e) a function of internal energy only

**6.79** An isentropic process is always

(a) irreversible and adiabatic
(b) reversible and isothermal
(c) frictionless and adiabatic
(d) frictionless and irreversible
(e) none of these answers

**6.80** The relation $p = \text{const } \rho^k$ holds only for those processes that are

(a) reversible polytropic
(b) isentropic
(c) frictionless isothermal
(d) adiabatic irreversible
(e) none of these answers

**6.81** The reversible polytropic process is

(a) adiabatic frictionless
(b) given by $p/\rho = \text{const}$
(c) given by $p\rho^k = \text{const}$
(d) given by $p/\rho^n = \text{const}$
(e) none of these answers

**6.82** A reversible polytropic process could be given by

(a) $\dfrac{T_1}{T_2} = \left(\dfrac{\rho_1}{\rho_2}\right)^{n-1}$
(b) $\dfrac{p_1}{p_2} = \left(\dfrac{\rho_2}{\rho_1}\right)^{n}$
(c) $\dfrac{T_1}{T_2} = \left(\dfrac{p_1}{p_2}\right)^{n-1}$

(d) $\dfrac{T_1}{T_2} = \left(\dfrac{\rho_1}{\rho_2}\right)^{(n-1)/n}$
(e) none of these answers

**6.83** In a reversible polytropic process

(a) some heat transfer occurs
(b) the entropy remains constant
(c) the enthalpy remains constant
(d) the internal energy remains constant
(e) the temperature remains constant

**6.84** The differential equation for energy in isentropic flow may take the form

(a) $dp + d(\rho V^2) = 0$
(b) $\dfrac{dV}{V} + \dfrac{d\rho}{\rho} + \dfrac{dA}{A} = 0$
(c) $2V\, dV + \dfrac{dp}{\rho} = 0$
(d) $V\, dV + \dfrac{dp}{\rho} = 0$
(e) none of these answers

**6.85**  Select the expression that does *not* give the speed of a sound wave:

(a) $\sqrt{kRT}$  (b) $\sqrt{p/\rho}$  (c) $\sqrt{dp/d\rho}$  (d) $\sqrt{kp/\rho}$
(e) $\sqrt{K/\rho}$

**6.86**  The speed of a sound wave in a gas is analogous to

(a) the speed of flow in an open channel
(b) the speed of an elementary wave in an open channel
(c) the change in depth in an open channel
(d) the speed of a disturbance traveling upstream in moving liquid
(e) none of these answers

**6.87**  The speed of sound in water, in feet per second, under ordinary conditions is about

(a) 460  (b) 1100  (c) 4600  (d) 11,000  (e) none of these answers

**6.88**  The speed of sound in an ideal gas varies directly as

(a) the density
(b) the absolute pressure
(c) the absolute temperature
(d) the bulk modulus of elasticity
(e) none of these answers

**6.89**  Select the correct statement regarding frictionless flow:

(a) In diverging conduits the velocity always decreases.
(b) The velocity is always sonic at the throat of a converging-diverging tube.
(c) In supersonic flow the area decreases for increasing velocity.
(d) Sonic velocity cannot be exceeded at the throat of a converging-diverging tube.
(e) At Mach zero the velocity is sonic.

**6.90**  In isentropic flow, the temperature

(a) cannot exceed the reservoir temperature
(b) cannot drop, then increase again downstream
(c) is independent of the Mach number
(d) is a function of Mach number only
(e) remains constant in duct flow

**6.91**  The critical pressure ratio for isentropic flow of carbon monoxide is

(a) 0.528  (b) 0.634  (c) 0.833  (d) 1.0  (e) none of these answers

**6.92**  Select the correct statement regarding flow through a converging-diverging tube.

(*a*) When the Mach number at exit is greater than unity no shock wave has developed in the tube.

(*b*) When the critical pressure ratio is exceeded, the Mach number at the throat is greater than unity.

(*c*) For sonic velocity at the throat, one and only one pressure or velocity can occur at a given downstream.

(*d*) The Mach number at the throat is always unity.

(*e*) The density increases in the downstream direction throughout the converging portion of the tube.

**6.93**  In a normal shock wave in one-dimensional flow the

(*a*) velocity, pressure, and density increase

(*b*) pressure, density, and temperature increase

(*c*) velocity, temperature, and density increase

(*d*) pressure, density, and momentum per unit time increase

(*e*) entropy remains constant

**6.94**  A normal shock wave

(*a*) is reversible

(*b*) may occur in a converging tube

(*c*) is irreversible

(*d*) is isentropic

(*e*) is none of these answers

**6.95**  A normal shock wave is analogous to

(*a*) an elementary wave in still liquid

(*b*) the hydraulic jump

(*c*) open-channel conditions with **F** $< 1$

(*d*) flow of liquid through an expanding nozzle

(*e*) none of these answers

**6.96**  Across a normal shock wave in a converging-diverging nozzle for adiabatic flow the following relationships are valid:

(*a*) continuity and energy equations, equation of state, isentropic relationship

(*b*) energy and momentum equations, equation of state, isentropic relationship

(*c*) continuity, energy, and momentum equations; equation of state

(*d*) equation of state, isentropic relationship, momentum equation, mass-conservation principle

(*e*) none of these answers

**6.97**   Across a normal shock wave there is an increase in

(a) $p$, **M**, $s$      (b) $p$, $s$; decrease in **M**      (c) $p$; decrease in $s$, **M**
(d) $p$, **M**; no change in $s$      (e) $p$, **M**, $T$

**6.98**   A Fanno line is developed from the following equations:

(a) momentum and continuity
(b) energy and continuity
(c) momentum and energy
(d) momentum, continuity, and energy
(e) none of these answers

**6.99**   A Rayleigh line is developed from the following equations:

(a) momentum and continuity
(b) energy and continuity
(c) momentum and energy
(d) momentum, continuity, and energy
(e) none of these answers

**6.100**   Select the correct statement regarding a Fanno or Rayleigh line:

(a) Two points having the same value of entropy represent conditions
   before and after a shock wave.
(b) $pV$ is held constant along the line.
(c) Mach number always increases with entropy.
(d) The subsonic portion of the curve is at higher enthalpy than the supersonic portion.
(e) Mach 1 is located at the maximum enthalpy point.

**6.101**   Choking in pipe flow means that

(a) a valve is closed in the line
(b) a restriction in flow area occurs
(c) the specified mass flow rate cannot occur
(d) shock waves always occur
(e) supersonic flow occurs somewhere in the line

**6.102**   In subsonic adiabatic flow with friction in a pipe

(a) $V$, **M**, $s$ increase; $p$, $T$, $\rho$ decrease
(b) $p$, $V$, **M** increase; $T$, $\rho$ decrease
(c) $p$, **M**, $s$ increase; $V$, $T$, $\rho$ decrease
(d) $\rho$, **M**, $s$ increase; $V$, $T$, $p$ decrease
(e) $T$, $V$, $s$ increase; **M**, $p$, $\rho$ decrease

**6.103**  In supersonic adiabatic flow with friction in a pipe

(a)  $V$, **M**, $s$ increase; $p$, $T$, $\rho$ decrease
(b)  $p$, $T$, $s$ increase; $\rho$, $V$, **M** decrease
(c)  $p$, **M**, $s$ increase; $V$, $T$, $\rho$ decrease
(d)  $p$, $T$, $\rho$, $s$ increase; $V$, **M** decrease
(e)  $p$, $\rho$, $s$ increase; $V$, **M**, $T$ decrease

**6.104**  Select the correct statement regarding frictionless duct flow with heat transfer:

(a)  Adding heat to supersonic flow increases the Mach number.
(b)  Adding heat to subsonic flow increases the Mach number.
(c)  Cooling supersonic flow decreases the Mach number.
(d)  The Fanno line is valuable in analyzing the flow.
(e)  The isentropic stagnation temperature remains constant along the pipe.

**6.105**  Select the correct trends in flow properties for frictionless duct flow with heat transferred to the pipe, **M** $< 1$:

(a)  $p$, $V$ increase; $\rho$, $T$, $T_0$ decrease
(b)  $V$, $T_0$ increase; $p$, $\rho$ decrease
(c)  $p$, $\rho$, $T$ increase; $V$, $T_0$ decrease
(d)  $V$, $T$ increase; $p$, $\rho$, $T_0$ decrease
(e)  $T_0$, $V$, $\rho$ increase; $p$, $T$ decrease

**6.106**  Select the correct trends for cooling in frictionless duct flow, **M** $> 1$:

(a)  $V$ increases; $p$, $\rho$, $T$, $T_0$ decrease
(b)  $p$, $V$ increase; $\rho$, $T$, $T_0$ decrease
(c)  $p$, $\rho$, $V$ increase; $T$, $T_0$ decrease
(d)  $p$, $\rho$ increase; $V$, $T$, $T_0$ decrease
(e)  $V$, $T$, $T_0$ increase; $p$, $\rho$ decrease

**6.107**  In steady, isothermal flow in long pipelines, the significant value of **M** for determining trends in flow properties is

(a)  $1/k$     (b)  $1/\sqrt{k}$     (c)  $1$     (d)  $\sqrt{k}$     (e)  $k$

**6.108**  Select the correct trends in fluid properties for isothermal flow in ducts for **M** $< 0.5$:

(a)  $V$ increases; **M**, $T_0$, $p$, $p_0$, $\rho$ decrease
(b)  $V$, **M** increase; $T_0$, $p$, $p_0$, $\rho$ decrease
(c)  $V$, **M**, $T_0$ increase; $p$, $p_0$, $\rho$ decrease
(d)  $V$, $T_0$ increase; **M**, $p$, $p_0$, $\rho$ decrease
(e)  $V$, **M**, $p_0$, $T_0$ increase; $p$, $\rho$ decrease

## references

Cambel, A. B., and B. H. Jennings: "Gas Dynamics," McGraw-Hill Book Company, New York, 1958.

Hunsaker, J. C., and B. G. Rightmire: "Engineering Applications of Fluid Mechanics," McGraw-Hill Book Company, New York, 1947.

Keenan, J. H., and J. Kaye: "Gas Tables," John Wiley & Sons, Inc., New York, 1948.

Keenan, J. H., and E. P. Neumann: Measurements of Friction in a Pipe for Subsonic and Supersonic Flow of Air, *J. Appl. Mech.*, vol. 13, no. 2, p. A-91, 1946.

Liepmann, H. W., and A. Roshko: "Elements of Gas Dynamics," John Wiley & Sons, Inc., New York, 1957.

Prandtl, L.: "Fluid Dynamics," Hafner Publishing Company, Inc., New York, 1952.

Shapiro, A. H.: "The Dynamics and Thermodynamics of Compressible Fluid Flow," vol. I, The Ronald Press Company, New York, 1953.

# 7
# ideal-fluid flow

In the preceding chapters most of the relationships have been developed for one-dimensional flow, i.e., flow in which the average velocity at each cross section is used and variations across the section are neglected. Many design problems in fluid flow, however, require more exact knowledge of velocity and pressure distributions, such as in flow over curved boundaries along an airplane wing, through the passages of a pump or compressor, or over the crest of a dam. An understanding of two- and three-dimensional flow of a nonviscous, incompressible fluid provides the student with a much broader approach to many real fluid-flow situations. There are also analogies that permit the same methods to apply to flow through porous media.

In this chapter the principles of irrotational flow of an ideal fluid are developed and applied to elementary flow cases. After the flow requirements are established, the vector operator $\nabla$ is introduced, Euler's equation is derived, and the velocity potential is defined. Euler's equation is then integrated to obtain Bernoulli's equation, and stream functions and boundary conditions are developed. Flow cases are then studied in three and two dimensions.

## 7.1 requirements for ideal-fluid flow

The Prandtl hypothesis, Sec. 5.6, states that, for fluids of low viscosity, the effects of viscosity are appreciable only in a narrow region surrounding the fluid boundaries. For incompressible-flow situations in which the boundary layer remains thin, ideal-fluid results may be applied to flow of a real fluid to a satisfactory degree of approximation. Converging or accelerating flow situations generally have thin boundary layers, but decelerating flow may have separation of the boundary layer and development of a large wake that is difficult to predict analytically.

An ideal fluid must satisfy the following requirements:

1. The continuity equation, Sec. 3.4, div $\mathbf{q}$ = 0, or

$$\frac{\partial u}{\partial x} + \frac{\partial v}{\partial y} + \frac{\partial w}{\partial z} = 0$$

2. Newton's second law of motion at every point at every instant.
3. Neither penetration of fluid into nor gaps between fluid and boundary at any solid boundary.

If, in addition to requirements 1, 2, and 3, the assumption of irrotational flow is made, the resulting fluid motion closely resembles real-fluid motion for fluids of low viscosity, outside boundary layers.

Using the above conditions, the application of Newton's second law to a fluid particle leads to the Euler equation which, together with the assumption of irrotational flow, may be integrated to obtain the Bernoulli equation. The unknowns in a fluid-flow situation with given boundaries are velocity and pressure at every point. Unfortunately, in most cases it is impossible to proceed directly to equations for velocity and pressure distribution from the boundary conditions.

## 7.2 the vector operator ∇

The vector operator $\nabla$ (pronounced "del"), which may act on a vector as a scalar or vector product or may act on a scalar function, is most useful in developing ideal-fluid-flow theory.

Let $U$ be the quantity acted upon by the operator. The operator $\nabla$ is defined by

$$\nabla U = \lim_{\upsilon \to 0} \frac{1}{\upsilon} \int_S \mathbf{n}_1 U \, dS \tag{7.2.1}$$

$U$ may be interpreted as $\cdot \mathbf{a}$, $\times \mathbf{a}$, where $\mathbf{a}$ is any vector, or as a scalar, say $\phi$. Consider a small volume $\upsilon$ with surface $S$ and surface element $dS$. $\mathbf{n}_1$ is a unit vector in the direction of the outwardly drawn normal $n$ of the surface element $dS$ (Fig. 7.1). This definition of the operator is now examined to develop the concepts of gradient, divergence, and curl.

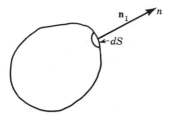

**Fig. 7.1** Notation for unit vector $\mathbf{n}_1$ normal to area element $dS$.

When $U$ is a scalar, say $\phi$, the *gradient* of $\phi$ is

$$\text{grad } \phi = \nabla\phi = \lim_{\upsilon\to 0} \frac{1}{\upsilon} \int_S \mathbf{n}_1\phi\, dS \qquad (7.2.2)$$

To interpret grad $\phi$, the volume element is taken as a small prism of cross-sectional area $dS$, of height $dn$, with one end area in the surface $\phi(x,y,z) = c$ and the other end area in the surface

$$\phi + \left(\frac{\partial\phi}{\partial n}\right) dn = \text{const}$$

(Fig. 7.2). As there is no change in $\phi$ in surfaces parallel to the end faces, by symmetry, $\int \mathbf{n}_1\phi\, dS$ over the curved surface of the element vanishes. Then

$$\int_S \mathbf{n}_1\phi\, dS = \mathbf{n}_1\left(\phi + \frac{\partial n}{\partial n} dn - \phi\right) dS$$

and the right-hand side of Eq. (7.2.2) becomes

$$\lim_{\upsilon\to 0} \frac{\mathbf{n}_1}{dS\, dn} \frac{\partial\phi}{\partial n} dn\, dS = \mathbf{n}_1 \frac{\partial\phi}{\partial n}$$

**Fig. 7.2** Surfaces of constant scalar $\phi$.

and

$$\text{grad } \phi = \nabla\phi = \mathbf{n}_1 \frac{\partial\phi}{\partial n} \qquad (7.2.3)$$

in which $\mathbf{n}_1$ is the unit vector, drawn normal to the surface over which $\phi$ is constant, positive in the direction of increasing $\phi$; grad $\phi$ is a vector.

By interpreting $U$ as the scalar (dot) product with $\nabla$, the *divergence* is obtained. Let $U$ be $\cdot\mathbf{q}$; then

$$\text{div } \mathbf{q} = \nabla \cdot \mathbf{q} = \lim_{\mathcal{v}\to 0} \frac{1}{\mathcal{v}} \int_S \mathbf{n}_1 \cdot \mathbf{q} \, dS \qquad (7.2.4)$$

This expression has been used (in somewhat different form) in deriving the general continuity equation in Sec. 3.4. It is the volume flux per unit volume at a point and is a scalar.

The *curl* $\nabla \times \mathbf{q}$ is a more difficult concept that deals with the *vorticity* or rotation of a fluid element:

$$\text{curl } \mathbf{q} = \nabla \times \mathbf{q} = \lim_{\mathcal{v}\to 0} \frac{1}{\mathcal{v}} \int_S \mathbf{n}_1 \times \mathbf{q} \, dS \qquad (7.2.5)$$

With reference to Fig. 7.3, $\mathbf{n}_1 \times \mathbf{q}$ is the velocity component tangent to the surface element $dS$ at a point, since the vector product is a vector at right angles to the plane of the two constituent vectors, with magnitude $q \sin \theta$, as $n_1 = 1$. Then $\mathbf{n}_1 \times \mathbf{q} \, dS$ is an elemental vector that is the product of tangential velocity and surface area element. Summing up over the surface, then dividing by the volume, with the limit taken as $\mathcal{v} \to 0$, yields the curl $\mathbf{q}$ at a point.

A special type of fluid motion is examined to demonstrate the connection between curl and rotation. Let a small circular cylinder of fluid be rotating

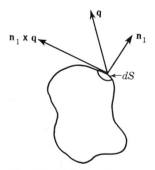

**Fig. 7.3** Notation for curl of the velocity vector.

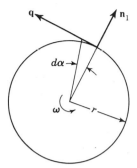

**Fig. 7.4** Small fluid cylinder rotating as a solid.

about its axis as if it were a solid (Fig. 7.4), with angular velocity $\omega$, which is a vector parallel to the axis of rotation.   The radius of the cylinder is $r$ and the length $l$.   $\mathbf{n}_1 \times \mathbf{q}$ at every point on the curved surface is a vector parallel to the axis having the magnitude $q = \omega r$.   Over the end areas the vector $\mathbf{n}_1 \times \mathbf{q}$ is equal and opposite at corresponding points on each end and contributes nothing to the curl.   Then, since $ds = lr\,d\alpha$,

$$\int_S \mathbf{n}_1 \times \mathbf{q}\,dS = \omega \int_0^{2\pi} rlr\,d\alpha = 2\pi r^2 l\omega$$

Equation (7.2.5) now yields

$$\text{curl } \mathbf{q} = \lim_{\upsilon \to 0} \frac{1}{\pi r^2 l} 2\pi r^2 l\omega = 2\omega$$

showing that for solid-body rotation the curl of the velocity at a point is twice the rotation vector.   If one considers the pure translation of a small element moving as a solid, then the curl $\mathbf{q}$ is always zero.   As any rigid body motion is a combination of a translation and a rotation, it is noted that the curl of the velocity vector is always twice the rotation vector.

A fluid, however, not only may translate and rotate but also may deform. The definition of curl $\mathbf{q}$ applies, and hence the *rotation of a fluid* at a point is defined by

$$\omega = \tfrac{1}{2}\text{curl } \mathbf{q} = \tfrac{1}{2}\nabla \times \mathbf{q} \tag{7.2.6}$$

When $\omega = 0$ throughout certain portions of a fluid, the motion there is described as *irrotational*.   The vorticity vector curl $\mathbf{q}$ has certain characteristics similar to the velocity vector $\mathbf{q}$.   Vortex lines are everywhere tangent to the vorticity vector, and vortex tubes, comprised of the vortex lines through a small closed curve, follow certain continuity principles; viz., the product of vorticity by area of the tube must remain constant along the vortex tube, or div (curl $\mathbf{q}$) = $\nabla \cdot (\nabla \times \mathbf{q}) = 0$.

The operator $\nabla$ acts like a vector but must be applied to a scalar or a vector to have physical significance.

*scalar components of vector relationships*

Any vector may be decomposed into three components along mutually perpendicular axes, say the $x$-, $y$-, $z$-axes. The component is a scalar, as only magnitude and sign (sense) are needed to specify it; $f_x = -3$ indicates the $x$-component of a vector $\mathbf{f}$ acting in the $-x$-direction.

The vector may be expressed in terms of its scalar components by use of the fixed unit vectors $\mathbf{i}$, $\mathbf{j}$, $\mathbf{k}$ parallel to the $x$-, $y$-, $z$-axes, respectively:

$$\mathbf{a} = \mathbf{i}a_x + \mathbf{j}a_y + \mathbf{k}a_z$$

The unit vectors combine as follows:

$$\mathbf{i} \cdot \mathbf{i} = \mathbf{j} \cdot \mathbf{j} = \mathbf{k} \cdot \mathbf{k} = 1 \qquad \mathbf{i} \cdot \mathbf{j} = \mathbf{j} \cdot \mathbf{k} = \mathbf{k} \cdot \mathbf{i} = 0$$
$$\mathbf{i} \times \mathbf{j} = \mathbf{k} \qquad \mathbf{j} \times \mathbf{k} = \mathbf{i} \qquad \mathbf{k} \times \mathbf{i} = \mathbf{j} = -\mathbf{i} \times \mathbf{k} \qquad \text{etc.}$$

The scalar product of two vectors $\mathbf{a} \cdot \mathbf{b}$ is

$$\begin{aligned}\mathbf{a} \cdot \mathbf{b} &= (\mathbf{i}a_x + \mathbf{j}a_y + \mathbf{k}a_z) \cdot (\mathbf{i}b_x + \mathbf{j}b_y + \mathbf{k}b_z) \\ &= a_x b_x + a_y b_y + a_x b_z\end{aligned}$$

The vector product of two vectors $\mathbf{a} \times \mathbf{b}$ is

$$\begin{aligned}\mathbf{a} \times \mathbf{b} &= (\mathbf{i}a_x + \mathbf{j}a_y + \mathbf{k}a_z) \times (\mathbf{i}b_x + \mathbf{j}b_y + \mathbf{k}b_z) \\ &= \mathbf{i}(a_y b_z - a_z b_y) + \mathbf{j}(a_z b_x - a_x b_z) + \mathbf{k}(a_x b_y - a_y b_x)\end{aligned}$$

It is conveniently written in determinant form:

$$\mathbf{a} \times \mathbf{b} = \begin{vmatrix} \mathbf{i} & \mathbf{j} & \mathbf{k} \\ a_x & a_y & a_z \\ b_x & b_y & b_z \end{vmatrix}$$

To find the scalar components of $\nabla\phi$, first consider $\mathbf{a} \cdot \nabla\phi$ (Fig. 7.5) in which $\mathbf{a}$ is any vector. By Eq. (7.2.3)

$$\mathbf{a} \cdot \nabla\phi = \mathbf{a} \cdot \mathbf{n}_1 \frac{\partial\phi}{\partial n} = a \cos\theta \frac{\partial\phi}{\partial n}$$

as $\theta$ is the angle between $\mathbf{a}$ and $\mathbf{n}_1$ and $n_1 = 1$. A change $da$ in magnitude

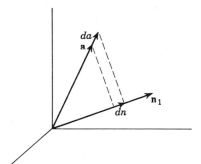

**Fig. 7.5** Change of vector $a$ corresponding to change in normal direction.

of **a** corresponds to a change in **n**, given by $da \cos \theta = dn$, hence

$$a \cos \theta \, \frac{\partial \phi}{\partial n} = a \, \frac{\partial \phi}{\partial a}$$

and

$$\mathbf{a} \cdot \nabla \phi = a \, \frac{\partial \phi}{\partial a} \tag{7.2.7}$$

The scalar components of $\nabla \phi$ are

$$\mathbf{i} \cdot \nabla \phi = \frac{\partial \phi}{\partial x} \qquad \mathbf{j} \cdot \nabla \phi = \frac{\partial \psi}{\partial y} \qquad \mathbf{k} \cdot \nabla \phi = \frac{\partial \phi}{\partial z}$$

and

$$\nabla \phi = \mathbf{i} \, \frac{\partial \phi}{\partial x} + \mathbf{j} \, \frac{\partial \phi}{\partial y} + \mathbf{k} \, \frac{\partial \phi}{\partial z} \tag{7.2.8}$$

The operator $\nabla$, in terms of its scalar components, is

$$\nabla = \mathbf{i} \, \frac{\partial}{\partial x} + \mathbf{j} \, \frac{\partial}{\partial y} + \mathbf{k} \, \frac{\partial}{\partial z} \tag{7.2.9}$$

The scalar product, say $\nabla \cdot \mathbf{q}$, becomes

$$\nabla \cdot \mathbf{q} = \left( \mathbf{i} \, \frac{\partial}{\partial x} + \mathbf{j} \, \frac{\partial}{\partial y} + \mathbf{k} \, \frac{\partial}{\partial z} \right) \cdot (\mathbf{i}u + \mathbf{j}v + \mathbf{k}w)$$

$$= \frac{\partial u}{\partial x} + \frac{\partial v}{\partial y} + \frac{\partial w}{\partial z} \tag{7.2.10}$$

as in Sec. 3.4.

The vector product $\nabla \times \mathbf{q}$, in scalar components, is

$$\nabla \times \mathbf{q} = \left(\mathbf{i}\frac{\partial}{\partial x} + \mathbf{j}\frac{\partial}{\partial y} + \mathbf{k}\frac{\partial}{\partial z}\right) \times (\mathbf{i}u + \mathbf{j}v + \mathbf{k}w)$$

$$= \mathbf{i}\left(\frac{\partial w}{\partial y} - \frac{\partial v}{\partial z}\right) + \mathbf{j}\left(\frac{\partial u}{\partial z} - \frac{\partial w}{\partial x}\right) + \mathbf{k}\left(\frac{\partial v}{\partial x} - \frac{\partial u}{\partial y}\right) \qquad (7.2.11)$$

The quantities in parentheses are vorticity components, which are twice the value of rotation components $\omega_x$, $\omega_y$, $\omega_z$, so

$$\nabla \times \mathbf{q} = \mathbf{i}2\omega_x + \mathbf{j}2\omega_y + \mathbf{k}2\omega_z \qquad (7.2.12)$$

## 7.3 Euler's equation of motion

In Sec. 3.5, Euler's equation was derived for steady flow of a frictionless fluid along a streamline. The assumption is made here that the flow is frictionless, and a continuum is assumed. Newton's second law of motion is applied to a fluid particle of mass $\rho\,\delta\mathcal{U}$. Three terms enter: the body force, the surface force, and mass times acceleration. Let $\mathbf{F}$ be the body force (such as gravity) per unit mass acting on the particle. Then $\mathbf{F}\rho\,\delta\mathcal{U}$ is the body-force vector. The surface force, from the preceding section, is $-\int_S \mathbf{n}_1 p\, dS$ if the fluid is frictionless or nonviscous, so that only normal forces act. The mass-times-acceleration term is $\rho\,\delta\mathcal{U}\,d\mathbf{q}/dt$. After assembling these terms,

$$\mathbf{F}\rho\,\delta\mathcal{U} - \int_S \mathbf{n}_1 p\, ds = \rho\,\delta\mathcal{U}\frac{d\mathbf{q}}{dt}$$

Now, dividing through by the mass of the element and taking the limit as $\delta\mathcal{U} \to 0$,

$$\mathbf{F} - \frac{1}{\rho}\lim_{\delta\mathcal{U}\to 0}\frac{1}{\mathcal{U}}\int_S \mathbf{n}_1 p\, dS = \frac{d\mathbf{q}}{dt}$$

By use of the operator $\nabla$,

$$\mathbf{F} - \frac{1}{\rho}\nabla p = \frac{d\mathbf{q}}{dt} \qquad (7.3.1)$$

This is Euler's equation of motion in vector notation. By forming the scalar product of each term with $\mathbf{i}$, then $\mathbf{j}$, then $\mathbf{k}$, the following scalar component equations are obtained:

$$X - \frac{1}{\rho}\frac{\partial p}{\partial x} = \frac{du}{dt}$$

$$Y - \frac{1}{\rho}\frac{\partial p}{\partial y} = \frac{dv}{dt} \tag{7.3.2}$$

$$Z - \frac{1}{\rho}\frac{\partial p}{\partial z} = \frac{dw}{dt}$$

in which $X$, $Y$, $Z$ are the body force components per unit mass.   The acceleration terms may be expanded.   In general $u = u(x,y,z,t)$, and so (see Appendix B)

$$du = \frac{\partial u}{\partial x}\,dx + \frac{\partial u}{\partial y}\,dy + \frac{\partial u}{\partial z}\,dz + \frac{\partial u}{\partial t}\,dt$$

For $du/dt$ to be the acceleration component of a particle in the $x$-direction, the $x$-, $y$-, $z$-coordinates of the moving particle become functions of time, and $du$ may be divided by $dt$, yielding

$$a_x = \frac{du}{dt} = \frac{\partial u}{\partial x}\frac{dx}{dt} + \frac{\partial u}{\partial y}\frac{dy}{dt} + \frac{\partial u}{\partial z}\frac{dz}{dt} + \frac{\partial u}{\partial t}$$

But

$$u = \frac{dx}{dt} \qquad v = \frac{dy}{dt} \qquad w = \frac{dz}{dt}$$

and

$$\frac{du}{dt} = u\frac{\partial u}{\partial x} + v\frac{\partial u}{\partial y} + w\frac{\partial u}{\partial z} + \frac{\partial u}{\partial t} \tag{7.3.3}$$

Similarly

$$\frac{dv}{dt} = u\frac{\partial v}{\partial x} + v\frac{\partial v}{\partial y} + w\frac{\partial v}{\partial z} + \frac{\partial v}{\partial t} \tag{7.3.4}$$

$$\frac{dw}{dt} = u\frac{\partial w}{\partial x} + v\frac{\partial w}{\partial y} + w\frac{\partial w}{\partial z} + \frac{\partial w}{\partial t} \tag{7.3.5}$$

If the extraneous force is *conservative*, it may be derived from a potential (**F** $= -$ grad $\Omega$):

$$X = -\frac{\partial \Omega}{\partial x} \qquad Y = -\frac{\partial \Omega}{\partial y} \qquad Z = -\frac{\partial \Omega}{\partial z} \tag{7.3.6}$$

In particular, if gravity is the only body force acting, $\Omega = gh$, with $h$ a direction measured vertically upward; thus

$$X = -g\frac{\partial h}{\partial x} \qquad Y = -g\frac{\partial h}{\partial y} \qquad Z = -g\frac{\partial h}{\partial z} \tag{7.3.7}$$

Remembering that $\rho$ is constant for an ideal fluid, substituting Eqs. (7.3.3) to (7.3.7) into Eqs. (7.3.2),

$$-\frac{1}{\rho}\frac{\partial}{\partial x}(p + \gamma h) = u\frac{\partial u}{\partial x} + v\frac{\partial u}{\partial y} + w\frac{\partial u}{\partial z} + \frac{\partial u}{\partial t} \tag{7.3.8}$$

$$-\frac{1}{\rho}\frac{\partial}{\partial y}(p + \gamma h) = u\frac{\partial v}{\partial x} + v\frac{\partial v}{\partial y} + w\frac{\partial v}{\partial z} + \frac{\partial v}{\partial t} \tag{7.3.9}$$

$$-\frac{1}{\rho}\frac{\partial}{\partial z}(p + \gamma h) = u\frac{\partial w}{\partial x} + v\frac{\partial w}{\partial y} + w\frac{\partial w}{\partial z} + \frac{\partial w}{\partial t} \tag{7.3.10}$$

The first three terms on the right-hand side of the equations are "convective acceleration" terms, depending upon changes of velocity with space. The last term is the "local acceleration," depending upon velocity change with time at a point.

*natural coordinates in two-dimensional flow*

Euler's equations in two dimensions are obtained from the general component equations by setting $w = 0$ and $\partial/\partial z = 0$; thus

$$-\frac{1}{\rho}\frac{\partial}{\partial x}(p + \gamma h) = u\frac{\partial u}{\partial x} + v\frac{\partial u}{\partial y} + \frac{\partial u}{\partial t} \tag{7.3.11}$$

$$-\frac{1}{\rho}\frac{\partial}{\partial y}(p + \gamma h) = u\frac{\partial v}{\partial x} + v\frac{\partial v}{\partial y} + \frac{\partial v}{\partial t} \tag{7.3.12}$$

By taking particular directions for the $x$- and $y$-axes, they may be reduced to a form that aids in understanding them. If the $x$-axis, called the $s$-axis, is taken parallel to the velocity vector at a point (Fig. 7.6), it is then tangent to the streamline through the point. The $y$-axis, called the $n$-axis, is drawn toward the center of curvature of the streamline. The velocity component $u$ is $v_s$, and the component $v$ is $v_n$. As $v_n$ is zero at the point, Eq. (7.3.11) becomes

$$-\frac{1}{\rho}\frac{\partial}{\partial s}(p + \gamma h) = v_s\frac{\partial v_s}{\partial s} + \frac{\partial v_s}{\partial t} \tag{7.3.13}$$

Although $v_n$ is zero at the point $(s,n)$, its rates of change with respect to $s$

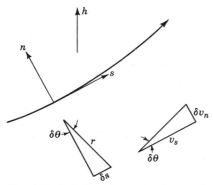

**Fig. 7.6** Notation for natural coordinates.

and $t$ are not necessarily zero.   Equation (7.3.12) becomes

$$-\frac{1}{\rho}\frac{\partial}{\partial n}(p + \gamma h) = v_s \frac{\partial v_n}{\partial s} + \frac{\partial v_n}{\partial t} \tag{7.3.14}$$

By considering the velocity at $s$ and at $s + \delta s$ along the streamline, $v_n$ changes from zero to $\delta v_n$.   With $r$ the radius of curvature of the streamline at $s$, from similar triangles (Fig. 7.6),

$$\frac{\delta s}{r} = \frac{\delta v_n}{v_s}$$

or

$$\frac{\partial v_n}{\partial s} = \frac{v_s}{r}$$

By substituting into Eq. (7.3.14),

$$-\frac{1}{\rho}\frac{\partial}{\partial n}(p + \gamma h) = \frac{v_s^2}{r} + \frac{\partial v_n}{\partial t} \tag{7.3.15}$$

For steady flow of an incompressible fluid Eqs. (7.3.11) and (7.3.15) may be written

$$-\frac{1}{\rho}\frac{\partial}{\partial s}(p + \gamma h) = \frac{\partial}{\partial s}\left(\frac{v_s^2}{2}\right) \tag{7.3.16}$$

and

$$-\frac{1}{\rho}\frac{\partial}{\partial n}(p + \gamma h) = \frac{v_s^2}{r} \tag{7.3.17}$$

Equation (7.3.16) may be integrated with respect to $s$ to produce Eq. (3.9.1), with the constant of integration varying with $n$, i.e., from one streamline to another. Equation (7.3.17) shows how pressure head varies across streamlines. With $v_s$ and $r$ known functions of $n$, Eq. (7.3.17) may be integrated.

**example 7.1** A container of liquid is rotated with angular velocity $\omega$ about a vertical axis as a solid. Determine the variation of pressure intensity in the liquid.

$n$ is the radial distance, measured inwardly, $n = -r$, $dn = -dr$, and $v_s = \omega r$. By integrating Eq. (7.3.17),

$$-\frac{1}{\rho}(p + \gamma h) = -\int \frac{\omega^2 r^2 \, dr}{r} + \text{const}$$

or

$$\frac{1}{\rho}(p + \gamma h) = \frac{\omega^2 r^2}{2} + \text{const}$$

To evaluate the constant, if $p = p_0$ when $r = 0$ and $h = 0$, then

$$p = p_0 - \gamma h + \rho \frac{\omega^2 r^2}{2}$$

which shows that the pressure is hydrostatic along a vertical line and increases as the square of the radius. Integration of Eq. (7.3.16) shows that the pressure is constant for a given $h$ and $v_s$, i.e., along a streamline.

## 7.4 irrotational flow. velocity potential

In this section it is shown that the assumption of irrotational flow leads to the existence of a velocity potential. By use of these relations and the assumption of a conservative body force, the Euler equations may be integrated.

The individual particles of a frictionless incompressible fluid initially at rest cannot be caused to rotate. This may be visualized by considering a small free body of fluid in the shape of a sphere. Surface forces act normal to its surface, since the fluid is frictionless, and therefore act through the center of the sphere. Similarly the body force acts at the mass center. Hence no torque can be exerted on the sphere, and it remains without rotation. Likewise, once an ideal fluid has rotation, there is no way of altering it, as no torque can be exerted on an elementary sphere of the fluid.

By assuming that the fluid has no rotation, i.e., it is irrotational, curl **q** = 0, or from Eq. (7.2.11)

$$\frac{\partial v}{\partial x} = \frac{\partial u}{\partial y} \qquad \frac{\partial w}{\partial y} = \frac{\partial v}{\partial z} \qquad \frac{\partial u}{\partial z} = \frac{\partial w}{\partial x} \tag{7.4.1}$$

These restrictions on the velocity must hold at every point (except special singular points or lines).   The first equation is the irrotational condition for two-dimensional flow.   It is the condition that the differential expression

$$u \, dx + v \, dy$$

is exact, say

$$u \, dx + v \, dy = -d\phi = -\frac{\partial \phi}{\partial x} dx - \frac{\partial \phi}{\partial y} dy \tag{7.4.2}$$

The minus sign is arbitrary; it is a convention that causes the value of $\phi$ to decrease in the direction of the velocity.   By comparing terms in Eq. (7.4.2), $u = -\partial\phi/\partial x$, $v = -\partial\phi/\partial y$.   This proves the existence, in two-dimensional flow, of a function $\phi$ such that its negative derivative with respect to any direction is the velocity component in that direction.   It may also be demonstrated for three-dimensional flow.   In vector form,

$$\mathbf{q} = -\text{grad } \phi = -\nabla\phi \tag{7.4.3}$$

is equivalent to

$$u = -\frac{\partial \phi}{\partial x} \qquad v = -\frac{\partial \phi}{\partial y} \qquad w = -\frac{\partial \phi}{\partial z} \tag{7.4.4}$$

The assumption of a velocity potential is equivalent to the assumption of irrotational flow, as

$$\text{curl} \, (-\text{grad } \phi) = -\nabla \times \nabla\phi = 0 \tag{7.4.5}$$

because $\nabla \times \nabla = 0$.   This is shown from Eq. (7.4.4) by cross differentiation:

$$\frac{\partial u}{\partial y} = -\frac{\partial^2 \phi}{\partial x \, \partial y} \qquad \frac{\partial v}{\partial x} = -\frac{\partial^2 \phi}{\partial y \, \partial x}$$

proving $\partial v/\partial x = \partial u/\partial y$, etc.

Substitution of Eqs. (7.4.4) into the continuity equation

$$\frac{\partial u}{\partial x} + \frac{\partial v}{\partial y} + \frac{\partial w}{\partial z} = 0$$

yields

$$\frac{\partial^2 \phi}{\partial x^2} + \frac{\partial^2 \phi}{\partial y^2} + \frac{\partial^2 \phi}{\partial z^2} = 0 \qquad\qquad (7.4.6)$$

In vector form this is

$$\nabla \cdot \mathbf{q} = -\nabla \cdot \nabla \phi = -\nabla^2 \phi = 0 \qquad\qquad (7.4.7)$$

and is written $\nabla^2 \phi = 0$.   Equation (7.4.6) or (7.4.7) is the *Laplace* equation. Any function $\phi$ that satisfies the Laplace equation is a possible irrotational fluid-flow case.   As there are an infinite number of solutions to the Laplace equation, each of which satisfies certain flow boundaries, the main problem is the selection of the proper function for the particular flow case.

Because $\phi$ appears to the first power in each term of Eq. (7.4.6), it is a linear equation, and the sum of two solutions is also a solution; e.g., if $\phi_1$ and $\phi_2$ are solutions of Eq. (7.4.6), then $\phi_1 + \phi_2$ is a solution; thus

$$\nabla^2 \phi_1 = 0 \qquad \nabla^2 \phi_2 = 0$$

then

$$\nabla^2 (\phi_1 + \phi_2) = \nabla^2 \phi_1 + \nabla^2 \phi_2 = 0$$

Similarly if $\phi_1$ is a solution, $C\phi_1$ is a solution if $C$ is constant.


## 7.5   integration of Euler's equations.   Bernoulli equation

Equation (7.3.8) may be rearranged so that every term contains a partial derivative with respect to $x$.   From Eq. (7.4.1)

$$v \frac{\partial u}{\partial y} = v \frac{\partial v}{\partial x} = \frac{\partial}{\partial x} \frac{v^2}{2} \qquad w \frac{\partial u}{\partial z} = w \frac{\partial w}{\partial x} = \frac{\partial}{\partial x} \frac{w^2}{2}$$

and from Eq. (7.4.4)

$$\frac{\partial u}{\partial t} = -\frac{\partial}{\partial x} \frac{\partial \phi}{\partial t}$$

Making these substitutions into Eq. (7.3.8) and rearranging,

$$\frac{\partial}{\partial x} \left( \frac{p}{\rho} + gh + \frac{u^2}{2} + \frac{v^2}{2} + \frac{w^2}{2} - \frac{\partial \phi}{\partial t} \right) = 0$$

As $u^2 + v^2 + w^2 = q^2$,

$$\frac{\partial}{\partial x} \left( \frac{p}{\rho} + gh + \frac{q^2}{2} - \frac{\partial \phi}{\partial t} \right) = 0 \qquad\qquad (7.5.1)$$

Similarly for the $y$- and $z$-directions,

$$\frac{\partial}{\partial y}\left(\frac{p}{\rho} + gh + \frac{q^2}{2} - \frac{\partial \phi}{\partial t}\right) = 0 \tag{7.5.2}$$

$$\frac{\partial}{\partial z}\left(\frac{p}{\rho} + gh + \frac{q^2}{2} - \frac{\partial \phi}{\partial t}\right) = 0 \tag{7.5.3}$$

The quantities within the parentheses are the same in Eqs. (7.5.1) to (7.5.3). Equation (7.5.1) states that the quantity is not a function of $x$, since the derivative with respect to $x$ is zero. Similarly the other equations show that the quantity is not a function of $y$ or $z$. Therefore it can be a function of $t$ only, say $F(t)$:

$$\frac{p}{\rho} + gh + \frac{q^2}{2} - \frac{\partial \phi}{\partial t} = F(t) \tag{7.5.4}$$

In steady flow $\partial \phi/\partial t = 0$ and $F(t)$ becomes a constant $E$:

$$\frac{p}{\rho} + gh + \frac{q^2}{2} = E \tag{7.5.5}$$

The available energy is everywhere constant throughout the fluid. This is Bernoulli's equation for an irrotational fluid.

The pressure term may be separated into two parts, the hydrostatic pressure $p_s$ and the dynamic pressure $p_d$, so that $p = p_s + p_d$. By inserting in Eq. (7.5.5),

$$gh + \frac{p_s}{\rho} + \frac{p_d}{\rho} + \frac{q^2}{2} = E$$

The first two terms may be written

$$gh + \frac{p_s}{\rho} = \frac{1}{\rho}(p_s + \gamma h)$$

with $h$ measured vertically upward. The expression is a constant, since it expresses the hydrostatic law of variation of pressure. These two terms may be included in the constant $E$. After dropping the subscript on the dynamic pressure, there remains

$$\frac{p}{\rho} + \frac{q^2}{2} = E \tag{7.5.6}$$

This simple equation permits the variation in pressure to be determined if the velocity is known, or vice versa. Assuming both the velocity $q_0$ and the dynamic pressure $p_0$ to be known at one point,

$$\frac{p_0}{\rho} + \frac{q_0^2}{2} = \frac{p}{\rho} + \frac{q^2}{2}$$

or

$$p = p_0 + \frac{\rho q_0^2}{2}\left[1 - \left(\frac{q}{q_0}\right)^2\right] \qquad\qquad (7.5.7)$$

**example 7.2** A submarine moves through water at a speed of 30 ft/sec. At a point $A$ on the submarine 5 ft above the nose, the velocity of the submarine relative to the water is 50 ft/sec. Determine the dynamic pressure difference between this point and the nose, and determine the difference in total pressure between the two points.

If the submarine is stationary and the water is moving past it, the velocity at the nose is zero, and the velocity at $A$ is 50 ft/sec. By selecting the dynamic pressure at infinity as zero, from Eq. (7.5.6)

$$E = 0 + \frac{q_0^2}{2} = \frac{(30)^2}{2} = 450$$

For the nose

$$\frac{p}{\rho} = E = 450 \qquad p = 450 \times 1.935 = 870 \text{ lb/ft}^2$$

For point $A$

$$\frac{p}{\rho} = E - \frac{q^2}{2} = 450 - \frac{(50)^2}{2}$$

and

$$p = 1.935\left[\frac{(30)^2}{2} - \frac{(50)^2}{2}\right] = -1548 \text{ lb/ft}^2$$

Therefore the difference in dynamic pressure is

$$-1548 - 870 = -2418 \text{ lb/ft}^2$$

The difference in total pressure may be obtained by applying Eq. (7.5.5) to point $A$ and to the nose $n$,

$$gh_A + \frac{p_A}{\rho} + \frac{q_A^2}{2} = gh_n + \frac{p_n}{\rho} + \frac{q_n^2}{2}$$

Hence

$$p_A - p_n = \rho \left( gh_n - gh_A + \frac{q_n{}^2 - q_A{}^2}{2} \right) = 1.935 \left[ -5g - \frac{(50)^2}{2} \right]$$

$$= -2740 \ \text{lb/ft}^2$$

It may also be reasoned that the actual pressure difference varies by $5\gamma$ from the dynamic pressure difference since $A$ is 5 ft above the nose, or $-2418 - 5 \times 62.4 = -2740 \ \text{lb/ft}^2$.

### 7.6   stream functions.   boundary conditions

Two stream functions are defined: one for two-dimensional flow, where all lines of motion are parallel to a fixed plane, say the $xy$-plane, and the flow is identical in each of these planes, and the other for three-dimensional flow with axial symmetry, i.e., all flow lines are in planes intersecting the same line or axis, and the flow is identical in each of these planes.

*two-dimensional stream function*

If $A$, $P$ represent two points in one of the flow planes, e.g., the $xy$-plane (Fig. 7.7), and if the plane has unit thickness, the rate of flow across any two lines $ACP$, $ABP$ must be the same, if the density is constant and no fluid is created or destroyed within the region, as a consequence of continuity. Now, if $A$ is a fixed point and $P$ a movable point, the flow rate across any line connecting the two points is a function of the position of $P$. If this function is $\psi$, and if it is taken as a sign convention that it denotes the flow rate from right to left as the observer views the line from $A$ looking

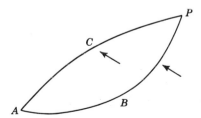

**Fig. 7.7** Fluid region showing the positive flow direction used in the definition of a stream function.

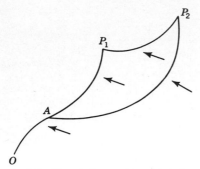

**Fig. 7.8** Flow between two points in a fluid region.

toward $P$, then

$$\psi = \psi(x,y)$$

is defined as the stream function.

If $\psi_1$, $\psi_2$ represent the values of stream function at points $P_1$, $P_2$ (Fig. 7.8), respectively, then $\psi_2 - \psi_1$ is the flow across $P_1P_2$ and is independent of the location of $A$. Taking another point $O$ in the place of $A$ changes the values of $\psi_1$, $\psi_2$ by the same amount, viz., the flow across $OA$. Then $\psi$ is indeterminate to the extent of an arbitrary constant.

The velocity component $u$, $v$ in the $x$-, $y$-directions may be obtained from the stream function. In Fig. 7.9$a$, the flow $\delta\psi$ across $\overline{AP} = \delta y$, from right to left, is $-u\,\delta y$, or

$$u = -\frac{\delta\psi}{\delta y} = -\frac{\partial\psi}{\partial y} \qquad\qquad (7.6.1)$$

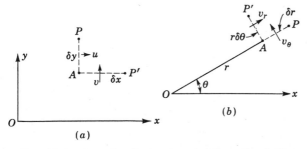

**Fig. 7.9** Selection of path to show relation of velocity components to stream function.

and similarly

$$v = \frac{\delta \psi}{\delta x} = \frac{\partial \psi}{\partial x} \tag{7.6.2}$$

In words, the partial derivative of the stream function with respect to any direction gives the velocity component $+90°$ (counterclockwise) to that direction.   In plane polar coordinates

$$v_r = -\frac{1}{r}\frac{\partial \psi}{\partial \theta} \qquad v_\theta = \frac{\partial \psi}{\partial r}$$

from Fig. 7.9$b$.

When the two points $P_1$, $P_2$ of Fig. 7.8 lie on the same streamline, $\psi_1 - \psi_2 = 0$ as there is no flow across a streamline.   Hence, a streamline is given by $\psi = $ const.   By comparing Eqs. (7.4.4) with Eqs. (7.6.1) and (7.6.2),

$$\frac{\partial \phi}{\partial x} = \frac{\partial \psi}{\partial y} \qquad \frac{\partial \phi}{\partial y} = -\frac{\partial \psi}{\partial x} \tag{7.6.3}$$

These are the Cauchy-Riemann equations.

By Eqs. (7.6.3) a stream function may be found for each velocity potential. If the velocity potential satisfies the Laplace equation, then the stream function also satisfies it.   Hence, the stream function may be considered as velocity potential for another flow case.

*Stokes' stream function for axially symmetric flow*

In any one of the planes through the axis of symmetry select two points $A$, $P$ such that $A$ is fixed and $P$ is variable.   Draw a line connecting $AP$. The flow through the surface generated by rotating $AP$ about the axis of symmetry is a function of the position of $P$.   Let this function be $2\pi\psi$, and let the axis of symmetry be the $x$-axis of a cartesian system of reference. Then $\psi$ is a function of $x$ and $\hat{\omega}$, where

$$\hat{\omega} = \sqrt{y^2 + z^2}$$

is the distance from $P$ to the $x$-axis.   The surfaces $\psi = $ const are stream surfaces.

To find the relation between $\psi$ and the velocity components $u$, $v'$ parallel to the $x$-axis and the $\hat{\omega}$-axis (perpendicular to the $x$-axis), respectively, a procedure is employed similar to that for two-dimensional flow.   Let $PP'$ be an infinitesimal step first parallel to $\hat{\omega}$ and then to $x$; i.e., $PP' = \delta\hat{\omega}$ and then $PP' = \delta x$.   The resulting relations between stream function and

velocity are given by

$$-2\pi\hat\omega\,\delta\hat\omega\,u = 2\pi\,\delta\psi \qquad \text{and} \qquad 2\pi\hat\omega\,\delta x\,v' = 2\pi\,\delta\psi$$

Solving for $u$, $v'$,

$$u = -\frac{1}{\hat\omega}\frac{\partial\psi}{\partial\hat\omega} \qquad v' = \frac{1}{\hat\omega}\frac{\partial\psi}{\partial x} \tag{7.6.4}$$

The same sign convention is used as in the two-dimensional case.

The relations between stream function and potential function are

$$\frac{\partial\phi}{\partial x} = \frac{1}{\hat\omega}\frac{\partial\psi}{\partial\hat\omega} \qquad \frac{\partial\phi}{\partial\hat\omega} = -\frac{1}{\hat\omega}\frac{\partial\psi}{\partial x} \tag{7.6.5}$$

In three-dimensional flow with axial symmetry, $\psi$ has the dimensions $L^3\,T^{-1}$, or volume per unit time.

The stream function is used for flow about bodies of revolution that are frequently expressed most readily in spherical polar coordinates. Let $r$ be the distance from the origin and $\theta$ be the polar angle; the meridian angle is not needed because of axial symmetry. Referring to Fig. 7.10$a$ and $b$,

$$2\pi r\,\sin\theta\,\delta r\,v_\theta = 2\pi\,\delta\psi$$
$$-2\pi r\,\sin\theta r\,\delta\theta\,v_r = 2\pi\,\delta\psi$$

from which

$$v_\theta = \frac{1}{r\sin\theta}\frac{\partial\psi}{\partial r} \qquad v_r = -\frac{1}{r^2\sin\theta}\frac{\partial\psi}{\partial\theta} \tag{7.6.6}$$

and

$$\frac{1}{\sin\theta}\frac{\partial\psi}{\partial\theta} = r^2\frac{\partial\phi}{\partial r} \qquad \frac{\partial\psi}{\partial r} = -\sin\theta\frac{\partial\phi}{\partial\theta} \tag{7.6.7}$$

(a)                                              (b)

**Fig. 7.10** Displacement of $P$ to show the relation between velocity components and Stokes' stream function.

**Fig. 7.11** Notation for boundary condition at a fixed boundary.

These expressions are useful in dealing with flow about spheres, ellipsoids, and disks and through apertures.

*boundary conditions*

At a fixed boundary the velocity component normal to the boundary must be zero at every point on the boundary (Fig. 7.11):

$$\mathbf{q} \cdot \mathbf{n}_1 = 0 \qquad\qquad (7.6.8)$$

$\mathbf{n}_1$ is a unit vector normal to the boundary. In scalar notation this is easily expressed in terms of the velocity potential

$$\frac{\partial \phi}{\partial n} = 0 \qquad\qquad (7.6.9)$$

at all points on the boundary. For a moving boundary (Fig. 7.12), where the boundary point has the velocity **V**, the fluid-velocity component normal to the boundary must equal the velocity of the boundary normal to the boundary; thus

$$\mathbf{q} \cdot \mathbf{n}_1 = \mathbf{V} \cdot \mathbf{n}_1 \qquad\qquad (7.6.10)$$

or

$$(\mathbf{q} - \mathbf{V}) \cdot \mathbf{n}_1 = 0 \qquad\qquad (7.6.11)$$

**Fig. 7.12** Notation for boundary condition at a moving boundary.

For two fluids in contact, a dynamical boundary condition is required; viz., the pressure must be continuous across the interface.

A stream surface in steady flow (fixed boundaries) satisfies the condition for a boundary and may be taken as a solid boundary.

### 7.7   the flow net

In two-dimensional flow the flow net is of great benefit; it is taken up in this section.

The line given by $\phi(x,y)$ = const is called an *equipotential* line.   It is a line along which the value of $\phi$ (the velocity potential) does not change. Since velocity $v_s$ in any direction $s$ is given by

$$v_s = -\frac{\partial \phi}{\partial s} = -\lim_{\Delta s \to 0}\frac{\Delta \phi}{\Delta s}$$

and $\Delta\phi$ is zero for two closely spaced points on an equipotential line, the velocity vector has no component in the direction defined by the line through the two points.   In the limit as $\Delta s \to 0$ this proves that there is no velocity component tangent to an equipotential line and, therefore, the velocity vector must be everywhere *normal* to an equipotential line (except at singular points where the velocity is zero or infinite).

The line $\psi(x,y)$ = const is a streamline, and is everywhere tangent to the velocity vector.   Streamlines and equipotential lines are therefore *orthogonal;* i.e., they intersect at right angles, except at singular points.   A *flow net* is composed of a family of equipotential lines and a corresponding family of streamlines with the constants varying in arithmetical progression. It is customary to let the change in constant between adjacent equipotential lines and adjacent streamlines be the same, e.g., $\Delta c$.   In Fig. 7.13, if the

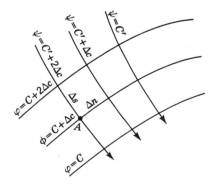

**Fig. 7.13**   Elements of a flow net.

distance between streamlines be $\Delta n$ and the distance between equipotential lines be $\Delta s$ at some small region in the flow net, the approximate velocity $v_s$ is then given in terms of the spacing of the equipotential lines [Eq. (7.4.4)],

$$v_s \approx -\frac{\Delta\phi}{\Delta s} = -\frac{-\Delta c}{\Delta s} = \frac{\Delta c}{\Delta s}$$

or in terms of the spacing of streamlines [Eqs. (7.6.1) and (7.6.2)],

$$v_s \approx \frac{\Delta\psi}{\Delta n} = \frac{\Delta c}{\Delta n}$$

These expressions are approximate when $\Delta c$ is finite, but when $\Delta c$ becomes very small the expressions become exact and yield velocity at a point.   As both velocities referred to are the same, the equations show that $\Delta s = \Delta n$, or that the flow net consists of an orthogonal grid that reduces to perfect squares in the limit as the grid size approaches zero.

Once a flow net has been found by any means to satisfy the boundary conditions and to form an orthogonal net reducing to perfect squares in the limit as the number of lines is increased, the flow net is the only solution for the particular boundaries as uniqueness theorems in hydrodynamics prove.   In steady flow when the boundaries are stationary, the boundaries themselves become part of the flow net as they are streamlines.   The problem of finding the flow net to satisfy given fixed boundaries may be considered purely as a *graphical* exercise, i.e., the construction of an orthogonal system of lines that compose the boundaries and that reduce to perfect squares in the limit as the number of lines increases.   This is one of the practical methods employed in two-dimensional-flow analysis, although it usually requires many attempts and much erasing.

Another practical method of obtaining a flow net for a particular set of fixed boundaries is the *electric analogy*.   The boundaries in a model are formed out of strips of nonconducting material mounted on a flat nonconducting surface, and the end equipotential lines are formed out of a conducting strip, e.g., brass or copper.   An electrolyte (conducting liquid) is placed at uniform depth in the flow space and a voltage potential applied to the two end conducting strips.   By means of a probe and a voltmeter, lines with constant drop in voltage from one end are mapped out and plotted.   These are equipotential lines.   By reversing the process and making the flow boundaries out of conducting material and the end equipotential lines from nonconducting material, the streamlines are mapped.

A special conducting paper, called *Teledeltos* paper, may be used in place of a tank with an electrolyte.   Silver ink is used to form a conducting strip or line having constant voltage.   One cuts the paper to the size and shape needed, places the constant-voltage lines on the paper with a heavy line of silver ink, then marks the intermediate points of constant voltage directly on the paper, using the same circuits as with an electrolyte.

The relaxation method[1] numerically determines the value of potential function at points throughout the flow, usually located at the intersections of a square grid. The Laplace equation is written as a difference equation, and it is shown that the value of potential function at a grid point is the average of the four values at the neighboring grid points. Near the boundaries special formulas are required. With values known at the boundaries, each grid point is computed based on the assumed values at the neighboring grid points; then these values are improved by repeating the process until the changes are within the desired accuracy. This method is particularly convenient for solution with high-speed digital computers.

*use of the flow net*

After a flow net for a given boundary configuration has been obtained, it may be used for all irrotational flows with geometrically similar boundaries. It is necessary to know the velocity at a single point and the pressure at one point. Then, by use of the flow net, the velocity can be determined at every other point. Application of the Bernoulli equation [Eq. (7.5.7)] produces the dynamic pressure. If the velocity is known, e.g., at $A$ (Fig. 7.13), $\Delta n$ or $\Delta s$ may be scaled from the adjacent lines. Then $\Delta c \cong \Delta n \, v_s \cong \Delta s \, v_s$. With the constant $\Delta c$ determined for the whole grid in this manner, measurement of $\Delta s$ or $\Delta n$ at any other point permits the velocity to be computed there,

$$v_s \approx \frac{\Delta c}{\Delta s} = \frac{\Delta c}{\Delta n}$$

The concepts underlying the flow net have been developed for irrotational flow of an ideal fluid. Because of the similarity of differential equations describing groundwater flow and irrotational flow, the flow net may also be used to determine streamlines and lines of constant piezometric head $(h + p/\gamma)$ for percolation through homogeneous porous media. The flow cases of Sec. 7.9 may then be interpreted in terms of the very rotational, viscous flow at extremely small velocities through a porous medium.

[1] C.-S. Yih, Ideal-fluid Flow, p. 4–67 in "Handbook of Fluid Dynamics," ed. by V. L. Streeter, McGraw-Hill Book Company, New York, 1961.

## 7.8   three-dimensional flow cases

Because of space limitations only a few three-dimensional cases are considered.   They are sources and sinks, the doublet, and uniform flow singly or combined.

### three-dimensional sources and sinks

A source in three-dimensional flow is a point from which fluid issues at a uniform rate in all directions.   It is entirely fictitious, as there is nothing resembling it in nature.   That does not, however, reduce its usefulness in obtained flow patterns.   The "strength" of the source $m$ is the rate of flow passing through any surface enclosing the source.

As the flow is outward and is uniform in all directions, the velocity, a distance $r$ from the source, is the strength divided by the area of the sphere through the point with center at the source, or

$$v_r = \frac{m}{4\pi r^2}$$

Since $v_r = -\partial\phi/\partial r$ and $v_\theta = 0$, hence $\partial\phi/\partial\theta = 0$, and the velocity potential can be found.

$$-\frac{\partial\phi}{\partial r} = \frac{m}{4\pi r^2}$$

and

$$\phi = \frac{m}{4\pi r} \tag{7.8.1}$$

A *negative source* is a *sink*.   Fluid is assumed to flow uniformly into a sink and there disappear.

### three-dimensional doublets

A *doublet*, or *double source*, is a combination of a source and a sink of equal strength, which are allowed to approach each other in such a manner that the product of their strength and the distance between them remains a constant in the limit.

Referring to Fig. 7.14, a source of strength $m$ is located at $(a,0)$ and a sink of the same strength at $(-a,0)$.   Since each satisfies the Laplace

**Fig. 7.14**   Auxiliary coordinate systems used for Rankine body.

equation, their sum also satisfies it:

$$\phi = \frac{m}{4\pi} \left( \frac{1}{r_1} - \frac{1}{r_2} \right)$$

(7.8.2)

By the law of sines and Fig. 7.14,

$$\frac{r_1}{\sin \theta_2} = \frac{r_2}{\sin \theta_1} = \frac{2a}{\sin (\theta_1 - \theta_2)}$$

$$= \frac{2a}{2 \sin \tfrac{1}{2}(\theta_1 - \theta_2) \cos \tfrac{1}{2}(\theta_1 - \theta_2)}$$

as the angle between $r_2$ and $r_1$ at $P$ is $\theta_1 - \theta_2$.   Solving for $r_2 - r_1$,

$$r_2 - r_1 = \frac{a(\sin \theta_1 - \sin \theta_2)}{\sin \tfrac{1}{2}(\theta_1 - \theta_2) \cos \tfrac{1}{2}(\theta_1 - \theta_2)}$$

$$= \frac{2a \cos \tfrac{1}{2}(\theta_1 + \theta_2)}{\cos \tfrac{1}{2}(\theta_1 - \theta_2)}$$

From Eq. (7.8.2)

$$\phi = \frac{m}{4\pi} \frac{r_2 - r_1}{r_1 r_2} = \frac{2am \cos \tfrac{1}{2}(\theta_1 + \theta_2)}{4\pi r_1 r_2 \cos \tfrac{1}{2}(\theta_1 - \theta_2)}$$

$$= \frac{\mu}{r_1 r_2} \frac{\cos \tfrac{1}{2}(\theta_1 + \theta_2)}{\cos \tfrac{1}{2}(\theta_1 - \theta_2)}$$

In the limit as $a$ approaches zero, $\theta_2 = \theta_1 = \theta$, $r_2 = r_1 = r$, and

$$\phi = \frac{\mu}{r^2} \cos \theta$$

(7.8.3)

which is the velocity potential for a doublet[1] at the origin with axis in the positive $x$-direction.   Equation (7.8.3) may be converted into the stream function by Eqs. (7.6.7).   The stream function is

$$\psi = -\frac{\mu\hat{\omega}^2}{r^3} = -\frac{\mu\sin^2\theta}{r} \tag{7.8.4}$$

Streamlines and equipotential lines for the doublet are drawn in Fig. 7.15.

### source in a uniform stream

The radial velocity $v_r$ due to a source at the origin

$$\phi = \frac{m}{4\pi r} \tag{7.8.1}$$

---

[1] L. M. Milne-Thompson, "Theoretical Hydrodynamics," p. 414, Macmillan & Co., Ltd., London, 1938.

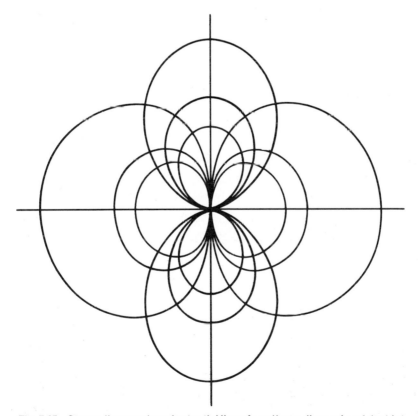

**Fig. 7.15**  Streamlines and equipotential lines for a three-dimensional doublet.

is

$$v_r = - \frac{\partial \phi}{\partial r} = \frac{m}{4\pi r^2}$$

which, when multiplied by the surface area of the sphere concentric with it, gives the strength $m$.   Since the flow from the source has axial symmetry, Stokes' stream function is defined.   For spherical polar coordinates, from Eqs. (7.6.7),

$$\frac{\partial \psi}{\partial r} = - \sin \theta \frac{\partial \phi}{\partial \theta} \qquad \frac{\partial \psi}{\partial \theta} = r^2 \sin \theta \frac{\partial \phi}{\partial r}$$

with Eq. (7.8.1),

$$\frac{\partial \psi}{\partial r} = 0 \qquad \frac{\partial \psi}{\partial \theta} = - \frac{m}{4\pi} \sin \theta$$

Integrating,

$$\psi = \frac{m}{4\pi} \cos \theta \qquad\qquad\qquad\qquad (7.8.5)$$

is the stream function for a source at the origin.   Equipotential lines and streamlines are shown in Fig. 7.16 for constant increments of $\phi$ and $\psi$.

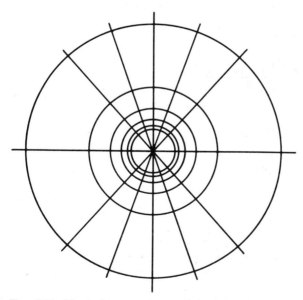

**Fig. 7.16** Streamlines and equipotential lines for a source.

A uniform stream of fluid having a velocity $U$ in the negative $x$-direction throughout space is given by

$$-\frac{\partial \phi}{\partial x} = -U \qquad \frac{\partial \phi}{\partial \hat{\omega}} = 0$$

Integrating,

$$\phi = Ux = Ur \cos \theta \tag{7.8.6}$$

The stream function is found in the same manner as above to be

$$\psi = \frac{U}{2} \hat{\omega}^2 = \frac{Ur^2}{2} \sin^2 \theta \tag{7.8.7}$$

The flow network is shown in Fig. 7.17.

Combining the uniform flow and the source flow, which may be accom-

**Fig. 7.17** Streamlines and equipotential lines for uniform flow in negative $x$-direction.

plished by adding the two velocity potentials and the two stream functions, gives

$$\phi = \frac{m}{4\pi r} + Ur \cos \theta$$

$$\psi = \frac{m}{4\pi} \cos \theta + \frac{Ur^2}{2} \sin^2 \theta \tag{7.8.8}$$

The resulting flow is everywhere the same as if the separate velocity vectors were added for each point in space.

A stagnation point is a point in the fluid where the velocity is zero.    The conditions for stagnation point, where spherical polar coordinates are used and when the flow has axial symmetry, are

$$v_r = -\frac{\partial \phi}{\partial r} = 0 \qquad v_\theta = -\frac{1}{r}\frac{\partial \phi}{\partial \theta} = 0$$

Use of these expressions with Eqs. (7.8.8) gives

$$\frac{m}{4\pi r^2} - U \cos \theta = 0 \qquad U \sin \theta = 0$$

which are satisfied by only one point in space, viz.,

$$\theta = 0 \qquad r = \sqrt{\frac{m}{4\pi U}}$$

Substituting this point back into the stream function gives $\psi = m/4\pi$, which is the stream surface through the stagnation point.    The equation of this surface is found from Eqs. (7.8.8):

$$\cos \theta + \frac{2\pi U}{m} r^2 \sin^2 \theta = 1 \tag{7.8.9}$$

The flow under consideration is steady, as the velocity potential does not change with the time.    Therefore, any stream surface satisfies the conditions for a boundary: The velocity component normal to the stream surface in steady flow is always zero.    Since stream surfaces through stagnation points usually split the flow, they are frequently the most interesting possible boundary.    This stream surface is plotted in Fig. 7.18.    Substituting $\hat{\omega} = r \sin \theta$ in Eq. (7.8.9), the distance of a point $(r,\theta)$ from the $x$-axis is given by

$$\hat{\omega}^2 = \frac{m}{2\pi U} (1 - \cos \theta)$$

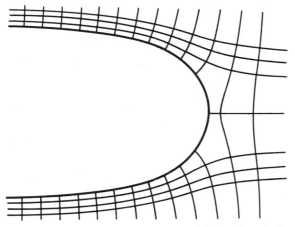

**Fig. 7.18**  Streamlines and equipotential lines for a half body.

which shows that $\hat{\omega}$ has a maximum value $\sqrt{m/\pi U}$ as $\theta$ approaches $\pi$, i.e., as $r$ approaches infinity.   Hence, $\hat{\omega} = \sqrt{m/\pi U}$ is an asymptotic surface to the dividing stream surface.   Equation (7.8.9) may be expressed in the form

$$r = \frac{1}{2}\sqrt{\frac{m}{\pi U}}\,\sec\frac{\theta}{2} \qquad (7.8.10)$$

from which the surface is easily plotted.   Such a figure of revolution is called a *half body*, as it extends to negative infinity, surrounding the negative $x$-axis.

The pressure at any point, i.e., the dynamic pressure from Eq. (7.5.7), is

$$p = \frac{\rho}{2}\,(U^2 - q^2)$$

in which the dynamic pressure at infinity is taken as zero.   $q$ is the speed at any point.   Evaluating $q$ from Eqs. (7.8.8),

$$q^2 = \left(\frac{\partial\phi}{\partial r}\right)^2 + \frac{1}{r^2}\left(\frac{\partial\phi}{\partial\theta}\right)^2 = U^2 + \frac{m^2}{16\pi^2 r^2} - \frac{mU\cos\theta}{2\pi r^2}$$

and

$$p = \frac{\rho}{2}\,U^2\left(\frac{m\cos\theta}{2\pi r^2 U} - \frac{m^2}{16\pi^2 r^4 U^2}\right) \qquad (7.8.11)$$

from which the pressure can be found for any point except the origin, which is a singular point. Substituting Eq. (7.8.10) into Eq. (7.8.11), the pressure is given in terms of $r$ for any point on the half body; thus

$$p = \frac{\rho}{2} U^2 \left( \frac{3m^2}{16\pi^2 r^4 U^2} - \frac{m}{2\pi r^2 U} \right) \tag{7.8.12}$$

This shows that the dynamic pressure approaches zero as $r$ increases downstream along the body.

*source and sink of equal strength in a uniform stream.   Rankine bodies*

A source of strength $m$, located at $(a,0)$, has the velocity potential at any point $P$ given by

$$\phi_1 = \frac{m}{4\pi r_1}$$

in which $r_1$ is the distance from $(a,0)$ to $P$, as shown in Fig. 7.14. Similarly, the potential function for a sink of strength $m$ at $(-a,0)$ is

$$\phi_2 = -\frac{m}{4\pi r_2}$$

Since both $\phi_1$ and $\phi_2$ satisfy the Laplace equation, their sum will also be a solution,

$$\phi = \frac{m}{4\pi} \left( \frac{1}{r_1} - \frac{1}{r_2} \right) \tag{7.8.13}$$

Because $r_1$, $r_2$ are measured from different points, this expression must be handled differently from the usual algebraic equation.

The stream functions for the source and sink may also be added to give the stream function for the combined flow,

$$\psi = \frac{m}{4\pi} (\cos \theta_1 - \cos \theta_2) \tag{7.8.14}$$

The stream surfaces and equipotential surfaces take the form shown in Fig. 7.19, which is plotted from Eqs. (7.8.13) and (7.8.14) by taking constant values of $\phi$ and $\psi$.

Superposing a uniform flow of velocity $U$ in the negative $x$-direction, $\phi = Ux$, $\psi = \frac{1}{2}U\hat{\omega}^2$, the potential and stream functions for source and

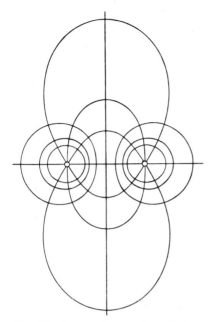

**Fig. 7.19** Streamlines and equipotential lines for a source and sink of equal strength.

sink of equal strength in a uniform flow (in direction of source to sink) are

$$\phi = Ux + \frac{m}{4\pi}\left(\frac{1}{r_1} - \frac{1}{r_2}\right)$$

$$= Ux + \frac{m}{4\pi}\left[\frac{1}{\sqrt{(x-a)^2 + \hat{\omega}^2}} - \frac{1}{\sqrt{(x+a)^2 + \hat{\omega}^2}}\right] \tag{7.8.15}$$

$$\psi = \tfrac{1}{2}Ur^2 \sin^2\theta + \frac{m}{4\pi}(\cos\theta_1 - \cos\theta_2) \tag{7.8.16}$$

As any stream surface may be taken as a solid boundary in steady flow, the location of a closed surface for this flow case will represent flow of a uniform stream around a body.   Examining the stream function, for $x > a$ and $\theta_1 = \theta_2 = 0$, $\psi = 0$.   For $x < -a$ and $\theta_1 = \theta_2 = \theta = \pi$, $\psi = 0$. Therefore, $\psi = 0$ must be the dividing streamline, since the $x$-axis is the axis of symmetry.   The equation of the dividing streamline is, from Eq. (7.8.16),

$$\hat{\omega}^2 + \frac{m}{2\pi U}(\cos\theta_1 - \cos\theta_2) = 0 \tag{7.8.17}$$

**Fig. 7.20**  Rankine body.

in which $\hat{\omega} = r \sin \theta$ is the distance of a point on the dividing stream surface from the $x$-axis.  Since $\cos \theta_1$ and $\cos \theta_2$ are never greater than unity, $\hat{\omega}$ cannot exceed $\sqrt{m/\pi U}$, which shows that the surface is closed and hence can be replaced by a solid body of exactly the same shape.  By changing the signs of $m$ and $U$ the flow is reversed and the body should change end for end.  From Eq. (7.8.17) it is seen that the equation is unaltered; hence, the body has symmetry with respect to the plane $x = 0$.  It is necessarily a body of revolution because of axial symmetry of the equations.

To locate the stagnation points $C$, $D$ (Fig. 7.20), which must be on the $x$-axis, it is known that the velocity is along the $x$-axis (it is a streamline). From Eq. (7.8.15) the velocity potential $\phi_x$ for points on the $x$-axis is given by

$$\phi_x = \frac{ma}{2\pi} \frac{1}{x^2 - a^2} + Ux$$

since

$$r_1 = x - a \qquad r_2 = x + a$$

Differentiating with respect to $x$ and setting the result equal to zero,

$$\frac{\partial \phi_x}{\partial x} = U - \frac{max_0}{\pi(x_0^2 - a^2)^2} = 0 \qquad\qquad (7.8.18)$$

where $x_0$ is the $x$-coordinate of the stagnation point.  This gives the point $C(x_0,0)$ (a trial solution).  The half breadth $h$ is determined as follows: From Fig. 7.20

$$\theta_1 = \pi - \alpha \qquad \theta_2 = \alpha$$

in which

$$\cos \alpha = \frac{a}{\sqrt{h^2 + a^2}}$$

Substituting into Eq. (7.8.17),

$$h^2 = \frac{m}{\pi U} \frac{a}{\sqrt{h^2 + a^2}} \qquad\qquad (7.8.19)$$

from which $h$ may be determined (also by trial solution).

Eliminating $m/U$ between Eqs. (7.8.18) and (7.8.19),

$$\frac{m}{U} = \frac{(x_0^2 - a^2)^2}{x_0} \frac{\pi}{a} = \frac{\pi}{a} h^2 \sqrt{h^2 + a^2}$$

the value of $a$ may be obtained for a predetermined body ($x_0$, $h$ specified). Hence, $U$ can be given any positive value and the pressure and velocity distribution can be determined.

In determining the velocity at points throughout the region it is convenient to find the velocity at each point due to each component of the flow, i.e., due to the source, the sink, and the uniform flow, separately, and add the components graphically or by $\hat{\omega}$- and $x$-components.

Bodies obtained from source-sink combinations with uniform flow are called *Rankine bodies*.

*translation of a sphere in an infinite fluid*

The velocity potential for a solid moving through an infinite fluid otherwise at rest must satisfy the following conditions:[1]

1.  The Laplace equation $\nabla^2 \phi = 0$ everywhere except at singular points.
2.  The fluid must remain at rest at infinity; hence, the space derivatives of $\phi$ must vanish at infinity.
3.  The boundary conditions at the surface of the solid must be satisfied.

For a sphere of radius $a$ with center at the origin moving with velocity $U$ in the positive $x$-direction, the velocity of the surface normal to itself is $U \cos \theta$, from Fig. 7.21. The fluid velocity normal to the surface is $-\partial \phi / \partial r$; hence the boundary condition is

$$-\frac{\partial \phi}{\partial r} = U \cos \theta$$

[1] G. G. Stokes, "Mathematical and Physical Papers," vol. 1, pp. 38–43, Cambridge University Press, London, 1880.

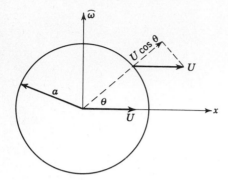

**Fig. 7.21** Sphere translating in the positive $x$-direction.

The velocity potential for the doublet [Eq. (7.8.3)]

$$\phi = \frac{\mu \cos \theta}{r^2}$$

satisfies $\nabla^2 \phi = 0$ for any constant value of $\mu$. Substituting it into the boundary condition,

$$-\frac{\partial \phi}{\partial r} = \frac{2\mu}{r^3} \cos \theta = U \cos \theta$$

which is satisfied for $r = a$ if $\mu = Ua^3/2$. It may also be noted that the velocity components,

$$-\frac{\partial \phi}{\partial r} \quad \text{and} \quad -\left(\frac{1}{r}\right)\left(\frac{\partial \phi}{\partial \theta}\right)$$

are zero at infinity. Therefore,

$$\phi = \frac{Ua^3}{2r^2} \cos \theta \tag{7.8.20}$$

satisfies all the conditions for translation of a sphere in an infinite fluid. This case is one of unsteady flow, solved for the instant when the center of the sphere is at the origin. Because this equation has been specialized for a particular instant, the pressure distribution cannot be found from it by use of Eq. (7.5.7). Streamlines and equipotential lines for the sphere are shown in Fig. 7.22.

The stream function for this flow case is

$$\psi = -\frac{Ua^3}{2r} \sin^2 \theta \tag{7.8.21}$$

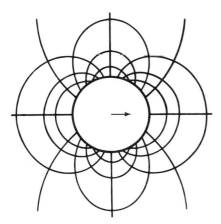

**Fig. 7.22** Streamlines and equipotential lines for a sphere moving through fluid.

*steady flow of an infinite fluid around a sphere*

The unsteady-flow case in the preceding section may be converted into a steady-flow case by superposing upon the flow a uniform stream of magnitude $U$ in the negative $x$-direction.   To prove this, add $\phi = Ux = Ur\cos\theta$ to the potential function [Eq. (7.8.20)]; thus

$$\phi = \frac{Ua^3}{2r^2}\cos\theta + Ur\cos\theta \tag{7.8.22}$$

The stream function corresponding to this is

$$\psi = -\frac{Ua^3}{2r}\sin^2\theta + \frac{Ur^2}{2}\sin^2\theta \tag{7.8.23}$$

Then from Eq. (7.8.23), $\psi = 0$ when $\theta = 0$ and when $r = a$.   Hence, the stream surface $\psi = 0$ is the sphere $r = a$, which may be taken as a solid, fixed boundary.   Streamlines and equipotential lines are shown in Fig. 7.23. Perhaps mention should be made that the equations give a flow pattern for the interior portion of the sphere as well.   No fluid passes through the surface of the sphere, however.

The velocity at any point on the surface of the sphere is

$$-\frac{1}{r}\frac{\partial\phi}{\partial\theta}\bigg]_{r=a} = q = \tfrac{3}{2}U\sin\theta$$

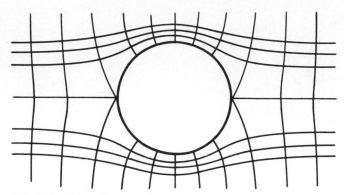

**Fig. 7.23** Streamlines and equipotential lines for uniform flow about a sphere at rest.

The stagnation points are at $\theta = 0$, $\theta = \pi$. The maximum velocity $\frac{3}{2}U$ occurs at $\theta = \pi/2$. The dynamic pressure distribution over the surface of the sphere is

$$p = \frac{\rho U^2}{2}(1 - \tfrac{9}{4}\sin^2\theta) \qquad\qquad (7.8.24)$$

for dynamic pressure of zero at infinity.

In Secs. 5.6 and 5.7 the flow around a sphere in a real fluid is discussed. Figure 5.20 shows the actual wake formation due to laminar and turbulent boundary-layer separation. The drag on a sphere in real fluids is given by the drag-coefficient data in Fig. 5.21. In the ideal-fluid-flow case the boundary condition does not permit separation. If the $x$-component of force exerted on the sphere by dynamic pressure is obtained from Eq. (7.8.24) by integration, it will be found to be zero. There is no drag on a body in ideal-fluid flow because the energy is everywhere constant and the high velocity of fluid obtained by flow over the front portion to the largest cross section is converted completely back to pressure in flowing over the downstream portion.

### 7.9 two-dimensional flow cases

Two simple flow cases that may be interpreted for flow along straight boundaries are first examined, then the source, vortex, doublet, uniform flow, and flow around a cylinder, with and without circulation, are discussed.

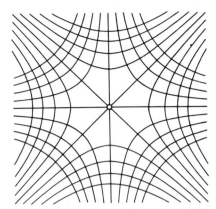

**Fig. 7.24**  Flow net for flow around 90°
bend.

*flow around a corner*

The potential function

$$\phi = A(x^2 - y^2)$$

has as its stream function

$$\psi = 2Axy = Ar^2 \sin 2\theta$$

in which $r$ and $\theta$ are polar coordinates.   It is plotted for equal increment
changes in $\phi$ and $\psi$ in Fig. 7.24.   Conditions at the origin are not defined,
as it is a stagnation point.   As any of the streamlines may be taken as
fixed boundaries, the plus axes may be taken as walls, yielding flow into a
90° corner.   The equipotential lines are hyperbolas having axes coincident
with the coordinate axes and asymptotes given by $y - \perp x$.   The streamlines are rectangular hyperbolas, having $y = \pm x$ as axes and the coordinate axes as asymptotes.   From the polar form of the stream function it
is noted that the two lines $\theta = 0$ and $\theta = \pi/2$ are the streamline $\psi = 0$.
    This case may be generalized to yield flow around a corner with angle $\alpha$.
By examining

$$\phi = Ar^{\pi/\alpha} \cos \frac{\pi\theta}{\alpha} \qquad \psi = Ar^{\pi/\alpha} \sin \frac{\pi\theta}{\alpha}$$

it is noted the streamline $\psi = 0$ is now given by $\theta = 0$ and $\theta = \alpha$.   Two
flow nets are shown in Fig. 7.25, for the cases $\alpha = 225°$ and $\alpha = 45°$.

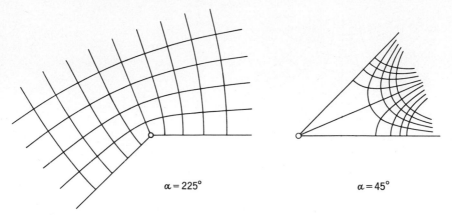

$\alpha = 225°$

$\alpha = 45°$

**Fig. 7.25** Flow net for flow along two inclined surfaces.

*source*

A line normal to the $xy$-plane, from which fluid is imagined to flow uniformly in all directions *at right angles* to it, is a source. It appears as a point in the customary two-dimensional flow diagram. The total flow per unit time per unit length of line is called the *strength* of the source. As the flow is in radial lines from the source, the velocity a distance $r$ from the source is determined by the strength divided by the flow area of the cylinder, or $2\pi\mu/2\pi r$, in which the strength is $2\pi\mu$. Then, since by Eq. (7.4.4) the velocity in any direction is given by the negative derivative of the velocity potential with respect to the direction,

$$-\frac{\partial\phi}{\partial r} = \frac{\mu}{r} \qquad \frac{\partial\phi}{\partial\theta} = 0$$

and

$$\phi = -\mu \ln r$$

is the velocity potential, in which ln indicates the natural logarithm and $r$ is the distance from the source. This value of $\phi$ satisfies the Laplace equation in two dimensions.

The streamlines are radial lines from the source, i.e.,

$$\frac{\partial\psi}{\partial r} = 0 \qquad -\frac{1}{r}\frac{\partial\psi}{\partial\theta} = \frac{\mu}{r}$$

From the second equation

$$\psi = -\mu\theta$$

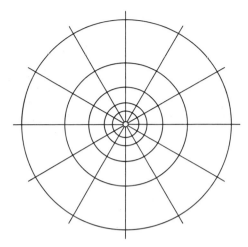

**Fig. 7.26**   Flow net for source or vortex.

Lines of constant $\phi$ (equipotential lines) and constant $\psi$ are shown in Fig. 7.26.   A *sink* is a negative source, a line into which fluid is flowing.

*vortex*

In examining the flow case given by selecting the stream function for the source as a velocity potential,

$$\phi = -\mu\theta \qquad \psi = \mu \ln r$$

which also satisfies the Laplace equation, it is seen that the equipotential lines are radial lines and the streamlines are circles.   The velocity is in a tangential direction only, since $\partial\phi/\partial r = 0$.   It is

$$q = -\left(\frac{1}{r}\right)\frac{\partial\phi}{\partial\theta} = \frac{\mu}{r}$$

since $r\,\delta\theta$ is the length element in the tangential direction.

In referring to Fig. 7.27, the *flow along a closed curve* is called the *circulation*.   The flow along an element of the curve is defined as the product of the length element $\delta s$ of the curve and the component of the velocity tangent to the curve, $q \cos \alpha$.   Hence the circulation $\Gamma$ around a closed path $C$ is

$$\Gamma = \int_C q \cos \alpha \, ds = \int_C \mathbf{q} \cdot d\mathbf{s}$$

The velocity distribution given by the equation $\phi = -\mu\theta$ is for the *vortex*

**Fig. 7.27**  Notation for definition of circulation.

and is such that the circulation around any closed path that contains the vortex is constant.  The value of the circulation is the strength of the vortex.  By selecting any circular path of radius $r$ to determine the circulation, $\alpha = 0°$, $q = \mu/r$, and $ds = r\,d\theta$; hence,

$$\Gamma = \int_C q \cos \alpha \; ds = \int_0^{2\pi} \frac{\mu}{r} r \; d\theta = 2\pi\mu$$

At the point $r = 0$, $q = \mu/r$ goes to infinity; hence, this point is called a singular point.  Figure 7.26 shows the equipotential lines and streamlines for the vortex.

### doublet

The two-dimensional doublet is defined as the limiting case as a source and sink of equal strength approach each other so that the product of their strength and the distance between them remains a constant $2\pi\mu$.  $\mu$ is called the *strength* of the doublet.  The axis of the doublet is from the sink toward the source, i.e., the line along which they approach each other.

In Fig. 7.28 a source is located at $(a,0)$ and a sink of equal strength at

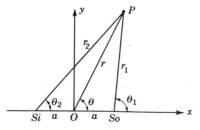

**Fig. 7.28**  Notation for derivation of two-dimensional doublet.

$(-a,0)$.   The velocity potential for both, at some point $P$, is

$$\phi = -m \ln r_1 + m \ln r_2$$

with $r_1$, $r_2$ measured from source and sink, respectively, to the point $P$. Thus, $2\pi m$ is the strength of source and sink. To take the limit as $a$ approaches zero for $2am = \mu$, the form of the expression for $\phi$ must be altered. The terms $r_1$ and $r_2$ may be expressed in terms of the polar coordinates $r$, $\theta$ by the cosine law, as follows:

$$r_1{}^2 = r^2 + a^2 - 2ar \cos \theta = r^2 \left[ 1 + \left(\frac{a}{r}\right)^2 - 2\frac{a}{r} \cos \theta \right]$$

$$r_2{}^2 = r^2 + a^2 + 2ar \cos \theta = r^2 \left[ 1 + \left(\frac{a}{r}\right)^2 + 2\frac{a}{r} \cos \theta \right]$$

After rewriting the expression for $\phi$, with these relations

$$\phi = -\frac{m}{2} (\ln r_1{}^2 - \ln r_2{}^2) = -\frac{m}{2} \left\{ \ln r^2 + \ln \left[ 1 + \left(\frac{a}{r}\right)^2 - 2\frac{a}{r} \cos \theta \right] \right.$$

$$\left. - \ln r^2 - \ln \left[ 1 + \left(\frac{a}{r}\right)^2 + 2\frac{a}{r} \cos \theta \right] \right\}$$

By using the series expression,

$$\ln (1 + x) = x - \frac{x^2}{2} + \frac{x^3}{3} - \frac{x^4}{4} + \cdots$$

$$\phi = -\frac{m}{2} \left\{ \left(\frac{a}{r}\right)^2 - 2\left(\frac{a}{r}\right) \cos \theta - \frac{1}{2} \left[ \left(\frac{a}{r}\right)^2 - 2\left(\frac{a}{r}\right) \cos \theta \right]^2 \right.$$

$$+ \frac{1}{3} \left[ \left(\frac{a}{r}\right)^2 - 2\left(\frac{a}{r}\right) \cos \theta \right]^3 - \cdots - \left[ \left(\frac{a}{r}\right)^2 + 2\left(\frac{a}{r}\right) \cos \theta \right]$$

$$+ \frac{1}{2} \left[ \left(\frac{a}{r}\right)^2 + 2\left(\frac{a}{r}\right) \cos \theta \right]^2 - \frac{1}{3} \left[ \left(\frac{a}{r}\right)^2 + 2\left(\frac{a}{r}\right) \cos \theta \right] + \cdots \right\}$$

After simplifying,

$$\phi = 2am \left[ \frac{\cos \theta}{r} + \left(\frac{a}{r}\right)^2 \frac{\cos \theta}{r} - \left(\frac{a}{r}\right)^4 \frac{\cos \theta}{r} - \frac{4}{3}\left(\frac{a}{r}\right)^2 \frac{\cos^3 \theta}{r} + \cdots \right]$$

Now, if $2am = \mu$ and if the limit is taken as $a$ approaches zero,

$$\phi = \frac{\mu \cos \theta}{r}$$

which is the velocity potential for a two-dimensional doublet at the origin, with axis in the $+x$-direction.

By using the relations

$$v_r = -\frac{\partial \phi}{\partial r} = -\frac{1}{r}\frac{\partial \psi}{\partial \theta} \qquad v_\theta = -\frac{1}{r}\frac{\partial \phi}{\partial \theta} = \frac{\partial \psi}{\partial r}$$

for the doublet,

$$\frac{\partial \psi}{\partial \theta} = -\frac{\mu \cos \theta}{r} \qquad \frac{\partial \psi}{\partial r} = \frac{\mu}{r^2}\sin \theta$$

After integrating,

$$\psi = -\frac{\mu \sin \theta}{r}$$

is the stream function for the doublet.   The equations in cartesian coordinates are

$$\phi = \frac{\mu x}{x^2 + y^2} \qquad \psi = -\frac{\mu y}{x^2 + y^2}$$

After rearranging,

$$\left(x - \frac{\mu}{2\phi}\right)^2 + y^2 = \frac{\mu^2}{4\phi^2} \qquad x^2 + \left(y + \frac{\mu}{2\psi}\right)^2 = \frac{\mu^2}{4\psi^2}$$

The lines of constant $\phi$ are circles through the origin with centers on the $x$-axis, and the streamlines are circles through the origin with centers on the $y$-axis, as shown in Fig. 7.29.   The origin is a singular point where the velocity goes to infinity.

*uniform flow*

Uniform flow in the $-x$-direction, $u = -U$, is expressed by

$$\phi = Ux \qquad \psi = Uy$$

In polar coordinates,

$$\phi = Ur \cos \theta \qquad \psi = Ur \sin \theta$$

*flow around a circular cylinder*

The addition of the flow due to a doublet and a uniform flow results in flow around a circular cylinder; thus

$$\phi = Ur \cos \theta + \frac{\mu \cos \theta}{r} \qquad \psi = Ur \sin \theta - \frac{\mu \sin \theta}{r}$$

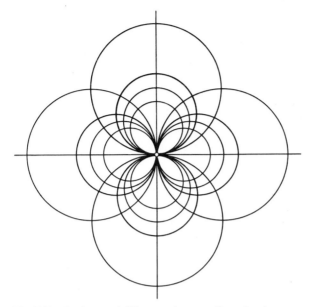

**Fig. 7.29**   Equipotential lines and streamlines for the two-dimensional doublet.

As a streamline in steady flow is a possible boundary, the streamline $\psi = 0$ is given by

$$0 = \left( Ur - \frac{\mu}{r} \right) \sin \theta$$

which is satisfied by $\theta = 0$, $\pi$, or by the value of $r$ that makes

$$Ur - \frac{\mu}{r} = 0$$

If this value is $r = a$, which is a circular cylinder, then

$$\mu = Ua^2$$

and the streamline $\psi = 0$ is the $x$-axis and the circle $r = a$.   The potential and stream functions for uniform flow around a circular cylinder of radius $a$ are, by substitution of the value of $\mu$,

$$\phi = U \left( r + \frac{a^2}{r} \right) \cos \theta \qquad \psi = U \left( r - \frac{a^2}{r} \right) \sin \theta$$

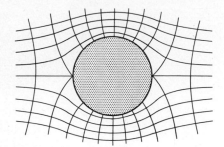

**Fig. 7.30** Equipotential lines and streamlines for flow around a circular cylinder.

for the uniform flow in the $-x$-direction. The equipotential lines and streamlines for this case are shown in Fig. 7.30.

The velocity at any point in the flow can be obtained from either the velocity potential or the stream function. On the surface of the cylinder the velocity is necessarily tangential and is expressed by $\partial\psi/\partial r$ for $r = a$; thus

$$q\Big|_{r=a} = U\left(1 + \frac{a^2}{r^2}\right)\sin\theta\Big|_{r=a} = 2U\sin\theta$$

The velocity is zero (stagnation point) at $\theta = 0, \pi$ and has maximum values of $2U$ at $\theta = \pi/2, 3\pi/2$. For the dynamic pressure zero at infinity, with Eq. (7.5.7) for $p_0 = 0$, $q_0 = U$,

$$p = \frac{\rho}{2}U^2\left[1 - \left(\frac{q}{U}\right)^2\right]$$

which holds for any point in the plane except the origin. For points on the cylinder,

$$p = \frac{\rho}{2}U^2(1 - 4\sin^2\theta)$$

The maximum pressure, which occurs at the stagnation points, is $\rho U^2/2$; and the minimum pressure, at $\theta = \pi/2, 3\pi/2$, is $-3\rho U^2/2$. The points of zero dynamic pressure are given by $\sin\theta = \pm\frac{1}{2}$, or $\theta = \pm\pi/6, \pm5\pi/6$. A cylindrical pitot-static tube is made by providing three openings in a cylinder, at 0 and $\pm30°$, as the difference in pressure between 0 and $\pm30°$ is the dynamic pressure $\rho U^2/2$.

The drag on the cylinder is shown to be zero by integration of the

$x$-component of the pressure force over the cylinder; thus

$$\text{Drag} = \int_0^{2\pi} pa \cos\theta\, d\theta = \frac{\rho a U^2}{2} \int_0^{2\pi} (1 - 4\sin^2\theta) \cos\theta\, d\theta = 0$$

Similarly, the lift force on the cylinder is zero.

*flow around a circular cylinder with circulation*

The addition of a vortex to the doublet and the uniform flow results in flow around a circular cylinder with circulation,

$$\phi = U\left(r + \frac{a^2}{r}\right) \cos\theta - \frac{\Gamma}{2\pi}\theta$$

$$\psi = U\left(r - \frac{a^2}{r}\right) \sin\theta + \frac{\Gamma}{2\pi} \ln r$$

The streamline $\psi = (\Gamma/2\pi) \ln a$ is the circular cylinder $r = a$, and, at great distances from the origin, the velocity remains $u = -U$, showing that flow around a circular cylinder is maintained with addition of the vortex. Some of the streamlines are shown in Fig. 7.31.

The velocity at the surface of the cylinder, necessarily tangent to the cylinder, is

$$q = \left.\frac{\partial\psi}{\partial r}\right|_{r=a} = 2U\sin\theta + \frac{\Gamma}{2\pi a}$$

Stagnation points occur when $q = 0$; i.e.,

$$\sin\theta = -\frac{\Gamma}{4\pi U a}$$

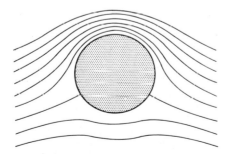

**Fig. 7.31** Streamlines for flow around a circular cylinder with circulation.

When the circulation is $4\pi U a$, the two stagnation points coincide at $r = a$, $\theta = -\pi/2$. For larger circulation, the stagnation point moves away from the cylinder.

The pressure at the surface of the cylinder is

$$p = \frac{\rho U^2}{2}\left[1 - \left(2 \sin \theta + \frac{\Gamma}{2\pi a U}\right)^2\right]$$

The drag again is zero. The lift, however, becomes

$$\text{Lift} = -\int_0^{2\pi} pa \sin \theta \, d\theta$$

$$= -\frac{\rho a U^2}{2}\int_0^{2\pi}\left[1 - \left(2 \sin \theta + \frac{\Gamma}{2\pi a U}\right)^2\right]\sin \theta \, d\theta = \rho U \Gamma$$

showing that the lift is directly proportional to the density of fluid, the approach velocity $U$, and the circulation $\Gamma$. This thrust, which acts at right angles to the approach velocity, is referred to as the *Magnus effect*. The Flettner rotor ship was designed to utilize this principle by the mounting of circular cylinders with axes vertical on a ship, and then mechanically rotating the cylinders to provide circulation. Air flow around the rotors produces the thrust at right angles to the relative wind direction. The close spacing of streamlines along the upper side of Fig. 7.31 indicates that the velocity is high there and that the pressure must then be correspondingly low.

The theoretical flow around a circular cylinder with circulation may be transformed[1] into flow around an airfoil with the same circulation and the same lift.

The airfoil develops its lift by producing a circulation around it due to its shape. It may be shown[1] that the lift is $\rho U \Gamma$ for any cylinder in two-dimensional flow. The angle of inclination of the airfoil relative to the approach velocity (angle of attack) greatly affects the circulation. For large angles of attack, the flow does not follow the wing profile, and the theory breaks down.

It should be mentioned that all two-dimensional ideal-fluid-flow cases may be conveniently handled by complex-variable theory and by a system of *conformal mapping*, which transforms a flow net from one configuration to another by a suitable complex-variable mapping function.

**example 7.3** A source with strength 6 cfs/ft and a vortex with strength 12 ft²/sec are located at the origin. Determine the equation for velocity

[1] V. L. Streeter, "Fluid Dynamics," pp. 137–155, McGraw-Hill Book Company, New York, 1948.

potential and stream function.   What are the velocity components at $x = 2$, $y = 3$?

The velocity potential for the source is

$$\phi = -\frac{6}{2\pi} \ln r$$

and the corresponding stream function is

$$\psi = -\frac{6}{2\pi} \theta$$

The velocity potential for the vortex is

$$\phi = -\frac{12}{2\pi} \theta$$

and the corresponding stream function is

$$\psi = \frac{12}{2\pi} \ln r$$

By adding the respective functions,

$$\phi = -\frac{3}{\pi} (\ln r + 2\theta)$$

and

$$\psi = -\frac{3}{\pi} (\theta - 2 \ln r)$$

The radial and tangential velocity components are

$$v_r = -\frac{\partial \phi}{\partial r} = \frac{3}{\pi r} \qquad v_\theta = -\frac{1}{r}\frac{\partial \phi}{\partial \theta} = \frac{6}{\pi r}$$

At (2,3), $r = \sqrt{2^2 + 3^2} = 3.61$, $v_r = 0.265$, $v_\theta = 0.53$.

## problems

**7.1**  Compute the gradient of the following two-dimensional scalar functions:

(a) $\phi = -2 \ln (x^2 + y^2)$     (b) $\phi = Ux + Vy$     (c) $\phi = 2xy$

**7.2**  Compute the divergence of the gradients of $\phi$ found in Prob. 7.1.

**7.3**  Compute the curl of the gradients of $\phi$ found in Prob. 7.1.

**Fig. 7.32**

**7.4**  For $\mathbf{q} = \mathbf{i}(x + y) + \mathbf{j}(y + z) + \mathbf{k}(x^2 + y^2 + z^2)$ find the components of rotation at (2,2,2).

**7.5**  Derive the equation of continuity for two-dimensional flow in polar coordinates by equating the net efflux from a small polar element to zero (Fig. 7.32).   It is

$$\frac{\partial v_r}{\partial r} + \frac{v_r}{r} + \frac{1}{r}\frac{\partial v_\theta}{\partial \theta} = 0$$

**7.6**  The $x$-component of velocity is $u = x^2 + z^2 + 5$, and the $y$-component is $v = y^2 + z^2$.   Find the simplest $z$-component of velocity that satisfies continuity.

**7.7**  A velocity potential in two-dimensional flow is $\phi = y + x^2 - y^2$. Find the stream function for this flow.

**7.8**  The two-dimensional stream function for a flow is $\psi = 9 + 6x - 4y + 7xy$.   Find the velocity potential.

**7.9**  Derive the partial differential equations relating $\phi$ and $\psi$ for two-dimensional flow in plane polar coordinates.

**7.10**  From the continuity equation in polar coordinates in Prob. 7.5, derive the Laplace equation in the same coordinate system.

**7.11**  Does the function $\phi = 1/r$ satisfy the Laplace equation in two dimensions?   In three-dimensional flow is it satisfied?

**7.12**  By use of the equations developed in Prob. 7.9 find the two-dimensional stream function for $\phi = \ln r$.

**7.13**  Find the Stokes stream function for $\phi = 1/r$.

**7.14**  For the Stokes stream function $\psi = 9r^2 \sin^2 \theta$, find $\phi$ in cartesian coordinates.

**7.15**  In Prob. 7.14 what is the discharge between stream surfaces through the points $r = 1$, $\theta = 0$ and $r = 1$, $\theta = \pi/4$?

**7.16**  Write the boundary conditions for steady flow around a sphere, of radius $a$, at its surface and at infinity.

**7.17**   A circular cylinder of radius $a$ has its center at the origin and is translating with velocity $V$ in the $y$-direction.   Write the boundary condition in terms of $\phi$ that is to be satisfied at its surface and at infinity.

**7.18**   A source of strength 30 cfs is located at the origin, and another source of strength 20 cfs is located at $(1,0,0)$.   Find the velocity components $u$, $v$, $w$ at $(-1,0,0)$ and $(1,1,1)$.

**7.19**   If the dynamic pressure is zero at infinity in Prob. 7.18, for $\rho = 2.00$ slugs/ft$^3$ calculate the dynamic pressure at $(-1,0,0)$ and $(1,1,1)$.

**7.20**   A source of strength $m$ at the origin and a uniform flow of 15 ft/sec are combined in three-dimensional flow so that a stagnation point occurs at $(1,0,0)$.   Obtain the velocity potential and stream function for this flow case.

**7.21**   By use of symmetry obtain the velocity potential for a three-dimensional sink of strength 25 cfs located 3 ft from a plane barrier.

**7.22**   Equations are wanted for flow of a uniform stream of 12 ft/sec around a Rankine body 4 ft long and 2 ft thick in a transverse direction.

**7.23**   A source of strength 10 cfs at $(1,0,0)$ and a sink of the same strength at $(-1,0,0)$ are combined with a uniform flow of 25 ft/sec in the $-x$-direction.   Determine the size of Rankine body formed by this flow.

**7.24**   A sphere of radius 3 ft, with center at the origin, has a uniform flow of 20 ft/sec in the $-x$-direction flowing around it.   At $(4,0,0)$ the dynamic pressure is 10 lb/ft$^2$ and $\rho = 1.935$ slugs/ft$^3$.   Find the equation for pressure distribution over the surface of the sphere.

**7.25**   By integration over the surface of the sphere of Prob. 7.24 show that the drag on the sphere is zero.

**7.26**   Show that if two stream functions $\psi_1$ and $\psi_2$ both satisfy the Laplace equation, $\nabla^2 \psi = 0$ for $\psi = \psi_1 + \psi_2$.

**7.27**   Show that if $u_1$, $v_1$ and $u_2$, $v_2$ are the velocity components of two velocity potentials $\phi_1$ and $\phi_2$ which satisfy the Laplace equation, then for $\phi = \phi_1 + \phi_2$ the velocity components are $u = u_1 + u_2$ and $v = v_1 + v_2$.

**7.28**   A two-dimensional source is located at $(1,0)$ and another one of the same strength at $(-1,0)$.   Construct the velocity vector at $(0,0)$, $(0,1)$, $(0,-1)$, $(0,-2)$, and $(1,1)$.   (*Hint:* Using the results of Prob. 7.27, draw the velocity components by adding the individual velocity components induced at the point in question by each source, without regard to the other, due to its strength and location.)

**7.29**   Determine the velocity potential for a source located at $(1,0)$.   Write the equation for the velocity potential for the source system described in Prob. 7.28.

**7.30**   Draw a set of streamlines for each of the sources described in Prob. 7.28 and from this diagram construct the streamlines for the combined flow.

(*Hint:* For each of the sources draw streamlines separated by an angle of $\pi/6$. Finally combine the intersection points of those rays for which $\psi_1 + \psi_2$ is constant.)

**7.31** Does the line $x = 0$ form a line in the flow field described in Prob. 7.28 for which there is no velocity component normal to it? Is this line a streamline? Could this line be the trace of a solid plane lamina that was submerged in the flow? Does the velocity potential determined in Prob. 7.29 describe the flow in the region $x > 0$ for a source located at a distance of unity from a plane wall? Justify your answers.

**7.32** Determine the equation for the velocity on the line $x = 0$ for the flow described in Prob. 7.28. Find an equation for the pressure on the surface whose trace is $x = 0$. What is the force on one side of this plane due to the source located at distance of unity from it? Water is the fluid.

**7.33** In two-dimensional flow what is the nature of the flow given by $\phi = 7x + 2 \ln r$?

**7.34** By using a method similar to that suggested in Prob. 7.30 draw the potential lines for the flow given in Prob. 7.33.

**7.35** By using the suggestion in Prob. 7.30 draw a flow net for a flow consisting of a source and a vortex which are located at the origin. Use the same value for $\mu$ in both the source and the vortex.

**7.36** A source discharging 20 cfs/ft is located at $(-1,0)$, and a sink of twice the strength is located at $(2,0)$. For dynamic pressure at the origin of 100 lb/ft², $\rho = 1.8$ slugs/ft³, find the velocity and dynamic pressure at $(0,1)$ and $(1,1)$.

**7.37** Select the strength of doublet needed to portray a uniform flow of 50 ft/sec around a cylinder of radius 5 ft.

**7.38** Develop the equations for flow around a "Rankine cylinder" formed by a source, an equal sink, and a uniform flow. If $2a$ is the distance between source and sink, their strength is $2\pi\mu$, and $U$ is the uniform velocity, develop an equation for length of the body.

**7.39** A circular cylinder 8 ft in diameter rotates at 500 rpm. When in an air stream, $\rho = 0.002$ slug/ft³, moving at 400 ft/sec, what is the lift force per foot of cylinder, assuming 90 per cent efficiency in developing circulation from the rotation?

**7.40** An unsteady-flow case may be transformed into a steady-flow case

(*a*) regardless of the nature of the problem
(*b*) when two bodies are moving toward each other in an infinite fluid
(*c*) when an unsymmetrical body is rotating in an infinite fluid
(*d*) when a single body translates in an infinite fluid
(*e*) under no circumstances

**7.41**   Select the value of $\phi$ that satisfies continuity.

(a) $x^2 + y^2$      (b) $\sin x$      (c) $\ln(x + y)$      (d) $x + y$
(e) none of these answers

**7.42**   The units for Euler's equations of motion are given by

(a) force per unit mass
(b) velocity
(c) energy per unit weight
(d) force per unit weight
(e) none of these answers

**7.43**   Euler's equations of motion can be integrated when it is assumed that

(a) the continuity equation is satisfied
(b) the fluid is incompressible
(c) a velocity potential exists and the density is constant
(d) the flow is rotational and incompressible
(e) the fluid is nonviscous

**7.44**   Euler's equations of motion are a mathematical statement that at every point

(a) rate of mass inflow equals rate of mass outflow
(b) force per unit mass equals acceleration
(c) the energy does not change with the time
(d) Newton's third law of motion holds
(e) the fluid momentum is constant

**7.45**   In irrotational flow of an ideal fluid

(a) a velocity potential exists
(b) all particles must move in straight lines
(c) the motion must be uniform
(d) the flow is always steady
(e) the velocity must be zero at a boundary

**7.46**   A function $\phi$ that satisfies the Laplace equation

(a) must be linear in $x$ and $y$
(b) is a possible case of rotational fluid flow
(c) does not necessarily satisfy the continuity equation
(d) is a possible fluid-flow case
(e) is none of these answers

**7.47**   If $\phi_1$ and $\phi_2$ are each solutions of the Laplace equation, which of the following is also a solution?

(a) $\phi_1 - 2\phi_2$      (b) $\phi_1\phi_2$      (c) $\phi_1/\phi_2$      (d) $\phi_1^2$      (e) none of these answers

**7.48**   Select the relation that must hold if the flow is irrotational.

(a) $\partial u/\partial y + \partial v/\partial x = 0$     (b) $\partial u/\partial x = \partial v/\partial y$
(c) $\partial^2 u/\partial x^2 + \partial^2 v/\partial y^2 = 0$     (d) $\partial u/\partial y = \partial v/\partial x$
(e) none of these answers

**7.49**   The Bernoulli equation in steady ideal-fluid flow states that

(a) the velocity is constant along a streamline
(b) the energy is constant along a streamline but may vary across streamlines
(c) when the speed increases, the pressure increases
(d) the energy is constant throughout the fluid
(e) the net flow rate into any small region must be zero

**7.50**   The Stokes stream function applies to

(a) all three-dimensional ideal-fluid-flow cases
(b) ideal (nonviscous) fluids only
(c) irrotational flow only
(d) cases of axial symmetry
(e) none of these cases

**7.51**   The Stokes stream function has the value $\psi = 1$ at the origin and the value $\psi = 2$ at (1,1,1).   The discharge through the surface between these points is

(a) 1     (b) $\pi$     (c) $2\pi$     (d) 4     (e) none of these answers

**7.52**   Select the relation that must hold in two-dimensional, irrotational flow:

(a) $\partial\phi/\partial x = \partial\psi/\partial y$     (b) $\partial\phi/\partial x = -\partial\psi/\partial y$     (c) $\partial\phi/\partial y = \partial\psi/\partial x$
(d) $\partial\phi/\partial x = \partial\phi/\partial y$     (e) none of these answers

**7.53**   The two-dimensional stream function

(a) is constant along an equipotential surface
(b) is constant along a streamline
(c) is defined for irrotational flow only
(d) relates velocity and pressure
(e) is none of these answers

**7.54**   In two-dimensional flow $\psi = 4$ ft$^2$/sec at (0,2) and $\psi = 2$ ft$^2$/sec at (0,1).   The discharge between the two points is

(a) from left to right     (b) $4\pi$ cfs/ft     (c) 2 cfs/ft     (d) $1/\pi$ cfs/ft
(e) none of these answers

**7.55**   The boundary condition for steady flow of an ideal fluid is that the

(*a*)  velocity is zero at the boundary
(*b*)  velocity component normal to the boundary is zero
(*c*)  velocity component tangent to the boundary is zero
(*d*)  boundary surface must be stationary
(*e*)  continuity equation must be satisfied

**7.56**   An equipotential surface

(*a*)  has no velocity component tangent to it
(*b*)  is composed of streamlines
(*c*)  is a stream surface
(*d*)  is a surface of constant dynamic pressure
(*e*)  is none of these answers

**7.57**   A source in two-dimensional flow

(*a*)  is a point from which fluid is imagined to flow outward uniformly in all directions
(*b*)  is a line from which fluid is imagined to flow uniformly in all directions at right angles to it
(*c*)  has a strength defined as the speed at unit radius
(*d*)  has streamlines that are concentric circles
(*e*)  has a velocity potential independent of the radius

**7.58**   The two-dimensional vortex

(*a*)  has a strength given by the circulation around a path enclosing the vortex
(*b*)  has radial streamlines
(*c*)  has a zero circulation around it
(*d*)  has a velocity distribution that varies directly as the radial distance from the vortex
(*e*)  creates a velocity distribution that has rotation throughout the fluid

# part two

# applications of fluid mechanics

In Part 1 the fundamental concepts and equations have been developed and illustrated by many examples and simple applications.   Fluid resistance, dimensional analysis, compressible flow, and ideal-fluid flow have been presented.   In Part 2 several of the important fields of application of fluid mechanics are explored: measurement of flow, turbomachinery, closed-conduit and open-channel flow, and unsteady flow.

# 8

# fluid measurement and control

Fluid measurements include the determination of pressure, velocity, discharge, shock waves, density gradients, turbulence, and viscosity. There are many ways these measurements may be taken, e.g., direct, indirect, gravimetric, volumetric, electronic, electromagnetic, and optical. Direct measurements for discharge consist in the determination of the volume or weight of fluid that passes a section in a given time interval. Indirect methods of discharge measurement require the determination of head, difference in pressure, or velocity at several points in a cross section, and with these the computing of discharge. The most precise methods are the gravimetric or volumetric determinations, in which the weight or volume is measured by weigh scales or by a calibrated tank for a time interval that is measured by a stop watch.

Pressure and velocity measurements are first undertaken in this chapter, followed by optical flow measurement, positive-displacement meters, rate meters, electromagnetic flow devices, and river-flow measurement, turbulence and viscosity measurement and concluding with fluid amplifiers and controls.

## 8.1 pressure measurement

The measurement of pressure is required in many devices that determine the velocity of a fluid stream or its rate of flow, because of the relationship between velocity and pressure given by the energy equation. The static

**Fig. 8.1**  Piezometer opening for measurement of static pressure.

pressure of a fluid in motion is its pressure when the velocity is undisturbed by the measurement.    Figure 8.1 indicates one method of measuring static pressure, the *piezometer* opening.    When the flow is parallel, as indicated, the pressure variation is hydrostatic normal to the streamlines; hence, by measuring the pressure at the wall, the pressure at any other point in the cross section may be determined.    The piezometer opening should be small, with length of opening at least twice its diameter, and should be normal to the surface, with no burrs at its edges because small eddies form and distort the measurement.    A small amount of rounding of the opening is permissible.    Any slight misalignment or roughness at the opening may cause errors in measurement; therefore, it is advisable to use several piezometer openings connected together into a *piezometer ring*.    When the surface is rough in the vicinity of the opening the reading is unreliable. For small irregularities it may be possible to smooth the surface around the opening.

For rough surfaces, the *static tube* (Fig. 8.2) may be used.    It consists

**Fig. 8.2**  Static tube.

of a tube that is directed upstream with the end closed.   It has radial holes in the cylindrical portion downstream from the nose.   The flow is presumed to be moving by the openings as if it were undisturbed.   There are disturbances, however, due to both the nose and the right-angled leg that is normal to the flow.   The static tube should be calibrated, as it may read too high or too low.   If it does not read true static pressure, the discrepancy $\Delta h$ normally varies as the square of the velocity of flow by the tube; i.e.,

$$\Delta h = C\frac{v^2}{2g}$$

in which $C$ is determined by towing the tube in still fluid where pressure and velocity are known or by inserting it into a smooth pipe that contains a piezometer ring.

Such tubes are relatively insensitive to the Reynolds number and to Mach numbers below unity.   Their alignment with the flow is not critical, so that an error of but a few per cent is to be expected for a yaw misalignment of 15°.

The distribution of static pressure around the surface of a body may be determined by taking pressure readings from a series of piezometer openings, as in Fig. 8.3.   The flow around a circular cylinder was discussed in Chap. 7, in which irrotational-flow theory was used.   At every point on the cylinder the pressure could be predicted, and if the pressures were known, one could equally well determine the free-stream velocity and direction with respect to some coordinate axis.   This predicted pressure distribution corresponds remarkably well with that which is observed on the front face of a cylinder in a real fluid for a wide range of Reynolds numbers. The same correspondence exists between the theoretical predictions for the flow around a sphere and the actual measurements that are observed on the sphere ahead of the point of separation (cf. Fig. 5.21).   An interesting probe has been developed which utilizes this fact to study the flow in a region where large changes in speed and direction are taking place and where one is interested in obtaining a local measurement.   By placing three holes on the equator of a small sphere and two more on a meridian, one hole above and one below the middle hole, and measuring the various

**Fig. 8.3**   Static pressure openings on a body submerged in a fluid.

pressure differences that exist at each of these taps, one can predict the horizontal and vertical velocity components. Because the theory and the experiment do not exactly agree, it is necessary to run a calibration curve for the instrument.

The pressure is often measured on U-tube manometers or micromanometers, which are described in Chap. 2. With a micromanometer it is possible to detect a change in the elevation of the manometer fluid of about 0.001 in. If the fluid has a specific gravity of unity, this corresponds to a pressure change of 0.000036 psi. Slightly greater sensitivities can be obtained by using special refinements to the micromanometer, e.g., the Chattock gage.[1]

The same sensitivities can be obtained with electric transducers, which sense the pressure changes by electrically measuring the displacement of a diaphragm or bellows. A schematic diagram of one arrangement is shown in Fig. 8.4. As the diaphragm is distended by a difference in pressure between the gas inside and outside the pressure chamber, the core of a differential transformer moves between the coils. The electric output of the transformer depends upon the position of the core, which, as has been said, is determined by the pressure difference at the two ports. Thus the transducer gives an electrical change for a pressure change. One can obtain such transducers to cover a wide variety of pressure ranges by having different elastic characteristics for the diaphragm.

The distortion of many types of elastic elements can also be detected with the *electric strain gage.* This is basically a piece of fine wire which is bonded to the piece that will be distorted. As the member changes shape,

[1] For a further descritpion of this gage see S. Goldstein, "Modern Developments in Fluid Mechanics," pp. 274–276, Oxford University Press, London, 1938.

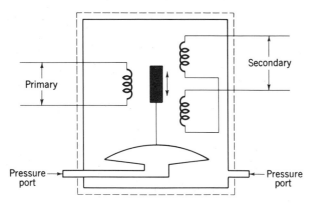

**Fig. 8.4** Schematic diagram of a pressure transducer using a differential transformer. (*Sanborn Co.*)

**Fig. 8.5**  Capacitance gage.

it stretches, thereby stretching the fine wire and altering its electric resistivity.   The change in the resistance can be measured with a Wheatstone-bridge circuit similar to the one shown in Fig. 8.11.   Now calibration is all that is needed to correlate the resistance changes to the pressure changes which caused the distortion of the elastic element.

Pressure may also be determined by making use of the *piezoelectric* properties of certain crystals, such as quartz or rochelle salt.   Pressure exerts a strain on the crystals that liberates a small electric charge that can be measured by electronic means.   Another method (Fig. 8.5) is the *capacitance* gage; the pressure distorts a diaphragm which varies the capacitance between plate and diaphragm.

## 8.2  velocity measurement

Since the determining of velocity at a number of points in a cross section permits the evaluating of discharge, the measuring of velocity is an important phase of measuring flow.   Velocity can be found by measuring the time an identifiable particle takes to move a known distance.   This is done whenever it is convenient or necessary.   This technique has been developed to study flow in regions which are so small that the normal flow would be greatly disturbed and perhaps diasppear if an instrument were introduced to measure the velocity.   A transparent viewing region must be made available, and by means of a strong light and a powerful microscope the very minute impurities in the fluid can be photographed with a high-speed motion-picture camera.   From such motion pictures the velocity of the particles, and therefore the velocity of the fluid in a small region, can be determined.

Normally, however, a device is used which does not measure velocity directly but yields a measurable quantity that can be related to velocity. The *pitot tube* operates on such a principle and is one of the most accurate methods of measuring velocity.   In Fig. 8.6 a glass tube or hypodermic needle with a right-angled bend is used to measure the velocity $v$ in an open channel.   The tube opening is directed upstream so that the fluid

**Fig. 8.6** Simple pitot tube.

flows into the opening until the pressure builds up within the tube sufficiently to withstand the impact of velocity against it.    Directly in front of the opening the fluid is at rest.    The streamline through 1 leads to the point 2, called the *stagnation point,* where the fluid is at rest, and there divides and passes around the tube.    The pressure at 2 is known from the liquid column within the tube.    Bernoulli's equation, applied between points 1 and 2, produces

$$\frac{v^2}{2g} + \frac{p_1}{\gamma} = \frac{p_2}{\gamma} = h_0 + \Delta h$$

since both points are at the same elevation.    As $p_1/\gamma = h_0$, the equation reduces to

$$\frac{v^2}{2g} = \Delta h \tag{8.2.1}$$

or

$$v = \sqrt{2g\,\Delta h} \tag{8.2.2}$$

Practically, it is very difficult to read the height $\Delta h$ from a free surface.

The pitot tube measures the stagnation pressure, which is also referred to as the *total* pressure.    The total pressure is composed of two parts, the static pressure $h_0$ and the dynamic pressure $\Delta h$, expressed in length of a column of the flowing fluid (Fig. 8.6).    The dynamic pressure is related to velocity head by Eq. (8.2.1).

By combining the static-pressure measurement and the total-pressure measurement, i.e., measuring each and connecting to opposite ends of a differential manometer, the dynamic pressure head is obtained.    Figure 8.7 illustrates one arrangement.    Bernoulli's equation applied from 1 to 2 is

$$\frac{v^2}{2g} + \frac{p_1}{\gamma} = \frac{p_2}{\gamma} \tag{8.2.3}$$

**Fig. 8.7** Use of pitot tube and piezometer opening for measurement of velocity.

The equation for the pressure through the manometer, in feet of water, is

$$\frac{p_1}{\gamma} S + kS + R'S_0 - (k + R')S = \frac{p_2}{\gamma} S$$

By simplifying,

$$\frac{p_2 - p_1}{\gamma} = R' \left( \frac{S_0}{S} - 1 \right) \tag{8.2.4}$$

After substituting for $(p_2 - p_1)/\gamma$ in Eq. (8.2.3) and solving for $v$,

$$v = \sqrt{2gR' \left( \frac{S_0}{S} - 1 \right)} \tag{8.2.5}$$

The pitot tube is also insensitive to flow alignment, and an error of only a few per cent occurs if the tube has a yaw misalignment of less than 15°. However, if the angle of yaw is around 45°, not only is the pressure that is sensed not easily related to the flow velocity, but minor changes in the yaw angle cause large changes in the pressure. This fact is used in the construction of a yaw meter. Two small pitot tubes are fastened to a common stem so that the plane of the sensing tubes is parallel to the flow and their axes are aligned $\pm 45°$ with the flow direction. In this condition the pressure difference between the two pitot tubes should be zero if the probe is well made. If the stem of the probe is now rotated so that the plane of the tubes is still parallel to the flow, one of the pitot tubes will make an angle with the velocity which is greater than 45° and the other, a smaller angle. This will result in a large pressure difference between the two pitot tubes. By carefully adjusting the yaw meter until a null reading

**Fig. 8.8**   Pitot-static tube.

is obtained, the flow direction can be determined.   Such probes can be made quite small for boundary-layer investigations.

The static tube and pitot tube may be combined into one instrument, called a *pitot-static tube* (Fig. 8.8).   Analyzing this system in a manner similar to that in Fig. 8.7 shows that the same relations hold; Eq. (8.2.5) expresses the velocity, but, owing to the uncertainty of the measurement of static pressure, a corrective coefficient $C$ is applied,

$$v = C \sqrt{2gR' \left( \frac{S_0}{S} - 1 \right)} \qquad\qquad (8.2.6)$$

A particular form of pitot-static tube with a blunt nose, the *Prandtl tube*, has been designed so that the disturbances due to nose and leg cancel, leaving $C = 1$ in the equation.   For other pitot-static tubes the constant $C$ must be determined by calibration.

Pitot-static tubes can be made so that the outside diameter is about $\frac{1}{8}$ in. However, the holes for the pressure taps are of such small size as to cause difficulty from clogging and also the trapping of air when they are used in liquids, problems which do not occur when such a probe is used for measuring gas velocities.

Once a probe is available which is small enough so that the measurement gives a local velocity, it is possible to survey a conduit to determine the quantity of flow.   The velocity readings are multiplied by an area for which the measurement is representative, and these results are summed to give the total flow rate.

The velocity probes are also used to survey a control surface surrounding a body that is submerged in a fluid in order to determine the net momentum efflux.   Wake surveys are made for determining the drag on airfoils, and the spherical probe which was mentioned in Sec. 8.1 was developed to examine the region behind a ship's hull to find the viscous drag.

*heated thermocouples*

A thermocouple can be made if two wires of different materials are joined to form a continuous loop.    If each of the junctions is at a different temperature, an electric current will flow in the loop as a result of the various thermoelectric effects which are present.    This current is directly related to the temperature difference between the two junctions, and if it can be measured, a relatively convenient means for determining temperature differences is available for use.    However, by further design refinements a velocity-measuring probe, using the Haystings patented principle, can be made (see Fig. 8.9).    A low-voltage a-c bridge circuit has two noble-metal thermocouples as sensing elements.    Thermocouples $A$ and $B$ are heated by alternating current.    A change in flow causes a change in the temperature of the thermocouples, resulting in a change in the d-c output from the thermocouples.    A third thermocouple $C$ is in the d-c meter circuit. This thermocouple is unheated and is the same size as those in the a-c circuit.    A change in ambient temperature develops voltages in all thermocouples; but the transient effects in heated and unheated elements are equal and opposite, so that the unheated thermocouple compensates for changes in ambient temperature.    If a probe is installed in pipe, duct, or line at the point of average velocity, the resultant indication multiplied by the cross-sectional area will equal the total volume flow rate.    Thus, these instruments can also be used as volume flowmeters.    Both directional and omnidirectional probes are available, the latter able to detect air speeds as low as 5 fpm.

**Fig. 8.9** Schematic diagram of a heated thermocouple velocity probe. (*U.S. patents 2,540,822, 2,652,723, 2,745,283, and patents pending, Haystings-Raydist, Inc.*)

Research is now going on to utilize heated thermistors, a solid-state device which undergoes a large change in resistance for small temperature changes, for measuring liquid flow velocities.

*velocity and temperature measurement in compressible flow*

The pitot-static tube may be used for velocity determinations in compressible flow.   In Fig. 8.8 the velocity reduction from free-stream velocity at 1 to zero at 2 takes place very rapidly without significant heat transfer, and friction plays a very small part, and so the compression may be assumed to be isentropic.   By applying Eq. (6.3.7) to points 1 and 2 of Fig. 8.8, with $V_2 = 0$,

$$\frac{V_1{}^2}{2} = \frac{k}{k-1}\left(\frac{p_2}{\rho_2} - \frac{p_1}{\rho_1}\right) = \frac{kR}{k-1}(T_2 - T_1) = c_p T_1\left(\frac{T_2}{T_1} - 1\right) \qquad (8.2.7)$$

The substitution of $c_p$ is from Eq. (6.1.8).   By use of Eq. (6.1.17)

$$\frac{V_1{}^2}{2} = c_p T_1\left[\left(\frac{p_2}{p_1}\right)^{(k-1)/k} - 1\right] = c_p T_2\left[1 - \left(\frac{p_1}{p_2}\right)^{(k-1)/k}\right] \qquad (8.2.8)$$

The static pressure $p_1$ may be obtained from the side openings of the pitot tube, and the stagnation pressure may be obtained from the impact opening leading to a simple manometer, or $p_2 - p_1$ may be found from the differential manometer.   If the tube is not designed so that true static pressure is measured, it must be calibrated and the true static pressure computed.

Temperature measurement of undisturbed flow of a compressible gas must be made indirectly, by measurement of the velocity of flow and the stagnation temperature.   By solving Eq. (8.2.7) for $T_1$,

$$T_1 = T_2 - \frac{V_1{}^2}{2c_p} \qquad (8.2.9)$$

$V_1$ is obtained from pitot-static tube measurements.   $T_2$, the true stagnation temperature, is difficult to obtain because of heat transfer to and from the temperature-sensing element.   Devices[1] comprising a thermocouple, with shielding such that true stagnation temperature is measured, have been developed.   Otherwise correction factors must be applied to the temperature readings, and the devices must be calibrated.

[1] A. Franz, Pressure and Temperature Measurements in Supercharger Investigations, *NACA Tech. Mem.* 953, 1940.

*the hot-wire anemometer*

Gas velocities are successfully measured with the *hot-wire anemometer*.   A short length of fine platinum wire is heated by an electric current.   The resistance to flow of electricity through the wire is a function of its temperature.   Flow of a gas around the hot wire cools it and thus changes its resistance.   By holding constant either the voltage across the wire or the current through the wire by a suitable circuit, the change in amperes or voltage, respectively, becomes a function of the speed of gas flow by the hot wire.   It may be calibrated by placing it in a gas stream of known velocity.   The hot-wire anemometer has a very quick response to changes in gas velocity and is the best practical means for measuring the rapid fluctuations caused by turbulence at a point.

In Figs. 8.10 and 8.11 circuits for the two systems are shown.   A Wheatstone-bridge circuit is utilized for both, with the hot wire forming one resistance and $R_1$, $R_2$, $R_3$ the other resistances.   In the constant-resistance circuit, the temperature of the wire is held constant and hence its resistance remains constant.   The circuit is first adjusted so that the galvanometer reads zero.   Then for a change in fluid flow over the wire, the variable resistance $B$ is adjusted to bring the galvanometer reading back to zero, and the voltmeter reading has changed.   By calibration in a stream of known velocity, voltmeter reading is related to fluid velocity.

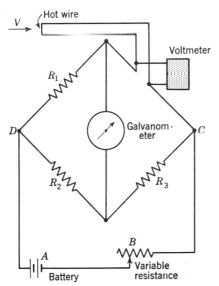

**Fig. 8.10**   Constant-resistance hot-wire anemometer.

**Fig. 8.11** Constant-voltage hot-wire anemometer.

In the constant-voltage circuit (Fig. 8.11) the variable resistance $B$ is first adjusted so that the galvanometer reads zero when the hot wire is exposed to fluid at rest.   Flow over the wire then cools the wire and varies its resistance, causing a change in galvanometer reading.   Calibration relates velocity to galvanometer reading.

Extending the use of the hot-wire anemometer to liquids, particularly water, has always been an attractive possibility.   In addition, the recent interest in liquid metals has opened up another area for the possible application of hot-wire instruments.   Efforts also have been exerted to develop hot-film anemometers.   These consist of a thin, electrically conducting film that is deposited upon an insulator so as to obtain low thermal inertia and the needed strength characteristics for operation in a liquid.

The results that have been achieved have been obtained by overcoming the difficulties that occur in liquids but not in gases.   Many liquids, including water unless it is extremely pure, have sufficient electric conductivity to interfere with the operation of the probe.   There is also a difficulty with entrained particles, which collect on the probes, alter their calibration, and are the cause of film erosion and wire breakage.   When using hot wires in air, this difficulty exists to a certain degree, because of the presence of dust.   However, in liquid applications one encounters the additional problem of keeping the sensing element free from the gases which come out of solution and collect on the sensor, thereby isolating it from the flow.

Despite these obstacles to a successful application, progress has been made. The recent introduction of an extremely thin quartz coating, which electrically insulates the hot wire or film without significantly reducing the frequency response of the probe, is very promising. An important incidental feature of this coating is that it reduces the tendency for contaminants to collect on the sensor.

The probe shown in Fig. 8.12 also extends the range of usefulness of the hot-film technique. Indeed, it is a cooled film for high-temperature applications. It consists of a 0.006-in.-diameter glass tube plated over with platinum and gold films, which carry away to a heat sink the heat picked up by the sensor in a hot fluid. The sink is cooled by water or low-temperature gas through a network of internal passages in the probe. The temperature of the sensor, a length of platinum film about $\frac{1}{16}$ in. long, will depend upon the flow velocity, which can now be measured by observing the changes in the film's resistance. The probes find application in severe environments, such as in combustors, plasmas, and rocket exhausts. Where measurements are to be made in combustion zones and electrically

0.038 in. diam

Cooled tube bundle

Gold plating over platinum

Sensing element (platinum)
0.006 in. diam

0.050 in.

**Fig. 8.12** Cooled film sensors are formed from a glass tube covered with a thin film of platinum. Gold plating isolates a short sensing element. Coolant flows through this glass tube. (*Thermo-Systems, Inc.*)

**Fig. 8.13** Price current meter. (*W. and L. E. Gurley.*)

conducting fluids, the above-mentioned quartz oxide films can be applied to eliminate any deleterious effects.

The *current meter* (Fig. 8.13) is used to measure the velocity of liquid flow in open channels.  The cups are shaped so that the drag varies with orientation, causing a relatively slow rotation.  With an electric circuit and headphones, an audible signal is detected for a fixed number of revolutions. The number of signals in a given time period is a function of the velocity. The meters are calibrated by towing them through liquid at known speeds. For measuring high-velocity flow a current meter with a propeller as rotating element is used, as it offers less resistance to the flow.

Air velocities are measured with cup-type or vane-(propeller) type anemometers (Fig. 8.14) which drive generators that indicate air velocity directly or drive counters that indicate the number of revolutions.

By designing the vanes so that they have very low inertia, employing

**Fig. 8.14**  Air anemometer.  (*Taylor Instrument Co.*)

precision bearings and optical tachometers which effectively take no power
to drive them, anemometers can be made to read very low air velocities.
They can be sensitive enough to measure the convection air currents which
the human body causes by its heat emission to the atmosphere.

## 8.3  force measurements

Force measurements are necessary in the study of fluids to determine such
physical properties as surface tension and such hydrodynamic forces as
lift and drag.   Elastic members are used, and their deflection is converted
to force through suitable calibration.   The various means used to detect
these deflections have been discussed previously.   By proper design of the
electronic force transducer, full-scale loads of $\pm 1$ gm can be obtained, and
the upper limit is dependent only upon the size of the elastic member that
can be used.

## 8.4 optical flow measurement

Three optical flow-measuring devices are described and illustrated in this section.   The principal advantage of the optical techniques is that the flow is undisturbed by the measurement.   Each method is based on the principle that changes in density of a medium change the angle of refraction of light; i.e., the denser the medium, the larger the angle of refraction.   The index of refraction $n$ of a substance is defined as the ratio of the speed of light in a vacuum to the speed of light through the medium; hence $n$ is always greater than unity.   The index of refraction varies with the wavelength of the light and tends to increase linearly with the density.   The relationship among angle of incidence $i$, angle of refraction $r$, and the two values of index of refraction $n_a$, $n_b$ (Fig. 8.15) is given by *Snell's law:*

$$n_a \sin i = n_b \sin r$$

When the light passes from a less dense medium to a more dense medium, the angle of refraction is less than the angle of incidence.   If the index of refraction is very close to unity, as is the case for most gases, the empirical *Gladstone-Dale* equation may be used:

$$\frac{n-1}{\rho} = \frac{n_a - 1}{\rho_a} = \frac{n_b - 1}{\rho_b}$$

*the schlieren method*

The schlieren system is illustrated in Fig. 8.16, where it is employed in flow across a two-dimensional test section.   Light from a source is collimated by the first lens and passed through the test section to a second lens, which

**Fig. 8.15** Angles of incidence and refraction.

**Fig. 8.16** Schlieren system.

brings it to a focus and then projects it on a screen or photographic plate. At the focal point a knife-edge is introduced which cuts off some of the light. For no flow in the test section the screen is uniformly illuminated. If the density within the test section is altered slightly by flow around a model, the light rays will be refracted in varying amounts. Where it is refracted so the rays are intercepted by the knife-edge, less light strikes the

**Fig. 8.17** Schlieren photograph of shock wave formed by ignition of explosive gas issuing from a tube. (*From doctoral thesis by W. P. Sommers, taken in Aeronautical and Astronautical Engineering Laboratories, The University of Michigan, 1961.*)

screen, and where it is refracted in the opposite direction, more light strikes the screen.    It is to be noted that this system portrays changes in density.    Figure 8.17 shows a schlieren photograph of a shock wave caused by propagation of an explosive wave due to detonation of a gas.

### the shadowgraph method

The same setup as the schlieren system may be used for shadowgraph studies, except that the knife-edge is not utilized.    For a uniform change in density all light rays are refracted the same amount and illumination of the screen remains uniform and of the same intensity.    Changes in the density gradient, however, will cause uneven refraction of the light waves which will project a pattern on the screen.    A shadowgraph view of a flame

**Fig. 8.18** Shadowgraph view of propane-air combustion.  Flame is stabilized around $\frac{1}{16}$ in.-diameter spherical flame holder at bottom.   Jet velocity 77 ft/sec.  (*Willow Run Research Center, The University of Michigan.*)

is shown in Fig. 8.18.   Schlieren and shadowgraph methods are generally qualitative, in that they aid in visualization of the flow.   The *interferometer* is used for quantitative measurement of density within the test section.

### the interferometer method

The interferometer makes use of a phase shift in the wave motion of light to obtain a pattern from which density changes may be read.   In the Mach-Zehnder interferometer (Fig. 8.19), light from a single source is split into two circuits, one including the test section, and is then recombined for projection onto a screen or photographic plate.   The first mirror is silvered over half of its surface; hence it transmits half of the light and reflects half of the light, forming the two circuits.   One circuit passes through the test section, and the other circuit through compensating plates.   These circuits are recombined, as indicated in the figure, by one being transmitted and the other reflected by the second half-silvered mirror and then projected onto a screen.

   When there is no flow through the test section and the fluid there has the same density as the surrounding fluid, the screen is uniformly bright, as both circuits have the same length and same light speed.   Now, if the density within the test section is uniformly changed, the speed of transmission of light is changed and the two streams are out of phase.   If the trough of one light wave coincides with the crest of the wave from the other circuit, the screen will be uniformly dark; hence the amount of light on the screen depends on the phase shift.   With flow around a model in

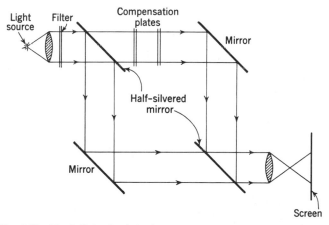

**Fig. 8.19**  Mach-Zehnder interferometer system.

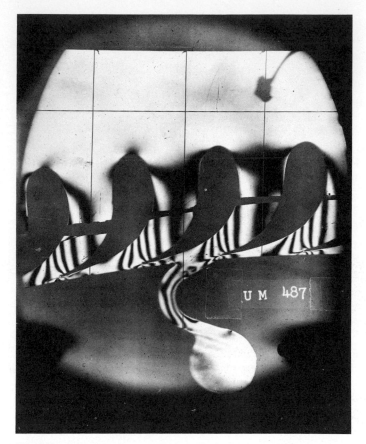

**Fig. 8.20**   Interferometer photograph of flow through nozzles and one bucket of model of a turbine.   The density change across each band (black or white) is $\frac{1}{2}$ per cent.   (*Photograph taken in Aeronautical and Astronautical Laboratories of The University of Michigan for the General Electric Co.*)

the test section, the zones of uniform density will appear as bands on the screen, as shown in Fig. 8.20.

## 8.5   positive-displacement meters

One volumetric meter is a positive-displacement meter that has pistons or partitions which are displaced by the flowing fluid and a counting mechanism that records the number of displacements in any convenient unit, such as gallons or cubic feet.

A common meter is the *disk* meter, or *wobble* meter (Fig. 8.21), used on many domestic water-distribution systems.  The disk oscillates in a passageway so that a known volume of fluid moves through the meter for each oscillation.   A stem normal to the disk operates a gear train, which in turn operates a counter.   When in good condition, these meters are accurate to within 1 per cent.   When worn, the error may be very large for small flows, such as those caused by a leaky faucet.

The flow of domestic gas at low pressure is usually measured by a volumetric meter with a traveling partition.   The partition is displaced by gas inflow to one end of the chamber in which it operates, and then, by a change in valving, it is displaced to the opposite end of the chamber.   The oscillations operate a counting mechanism.

Oil flow or high-pressure gas flow in a pipeline is frequently measured by a rotary meter in which cups or vanes move about an annular opening and displace a fixed volume of fluid for each revolution.   Radial or axial pistons may be arranged so that the volume of a continuous flow through them is determined by rotations of a shaft.

Positive-displacement meters normally have no timing equipment that measures the rate of flow.   The rate of steady flow may be determined

**Fig. 8.21**   Disk meter.   (*Neptune Meter Co.*)

with a stop watch to record the time for displacement of a given volume of fluid.

### 8.6 rate meters

A *rate meter* is a device that determines, generally by a single measurement, the quantity (weight or volume) per unit time that passes a given cross section. Included among rate meters are the *orifice, nozzle, venturi meter, rotameter, weir,* and *mass meter,* which are discussed in this section.

### *orifice in a reservoir*

An orifice may be used for measuring the rate of flow out of a reservoir or through a pipe. An orifice in a reservoir or tank may be in the wall or in the bottom. It is an opening, usually round, through which the fluid flows, as in Fig. 8.22. It may be square-edged, as shown, or rounded, as in Fig. 3.14. The area of the orifice is the area of the opening. With the square-edged orifice, the fluid jet contracts during a short distance of about one-half diameter downstream from the opening. That portion of the flow that approaches along the wall cannot make a right-angled turn at the opening, and so it maintains a radial velocity component that reduces the jet area. The cross section where the contraction is greatest is called the *vena contracta.* The streamlines are parallel throughout the jet at this section, and the pressure is atmospheric.

The head on the orifice, $H$, is measured from the center of the orifice to

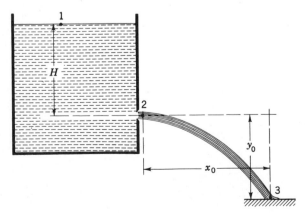

**Fig. 8.22** Orifice in a reservoir.

the free surface. The head is assumed to be held constant. Bernoulli's equation applied from a point 1 on the free surface to the center of the *vena contracta*, point 2, with local atmospheric pressure as datum and point 2 as elevation datum, neglecting losses, is written

$$\frac{V_1{}^2}{2g} + \frac{p_1}{\gamma} + z_1 = \frac{V_2{}^2}{2g} + \frac{p_2}{\gamma} + z_2$$

By inserting the values,

$$0 + 0 + H = \frac{V_2{}^2}{2g} + 0 + 0$$

or

$$V_2 = \sqrt{2gH} \tag{8.6.1}$$

This is only the *theoretical* velocity because the losses between the two points were neglected. The ratio of the *actual* velocity $V_a$ to the theoretical velocity $V_t$ is called the *velocity coefficient* $C_v$; that is,

$$C_v = \frac{V_a}{V_t} \tag{8.6.2}$$

Hence

$$V_{2a} = C_v \sqrt{2gH} \tag{8.6.3}$$

The actual discharge from the orifice, $Q_a$, is the product of the actual velocity at the *vena contracta* and the area of the jet. The ratio of jet area $A_2$ at *vena contracta* to area of orifice $A_0$ is symbolized by another coefficient, called the *coefficient of contraction*, $C_c$,

$$C_c = \frac{A_2}{A_0} \tag{8.6.4}$$

The area at the *vena contracta* is $C_c A_0$. The actual discharge is thus

$$Q_a = C_v C_c A_0 \sqrt{2gH} \tag{8.6.5}$$

It is customary to combine the two coefficients into a *discharge coefficient* $C_d$,

$$C_d = C_v C_c \tag{8.6.6}$$

from which

$$Q_a = C_d A_0 \sqrt{2gH} \tag{8.6.7}$$

There is no way to compute the losses between points 1 and 2; hence,

$C_v$ must be determined experimentally. It varies from 0.95 to 0.99 for the square-edged or rounded orifice. For most orifices, such as the square-edged one, the amount of contraction cannot be computed, and test results must be used. There are several methods for obtaining one or more of the coefficients. By measuring area $A_0$, the head $H$, and the discharge $Q_a$ (by gravimetric or volumetric means), $C_d$ is obtained from Eq. (8.6.7). Determination of either $C_v$ or $C_c$ then permits determination of the other by Eq. (8.6.6). Several methods follow:

1. Trajectory method. By measuring the position of a point on the trajectory of the free jet downstream from the *vena contracta* (Fig. 8.22) the actual velocity $V_a$ may be determined if air resistance is neglected. The $x$-component of velocity does not change; therefore, $V_a t = x_0$, in which $t$ is the time for a fluid particle to travel from the *vena contracta* to the point 3. The time for a particle to drop a distance $y_0$ under the action of gravity when it has no initial velocity in that direction is expressed by $y_0 = gt^2/2$. After eliminating $t$ in the two relations,

$$V_a = \frac{x_0}{\sqrt{2y_0/g}}$$

With $V_{2t}$ determined by Eq. (8.6.1) the ratio $V_a/V_t = C_v$ is known.

2. Direct measuring of $V_a$. With a pitot tube placed at the *vena contracta*, the actual velocity $V_a$ is determined.

3. Direct measuring of jet diameter. With outside calipers, the diameter of jet at the *vena contracta* may be approximated. This is not a precise measurement and, in general, is less satisfactory than the other methods.

4. Use of momentum equation. When the reservoir is of such size that it may be suspended on knife-edges, as in Fig. 8.23, it is possible to

**Fig. 8.23** Momentum method for determination of $C_v$ and $C_c$.

determine the force $F$ that creates the momentum in the jet.    With the orifice opening closed, the tank is leveled by adding or subtracting weights.    With the orifice discharging, a force creates the momentum in the jet and an equal and opposite force $F'$ acts against the tank.    By addition of sufficient weights, $W$, the tank is again leveled.    From the figure, $F' = Wx_0/y_0$.    With the momentum equation,

$$\Sigma F_x = \frac{Q\gamma}{g} (V_{x\text{out}} - V_{x\text{in}})$$

or

$$\frac{Wx_0}{y_0} = \frac{Q_a\gamma V_a}{g}$$

as $V_{x\text{in}}$ is zero and $V_a$ is the final velocity.    Since the actual discharge is measured, $V_a$ is the only unknown in the equation.

## losses in orifice flow

The head loss in flow through an orifice is determined by applying the energy equation with a loss term for the distance between points 1 and 2 (Fig. 8.22),

$$\frac{V_{1a}^2}{2g} + \frac{p_1}{\gamma} + z_1 = \frac{V_{2a}^2}{2g} + \frac{p_2}{\gamma} + z_2 + \text{losses}$$

By substituting the values for this case,

$$\text{Losses} = H - \frac{V_{2a}^2}{2g} = H(1 - C_v^2) = \frac{V_{2a}^2}{2g} \left( \frac{1}{C_v^2} - 1 \right) \qquad (8.6.8)$$

in which Eq. (8.6.3) has been used to obtain the losses in terms of $H$ and $C_v$, or $V_{2a}$ and $C_v$.

**example 8.1**    A 3-in.-diameter orifice under a head of 16.0 ft discharges 2000 lb water in 32.6 sec.    The trajectory was determined by measuring $x_0 = 15.62$ ft for a drop of 4.0 ft.    Determine $C_v$, $C_c$, $C_d$, the head loss per unit weight, and the horsepower loss.
    The theoretical velocity $V_{2t}$ is

$$V_{2t} = \sqrt{2gH} = \sqrt{64.4 \times 16} = 32.08 \text{ ft/sec}$$

The actual velocity is determined from the trajectory.    The time to drop

4 ft is

$$t = \sqrt{\frac{2y_0}{g}} = \sqrt{\frac{2 \times 4}{32.2}} = 0.498 \text{ sec}$$

and the velocity is expressed by

$$x_0 = V_{2a}t \qquad V_{2a} = \frac{15.62}{0.498} = 31.4 \text{ ft/sec}$$

Then

$$C_v = \frac{V_{2a}}{V_{2t}} = \frac{31.4}{32.08} = 0.98$$

The actual discharge $Q_a$ is

$$Q_a = \frac{2000}{62.4 \times 32.6} = 0.984 \text{ cfs}$$

With Eq. (8.6.7)

$$C_d = \frac{Q_a}{A_0 \sqrt{2gH}} = \frac{0.984}{(\pi/64) \sqrt{64.4 \times 16}} = 0.625$$

Hence, from Eq. (8.6.6),

$$C_c = \frac{C_d}{C_v} = \frac{0.625}{0.98} = 0.638$$

The head loss, from Eq. (8.6.8), is

Loss $= H(1 - C_v^2) = 16[1 - (0.98)^2] = 0.63$ ft-lb/lb

The horsepower loss is

$$\frac{0.63 \times 2000}{550 \times 32.6} = 0.070 \text{ hp}$$

The Borda mouthpiece (Fig. 8.24), a short, thin-walled tube about one diameter long that projects into the reservoir (re-entrant), permits application of the momentum equation, which yields one relation between $C_v$ and $C_d$. The velocity along the wall of the tank is almost zero at all points; hence, the pressure distribution is hydrostatic. With the component of force exerted on the liquid by the tank parallel to the axis of the tube, there is an unbalanced force due to the opening, which is $\gamma H A_0$. The final velocity is $V_{2a}$, the initial velocity is zero, and $Q_a$ is the actual discharge.

**Fig. 8.24**  The Borda mouthpiece.

Then

$$\gamma H A_0 = Q_a \frac{\gamma}{g} V_{2a}$$

So

$$Q_a = C_d A_0 \sqrt{2gH} \qquad V_{2a} = C_v \sqrt{2gH}$$

By substituting for $Q_a$ and $V_{2a}$, and simplifying,

$$1 = 2C_dC_v = 2C_v{}^2C_c$$

In the orifice situations considered, the liquid surface in the reservoir has been assumed to be held constant.  An unsteady-flow case of some practical interest is that of determining the time to lower the reservoir surface a given distance.  Theoretically, Bernoulli's equation applies only to steady flow, but if the reservoir surface drops slowly enough, the error from using Bernoulli's equation is negligible.  The volume discharged from the orifice in time $\delta t$ is $Q\, \delta t$, which must just equal the reduction in volume in the reservoir in the same time increment (Fig. 8.25), $A_R(-\delta y)$, in which

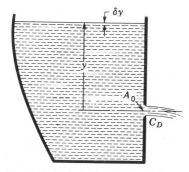

**Fig. 8.25**  Notation for falling head.

$A_R$ is the area of liquid surface at height $y$ above the orifice.    By equating the two expressions,

$$Q \, \delta t = -A_R \, \delta y$$

By solving for $\delta t$ and integrating between the limits $y = y_1$, $t = 0$ and $y = y_2$, $t = t$,

$$t = \int_0^t dt = -\int_{y_1}^{y_2} \frac{A_R \, dy}{Q}$$

The orifice discharge $Q$ is $C_d A_0 \sqrt{2gy}$.    After substituting for $Q$,

$$t = -\frac{1}{C_d A_0 \sqrt{2g}} \int_{y_1}^{y_2} A_R y^{-1/2} \, dy$$

When $A_R$ is known as a function of $y$, the integral can be evaluated.    Consistent with other English units, $t$ is in seconds.    For the special case of a tank with constant cross section,

$$t = -\frac{A_R}{C_d A_0 \sqrt{2g}} \int_{y_1}^{y_2} y^{-1/2} \, dy = \frac{2A_R}{C_d A_0 \sqrt{2g}} (\sqrt{y_1} - \sqrt{y_2})$$

**example 8.2**    A tank has a horizontal cross-sectional area of 20 ft² at the elevation of the orifice, and the area varies linearly with elevation so that it is 10 ft² at a horizontal cross section 10 ft above the orifice.    For a 4-in.-diameter orifice, $C_d = 0.65$, compute the time in seconds to lower the surface from 8 ft to 4 ft above the orifice.

$$A_R = 20 - y \text{ ft}^2$$

and

$$t = -\frac{1}{0.65(\pi/36) \sqrt{64.4}} \int_8^4 (20 - y)y^{-1/2} \, dy = 51.3 \text{ sec}$$

*venturi meter*

The venturi meter is used to measure the rate of flow in a pipe.    It is generally a casting (Fig. 8.26) consisting of an upstream section which is the same size as the pipe, has a bronze liner, and contains a piezometer ring for measuring static pressure; a converging conical section; a cylindrical throat with a bronze liner containing a piezometer ring; and a gradually diverging conical section leading to a cylindrical section the size of the pipe. A differential manometer is attached to the two piezometer rings.    The

**Fig. 8.26**   Venturi meter.

size of a venturi meter is specified by the pipe and throat diameter; e.g., a 6- by 4-in. venturi meter fits a 6-in.-diameter pipe and has a 4-in.-diameter throat.   For accurate results the venturi meter should be preceded by at least 10 diameters of straight pipe.   In the flow from the pipe to the throat, the velocity is greatly increased and the pressure correspondingly decreased.   The amount of discharge in incompressible flow is shown to be a function of the manometer reading.

The pressures at the upstream section and throat are *actual pressures*, and the velocities from Bernoulli's equation without a loss term are *theoretical velocities*.   When losses are considered in the energy equation, the velocities are *actual velocities*.   First, with the Bernoulli equation (i.e., without a head-loss term) the theoretical velocity at the throat is obtained. Then by multiplying this by the velocity coefficient $C_v$, the actual velocity is obtained.   The actual velocity times the actual area of the throat determines the actual discharge.   From Fig. 8.26,

$$\frac{V_{1t}^2}{2g} + \frac{p_1}{\gamma} + h = \frac{V_{2t}^2}{2g} + \frac{p_2}{\gamma} \tag{8.6.9}$$

in which elevation datum is taken through point 2.   $V_1$ and $V_2$ are average velocities at sections 1 and 2, respectively; hence, $\alpha_1$, $\alpha_2$ are assumed to be unity.   With the continuity equation $V_1 D_1^2 = V_2 D_2^2$,

$$\frac{V_1^2}{2g} = \frac{V_2^2}{2g}\left(\frac{D_2}{D_1}\right)^4 \tag{8.6.10}$$

which holds for either the actual velocities or the theoretical velocities. Equation (8.6.9) may be solved for $V_{2t}$,

$$\frac{V_{2t}^2}{2g}\left[1 - \left(\frac{D_2}{D_1}\right)^4\right] = \frac{p_1 - p_2}{\gamma} + h$$

and

$$V_{2t} = \sqrt{\frac{2g[h + (p_1 - p_2)/\gamma]}{1 - (D_2/D_1)^4}} \qquad (8.6.11)$$

By introducing the velocity coefficient, $V_{2a} = C_v V_{2t}$,

$$V_{2a} = C_v \sqrt{\frac{2g[h + (p_1 - p_2)/\gamma]}{1 - (D_2/D_1)^4}} \qquad (8.6.12)$$

After multiplying by $A_2$, the actual discharge $Q$ is determined to be

$$Q = C_v A_2 \sqrt{\frac{2g[h + (p_1 - p_2)/\gamma]}{1 - (D_2/D_1)^4}} \qquad (8.6.13)$$

The gage difference $R'$ may now be related to the pressure difference by writing the equation for the manometer. In feet of water ($S_1$ is the specific gravity of flowing fluid and $S_0$ the specific gravity of manometer liquid),

$$\frac{p_1}{\gamma} S_1 + (h + k + R')S_1 - R'S_0 - kS_1 = \frac{p_2}{\gamma} S_1$$

After simplifying,

$$h + \frac{p_1 - p_2}{\gamma} = R'\left(\frac{S_0}{S_1} - 1\right) \qquad (8.6.14)$$

By substituting into Eq. (8.6.14),

$$Q = C_v A_2 \sqrt{\frac{2gR'[(S_0/S_1) - 1]}{1 - (D_2/D_1)^4}} \qquad (8.6.15)$$

which is the venturi-meter equation for incompressible flow. The contraction coefficient is unity; hence, $C_v = C_d$. It should be noted that $h$ has dropped out of the equation. The discharge depends upon the gage difference $R'$ regardless of the orientation of the venturi meter; whether it is horizontal, vertical, or inclined, exactly the same equation holds.

$C_v$ is determined by calibration, i.e., by measuring the discharge and the gage difference and solving for $C_v$, which is usually plotted against the Reynolds number. Experimental results for venturi meters are given in

**Fig. 8.27** Coefficient $C_v$ for venturi meters. ("*Fluid Meters: Their Theory and Application*," 5th ed., *American Society of Mechanical Engineers, 1959.*)

Fig. 8.27.    They are applicable to diameter ratios $D_2/D_1$ from 0.25 to 0.75 within the tolerances shown by the dotted lines.    Where feasible, a venturi meter should be selected so that its coefficient is constant over the range of Reynolds numbers for which it is to be used.

The coefficient may be slightly greater than unity for venturi meters that are unusually smooth inside.    This does not mean that there are no losses but results from neglecting the kinetic-energy correction factors $\alpha_1$, $\alpha_2$ in the Bernoulli equation.    Generally $\alpha_1$ is greater than $\alpha_2$ since the reducing section acts to make the velocity distribution uniform across section 2.

The venturi meter has a low over-all loss, due to the gradually expanding concial section, which aids in reconverting the high kinetic energy at the throat into pressure energy.    The loss is about 10 to 15 per cent of the head change between sections 1 and 2.

*venturi meter for compressible flow*

The theoretical mass flow rate through a venturi meter in compressible flow is given by Eq. (6.3.24) for isentropic flow through a converging-diverging duct when the throat velocity is less than sonic velocity.    When multiplied by $C_v$, the velocity coefficient, it yields the actual mass flow rate $\dot{m}$.    Equation (8.6.13), for incompressible flow, may be written in

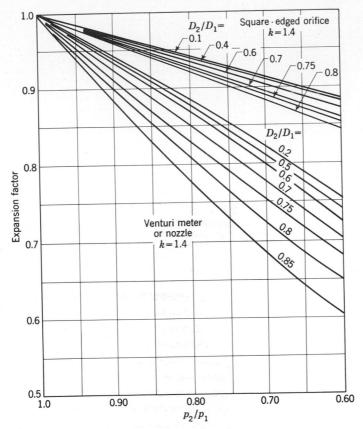

**Fig. 8.28**  Expansion factors.

terms of mass flow rate,

$$\dot{m} = C_v\rho_1 A_2 \sqrt{\frac{2\Delta p/\rho_1}{1 - (D_2/D_1)^4}} = C_v A_2 \sqrt{\frac{2\rho_1 \Delta p}{1 - (D_2/D_1)^4}} \tag{8.6.16}$$

($h$ is dropped because it is negligible for gas flow).   This equation may be modified by insertion of an *expansion factor* $Y$, so that it applies to compressible flow:

$$\dot{m} = C_v Y A_2 \sqrt{\frac{2\rho_1 \Delta p}{1 - (D_2/D_1)^4}} \tag{8.6.17}$$

$Y$ may be found by solving Eqs. (8.6.17) and (6.3.24) with coefficient $C_v$ inserted and is shown to be a function of $k$, $p_2/p_1$, and $A_2/A_1$.   Values of $Y$ are plotted in Fig. 8.28 for $k = 1.40$; hence, by the use of Eq. (8.6.17) and Fig. 8.28 compressible flow may be computed for a venturi meter.

*flow nozzle*

The ISA (Instrument Society of America) flow nozzle (originally the VDI flow nozzle) is shown in Fig. 8.29.   It has no contraction of the jet other than that of the nozzle opening, therefore the contraction coefficient is unity.

Equations (8.6.13) and (8.6.15) hold equally well for the flow nozzle.   For a horizontal pipe ($h = 0$), Eq. (8.6.13) may be written

$$Q = CA_2 \sqrt{\frac{2\Delta p}{\rho}} \tag{8.6.18}$$

in which

$$C = \frac{C_v}{\sqrt{1 - (D_2/D_1)^4}} \tag{8.6.19}$$

and $\Delta p = p_1 - p_2$.   The value of coefficient $C$ in Fig. 8.29 is for use in Eq. (8.6.18).   When the coefficient given in the figure is to be used, it is important that the dimensions shown shall have been closely adhered to,

**Fig. 8.29**  ISA (VDI) flow nozzle and discharge coefficients.  (*NACA Tech. Mem. 952, Ref. 11.*)

particularly in the location of the piezometer openings (two methods shown) for measuring pressure drop.   At least 10 diameters of straight pipe should precede the nozzle.

The flow nozzle is less costly than the venturi meter.   It has the disadvantage that the over-all losses are much higher because of the lack of guidance of jet downstream from the nozzle opening.

Compressible flow through a nozzle is found by Eq. (8.6.17) and Fig. 8.28, if $k = 1.4$.   For other values of specific-heat ratio $k$, Eq. (6.3.24) may be used and then modified with the velocity coefficient.

**example 8.3**   Determine the flow through a 6-in.-diameter water line that contains a 4-in.-diameter flow nozzle.   The mercury-water differential manometer has a gage difference of 10 in.   Water temperature is 60°F.

From the data given, $S_0 = 13.6$, $S_1 = 1.0$, $R' = \frac{10}{12} = 0.833$ ft, $A_2 = \pi/36 = 0.0873$ ft$^2$, $\rho = 1.935$ slugs/ft$^3$, $\mu = 0.01/479 = 2.09 \times 10^{-5}$ lb-sec/ft$^2$. By substituting Eq. (8.6.19) into Eq. (8.6.15),

$$Q = CA_2 \sqrt{2gR' \left( \frac{S_0}{S_1} - 1 \right)}$$

From Fig. 8.29, for $A_2/A_1 = (\frac{4}{6})^2 = 0.444$, assume that the horizontal region of the curves applies; hence, $C = 1.056$; then compute the flow and the Reynolds number.

$$Q = 1.056 \times 0.0873 \sqrt{64.4 \times 0.833 \left( \frac{13.6}{1.0} - 1.0 \right)} = 2.39 \text{ cfs}$$

Then

$$V_1 = \frac{Q}{A_1} = \frac{2.39}{\pi/16} = 12.19 \text{ ft/sec}$$

and

$$\mathbf{R} = \frac{V_1 D_1 \rho}{\mu} = \frac{12.19 \times 1.935}{2 \times 2.09 \times 10^{-5}} = 565,000$$

The chart shows the value of $C$ to be correct; therefore, the discharge is 2.39 cfs.

*orifice in a pipe*

The square-edged orifice in a pipe (Fig. 8.30) causes a contraction of the jet downstream from the orifice opening.   For incompressible flow Bernoulli's

**Fig. 8.30**  Orifice in a pipe.

equation applied from section 1 to the jet at its *vena contracta*, section 2, is

$$\frac{V_{1t}^2}{2g} + \frac{p_1}{\gamma} = \frac{V_{2t}^2}{2g} + \frac{p_2}{\gamma}$$

The continuity equation relates $V_{1t}$ and $V_{2t}$ with the contraction ceofficient $C_c = A_2/A_0$,

$$V_1\frac{\pi D_1^2}{4} - V_2 C_c \frac{\pi D_0^2}{4} \tag{8.6.20}$$

After eliminating $V_{1t}$,

$$\frac{V_{2t}^2}{2g}\left[1 - C_c^2\left(\frac{D_0}{D_1}\right)^4\right] = \frac{p_1 - p_2}{\gamma}$$

and by solving for $V_{2t}$,

$$V_{2t} = \sqrt{\frac{2g(p_1 - p_2)/\gamma}{1 - C_c^2(D_0/D_1)^4}}$$

By multiplying by $C_v$ to obtain the actual velocity at the *vena contracta*,

$$V_{2a} = C_v\sqrt{\frac{2(p_1 - p_2)/\rho}{1 - C_c^2(D_0/D_1)^4}}$$

and, finally multiplying by the area of the jet, $C_cA_0$, produces the actual discharge $Q$,

$$Q = C_dA_0\sqrt{\frac{2(p_1 - p_2)/\rho}{1 - C_c^2(D_0/D_1)^4}} \tag{8.6.21}$$

**Fig. 8.31** VDI orifice and discharge coefficients. (*NACA Tech. Mem. 952,* *Ref. 11.*)

in which $C_d = C_v C_c$.  In terms of the gage difference $R'$, Eq. (8.6.21) becomes

$$Q = C_d A_0 \sqrt{\frac{2gR'[(S_0/S_1) - 1]}{1 - C_c^2(D_0/D_1)^4}} \qquad (8.6.22)$$

Because of the difficulty in determining the two coefficients separately, a simplified formula is generally used, Eq. (8.6.18),

$$Q = C A_0 \sqrt{\frac{2\Delta p}{\rho}} \qquad (8.6.23)$$

or its equivalent,

$$Q = C A_0 \sqrt{2gR' \left(\frac{S_0}{S_1} - 1\right)} \qquad (8.6.24)$$

Values of $C$ are given in Fig. 8.31 for the VDI orifice.

Experimental values of expansion factor, for $k = 1.4$, are given in Fig. 8.28.  Equation (8.6.23) for actual mass flow rate in compressible flow becomes

$$\dot{m} = C Y A_0 \sqrt{2\rho_1 \Delta p} \qquad (8.6.25)$$

The location of the pressure taps is usually specified in order that an orifice can be installed in a conduit and used with sufficient accuracy without performing a calibration at the site.

*elbow meter*

The elbow meter for incompressible flow is one of the simplest flow-rate measuring devices.   Piezometer openings on the inside and on the outside of the elbow are connected to a differential manometer.   Because of centrifugal force at the bend, the difference in pressures is related to the discharge.   A straight calming length should precede the elbow, and, for accurate results, the meter should be calibrated in place.[1]   As most pipelines have an elbow, it may be used as the meter.   After calibration the results are as reliable as with a venturi meter or a flow nozzle.

*rotameter*

The rotameter (Fig. 8.32) is a variable-area meter that consists of an enlarging transparent tube and a metering "float" (actually heavier than

[1] W. M. Lansford, The Use of an Elbow in a Pipe Line for Determining the Rate of Flow in a Pipe, *Univ. Illinois Eng. Exp. Sta. Bull.* 289, December, 1936.

**Outlet**

**Metering float**

**Inlet**

**Fig. 8.32** Rotameter. (*Fischer & Porter Co.*)

the liquid) that is displaced upward by the upward flow of fluid through the tube.   The tube is graduated to read the flow directly.   Notches in the float cause it to rotate and thus maintain a central position in the tube. The greater the flow, the higher the position that the float assumes.

### turbine flowmeters

The fact that the change of momentum in a flow through a set of curved vanes causes a force or torque to be exerted on the vanes is utilized in the anemometer shown in Fig. 8.14.   If the outer shroud of such an anemometer is made a part of the conduit in which the air is flowing, the output of the meter can be given as a volume rate, since now the area of flow is specified.   The turbine-type flowmeters are essentially units similar to the one just described.   They are made waterproof and inserted into a pipeline to measure the flow rates of various fluids under widely varying temperature and corrosion conditions.   The hub of the vane assembly may contain a magnet, which, as the rotor turns, yields a varying magnetic field. The field is detected in an electric coil that is built into the external casing of the unit.   The frequency of the magnetic pulses indicates the flow rate on suitable read-out equipment that is attached by a simple electrical connection.

### weirs

Open-channel flow may be measured by a *weir*, which is an obstruction in the channel that causes the liquid to back up behind it and to flow over it or through it.   By measuring the height of upstream water surface, the rate of flow is determined.   Weirs constructed from a sheet of metal or other material so that the jet, or *nappe*, springs free as it leaves the

**Fig. 8.33** Sharp-crested, rectangular weir.

**Fig. 8.34**  Weir nappe without contractions.

upstream face are called *sharp-crested* weirs.  Other weirs such as the *broad-crested* weir support the flow in a longitudinal direction.

The sharp-crested, rectangular weir (Fig. 8.33) has a horizontal crest. The nappe is contracted at top and bottom as shown.  An equation for discharge may be derived if the contractions are neglected.  Without contractions the flow appears as in Fig. 8.34.  The nappe has parallel streamlines with atmospheric pressure throughout.

Bernoulli's equation applied between 1 and 2 is

$$H + 0 + 0 = \frac{v^2}{2g} + H - y + 0$$

in which the velocity head at section 1 is neglected.  By solving for $v$,

$$v = \sqrt{2gy}$$

The theoretical discharge $Q_t$ is

$$Q_t = \int v \, dA = \int_0^H vL \, dy = \sqrt{2g} \, L \int_0^H y^{1/2} \, dy = \tfrac{2}{3} \sqrt{2g} \, LH^{3/2}$$

in which $L$ is the width of weir.  Experiment shows that the exponent of $H$ is correct but that the coefficient is too great.  The contractions and losses reduce the actual discharge to about 60 per cent of the theoretical, or

$$Q = 3.33 \, LH^{3/2} \tag{8.6.26}$$

in which $Q$ is in cubic feet per second, $L$ and $H$ in feet.

When the weir does not extend completely across the width of the channel, it has *end contractions*, illustrated in Fig. 8.35.  An empirical correction for the reduction of flow is accomplished by subtracting $0.1H$ from $L$ for each end contraction.  The weir in Fig. 8.33 is said to have its end contractions *suppressed*.

The head $H$ is measured upstream from the weir a sufficient distance to avoid the surface contraction.  A hook gage mounted in a stilling pot

**Fig. 8.35** Weir with end contractions.

connected to a piezometer opening determines the water-surface elevation from which the head is determined.

When the height $P$ of weir (Fig. 8.33) is small, the velocity head at 1 cannot be neglected. A correction may be added to the head,

$$Q = CL \left( H + \alpha \frac{V^2}{2g} \right)^{3/2}$$ 

$$(8.6.27)$$

in which $V$ is velocity and $\alpha$ is greater than unity, usually taken around 1.4, which accounts for the nonuniform velocity distribution. Equation (8.6.27) must be solved for $Q$ by trial since $Q$ and $V$ are both unknown. As a first trial, the term $\alpha V^2/2g$ may be neglected to approximate $Q$; then with this trial discharge a value of $V$ is computed, since

$$V = \frac{Q}{L(P + H)}$$

For small discharges the V-notch weir is particularly convenient. Neglecting contraction of the nappe, the theoretical discharge is computed (Fig. 8.36) as follows:

The velocity at depth $y$ is $v = \sqrt{2gy}$, and the theoretical discharge is

$$Q_t = \int v \, dA = \int_0^H vx \, dy$$

By similar triangles, $x$ may be related to $y$,

$$\frac{x}{H - y} = \frac{L}{H}$$

After substituting for $v$ and $x$,

$$Q_t = \sqrt{2g} \, \frac{L}{H} \int_0^H y^{1/2} (H - y) \, dy = \frac{4}{15} \sqrt{2g} \, \frac{L}{H} H^{5/2}$$

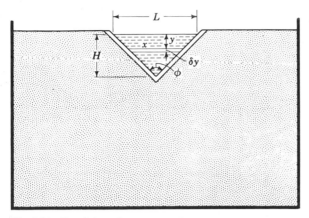

**Fig. 8.36**  V-notch weir.

By expressing $L/H$ in terms of the angle $\phi$ of the V-notch,

$$\frac{L}{2H} = \tan \frac{\phi}{2}$$

Hence,

$$Q_t = \frac{8}{15} \sqrt{2g} \, \tan \frac{\phi}{2} \, H^{5/2}$$

The exponent in the equation is approximately correct, but the coefficient must be reduced by about 40 per cent.   An approximate equation for a 90° V-notch weir is

$$Q = 2.50H^{2.50} \tag{8.6.28}$$

in which $Q$ is in cubic feet per second and $H$ is in feet.   Experiments show that the coefficient is increased by roughening the upstream side of the weir plate, which causes the boundary layer to grow thicker.   The greater amount of slow-moving liquid near the wall is more easily turned, and hence there is less contraction of the nappe.

The broad-crested weir (Fig. 8.37$a$) supports the nappe so that the pressure variation is hydrostatic at section 2.   Bernoulli's equation applied between points 1 and 2 can be used to find the velocity $v_2$ at height $z$, neglecting the velocity of approach,

$$H + 0 + 0 = \frac{v_2{}^2}{2g} + z + (y - z)$$

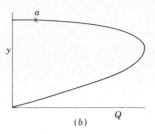

(a)                                              (b)

**Fig. 8.37**  Broad-crested weir.

In solving for $v_2$,

$$v_2 = \sqrt{2g(H - y)}$$

$z$ drops out; hence, $v_2$ is constant at section 2.   For a weir of width $L$ normal to the plane of the figure, the theoretical discharge is

$$Q = v_2 Ly = Ly \sqrt{2g(H - y)} \tag{8.6.29}$$

A plot of $Q$ as abscissa against the depth $y$ as ordinate, for constant $H$, is given in Fig. 8.37$b$.   The depth is shown to be that which yields the maximum discharge, by the following reasoning:

A gate or other obstruction placed at section 3 of Fig. 8.37$a$ can completely stop the flow by making $y = H$.   Now, if a small flow is permitted to pass section 3 (holding $H$ constant), the depth $y$ becomes a little less than $H$, and the discharge is, for example, as shown by point $a$ on the depth-discharge curve.   By further lifting of the gate or obstruction at section 3 the discharge-depth relationship follows the upper portion of the curve until the maximum discharge is reached.   Any additional removal of downstream obstructions, however, has no effect upon the discharge, because the velocity of flow at section 2 is $\sqrt{gy}$, which is exactly the speed that an elementary wave can travel in still liquid of depth $y$.   Hence, the effect of any additional lowering of the downstream surface elevation cannot travel upstream to affect further the value of $y$, and the discharge occurs at the maximum value.   This depth $y$, called the *critical depth*, is discussed in Sec. 11.4.   The speed of an elementary wave is derived in Sec. 12.10.

By taking $dQ/dy$ and with the result set equal to zero, for constant $H$,

$$\frac{dQ}{dy} = 0 = L\sqrt{2g(H - y)} + Ly\,\frac{1}{2}\frac{(-2g)}{\sqrt{2g(H - y)}}$$

and by solving for $y$,

$$y = \tfrac{2}{3}H$$

After inserting the value of $H$, that is, $3y/2$, into the equation for velocity $v_2$,

$$v_2 = \sqrt{gy}$$

After substituting the value of $y$ into Eq. (8.6.29),

$$Q_t = 3.09LH^{3/2} \tag{8.6.30}$$

Experiments show that for a well-rounded upstream edge the discharge is

$$Q = 3.03LH^{3/2} \tag{8.6.31}$$

which is within 2 per cent of the theoretical value.   The flow, therefore, adjusts itself to discharge at the maximum rate.

Viscosity and surface tension have a minor effect on the discharge coefficients of weirs.   Therefore, a weir should be calibrated with the liquid that it will measure.

**example 8.4**   Tests on a 60° V-notch weir yield the following values of head $H$ on the weir and discharge $Q$:

| $H$, ft | 0.345 | 0.356 | 0.456 | 0.537 | 0.568 | 0.594 | 0.619 | 0.635 | 0.654 | 0.665 |
|---------|-------|-------|-------|-------|-------|-------|-------|-------|-------|-------|
| $Q$, cfs | 0.107 | 0.110 | 0.205 | 0.303 | 0.350 | 0.400 | 0.435 | 0.460 | 0.490 | 0.520 |

By means of the theory of least squares, determine the constants in $Q = CH^m$ for this weir.

By taking the logarithm of each side of the equation

$$\ln Q = \ln C + m \ln H$$

or

$$Y = B + mX$$

it is noted that the best values of $B$ and $m$ are needed for a straight line through the data, when plotted on log-log paper.

By the theory of least squares, the best straight line through the data points is the one yielding a minimum value of the sums of the squares of vertical displacements of each point from the line; or, from Fig. 8.38,

$$F = \sum_{i=1}^{i=n} s_i^2 = \Sigma[y_i - (B + mx_i)]^2$$

To minimize $F$, $\partial F/\partial B$ and $\partial F/\partial m$ are taken and set equal to zero, yielding

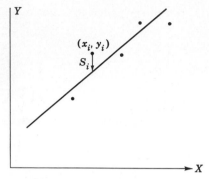

**Fig. 8.38** Log-log plot of $Q$ vs. $H$ for V-notch weir.

two equations in the two unknowns $B$ and $m$, as follows:

$$\frac{\partial F}{\partial B} = 0 = 2\Sigma[y_i - (B + mx_i)](-1)$$

from which

$$\Sigma y_i - nB - m\Sigma x_i = 0 \tag{1}$$

and

$$\frac{\partial F}{\partial m} = 0 = 2\Sigma[y_i - (B + mx_i)](-x_i)$$

or

$$\Sigma x_i y_i - B\Sigma x_i - m\Sigma x_i^2 = 0 \tag{2}$$

After solving Eqs. (1) and (2) for $m$,

$$m = \frac{\Sigma x_i y_i / \Sigma x_i - \Sigma y_i / n}{\Sigma x_i^2 / \Sigma x_i - \Sigma x_i / n}$$

$$B = \frac{\Sigma y_i - m\Sigma x_i}{n}$$

The logarithms of $Q_i$ and $H_i$ may be looked up, and the summations taken by desk calculator. This problem, however, is very easily handled by digital computer with the following program:

```
REAL M,LH,LQ
DIMENSION Q(10),H(10)
NAMELIST/DIN/Q,H,N,M,C
```

```
    READ(5,DIN,END=99)
    X=.0
    Y=.0
    XX=.0
    XY=.0
    DO 1 I=1,N
    LH=ALOG(H(I))
    LQ=ALOG(Q(I))
    X=X+LH
    Y=Y+LQ
    XX=XX+LH**2
  1 XY=XY+LH*LQ
    M=(XY/X-Y/N)/(XX/X-X/N)
    B=(Y-M*X)/N
    C=EXP(B)
    WRITE(6,DIN)
 99 CALL SYSTEM
    END
```

N = 10,Q(1) = .107, .110, .205, .303, .35,  .4,   .435, .46,  .49,  .52
          H(1) = .345, .356, .456, .537, .568, .594, .619, .635, .654, .665

For the data of this problem, $m = 2.437$, $C = 1.395$.

*mass meter*

Most rate meters determine the volumetric flow rate, which requires a separate determination of density before the mass flow rate can be found. By means of the moment-of-momentum principle, measurement of torque on an impeller may be related to the mass flow rate.   Consider the impeller of Fig. 8.39, in which fluid flows into the impeller without prerotation, i.e.,

**Fig. 8.39**  Schematic view of impeller with radial closed blades for use as a mass meter.

with $V_{u1} = 0$. The impeller has many blades, which are radial at the exit section, so that $V_{u2} = r_2\omega$, with $\omega$ the speed of rotation. Then, from Eq. (3.12.5)

$$T = \dot{m} V_{u2} r_2 = \dot{m}\omega r_2{}^2 \tag{8.6.32}$$

in which $T$ is the torque applied and $\dot{m}$ is the mass per unit time being discharged. By determination of torque, speed, and radius the mass rate may be computed. The torque must be corrected for torque losses due to bearings and disk friction. Practical details of mass meters are discussed in the literature.[1]

## 8.7 electromagnetic flow devices

If a magnetic field is set up across a nonconducting tube and a conducting fluid flows through the tube, an induced voltage is produced across the flow which may be measured if electrodes are embedded in the tube walls.[2] The voltage is a linear function of the volume rate passing through the tube. Either an alternating- or a direct-current field may be used, with a corresponding signal generated at the electrodes. A disadvantage of the method is the small signal received and the large amount of amplification needed. The device has been used to measure the flow in blood vessels.

## 8.8 measurement of river flow

Daily records of the discharge of rivers over long periods of time are essential to economic planning for utilization of their water resources or for protection against floods. The daily measurement of discharge by determining velocity distribution over a cross section of the river is costly. To avoid this and still obtain daily records, *control sections* are established where the river channel is stable, i.e., with little change in bottom or sides of the stream bed. The control section is frequently at a break in slope of the river bottom where it becomes steeper downstream.

A gage rod is mounted at the control section so that the elevation of water surface is determined by reading the water line on the rod; in some installations float-controlled recording gages keep a continuous record of

---

[1] V. A. Olando and F. B. Jennings, Momentum Principle Measures Mass Rate of Flow, *Trans. ASME*, vol. 76, p. 961, August, 1954. V. T. Li and S. Y. Lee, A Fast Responsive True Mass-rate Flowmeter, *Trans. ASME*, vol. 75, p. 835, July, 1953.

[2] H. G. Elrod, Jr., and R. R. Fouse, An Investigation of Electromagnetic Flowmeters, *Trans. ASME*, vol. 74, p. 589, May, 1952.

river elevation.   A *gage height-discharge* curve is established by taking current-meter measurements from time to time as the river discharge changes and plotting the resulting discharge against the gage height.

With a stable control section the gage height-discharge curve changes very little, and current-meter measurements are infrequent.   For unstable control sections the curve changes continuously, and discharge measurement must be made every few days to maintain an accurate curve.

Daily readings of gage height produce a daily record of the river discharge.

## 8.9   measurement of turbulence

Turbulence is a characteristic of the flow.   It affects the calibration of measuring instruments and has an important effect upon heat transfer, evaporation, diffusion, and many other phenomena connected with fluid movement.

Turbulence is generally specified by two quantities, the *size* and the *intensity* of the fluctuations.   In steady flow the temporal mean velocity components at a point are constant.   If these mean values be $\bar{u}$, $\bar{v}$, $\bar{w}$ and the velocity components at an instant be $u$, $v$, $w$, the fluctuations are given by $u'$, $v'$, $w'$, in

$$u = \bar{u} + u'$$
$$v = \bar{v} + v'$$
$$w = \bar{w} + w'$$

The root-mean-square of measured values of the fluctuations (Fig. 8.40) is a measure of the intensity of the turbulence.   These are $\sqrt{(\bar{u}')^2}$, $\sqrt{(\bar{v}')^2}$, $\sqrt{(\bar{w}')^2}$.

**Fig. 8.40**  Turbulent fluctuations in direction of flow.

The size of the fluctuation is an average measure of the size of eddy, or vortex, in the flow. When two velocity measuring instruments (hot-wire anemometers) are placed adjacent to each other in a flow, the velocity fluctuations are correlated, i.e., they tend to change in unison. Separating these instruments reduces this correlation. The distance between instruments for zero correlation is a measure of the size of the fluctuation. Another method for determining turbulence is discussed in Sec. 5.6.

## 8.10   measurement of viscosity

The treatment of fluid measurement is concluded with a discussion of methods for determining viscosity. Viscosity may be measured in a number of ways: (1) by use of Newton's law of viscosity; (2) by use of the Hagen-Poiseuille equation; (3) by methods that require calibration with fluids of known viscosity.

By measurement of the velocity gradient $du/dy$ and the shear stress $\tau$, in Newton's law of viscosity [Eq. (1.1.1)],

$$\tau = \mu \frac{du}{dy} \tag{8.10.1}$$

the dynamic or absolute viscosity can be computed. This is the most basic method as it determines all other quantities in the defining equation for viscosity. By means of a cylinder that rotates at a known speed with respect to an inner concentric stationary cylinder, $du/dy$ is determined. By measurement of torque on the stationary cylinder, the shear stress may be computed. The ratio of shear stress to rate of change of velocity expresses the viscosity.

A schematic view of a concentric-cylinder viscometer is shown in Fig. 8.41. When the speed of rotation is $N$ rpm and the radius is $r_2$ ft, the fluid velocity at the surface of the outer cylinder is $2\pi r_2 N/60$. With clearance $b$ ft

$$\frac{du}{dy} = \frac{2\pi r_2 N}{60b}$$

The equation is based on $b \ll r_2$. The torque $T_c$ on the inner cylinder is measured by a torsion wire from which it is suspended. By attaching a disk to the wire, its rotation may be determined by a fixed pointer. If the torque due to fluid below the bottom of the inner cylinder is neglected, the shear stress is

$$\tau = \frac{T_c}{2\pi r_1^2 h}$$

**Fig. 8.45** Switching sequence in a fluid-amplifier model. (*Department of Mechanical Engineering, The University of Michigan.*)

(*a*) White fluid jet (main jet) that has green tracer filaments entering from the middle of the left side of the fluid-amplifier model and flowing into the lower passage.

(*b*) Red fluid begins to enter from a lateral port. Note the tufts on the lower surface which indicate the flow direction.

(*c*) The control jet continues to flow. Only the initial portion of the control jet was colored, so that the fluid model would not become opaque through the heavy color concentration. The initial surge of the control jet carried some of the fluid through the main jet. Just to the right of the control-jet opening there are tufts which have changed their angle of inclination, indicating the development of a vortex in this region.

*d*

*e*

(*d*) The main jet is at the point where flow is beginning to
occur in the upper channel.  The control jet is still on.
(*e*) Switching has occurred.

(*f*) The main jet has now become attached to the upper wall.  Note the vortices that are being shed from both the main and control jets.

(*g*) Flow continues in the upper channel with a tendency to aspirate fluid out of the lower one.  The tufts indicate almost no flow in the lower channel; however, the white region at the lower right will proceed to the left.

*f*

*g*

*h*

*i*

*j*

(*h*) The control jet has been turned off.
(*i*) The main-jet flow direction continues in the upper channel.
(*j*) The flow into the upper channel will persist until the unit is again switched by operating the control jet at the top.

**Fig. 8.41**  Concentric-cylinder
viscometer.

By substituting into Eq. (8.10.1) and solving for the viscosity,

$$\mu = \frac{15 T_c b}{\pi^2 r_1{}^2 r_2 h N} \tag{8.10.2}$$

When the clearance $a$ is so small that the torque contribution from the
bottom is appreciable, it may be calculated in terms of the viscosity.

Referring to Fig. 8.42,

$$\delta T = r\tau \, \delta A = r\mu \frac{\omega r}{a} \, r \, \delta r \, \delta \theta$$

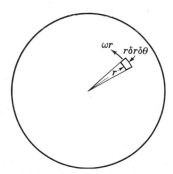

**Fig. 8.42**  Notation for determination of torque on a disk.

in which the velocity change is $\omega r$ in the distance $a$ ft.   By integrating over the circular area of the disk and letting $\omega = 2\pi N/60$,

$$T_d = \frac{\mu}{a}\frac{\pi}{30}N\int_0^{r_1}\int_0^{2\pi}r^3\,dr\,d\theta = \frac{\mu\pi^2}{a60}Nr_1{}^4 \tag{8.10.3}$$

The torque due to disk and cylinder must equal the torque $T$ in the torsion wire, so that

$$T = \frac{\mu\pi^2Nr_1{}^4}{a60} + \frac{\mu\pi^2r_1{}^2r_2hN}{15b} = \frac{\mu\pi^2Nr_1{}^2}{15}\left(\frac{r_1{}^2}{4a} + \frac{r_2h}{b}\right) \tag{8.10.4}$$

in which all quantities are known except $\mu$.   The flow between the surfaces must be laminar for Eqs. (8.10.2) to (8.10.4) to be valid.

Often the geometry of the inner cylinder is altered so as to eliminate the torque which acts on the lower surface.   If the bottom surface of the inner cylinder is made concave, a pocket of air will be trapped between the bottom surface of the inner cylinder and the fluid in the rotating outer cup. A well-designed cup and a careful filling procedure will ensure the condition whereby the torque measured will consist of that produced in the annulus between the two cylinders and a minute amount resulting from the action of the air on the bottom surface.   Naturally the viscometer must be provided with a temperature-controlled bath and a variable-speed drive which can be carefully regulated.   Such design refinements are needed in order to obtain the rheological diagrams (cf. Fig. 1.2) for the fluid under test.

The measurement of all quantities in the Hagen-Poiseuille equation, except $\mu$, by a suitable experimental arrangement, is another basic method for determination of viscosity.   A setup as in Fig. 8.43 may be used.   Some distance is required for the fluid to develop its characteristic velocity distribution after it enters the tube; therefore, the head or pressure must be measured by some means at a point along the tube.   The volume $\mho$ of flow

**Fig. 8.43** Determination of viscosity by flow through a capillary tube.

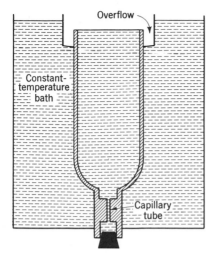

**Fig. 8.44**  Schematic view of Saybolt viscometer.

can be measured over a time $t$ where the reservoir surface is held at a constant level.   This yields $Q$, and, by determining $\gamma$, $\Delta p$ may be computed. Then with $L$ and $D$ known, from Eq. (5.2.10a),

$$\mu = \frac{\Delta p \, \pi D^4}{128 Q L}$$

An adaptation of the capillary tube for industrial purposes is the $Saybolt$ viscometer (Fig. 8.44).   A short capillary tube is utilized, and the time is measured for 60 cm³ of fluid to flow through the tube under a falling head. The time in seconds is the Saybolt reading.   This device measures kinematic viscosity, evident from a rearrangement of Eq. (5.2.10a).   When $\Delta p = \rho g h$, $Q = \text{vol}/t$, and when the terms are separated that are the same regardless of the fluid,

$$\frac{\mu}{\rho t} = \frac{g h \pi D^4}{128 (\text{vol}) L} = C_1$$

Although the head $h$ varies during the test, it varies over the same range for all liquids; and the terms on the right-hand side may be considered as a constant of the particular instrument.   Since $\mu/\rho = \nu$, the kinematic viscosity is

$$\nu = C_1 t$$

which shows that the kinematic viscosity varies directly as the time $t$.   The capillary tube is quite short, and so the velocity distribution is not established.   The flow tends to enter uniformly, and then, owing to viscous drag at the walls, to slow down there and speed up in the center region.   A correction in the above equation is needed, which is of the form $C/t$; hence

$$\nu = C_1 t + \frac{C_2}{t}$$

The approximate relationship between viscosity and Saybolt seconds is expressed by

$$\nu = 0.0022t - \frac{1.80}{t}$$

in which $\nu$ is in stokes and $t$ in seconds.

For measuring viscosity there are many other industrial methods that generally have to be calibrated for each special case to convert to the absolute units.   One consists of several tubes containing "standard" liquids of known graduated viscosities with a steel ball in each of the tubes. The time for the ball to fall the length of the tube depends upon the viscosity of the liquid.    By placing the test sample in a similar tube, its viscosity may be approximated by comparison with the other tubes.

The flow of a fluid in a capillary tube is the basis for viscometers of the Oswald-Cannon-Fenske or Ubbelohde type.   In essence the viscometer is a U-tube, one leg of which is a fine capillary tube connected to a reservoir above.   The tube is held vertically, and a known quantity of fluid is placed in the reservoir and allowed to flow by gravity through the capillary.   The time is recorded for the free surface in the reservoir to fall between two scribed marks.   A calibration constant for each instrument takes into account the variation of the capillary's bore from the standard, the bore's uniformity, entrance conditions, and the slight unsteadiness due to the falling head during the 1- to 2-min test.   Various bore sizes can be obtained to cover a wide range of viscosities.   Exact procedures for carrying out the tests are contained in the standards of the American Society for Testing and Materials.

## 8.11  fluid amplifiers

The photographs shown in Fig. 8.45 illustrate the operation of one kind of fluid amplifier or, in this case, fluid switch.   Many forms of this device have a geometry which is similar to that shown in the figure.   Basically, all that is needed for such a fluid amplifier is a flat piece of metal or plastic into which has been machined or etched shallow passages in which the fluid (e.g., air, water) can flow.   The arrangement of the passages and chambers differs for each type of fluid amplifier, but in principle all have a main, or power, stream which changes its direction or some other flow characteristic through the action of a control jet.   For example, a marginally stable laminar flow could be made turbulent by a control jet.

The control jet shown in Fig. 8.45 not only changes the direction of the power jet, thus acting as a switch, but also acts as an amplifier.   The linear momentum of the power jet is greater than that of the control jet, and their ratio can be taken as a measure of the amplification which occurred in the switching operation.   The over-all amplification of fluid devices of the type being discussed can be increased by connecting them together so that the power-jet openings of the first device (the upper and lower channels in Fig. 8.45) are connected to the control-jet openings of the second device and so forth.

Naturally, the high amplification that results from multistaging is very desirable, but equally important is the fact that once the power jet has been "switched" it will remain switched after the control jet has been turned off.   The phenomenon which determines this behavior is called the Coanda effect, in honor of one of the first men to observe and utilize the phenomenon.   He and others were actively engaged in studying the fluid dynamics of channels which have a shape similar to that shown in Fig. 8.45. This research occurred largely in the 1930s but received little notice or encouragement because of the state of other technologies.   If one wanted amplification, one could obtain it through the already available and rapidly expanding electronic means.   However, at the close of the 1950s the idea was revived and may find use in applications that were not considered or possible 25 years earlier.

The investigations showed that if a fluid stream entered a converging channel, the flow would have a velocity distribution which was symmetric with respect to the center line.   The velocities would increase as the passage area became smaller.   The boundary-layer thickness would decrease as the fluid proceeded into the converging section because of the increase of the center-line velocity and consequently the local Reynolds number. Furthermore, the flow was very stable against disturbances which were induced in the flow field.

The situation was greatly different, however, if the flow direction was reversed.   If the walls diverged at an angle of less than 4° with the center line, the velocity profile was completely symmetrical.   For channels having a semiangle that was greater than 4°, there was a marked change in the velocity distribution.   First of all, the outgoing stream seemed to prefer one side of the channel, so that on the other side there was an induced vortex or swirl.   Second, the flow was unstable and would switch from one side of the channel to the other, depending on the disturbances in the fluid supply system.   This tendency of the fluid to choose one side of a symmetric diverging channel and flow in an unsymmetric way is the Coanda effect.

Subsequent work has shown how this effect can be modified by the use and location of a center section, or splitter, in the diverging passage.   If the symmetrically placed splitter shown in Fig. 8.45 is very close to the entrance part of the main or power jet, one finds that this jet divides equally into both channels.   If a control jet is activated on one side, the power jet is deflected to flow entirely into the opposite channel.   After the control jet is turned off, the original divided flow occurs again.

If the splitter is withdrawn from the direct region of the power-jet opening (about four diameters), the flow again divides around the splitter but now unsymmetrically, more going to one side.   If the control jet on this side is activated, all the flow will be diverted to the opposite side, the side which originally had the smaller flow.   After the control jet is turned off, the power jet will return spontaneously to its original path.

Upon moving the point of the splitter to a distance of more than five diameters from the power-jet opening, one observes sustained switching. This is the situation shown in Fig. 8.45.   Once again the power jet prefers one of the two channels, but now it does so completely.   If the control jet on this side is activated, the power jet will be deflected to the other channel and remain there even after the power jet is turned off.

The splitter can be withdrawn even further to yield a substantial inter-action chamber between it and the inlet port of the power jet.   This chamber can be utilized to give the fluid amplifier a memory.   This geometry affects neither the preference of the power jet for one channel nor its diversion to, and retention in, the other channel as a result of a short pulse of the control jet.   But when the fluid is flowing in one channel, a vortex is induced in the interaction chamber on the side of the chamber opposite to that on which the power jet is flowing (upper left-hand corner of Fig. 8.45a). This vortex will try to persist even if there are changes in the flow which caused it.   If the outlet of the channel in which the power jet is flowing is mechanically blocked off, the power jet will naturally be forced to flow in the other channel.   The vortex which had been induced is now squeezed in between the diverted power jet and the wall of the interaction chamber. When the mechanical blockage of the channel in which the power jet first flowed is removed, the trapped vortex expands and forces the power jet back to its original course, which is now open.

Engineers have quite naturally been seeking other ways to achieve fluid amplification and switching.   One such device can be made by having a jet of fluid from a tube of small diameter aimed at the inlet of a somewhat larger tube that is concentric with the smaller one.   The power jet enters the larger tube after flowing across a small gap.   If there are some lateral control tubes, they can be activated to yield a side flow, at right angles to the power jet, which will cause the power jet to go from a laminar to a turbulent state with a resultant decrease in the quantity of fluid which enters the larger tube.   Again one can achieve a large effect from a small cause.   In Prandtl's original discussion of boundary-layer theory in 1904 he showed photographs of how the location of boundary-layer separation could be controlled (see Chap. 5 for boundary-layer separation on plates and spheres).   These methods of controlling the boundary layer are being employed today in fluid amplifiers to achieve specific effects for particular applications.

The fluid amplifier cannot match the performance of an electronic unit near room temperature, but at very high and very low temperatures the fluid amplifier's advantageous temperature stability greatly outweighs its disadvantageous lower operating speed.   Thus, reliable fluid controllers and computing circuits can be made to operate at extreme temperatures.

The fluid amplifier is easily used in computing devices since each of the two channels shown in Fig. 8.45 could be viewed as being "yes" or "no," "plus" or "minus," 0 or 1.   By proper location of the channels with respect to the control jets, "and" and "or" circuits can be made, so that logic and adding devices are possible.   Such digital units, which give a discrete response, can be augmented with analogue units, which give a continuously varying output depending on the degree to which the control jet is employed.

In the fluid amplifier discussed above, which has two concentric tubes connected by a fluid jet, the output can be made to depend continuously on the control jets.   For if the control jet is only slightly activated, the power jet is made only slightly turbulent, and most of it flows from the smaller tube into the larger.   But if the control jet is applied strongly, then very little of the power jet gets into the larger tube.

The device just mentioned, as well as the diverging channel and many others, are the fluid counterparts of electric devices which are directionally sensitive.   It is clear that when one sends a jet from a small tube into a larger one, there will be a greater percentage of the flow entering the second tube than when the jet goes from the larger tube into the smaller.   In a similar way the flow in a diverging channel is greatly different from that in a converging channel.

These varied characteristics of fluid flow in specially designed channels have stirred the imagination of many engineers.   They have found application in rocket systems, where there are severe vibration and environmental conditions, as well as in recent biomedical work.   An artificial heart pump has been developed, as well as an automatic respirator to help patients breathe.

## 8.12   principles of pressure and flow control

The preceding sections of this chapter have been concerned with the measurement of fluid properties and quantities.   In present-day fluid systems it is not enough just to measure these quantities; it is also necessary to control them.   This section discusses the principles of pressure and flow control by the use of pneumatic feedback systems of valve operation.

To alter the flow in a system the amount of opening of a valve is adjusted. The valve plug introduces losses into the system, generally proportional to the square of the discharge, $KV^2/2g$ (Sec. 5.10), in which $K$ is primarily a function of the valve opening.   For a closed valve $K$ is infinite.   Application of the energy equation, with the valve-loss term included, permits calculation of flow.   As the flow and pressure (or pressure drop) are related in a system, the flow may be controlled by suitable pressure control.

*control valves*

Valves may be broadly classified into two categories, stop valves and control valves.   A stop valve, such as a gate valve, normally is wide open or completely closed.   A control valve operates to throttle the flow or introduce losses into the system.   To be a good control valve it must withstand the erosive action of the high-velocity fluid passing through its opening, and it must also be sensitive to stem movement over the complete operating range.   This may be accomplished by careful guidance of the valve stem and by suitable profiling of the valve plug (or movable portion).   Figure 8.46 is a cross section through a double-ported, top-and-bottom guided, profiled valve plug, together with an actuator that provides the power to move the plug by means of a diaphragm, spring, and compressed air.   The plug profile shown yields equal-percentage flow change for a given stem displacement over the whole range of travel for a given pressure drop. Many other special valve plug profiles are available for the various flow-control situations.

*elements of control systems*

The valve positioner, pressure controller, and pneumatic position transmitter are described and then incorporated into a system.

**Fig. 8.46**  Double-ported control valve, top- and bottom-guided, with diaphragm air-pressure actuator. (*Fisher Governor Co.*)

When it is desired that a valve take a specific opening for a given control signal to it, a *valve positioner* is used, which by feedback control places the plug in the position irrespective of the fluid pressures or unbalanced forces acting on the plug.    Figure 8.47 is a schematic view of the positioner.    The signal (assumed to be a positive increment of pressure) indicating the desired setting is applied to the interior of the bellows.    The bellows extends and causes the beam-and-flapper assembly further to restrict the nozzle.    Supply air bleeds through a small restriction of much less area

Bellows

Instrument

Exhaust

Beam and flapper assembly

Nozzle

Relay

Restriction

Supply

| | Instrument pressure | | Nozzle pressure |
| | Supply pressure | | Exhaust |
| | Diaphragm pressure | | |

**Fig. 8.47**  Schematic control circuit for valve positioner.  (*Fisher Governor Co.*)

than the nozzle into the nozzle chamber.   When the air behind the nozzle is further restricted by the movement of the beam assembly toward it, the pressure builds up and moves a relay-diaphragm assembly to open the supply valve to the upper side of the valve actuator.   As the valve stem moves downward, feedback is provided by the cam, which rotates and moves the beam assembly away from the nozzle. Nozzle pressure decreases, and the relay supply valve closes to prevent any further increase in output pressure.   The positioner is again in equilibrium but at a higher instrument (signal) pressure and a new valve-plug position.

**Fig. 8.48** Schematic control circuit for a pressure controller. (*Fisher Governor Co.*)

Diaphragm pressure

Pilot exhaust

Proportional pressure

Nozzle pressure

Controlled pressure

Pilot supply pressure

Vent or remote control point setting connection

20 psi supply

I

K

J

L

H

G

F

E

B

C

D

T

S

M

When the instrument pressure decreases, the bellows contracts to move the beam and uncover the nozzle. The relay acts under the lowered pressure to open the exhaust valve in the relay and permit the valve stem to move upward. Stem movement is fed back to the cam, which repositions the beam and flapper when equilibrium conditions are obtained. The exhaust valve closes to prevent any further change in case pressure.

A *pressure controller* is used to hold the pressure in a conduit at a desired value by suitable positioning of a control valve. In Fig. 8.48 the downstream pressure is to be controlled to the value set on the dial, which positions the bellows assembly that is attached to one end of the beam $C$. The other end is attached to the bourdon tube $T$. The bourdon tube is connected to the conduit and senses its pressure, tending to straighten out and lift the beam for increasing pressure. The relay assembly is similar to that of the valve positioner and causes air to be supplied to the top of the valve casing or be exhausted from it as the beam covers or uncovers the nozzle. The feedback mechanism $M$ repositions the beam after an adjustment of pressure, and is adjustable so that it may cover full valve travel for the desired pressure range being monitored.

In place of the manual setting of the dial to the pressure to be controlled, the lower bellows of Fig. 8.48 can take a position depending upon the pressure within it, which sets one end of the beam; hence a remote setting of the desired pressure can be obtained. Also, this signal may be varied as a function of time.

If the pressure at one section of a pipe, upstream from a valve, is to be made to vary as an arbitrary function of time, the desired pressure may be

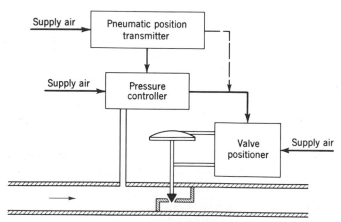

**Fig. 8.49** Diagram of control system for variation of pressure in a pipeline in an arbitrary determined manner.

produced as a signal to the pressure controller by a *pneumatic position transmitter*. The desired signal may first be cut into a template that rotates at constant speed, causing the cam of a valve positioner to be displaced (Fig. 8.49). A pressure is set up in the positioner circuit proportional to the displacement of the cam; hence, from a template, an air pressure signal is generated; this signal to the pressure controller causes it to signal the positioner to move the valve so that the fluid pressure is obtained in the pipe.

If a certain *position* of the valve plug is desired, as a function of time, this position is indicated by the height of a template which operates the cam of the pneumatic position transmitter. By having this signal go directly to the valve positioner, the plug is placed in the required position.

## problems

**8.1** A static tube (Fig. 8.2) indicates a static pressure that is 0.12 psi too low when liquid is flowing at 8 ft/sec. Calculate the correction to be applied to the indicated pressure for the liquid flowing at 18 ft/sec.

**8.2** Four piezometer openings in the same cross section of a cast-iron pipe indicate the following pressures for simultaneous readings: 4.30, 4.26, 4.24, 3.7 psi. What value should be taken for the pressure?

**8.3** A simple pitot tube (Fig. 8.6) is inserted into a small stream of flowing oil, $\gamma = 55$ lb/ft$^3$, $\mu = 0.65$ poise, $\Delta h = 1.5$ in., $h_0 = 5$ in. What is the velocity at point 1?

**8.4** A stationary body immersed in a river has a maximum pressure of 10 psi exerted on it at a distance of 18 ft below the free surface. Calculate the river velocity at this depth.

**8.5** From Fig. 8.7 derive the equation for velocity at 1.

**8.6** In Fig. 8.7 air is flowing ($p = 16$ psia, $t = 40°F$) and water is in the manometer. For $R' = 1.2$ in., calculate the velocity of air.

**8.7** In Fig. 8.7 air is flowing ($p = 16$ psia, $t_1 = 40°F$) and mercury is in the manometer. For $R' = 8$ in., calculate the velocity at 1 ($a$) for isentropic compression of air between 1 and 2 and ($b$) for air considered incompressible.

**8.8** A pitot-static tube directed into a 12 ft/sec water stream has a gage difference of 1.47 in. on a water-mercury differential manometer. Determine the coefficient for the tube.

**8.9** A pitot-static tube, $C = 1.12$, has a gage difference of 2.7 in. on a water-mercury manometer when directed into a water stream. Calculate the velocity.

**8.10** A pitot-static tube of the Prandtl type has the following value of gage difference $R'$ for the radial distance from center of a 3-ft-diameter pipe:

| $r$, ft | 0 | 0.3 | 0.6 | 0.9 | 1.2 | 1.48 |
|---------|---|-----|-----|-----|-----|------|
| $R'$, in. | 4 | 3.91 | 3.76 | 3.46 | 3.02 | 2.40 |

Water is flowing, and the manometer fluid has a specific gravity of 2.93. Calculate the discharge.

**8.11** What would be the gage difference on a water-nitrogen manometer for flow of nitrogen at 600 ft/sec, using a pitot-static tube? The static pressure is 25 psia, and corresponding temperature 80°F. True static pressure is measured by the tube.

**8.12** Measurements in an air stream indicate that the stagnation pressure is 15 psia, the static pressure is 10 psia, and the stagnation temperature is 102°F. Determine the temperature and velocity of the air stream.

**8.13** 0.1 $lb_m$/sec nitrogen flows through a 2-in.-diameter tube with stagnation temperature of 100°F and undisturbed temperature of 70°F. Find the velocity and static and stagnation pressures.

**8.14** A disk meter has a volumetric displacement of 1.73 in.$^3$ for one complete oscillation. Calculate the flow in gallons per minute for 86.5 oscillations per minute.

**8.15** A disk water meter with volumetric displacement of 2.40 in.$^3$ per oscillation requires 470 oscillations per minute to pass 5 gpm and 3840 oscillations per minute to pass 40 gpm. Calculate the per cent error, or slip, in the meter.

**8.16** A volumetric tank 4 ft in diameter and 5 ft high was filled with oil in 16 min 32.4 sec. What is the average discharge in gallons per minute?

**8.17** A weigh tank receives 16.3 lb liquid, sp gr 0.86, in 14.9 sec. What is the flow rate in gallons per minute?

**8.18** Determine the equation for trajectory of a jet discharging horizontally from a small orifice with head of 15 ft and velocity coefficient of 0.96. Neglect air resistance.

**8.19** An orifice of area 0.03 ft$^2$ in a vertical plate has a head of 3.6 ft of oil, sp gr 0.91. It discharges 1418 lb of oil in 79.3 sec. Trajectory measurements yield $X = 7.38$ ft, $Y = 4.025$ ft. Determine $C_v$, $C_c$, $C_d$.

**8.20** Calculate $Y$, the maximum rise of a jet from an inclined plate (Fig. 8.50), in terms of $H$ and $\alpha$. Neglect losses.

**Fig. 8.50**

**8.21** In Fig. 8.50, for $\alpha = 45°$, $Y = 0.48H$. Neglecting air resistance of the jet, find $C_v$ for the orifice.

**8.22** Show that the locus of maximum points of the jet of Fig. 8.50 is given by

$$X^2 = 4Y(H - Y)$$

when losses are neglected.

**8.23** A 3-in.-diameter orifice discharges 64 ft³ liquid, sp gr 1.07, in 82.2 sec under a 9-ft head. The velocity at the *vena contracta* is determined by a pitot-static tube with coefficient 1.0. The manometer liquid is acetylene tetrabromide, sp gr 2.96, and the gage difference is $R' = 3.35$ ft. Determine $C_v$, $C_c$, and $C_d$.

**8.24** A 4-in.-diameter orifice discharges 1.575 cfs water under a head of 9 ft. A flat plate held normal to the jet just downstream from the *vena contracta* requires a force of 69.7 lb to resist impact of the jet. Find $C_d$, $C_v$, and $C_c$.

**8.25** Compute the discharge from the tank shown in Fig. 8.51.

**8.26** For $C_v = 0.96$ in Fig. 8.51, calculate the losses in foot-pounds per pound and in foot-pounds per second.

**Fig. 8.51**

**Fig. 8.52**

**8.27**  Calculate the discharge through the orifice of Fig. 8.52.

**8.28**  For $C_v = 0.93$ in Fig. 8.52, determine the losses in foot-pounds per pound and in foot-pounds per second.

**8.29**  A 4-in.-diameter orifice discharges 1.60 cfs liquid under a head of 11.8 ft.  The diameter of jet at the *vena contracta* is found by calipering to be 3.47 in.  Calculate $C_v$, $C_d$, and $C_c$.

**8.30**  A Borda mouthpiece 2 in. in diameter has a discharge coefficient of 0.51.  What is the diameter of the issuing jet?

**8.31**  A 3-in.-diameter orifice, $C_d = 0.82$, is placed in the bottom of a vertical tank that has a diameter of 4 ft.  How long does it take to draw the surface down from 8 to 6 ft?

**8.32**  Select the size of orifice that permits a tank of horizontal cross section 16 ft² to have the liquid surface drawn down at the rate of 0.6 ft/sec for 11 ft head on the orifice.  $C_d = 0.63$.

**8.33**  A 4-in.-diameter orifice in the side of a 6-ft-diameter tank draws the surface down from 8 to 4 ft above the orifice in 83.7 sec.  Calculate the discharge coefficient.

**Fig. 8.53**

$A_R = 16$ ft$^2$        $A_R = 20$ ft$^2$

**Fig. 8.54**

**8.34**   Select a reservoir of such size and shape that the liquid surface drops 3 ft/min over a 10-ft distance for flow through a 4-in.-diameter orifice. $C_d = 0.74$.

**8.35**   In Fig. 8.53 the truncated cone has an angle $\theta = 60°$.   How long does it take to draw the liquid surface down from $y = 12$ ft to $y = 4$ ft?

**8.36**   Calculate the dimensions of a tank such that the surface velocity varies inversely as the distance from the center line of an orifice draining the tank.   When the head is 1 ft, the velocity of fall of the surface is 0.1 ft/sec. 0.5-in.-diameter orifice, $C_d = 0.66$.

**8.37**   Determine the time required to raise the right-hand surface of Fig. 8.54 by 2 ft.

**8.38**   How long does it take to raise the water surface of Fig. 8.55 6 ft?   The left-hand surface is a large reservoir of constant water-surface elevation.

**8.39**   Show that for incompressible flow the losses per unit weight of fluid between the upstream section and throat of a venturi meter are $K V_2{}^2/2g$ if $K = [(1/C_v)^2 - 1][1 - (D_2/D_1)^4]$.

**Fig. 8.55**

**8.40**  A 200- by 100-in. venturi meter carries water at 80°F.  A water-air differential manometer has a gage difference of 2.4 in.  What is the discharge?

**8.41**  What is the pressure difference between the upstream section and throat of a 6- by 3-in. horizontal venturi meter carrying 800 gpm water at 120°F?

**8.42**  A 12- by 6-in. venturi meter is mounted in a vertical pipe with the flow upward.  1000 gpm oil, sp gr 0.80, $\mu = 1$ poise, flows through the pipe. The throat section is 4 in. above the upstream section.  What is $p_1 - p_2$?

**8.43**  Air flows through a venturi meter in a 2-in.-diameter pipe having a throat diameter of 1.25 in., $C_v = 0.97$.  For $p_1 = 120$ psia, $t_1 = 60°F$, $p_2 = 90$ psia, calculate the mass per second flowing.

**8.44**  Oxygen, $p_1 = 40$ psia, $t_1 = 120°F$, flows through a 1- by $\frac{1}{2}$-in. venturi meter with a pressure drop of 6 psi.  Find the mass per second flowing and the throat velocity.

**8.45**  Air flows through a 3-in.-diameter ISA flow nozzle in a 4-in.-diameter pipe.  $p_1 = 20$ psia, $t_1 = 40°F$, and a differential manometer with liquid, sp gr 2.93, has a gage difference of 2.7 ft when connected between the pressure taps.  Calculate the mass rate of flow.

**8.46**  A 2.5-in.-diameter ISA nozzle is used to measure flow of water at 40°F in a 6-in.-diameter pipe.  What gage difference on a water-mercury manometer is required for 300 gpm?

**8.47**  Determine the discharge in a 12-in.-diameter line with a 9-in.-diameter VDI orifice for water at 68°F when the gage difference is 12 in. on an acetylene tetrabromide (sp gr 2.94)-water differential manometer.

**8.48**  A $\frac{1}{2}$-in.-diameter VDI orifice is installed in a 1-in.-diameter pipe carrying nitrogen at $p_1 = 120$ psia, $t_1 = 120°F$.  For a pressure drop of 20 psi across the orifice, calculate the mass flow rate.

**8.49**  Air at 14.7 psia, $t = 72°F$, flows through a 36-in.-square duct that contains an 18-in.-diameter square-edged orifice.  With a 3-in. water head loss across the orifice, compute the flow in cubic feet per minute.

**8.50**  A 6-in.-diameter VDI orifice is installed in a 12-in.-diameter oil line, $\mu = 0.06$ poise, $\gamma = 52$ lb/ft³.  An oil-air differential manometer is used. For a gage difference of 22 in. determine the flow rate in gallons per minute.

**8.51**  A rectangular sharp-crested weir 12 ft long with end contractions suppressed is 4 ft high.  Determine the discharge when the head is 0.81 ft.

**8.52**  In Fig. 8.33, $L = 10$ ft, $P = 1.8$ ft, $H = 0.80$ ft.  Estimate the discharge over the weir.  $C = 3.33$.

**8.53**  A rectangular sharp-crested weir with end contractions is 4 ft long. How high should it be placed in a channel to maintain an upstream depth of 6 ft for 16 cfs flow?

**8.54**  Determine the head on a 60° V-notch weir for discharge of 6 cfs.

**8.55**  Tests on a 90° V-notch weir gave the following results: $H = 0.60$ ft, $Q = 0.685$ cfs; $H = 1.35$ ft, $Q = 5.28$ cfs.  Determine the formula for the weir.

**8.56**  A sharp-crested rectangular weir 3 ft long with end contractions suppressed and a 90° V-notch weir are placed in the same weir box, with the vertex of the 90° V-notch weir 6 in. below the rectangular weir crest.  Determine the head on the V-notch weir $(a)$ when the discharges are equal and $(b)$ when the rectangular weir discharges its greatest amount above the discharge of the V-notch weir.

**8.57**  A broad-crested weir 5 ft high and 10 ft long has a well-rounded upstream corner.  What head is required for a flow of 100 cfs?

**8.58**  A circular disk 8 in. in diameter has a clearance of 0.012 in. from a flat plate.  What torque is required to rotate the disk 800 rpm when the clearance contains oil, $\mu = 0.8$ poise?

**8.59**  The concentric-cylinder viscometer (Fig. 8.41) has the following dimensions: $a = 0.012$ in.; $b = 0.05$ in.; $r_1 = 2.8$ in.; $h = 6.0$ in.  The torque is 24 lb-in. when the speed is 160 rmp.  What is the viscosity?

**8.60**  With the apparatus of Fig. 8.43, $D = 0.020$ in., $L = 36$ in., $H = 2.4$ ft, and 60 cm³ was discharged in 1 hr 30 min.  What is the viscosity in poises? $\gamma = 52$ lb/ft³.

**8.61**  The piezoelectric properties of quartz are used to measure

$(a)$ temperature   $(b)$ density   $(c)$ velocity   $(d)$ pressure
$(e)$ none of these answers

**8.62**  A static tube is used to measure

$(a)$ the pressure in a static fluid
$(b)$ the velocity in a flowing stream
$(c)$ the total pressure
$(d)$ the dynamic pressure
$(e)$ the undisturbed fluid pressure

**8.63**  A piezometer opening is used to measure

$(a)$ the pressure in a static fluid
$(b)$ the velocity in a flowing stream
$(c)$ the total pressure
$(d)$ the dynamic pressure
$(e)$ the undisturbed fluid pressure

**8.64**   The simple pitot tube measures the

(a) static pressure
(b) dynamic pressure
(c) total pressure
(d) velocity at the stagnation point
(e) difference in total and dynamic pressure

**8.65**   A pitot-static tube ($C = 1$) is used to measure air speeds.   With water in the differential manometer and a gage difference of 3 in., the air speed for $\gamma = 0.0624$ lb/ft$^3$, in feet per second, is

(a) 4.01      (b) 15.8      (c) 24.06      (d) 127      (e) none of these answers

**8.66**   The pitot-static tube measures

(a) static pressure
(b) dynamic pressure
(c) total pressure
(d) difference in static and dynamic pressure
(e) difference in total and dynamic pressure

**8.67**   The temperature of a known flowing gas may be determined from measurement of

(a) static and stagnation pressure only
(b) velocity and stagnation pressure only
(c) velocity and dynamic pressure only
(d) velocity and stagnation temperature only
(e) none of these answers

**8.68**   The velocity of a known flowing gas may be determined from measurement of

(a) static and stagnation pressure only
(b) static pressure and temperature only
(c) static and stagnation temperature only
(d) stagnation temperature and stagnation pressure only
(e) none of these answers

**8.69**   The hot-wire anemometer is used to measure

(a) pressure in gases
(b) pressure in liquids
(c) wind velocities at airports
(d) gas velocities
(e) liquid discharges

**8.70**   Snell's law relates

($a$)  pressure and density in optical measurements
($b$)  angle of incidence, angle of refraction, and index of refraction
($c$)  velocity, pressure, and piezoelectric properties of crystals
($d$)  density and index of refraction
($e$)  none of these answers

**8.71**   The Gladstone-Dale equation relates

($a$)  pressure and density in optical measurements
($b$)  angle of incidence, angle of refraction, and index of refraction
($c$)  velocity, pressure, and piezoelectric properties of crystals
($d$)  density and index of refraction
($e$)  none of these answers

**8.72**   The schlieren optical system portrays

($a$)  temperature changes in gas flow
($b$)  pressure changes in gas flow
($c$)  density changes in gas flow
($d$)  density gradient changes in gas flow
($e$)  none of these answers

**8.73**   The shadowgraph optical system portrays

($a$)  temperature changes in gas flow
($b$)  pressure changes in gas flow
($c$)  density changes in gas flow
($d$)  density gradient changes in gas flow
($e$)  none of these answers

**8.74**   The interferometer optical system

($a$)  makes use of a knife-edge
($b$)  requires two light sources
($c$)  depends upon a phase shift in light wave motion
($d$)  splits the light from a single source into three circuits
($e$)  satisfies none of these answers

**8.75**   A piston-type displacement meter has a volume displacement of 2.15 in.³ per revolution of its shaft.   The discharge in gallons per minute for 1000 rpm is

($a$)  0.497      ($b$)  1.23      ($c$)  9.3      ($d$)  10.72      ($e$)  none of these
answers

**8.76**   Water for a pipeline was diverted into a weigh tank for exactly 10 min. The increased weight in the tank was 4765 lb.   The average flow rate in gallons per minute was

(a) 66.1      (b) 57.1      (c) 7.95      (d) 0.13      (e) none of these
answers

**8.77**   A rectangular tank with cross-sectional area of 90 ft² was filled to a depth of 4.00 ft by a steady flow of liquid for 12 min.   The rate of flow in cubic feet per second was

(a) 0.50      (b) 30      (c) 31.2      (d) 224      (e) none of these
answers

**8.78**   Which of the following measuring instruments is a rate meter?

(a) current meter      (b) disk meter      (c) hot-wire anemometer
(d) pitot tube      (e) venturi meter

**8.79**   The actual velocity at the *vena contracta* for flow through an orifice from a reservoir is expressed by

(a) $C_v \sqrt{2gH}$      (b) $C_c \sqrt{2gH}$      (c) $C_d \sqrt{2gH}$      (d) $\sqrt{2gH}$
(e) $C_v V_a$

**8.80**   A fluid jet discharging from a 2-in.-diameter orifice has a diameter 1.75 in. at its *vena contracta*.   The coefficient of contraction is

(a) 1.31      (b) 1.14      (c) 0.875      (d) 0.766      (e) none of these
answers

**8.81**   The ratio of actual discharge to theoretical discharge through an orifice is

(a) $C_c C_v$      (b) $C_c C_d$      (c) $C_v C_d$      (d) $C_d/C_v$      (e) $C_d/C_c$

**8.82**   The losses in orifice flow are

(a) $\dfrac{1}{C_v^2}\left(\dfrac{V_{2a}^2}{2g} - 1\right)$      (b) $\dfrac{V_{2t}^2}{2g} - \dfrac{V_{2a}^2}{2g}$      (c) $H(C_v^2 - 1)$
(d) $H - V_{2t}^2/2g$      (e) none of these answers

**8.83**   For a liquid surface to lower at a constant rate, the area of reservoir $A_R$ must vary with head $y$ on the orifice, as

(a) $\sqrt{y}$      (b) $y$      (c) $1/\sqrt{y}$      (d) $1/y$      (e) none of these
answers

**8.84**   A 2-in.-diameter Borda mouthpiece discharges 0.268 cfs under a head of 9.0 ft.   The velocity coefficient is

(a) 0.96      (b) 0.97      (c) 0.98      (d) 0.99      (e) none of these
answers

**8.85**   The discharge coefficient for a 4- by 2-in. venturi meter at a Reynolds number of 200,000 is

(a) 0.95      (b) 0.96      (c) 0.97      (d) 0.98      (e) 0.99

**8.86**  Select the correct statement:

(a)  The discharge through a venturi meter depends upon $\Delta p$ only and is independent of orientation of the meter.

(b)  A venturi meter with a given gage difference $R'$ discharges at a greater rate when the flow is vertically downward through it than when the flow is vertically upward.

(c)  For a given pressure difference the equations show that the discharge of gas is greater through a venturi meter when compressibility is taken into account than when it is neglected.

(d)  The coefficient of contraction of a venturi meter is unity.

(e)  The over-all loss is the same in a given pipeline whether a venturi meter or a nozzle with the same $D_2$ is used.

**8.87**  The expansion factor $Y$ depends upon

(a)  $k$, $p_2/p_1$, and $A_2/A_1$
(b)  $R$, $p_2/p_1$, and $A_2/A_1$
(c)  $k$, $R$, and $p_2/p_1$
(d)  $k$, $R$, and $A_2/A_1$
(e)  none of these answers

**8.88**  The discharge through a V-notch weir varies as

(a)  $H^{-1/2}$     (b)  $H^{1/2}$     (c)  $H^{3/2}$     (d)  $H^{5/2}$     (e)  none of these answers

**8.89**  The discharge of a rectangular sharp-crested weir with end contractions is less than for the same weir with end contractions suppressed by

(a)  5%     (b)  10%     (c)  15%     (d)  no fixed percentage
(e)  none of these answers

**8.90**  A mass meter, with radius at exit of impeller of 6 in., turns at 1200 rpm and has a torque applied of 36 lb-in.   The mass per second flowing is, in pounds mass per second,

(a)  0.00796     (b)  0.096     (c)  0.478     (d)  3.08     (e)  none of these answers

**8.91**  A homemade viscometer of the Saybolt type is calibrated by two measurements with liquids of known kinematic viscosity.   For $\nu = 0.461$ stoke, $t = 97$ sec and for $\nu = 0.18$ stoke, $t = 46$ sec.   The coefficients $C_1$, $C_2$ in $\nu = C_1 t + C_2/t$ are

(a)  $C_1 = 0.005$      (b)  $C_1 = 0.0044$      (c)  $C_1 = 0.0046$
    $C_2 = -2.3$          $C_2 = 3.6$              $C_2 = 1.55$
(d)  $C_1 = 0.00317$     (e)  none of these answers
    $C_2 = 14.95$

## references

Addison, Herbert: "Hydraulic Measurements," John Wiley & Sons, Inc., New York, 1946.

Binder, R. C.: Flow Measurement, sec. 14 in "Handbook of Fluid Dynamics," ed. by V. L. Streeter, McGraw-Hill Book Company, New York, 1961.

Dryden, H. L., and A. M. Keuthe: The Measurement of Fluctuations of Air Speed by the Hot-wire Anemometer, *NACA Rept.* 320, 1929.

"Flow Measurement," American Society of Mechanical Engineers, 1940.

"Fluid Meters: Their Theory and Application," 5th ed., American Society of Mechanical Engineers, 1959.

Goldstein, S.: "Modern Developments in Fluid Mechanics," Oxford University Press, London, 1938.

Horton, Robert E.: Weir Experiments, Coefficients, and Formulas, *U.S. Geol. Surv. Water Supply and Irrigation Paper* 200, 1907.

Howarth, L.: "Modern Developments in Fluid Mechanics: High Speed Flow," Oxford University Press, London, 1953.

King, H. W., and E. F. Brater: "Handbook of Hydraulics," 5th ed., McGraw-Hill Book Company, New York, 1963.

Landenburg, R. W., B. Lewis, R. N. Pease, and H. S. Taylor: "Physical Measurements in Gas Dynamics and Combustion," Princeton University Press, Princeton, N.J., 1954.

Pankhurst, R. C., and D. W. Holder, "Wind-tunnel Technique," Sir Isaac Pitman & Sons, Ltd., London, 1952.

# 9

# turbomachinery

The turning of a fluid stream or the changing of the magnitude of its velocity requires that forces be applied. When a moving vane deflects a fluid jet and changes its momentum, forces are exerted between vane and jet and work is done by displacement of the vane. Turbomachines make use of this principle: The axial and centrifugal pumps, blowers, and compressors, by continuously doing work on the fluid, add to its energy; the impulse, Francis, and propeller turbines and steam and gas turbines continuously extract energy from the fluid and convert it into torque on a rotating shaft; the fluid coupling and the torque converter, each consisting of a pump and a turbine built together, make use of the fluid to transmit power smoothly. The designing of efficient turbomachines utilizes both theory and experimentation. A good design of given size and speed may be readily adapted to other speeds and other geometrically similar sizes by application of the theory of scaled models, as outlined in Sec. 4.5.

Similarity relationships are first discussed in this chapter by consideration of homologous units and specific speed. Elementary cascade theory is next taken up, before considering the theory of turbomachines. Water turbines and pumps are then considered, followed by blowers, centrifugal compressors, and fluid couplings and torque converters. The chapter closes with a discussion of cavitation.

## 9.1 homologous units. specific speed

In utilizing scaled models in the designing of turbomachines, geometric similitude is required as well as geometrically similar velocity vector diagrams at entrance to or exit from the impellers. Viscous effects must, unfortunately, be neglected, as it is generally impossible to satisfy the two above conditions and have equal Reynolds numbers in model and proto-type. Two geometrically similar units having similar velocity vector dia-grams are *homologous*. They will also have geometrically similar streamlines.

The velocity vector diagram in Fig. 9.1 at exit from a pump impeller may be used to formulate the condition for similar streamline patterns. The blade angle is $\beta$, $u$ is the peripheral speed of the impeller at the end of the vane or blade, $v$ is the velocity of fluid *relative* to the vane, and $V$ is the absolute velocity leaving the impeller, the vector sum of $u$ and $v$; $V_r$ is the radial component of $V$ and is proportional to the discharge; $\alpha$ is the angle which the absolute velocity makes with $u$, the tangential direction. According to geometric similitude, $\beta$ must be the same for two units, and for similar streamlines $\alpha$ must also be the same in each case.

It is convenient to express the fact that $\alpha$ is to be the same in any of a series of turbomachines, called homologous units, by relating the speed of rotation $N$, the impeller diameter (or other characteristic dimension) $D$, and the flow rate $Q$. For constant $\alpha$, $V_r$ is proportional to $V$ ($V_r = V \sin \alpha$) and $u$ is proportional to $V_r$. Hence the conditions for constant $\alpha$ in a homologous series of units may be expressed as

$$\frac{V_r}{u} = \text{const}$$

The discharge $Q$ is proportional to $V_r D^2$, since any cross-sectional flow area is proportional to $D^2$. The speed of rotation $N$ is proportional to

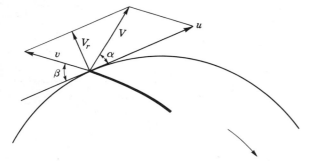

**Fig. 9.1** Velocity vector diagram for exit from a pump impeller.

$u/D$.   By inserting these values,

$$\frac{Q}{ND^3} = \text{const} \tag{9.1.1}$$

expresses the condition in which geometrically similar units are homologous.

The discharge $Q$ through homologous units may be related to head $H$ and cross-sectional flow path $A$ by the orifice formula

$$Q = C_d A \sqrt{2gH}$$

in which $C_d$, the discharge coefficient, varies slightly with the Reynolds number and so causes a small change in efficiency with size in a homologous series.   The change in discharge with the Reynolds number is referred to as "scale effect."   The smaller machines, having smaller hydraulic radii of passages, will have lower Reynolds numbers and correspondingly higher friction factors; hence they are less efficient.   The change in efficiency from model to prototype may be from 1 to 4 per cent.   However, in the homologous theory, the scale effect must be neglected, and so an empirical correction for change in efficiency with size is used [see Eq. (9.5.1)].   As $A \sim D^2$, the discharge equation may be

$$\frac{Q}{D^2 \sqrt{H}} = \text{const} \tag{9.1.2}$$

After eliminating $Q$ between Eqs. (9.1.1) and (9.1.2),

$$\frac{H}{N^2 D^2} = \text{const} \tag{9.1.3}$$

Equations (9.1.1) and (9.1.3) are most useful in determining performance characteristics for one unit from those of a homologous unit of different size and speed.[1]

---

[1] Application of dimensional analysis is illuminating.   The variables appearing to be pertinent to the flow relations for similar units would be

$$F(H,Q,N,D,g) = 0$$

There are two dimensions involved, $L$ and $T$; $N$ and $D$ may be selected as the repeating variables, yielding

$$f\left(\frac{Q}{ND^3}, \frac{H}{D}, \frac{g}{N^2 D}\right) = 0$$

After solving for $H$,

$$H = D f_1\left(\frac{Q}{ND^3}, \frac{g}{N^2 D}\right)$$

*(For balance of footnote see next page)*

**example 9.1**    A prototype test of a mixed-flow pump with a 72-in.-diameter discharge opening, operating at 225 rpm, resulted in the following characteristics:

| $H_{ft}$ | $Q_{cfs}$ | $e\%$ | $H_{ft}$ | $Q_{cfs}$ | $e\%$ |
|------|------|------|------|------|------|
| 60   | 200  | 69   | 40   | 382  | 86.3 |
| 57.5 | 228  | 75   | 37.5 | 396  | 84.4 |
| 55   | 256  | 80   | 35   | 411  | 82   |
| 52.5 | 280  | 83.7 | 32.5 | 425  | 79   |
| 50   | 303  | 86   | 30   | 438  | 75   |
| 47.5 | 330  | 87.3 | 27.5 | 449  | 71   |
| 45   | 345  | 88   | 25   | 459  | 66.5 |
| 42.5 | 362  | 87.4 |      |      |      |

What size and synchronous speed of homologous pump should be used to produce 200 cfs at 60 ft head at point of best efficiency?    Find the characteristic curves for this case.

   Subscript 1 refers to the 72-in. pump.    For best efficiency $H_1 = 45, Q_1 = 345, e = 88$ per cent.    With Eqs. (9.1.1) and (9.1.3),

$$\frac{H}{N^2 D^2} = \frac{H_1}{N_1^2 D_1^2} \qquad \frac{Q}{ND^3} = \frac{Q_1}{N_1 D_1^3}$$

or

$$\frac{60}{N^2 D^2} = \frac{45}{(225)^2 (72)^2} \qquad \frac{200}{ND^3} = \frac{345}{225(72)^3}$$

Experiment shows that the second dimensionless parameter actually occurs to the power $-1$; hence

$$H = \frac{N^2 D^2}{g} f_2 \left( \frac{Q}{ND^3} \right)$$

or

$$\frac{gH}{N^2 D^2} = f_2 \left( \frac{Q}{ND^3} \right)$$

   The characteristic curve for a pump in dimensionless form is the plot of $Q/ND^3$ as abscissa against $H/(N^2D^2/g)$ as ordinate.    This curve, obtained from tests on one unit of the series, then applies to all homologous units, and may be converted to the usual characteristic curve by selecting desired values of $N$ and $D$.    As power is proportional to $\gamma QH$, the dimensionless power term is

$$\frac{\gamma}{\gamma} \times \frac{Q}{ND^3} \times \frac{H}{N^2 D^2 / g} = \frac{\text{power}}{\rho N^3 D^5}$$

After solving for $N$ and $D$,

$$N = 366 \qquad D = 51.1$$

The nearest synchronous speed (3600 divided by number of pairs of poles) is 360 rpm. To maintain the desired head of 60 ft, a new $D$ is necessary. Its size may be computed:

$$D = \sqrt{\tfrac{60}{45}} \times \tfrac{225}{360} \times 72 = 52 \text{ in.}$$

The discharge at best efficiency is then

$$Q = \frac{Q_1 N D^3}{N_1 D_1{}^3} = 345 \times \frac{360}{225}\left(\frac{52}{72}\right)^3 = 208 \text{ cfs}$$

which is slightly more capacity than required. With $N = 360$ and $D = 52$, equations for transforming the corresponding values of $H$ and $Q$ for any efficiency may be obtained:

$$H = H_1\left(\frac{ND}{N_1 D_1}\right)^2 = H_1\left(\frac{360}{225} \times \frac{52}{72}\right)^2 = 1.336 H_1$$

and

$$Q = Q_1 \frac{ND^3}{N_1 D_1{}^3} = Q_1 \frac{360}{225} \times \left(\frac{52}{72}\right)^3 = 0.605 Q_1$$

The characteristics of the new pump are

| $H_{\text{ft}}$ | $Q_{\text{cfs}}$ | $e\%$ | $H_{\text{ft}}$ | $Q_{\text{cfs}}$ | $e\%$ |
|---|---|---|---|---|---|
| 80 | 121 | 69 | 53.5 | 231 | 86.3 |
| 76.7 | 138 | 75 | 50 | 239 | 84.4 |
| 73.4 | 155 | 80 | 46.7 | 248 | 82 |
| 70 | 169 | 83.7 | 43.4 | 257 | 79 |
| 66.7 | 183 | 86 | 40 | 264 | 75 |
| 63.5 | 200 | 87.3 | 36.7 | 271 | 71 |
| 60 | 208 | 88 | 33.4 | 277 | 66.5 |
| 56.7 | 219 | 87.4 | | | |

The efficiency of the 52-in. pump might be a fraction of a per cent less than that of the 72-in. pump, as the hydraulic radii of flow passages are smaller, so that the Reynolds number would be less.

*specific speed*

The specific speed of a homologous unit is a constant that is widely used in the selection of type of unit and in preliminary design. It is usually defined differently for a pump than for a turbine.

The specific speed $N_s$ of a homologous series of pumps is defined as the speed of some one unit of the series of such a size that it delivers unit discharge at unit head. It is obtained as follows: By eliminating $D$ in Eqs. (9.1.1) and (9.1.3) and rearranging,

$$\frac{N\sqrt{Q}}{H^{\frac{3}{4}}} = \text{const} \tag{9.1.4}$$

By definition of specific speed, the constant is $N_s$, the speed of a unit for $Q = 1$, $H = 1$:

$$N_s = \frac{N\sqrt{Q}}{H^{\frac{3}{4}}} \tag{9.1.5}$$

The specific speed of a series is usually defined for the point of best efficiency, i.e., for the speed, discharge, and head that is most efficient.

The specific speed of a homologous series of turbines is defined as the speed of a unit of the series of such a size that it produces unit horsepower with unit head. Since power $P$ is proportional to $QH$,

$$\frac{P}{QH} = \text{const} \tag{9.1.6}$$

The terms $D$ and $Q$ may be eliminated from Eqs. (9.1.1), (9.1.3), and (9.1.6) to produce

$$\frac{N\sqrt{P}}{H^{\frac{5}{4}}} = \text{const} \tag{9.1.7}$$

For unit power and unit head the constant of Eq. (9.1.7) becomes the speed, or the specific speed, $N_s$, of the series, so that

$$N_s = \frac{N\sqrt{P}}{H^{\frac{5}{4}}} \tag{9.1.8}$$

The specific speed of a unit required for a given discharge and head can be estimated from Eqs. (9.1.5) and (9.1.8). For pumps handling large discharges at low heads a high specific speed is indicated; for a high-head turbine producing relatively low power (small discharge) the specific speed is low. Experience has shown that for best efficiency one particular type of pump or turbine is usually indicated for a given specific speed.

Centrifugal pumps have low specific speeds; mixed-flow pumps have medium specific speeds; and axial-flow pumps have high specific speeds. Impulse turbines have low specific speeds; Francis turbines have medium specific speeds; and propeller turbines have high specific speeds.

## 9.2  elementary cascade theory

Turbomachines either do work on a fluid or extract work from it in a continuous manner by having it flow through a series of moving (and possibly fixed) vanes.  By examination of flow through a series of similar blades or vanes, called a *cascade*, some of the requirements of an efficient system may be developed.  Consider, first, flow through the simple fixed cascade system of Fig. 9.2.  It is seen that the velocity vector representing the fluid has been turned through the angle $\theta$ by the presence of the cascade system.  A force has been exerted on the fluid, but neglecting friction effects and turbulence, no work is done on the fluid.  Section 3.11 deals with forces on a single vane.

Since turbomachines are rotational devices, the cascade system may be arranged symmetrically around the periphery of a circle, as in Fig. 9.3. If the fluid approaches the fixed cascade in a radial direction, it has its moment of momentum changed from zero to a value dependent upon the mass per unit time flowing, the tangential component of velocity $V_t$ developed, and the radius, from Eq. (3.12.5),

$$T = \rho Q r V_t \qquad (9.2.1)$$

Again, no work is done by the fixed-vane system.

Consider now another series of vanes (Fig. 9.4) that are rotating within the fixed vane system at a speed $\omega$.  For efficient operation of the system it is important that the fluid flow onto the moving vanes with the least dis-

**Fig. 9.2**  Simple cascade system.

**Fig. 9.3** Cascade arranged on the periphery of a circular cylinder.

turbance, i.e., in a tangential manner, as illustrated in Fig. 9.5.   When the relative velocity is not tangent to the blade at its entrance, separation may occur, as shown in Fig. 9.6.   The losses tend to increase rapidly (about as the square) with angle from the tangential and radically impair the efficiency of the machine.   Separation also frequently occurs when the approaching relative velocity is tangential to the vane, owing to curvature of the vanes or to expansion of the flow passages, which causes the boundary layer to thicken and come to rest.   These losses are called *shock* or *turbulence* losses.   When the fluid exits from the moving cascade, it will generally have its velocity altered in both magnitude and direction, thereby changing its moment of momentum and either doing work on the cascade or having work done on it by the moving cascade.   In the case of a turbine it is desired to have the fluid leave with no moment of momentum.   An old saying in

**Fig. 9.4** Moving cascade within fixed cascade.

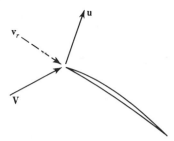

**Fig. 9.5** Relative velocity tangent to blade.

turbine design is "have the fluid enter without shock and leave without velocity."

Turbomachinery design requires the proper arrangement and shaping of passages and vanes so that the purpose of the design can be most efficiently met. The particular design depends upon the purpose of the machine, the amount of work to be done per unit mass of fluid, and the fluid density.

## 9.3  theory of turbomachines

Turbines extract useful work from fluid energy; and pumps, blowers, and turbocompressors add energy to fluids by means of a runner consisting of vanes rigidly attached to a shaft.   Since the only displacement of the vanes is in the tangential direction, work is done by the displacement of the tangential components of force on the runner.   The radial components of force on the runner have no displacement in a radial direction and, hence, can do no work.

In turbomachine theory, friction is neglected and the fluid is assumed to have perfect guidance through the machine, i.e., an infinite number of thin vanes, and so the relative velocity of the fluid is always tangent to the vane.

**Fig. 9.6** Flow separation, or "shock," from blade with relative velocity not tangent to leading edge.

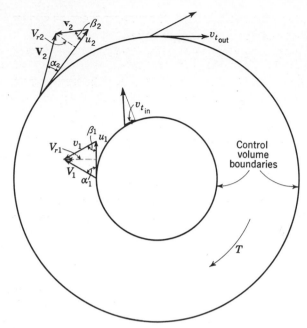

**Fig. 9.7** Steady flow through control volume with circular symmetry.

This yields circular symmetry and permits the moment-of-momentum equation, Sec. 3.12, to take the simple form of Eq. (3.12.5), for steady flow,

$$T = \rho Q[(rv_t)_{\text{out}} - (rv_t)_{\text{in}}] \tag{9.3.1}$$

in which $T$ is the torque acting on the fluid within the control volume (Fig. 9.7) and $\rho Q(rV_t)_{\text{out}}$ and $\rho Q(rv_t)_{\text{in}}$ represent the moment of momentum leaving and entering the control volume, respectively.

The polar vector diagram is generally used in studying vane relationships (Fig. 9.8), with subscript 1 for entering fluid and subscript 2 for exiting fluid. $V$ is the absolute fluid velocity, $u$ the peripheral velocity of the runner, and $v$ the fluid velocity relative to the runner. The absolute velocities

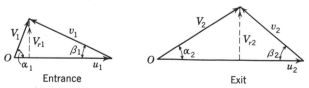

**Fig. 9.8** Polar vector diagrams.

$V$, $u$ are laid off from 0, and the relative velocity connects them as shown. $V_u$ is designated as the component of absolute velocity in the tangential direction.   $\alpha$ is the angle the absolute velocity $V$ makes with the peripheral velocity $u$, and $\beta$ is the angle the relative velocity makes with $-u$, or it is the *blade angle*, as perfect guidance is assumed.   $V_r$ is the absolute velocity component normal to the periphery.   In this notation Eq. (9.3.1) becomes

$$T = \rho Q(r_2 V_2 \cos \alpha_2 - r_1 V_1 \cos \alpha_1)$$
$$= \rho Q(r_2 V_{u2} - r_1 V_{u1}) = \dot{m}(r_2 V_{u2} - r_1 V_{u1}) \tag{9.3.2}$$

The mass per unit time flowing is $\dot{m} = \rho Q = (\rho Q)_{\text{out}} = (\rho Q)_{\text{in}}$.   In the form above, when $T$ is positive, the fluid moment of momentum increases through the control volume, as for a pump.   For $T$ negative, moment of momentum of the fluid is decreased, as for a turbine runner.   When $T = 0$, as in passages where there are no vanes,

$$rV_u = \text{const}$$

This is *free-vortex* motion, with the tangential component of velocity varying inversely with radius.   It is discussed in Sec. 7.9 and compared with the forced vortex in Sec. 2.9.

**example 9.2**   The wicket gates of Fig. 9.9 are turned so that the flow makes an angle of 45° with a radial line at section 1, where the speed is 8 ft/sec. Determine the magnitude of tangential velocity component $V_u$ over section 2.

**Fig. 9.9**   Schematic view of propeller turbine.

Since no torque is exerted on the flow between sections 1 and 2, the moment of momentum is constant and the motion follows the free-vortex law

$$V_u r = \text{const}$$

At section 1

$$V_{u1} = 8 \cos 45° = 5.65 \text{ ft/sec}$$

Then

$$V_{u1}r_1 = 5.65 \times 4 = 22.6 \text{ ft}^2/\text{sec}$$

Across section 2

$$V_{u2} = \frac{22.6}{r}$$

At the hub $V_u = 22.6/0.75 = 30.1$ ft/sec, and at the outer edge $V_u = 22.6/2 = 11.3$ ft/sec.

*head and energy relations*

By multiplying Eq. (9.3.2) by the rotational speed $\omega$ of runner,

$$\begin{aligned} T\omega &= \rho Q(\omega r_2 V_{u2} - \omega r_1 V_{u1}) \\ &= \rho Q(u_2 V_{u2} - u_1 V_{u1}) \end{aligned} \tag{9.3.3}$$

For no losses the power available from a turbine is $Q\,\Delta p = Q\gamma H$, in which $H$ is the head on the runner, since $Q$ is the weight per unit time and $H$ the potential energy per unit weight.   Similarly a pump runner produces work $Q\gamma H$ in which $H$ is the pump head.   The power exchange is

$$T\omega = Q\gamma H \tag{9.3.4}$$

By solving for $H$, using Eq. (9.3.3) to eliminate $T$,

$$H = \frac{u_2 V_{u2} - u_1 V_{u1}}{g} \tag{9.3.5}$$

For turbines the sign is reversed in Eq. (9.3.5).
     For pumps the *actual* head $H_p$ produced is

$$H_p = e_h H = H - H_L \tag{9.3.6}$$

and for turbines the actual head $H_t$ is

$$H_t = \frac{H}{e_h} = H + H_L \tag{9.3.7}$$

in which $e_h$ is the hydraulic efficiency of the machine and $H_L$ represents all the internal fluid loss in the machine. The over-all efficiency of the machines is further reduced by bearing friction, by friction caused by fluid between runner and housing, and by leakage or flow that passes around the runner without going through it. These losses do not affect the head relations.

Pumps are generally designed so that the angular momentum of fluid entering the runner (impeller) is zero. Then

$$H = \frac{u_2 V_2 \cos \alpha_2}{g} \tag{9.3.8}$$

Turbines are designed so that the angular momentum is zero at the exit section of the runner for conditions at best efficiency; hence,

$$H = \frac{u_1 V_1 \cos \alpha_1}{g} \tag{9.3.9}$$

In writing the energy equation for a pump, with Eqs. (9.3.5) and (9.3.6),

$$H_p = \left(\frac{V_2{}^2}{2g} + \frac{p_2}{\gamma} + z_2\right) - \left(\frac{V_1{}^2}{2g} + \frac{p_1}{\gamma} + z_1\right)$$

$$= \frac{u_2 V_2 \cos \alpha_2 - u_1 V_1 \cos \alpha_1}{g} - H_L \tag{9.3.10}$$

for which it is assumed that all streamlines through the pump have the same total energy. With the relations among the absolute velocity $V$, the velocity $v$ relative to the runner, and the velocity $u$ of runner, from the vector diagrams (Fig. 9.8) by the law of cosines,

$$u_1{}^2 + V_1{}^2 - 2u_1 V_1 \cos \alpha_1 = v_1{}^2$$
$$u_2{}^2 + V_2{}^2 - 2u_2 V_2 \cos \alpha_2 = v_2{}^2$$

After eliminating the absolute velocities $V_1$, $V_2$ in these relations and in Eq. (9.3.10),

$$H_L = \frac{u_2{}^2 - u_1{}^2}{2g} - \frac{v_2{}^2 - v_1{}^2}{2g} - \frac{p_2 - p_1}{\gamma} - (z_2 - z_1) \tag{9.3.11}$$

or

$$H_L = \frac{u_2{}^2 - u_1{}^2}{2g} - \left[\left(\frac{v_2{}^2}{2g} + \frac{p_2}{\gamma} + z_2\right) - \left(\frac{v_1{}^2}{2g} + \frac{p_1}{\gamma} + z_1\right)\right] \tag{9.3.12}$$

The losses are the difference in centrifugal head, $(u_2{}^2 - u_1{}^2)/2g$, and in the head change in the relative flow. For no loss, the increase in pressure head, from Eq. (9.3.11), is

$$\frac{p_2 - p_1}{\gamma} + z_2 - z_1 = \frac{u_2{}^2 - u_1{}^2}{2g} - \frac{v_2{}^2 - v_2{}^1}{2g} \tag{9.3.13}$$

With no flow through the runner, $v_1$, $v_2$ are zero, and the head rise is as expressed in the relative equilibrium relationships [Eq. (2.9.7)]. When flow occurs, the head rise is equal to the centrifugal head minus the difference in relative velocity heads.

For the case of a turbine, exactly the same equations result.

**example 9.3**   A centrifugal pump with a 24-in.-diameter impeller runs at 1800 rpm.   The water enters without whirl, and $\alpha_2 = 60°$.   The actual head produced by the pump is 50 ft.   Find its hydraulic efficiency when $V_2 = 20$ ft/sec.

From Eq. (9.3.8) the theoretical head is

$$H = \frac{u_2 V_2 \cos \alpha_2}{g} = \frac{1800 \times 2\pi \times 20 \times 0.50}{60 \times 32.2} = 58.6 \text{ ft}$$

The actual head is 50.0 ft; hence, the hydraulic efficiency is

$$e_h = \frac{50}{58.6} = 85.4\%$$

## 9.4  impulse turbines

The impulse turbine is one in which all available energy of the flow is converted by a nozzle into kinetic energy at atmospheric pressure before the fluid contacts the moving blades.   Losses occur in flow from the reservoir through the pressure pipe (penstock) to the base of the nozzle, which may be computed from pipe friction data. At the base of the nozzle the available energy, or total head, is

$$h_a = \frac{p_1}{\gamma} + \frac{V_1{}^2}{2g} \tag{9.4.1}$$

from Fig. 9.10.   With $C_v$ the nozzle coefficient, the jet velocity $V_2$ is

$$V_2 = C_v \sqrt{2gh_a} = C_v \sqrt{2g\left(\frac{p_1}{\gamma} + \frac{V_1{}^2}{2g}\right)} \tag{9.4.2}$$

The head lost in the nozzle is

$$h_a - \frac{V_2{}^2}{2g} = h_a - C_v{}^2 h_a = h_a(1 - C_v{}^2) \tag{9.4.3}$$

**Fig. 9.10**  Impulse turbine system.

and the efficiency of the nozzle is

$$\frac{V_2{}^2/2g}{h_a} = \frac{C_v{}^2 h_a}{h_a} = C_v{}^2 \tag{9.4.4}$$

The jet, with velocity $V_2$, strikes double-cupped buckets (Figs. 9.11 and 9.12) which split the flow and turn the relative velocity through the angle $\theta$ (Fig. 9.12).

The $x$-component of momentum is changed by (Fig. 9.12)

$$F = \rho Q(v_r - v_r \cos \theta)$$

and the work done by the vanes is

$$Fu = \rho Q u v_r (1 - \cos \theta) \tag{9.4.5}$$

To maximize the work done, theoretically, $\theta = 180°$, and $u v_r$ must be a maximum; i.e., $u(V_2 - u)$ must be a maximum.  By differentiating with respect to $u$ and equating to zero,

$$(V_2 - u) + u(-1) = 0$$

$u = V_2/2$.  After making these substitutions into Eq. (9.4.5),

$$Fu = \rho Q \frac{V_2}{2}\left(V_2 - \frac{V_2}{2}\right)(1 - -1) = \gamma Q \frac{V_2{}^2}{2g} \tag{9.4.6}$$

which accounts for the total kinetic energy of the jet.  The velocity diagram for these values shows that the absolute velocity leaving the vanes is zero.

Practically, when vanes are arranged on the periphery of a wheel (Fig. 9.11), it is necessary that the fluid retain enough velocity to move out of the way of the following bucket.  Most of the practical impulse turbines

**Fig. 9.11** Southern California Edison, Big Creek 2A, 1948. $8\frac{1}{2}$-in.-diameter jet impulse buckets and disk in process of being reamed. 56,000 hp, 2200 ft head, 300 rpm. (*Allis-Chalmers Mfg. Co.*)

are Pelton wheels. The jet is split in two, turned in a horizontal plane, and half is discharged from each side to avoid any unbalanced thrust on the shaft. There are losses due to the splitter and to friction between jet and bucket surface, which make the most economical speed somewhat less than $V_1/2$. It is expressed in terms of the *speed factor*

$$\phi = \frac{U}{\sqrt{2gh_a}} \tag{9.4.7}$$

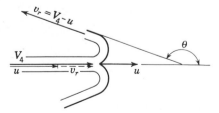

**Fig. 9.12** Flow through bucket.

For most efficient turbine operation $\phi$ has been found to be dependent upon specific speed as shown in the table.[1]   The angle $\theta$ of the bucket is

| $N_s$ | 2 | 3 | 4 | 5 | 6 | 7 |
|---|---|---|---|---|---|---|
| $\phi$ | 0.47 | 0.46 | 0.45 | 0.44 | 0.433 | 0.425 |

usually 173 to 176°.   If the diameter of the jet is $d$ and the diameter of the wheel is $D$ at the center line of the buckets, it has been found in practice that the diameter ratio $D/d$ should be about $54/N_s$ for maximum efficiency.

In the majority of installations only one jet is used, which discharges horizontally against the lower periphery of the wheel as shown in Fig. 9.10. The wheel speed is carefully regulated for the generation of electric power. A governor operates a needle valve that controls the jet discharge by changing its area.   So $V_0$ remains practically constant for a wide range of positions of the needle valve.

The efficiency of the power conversion drops off rapidly with change in head (which changes $V_0$), as is evident when power is plotted against $V_0$ for constant $u$ in Eq. (9.4.5).   The wheel operates in atmospheric air although it is enclosed by a housing.   It is therefore essential that the wheel be placed above the maximum flood water level of the river into which it discharges.   The head from nozzle to tailwater is wasted. Because of their inefficiency at other than the design head and because of the wasted head, Pelton wheels usually are employed for high heads, e.g., from 600 ft to more than a mile.   For high heads, the efficiency of the complete installation, from headwater to tailwater, may be in the high 80's.

Impulse wheels with a single nozzle are most efficient in the specific speed range of 2 to 6, when $P$ is in horsepower, $H$ is in feet, and $N$ is in revolutions per minute.   Multiple nozzle units are designed in the specific speed range of 6 to 12.

**example 9.4**   A Pelton wheel is to be selected to drive a generator at 600 rpm.   The water jet is 3 in. in diameter and has a velocity of 300 ft/sec. With the blade angle at 170°, the ratio of vane speed to initial jet speed at 0.47, and neglecting losses, determine (a) diameter of wheel to center line of buckets (vanes), (b) horsepower developed, and (c) kinetic energy per pound remaining in the fluid.

---

[1] J. W. Daily, Hydraulic Machinery, in "Engineering Hydraulics," ed. by H. Rouse, p. 943, John Wiley & Sons, Inc., New York, 1950.

($a$)  The peripheral speed of wheel is

$$u = 0.47 \times 300 = 141 \text{ ft/sec}$$

Then

$$\frac{600}{60} 2\pi \frac{D}{2} = 141 \quad \text{or} \quad D = 4.49 \text{ ft}$$

($b$)  From Eq. (9.4.5), the power, in foot-pounds per second, is computed to be

$$1.935 \times \frac{\pi}{4} \times \frac{3^2}{144} \times 300(300 - 141)141[1 - (-0.9848)] = 1{,}270{,}000$$

and

$$\text{hp} = \frac{1{,}270{,}000}{550} = 2305$$

($c$)  From Fig. 3.32, the absolute velocity components leaving the vane are determined to be

$$V_x = (300 - 141)(-0.9848) + 141 = -15.5 \text{ ft/sec}$$
$$V_y = (300 - 141)(0.1736) = 27.6 \text{ ft/sec}$$

The kinetic energy remaining in the jet is

$$\frac{(15.5)^2 + (27.6)^2}{64.4} = 15.6 \text{ ft-lb/lb}$$

**example 9.5**   A small impulse wheel is to be used to drive a generator for 60-cycle power.  The head is 300 ft, and the discharge 1.40 cfs.  Determine the diameter of the wheel at the center line of the buckets and the speed of the wheel.  $C_v = 0.98$.  Assume efficiency of 80 per cent.

The power is

$$P = \frac{\gamma Q H e}{550} = \frac{62.4 \times 1.4 \times 300 \times 0.80}{550} = 38.2 \text{ hp}$$

Taking a trial value of $N_s$ of 4,

$$N = \frac{N_s H^{5/4}}{\sqrt{P}} = \frac{4 \times (300)^{5/4}}{38.2} = 809 \text{ rpm}$$

For 60-cycle power the speed must be 3600 divided by the number of pairs of poles in the generator.  For five pairs of poles the speed would be $\frac{3600}{5} = 720$ rpm and for four pairs of poles $\frac{3600}{4} = 900$ rpm.  The closer speed 720 is selected, although some engineers prefer an even number of pairs of poles in the generator.  Then

$$N_s = \frac{N\sqrt{P}}{H^{5/4}} = \frac{720\sqrt{38.2}}{300^{5/4}} = 3.56 \text{ rpm}$$

For $N_s = 3.56$, take $\phi = 0.455$,

$$u = \phi\sqrt{2gH} = 0.455\sqrt{2 \times 32.2 \times 300} = 63.2 \text{ ft/sec}$$

and

$$\omega = \tfrac{720}{60} 2\pi = 75.4 \text{ rad/sec}$$

The peripheral speed $u$ and $D$ and $\omega$ are related:

$$u = \frac{\omega D}{2} \qquad D = \frac{2u}{\omega} = \frac{2 \times 63.2}{75.4} = 1.676 \text{ ft} = 20.1 \text{ in.}$$

The diameter $d$ of the jet is obtained from the jet velocity $V_2$; thus

$$V_2 = C_v\sqrt{2gH} = 0.98\sqrt{2 \times 32.2 \times 300} = 136 \text{ ft/sec}$$

$$a = \frac{Q}{V_2} = \frac{1.40}{136} \times 144 = 1.482 \text{ in.}^2$$

and

$$d = \sqrt{\frac{4a}{\pi}} = \sqrt{\frac{1.482}{0.7854}} = 1.375 \text{ in.}$$

Hence the diameter ratio $D/d$ is

$$\frac{D}{d} = \frac{20.1}{1.375} = 14.6$$

The desired diameter ratio for best efficiency is

$$\frac{D}{d} = \frac{54}{N_s} = \frac{54}{3.56} = 15.15$$

which is satisfactory.  Hence the wheel diameter is 20.1 in. and speed 720 rpm.

## 9.5  reaction turbines

In the *reaction* turbine a portion of the energy of the fluid is converted into kinetic energy by the fluid's passing through adjustable gates (Fig. 9.13)

**Fig. 9.13**  Stay ring and wicket gates for reaction turbine.  (*Allis-Chalmers Mfg. Co.*)

before entering the runner, and the remainder of the conversion takes place through the runner.   All passages are filled with liquid including the passage (draft tube) from the runner to the downstream liquid surface. The static fluid pressure occurs on both sides of the vanes and, hence, does no work.   The work done is entirely due to the conversion to kinetic energy.

The reaction turbine is quite different from the impulse turbine discussed in Sec. 9.4.   In an impulse turbine all the available energy of the fluid is converted into kinetic energy by a nozzle that forms a free jet.   The energy is then taken from the jet by suitable flow through moving vanes. The vanes are partly filled, with the jet open to the atmosphere throughout its travel through the runner.

In contrast, in the reaction turbine the kinetic energy is appreciable as the fluid leaves the runner and enters the draft tube.   The function of the draft tube is to reconvert the kinetic energy to flow energy by a gradual expansion of the flow cross section.   Application of the energy equation between the two ends of the draft tube shows that the action of the tube is to reduce the pressure at its upstream end to less than atmospheric pressure, thus increasing the effective head across the runner to the difference in elevation between headwater and tailwater, less losses.

**Fig. 9.14**  Draft tube.

By referring to Fig. 9.14, the energy equation from 1 to 2 yields

$$z_s + \frac{V_1{}^2}{2g} + \frac{p_1}{\gamma} = 0 + 0 + 0 + \text{losses}$$

The losses include friction plus velocity head loss at the exit from the draft tube, both of which are quite small; hence

$$\frac{p_1}{\gamma} = -z_s - \frac{V_1{}^2}{2g} + \text{losses} \qquad (9.5.1)$$

shows that considerable vacuum is produced at section 1, which effectively increases the head across the turbine runner.  The turbine setting may not be too high, or cavitation occurs in the runner and draft tube (see Sec. 9.9).

**example 9.6**  A turbine has a velocity of 20 ft/sec at the entrance to the draft tube and a velocity of 4.0 ft/sec at its exit.  For friction losses of 0.3 ft and a tailwater 16 ft below the entrance to the draft tube, find the pressure head at the entrance.

From Eq. (9.5.1)

$$\frac{p_1}{\gamma} = -16 - \frac{20^2}{2 \times 32.2} + \frac{4^2}{2 \times 32.2} + 0.3 = -21.7$$

as the kinetic energy at the exit from the draft tube is lost.  Hence a suction head of 21.7 ft is produced by the presence of the draft tube.

There are two forms of the reaction turbine in common use, the *Francis* turbine (Fig. 9.15) and the *propeller* (axial-flow) turbine (Fig. 9.16).  In both, all passages flow full, and energy is converted to useful work entirely by the changing of the moment of momentum of the liquid.  The flow passes first through the wicket gates, which impart a tangential and a radially inward velocity to the fluid.  A space between the wicket gates and the runner permits the flow to close behind the gates and move as a free vortex, without external torque being applied.

In the Francis turbine (Fig. 9.17) the fluid enters the runner so that the

**Fig. 9.15**  Section through a hydroelectric unit installed and put in operation at Hoover Dam in 1952.   The turbine is rated 115,000 hp at 180 rpm under 480 ft head.   (*Allis-Chalmers Mfg. Co.*)

relative velocity is tangent to the leading edge of the vanes.   The radial component is gradually changed to an axial component, and the tangential component is reduced as the fluid traverses the vane, so that at the runner exit the flow is axial with very little whirl (tangential component) remaining. The pressure has been reduced to less than atmospheric and most of the remaining kinetic energy is reconverted to flow energy by the time it discharges from the draft tube.   The Francis turbine is best suited to medium-head installations from 80 to 600 ft and has an efficiency between 90 and 95 per cent for the larger installations.    Francis turbines are designed in the specific speed range of 10 to 110 with best efficiency in the range 40 to 60.

In the propeller turbine (Fig. 9.9), after passing through the wicket gates, the flow moves as a free vortex and has its radial component changed to axial component by guidance from the fixed housing.  The moment of momentum is constant, and the tangential component of velocity is increased through the reduction in radius.  The blades are few in number, relatively flat, with very little curvature, and placed so that the relative flow entering the runner is tangential to the leading edge of the blade.  The

**Fig. 9.16**  Field view of installation of runner of 24,500 hp, 100 rpm, 41 ft head, Kaplan adjustable-runner hydraulic turbine.  Box Canyon Project, Public Utility District No. 1 of Pend Oreille County, Washington.  Plant placed in operation in 1955.  (*Allis-Chalmers Mfg. Co.*)

44 in. diam

Speed ring

Wicket gates

2 ft $10\frac{3}{8}$ in.

197 in. diam
runner

5 ft 0 in.

14 ft 4 in. diam

Turbine data
150,000 hp
330 ft hd
120 rpm

**Fig. 9.17** Francis turbine for Grand Coulee, Columbia Basin Project. (*Newport News Shipbuilding and Dry Dock Co.*)

relative velocity is high, as with the Pelton wheel, and changes slightly in traversing the blade. The velocity diagrams in Fig. 9.18 show how the tangential component of velocity is reduced. Propeller turbines are made with blades that pivot around the hub, thus permitting the blade angle to be adjusted for different gate openings and for changes in head. They are particularly suited for low-head installations, up to 100 ft, and have top efficiencies around 94 per cent. Axial-flow turbines are designed in the specific speed range of 100 to 210 with best efficiency from 120 to 160.

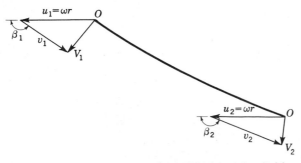

**Fig. 9.18** Velocity diagrams for entrance and exit of a propeller turbine blade at fixed radial distance.

The windmill is a form of axial-flow turbine.   It has no fixed vanes to give an initial tangential component to the air stream and hence must impart the tangential component to the air with the moving vanes.   The air stream expands in passing through the vanes with a reduction in its axial velocity.

**example 9.7**   Assuming uniform axial velocity over section 2 of Fig. 9.9 and using the data of Example 9.2, determine the angle of the leading edge of the propeller at $r = 0.75$, 1.50, and 2.0 ft, for a propeller speed of 240 rpm.

At $r = 0.75$,

$u = \frac{240}{60} \times 2\pi \times 0.75 = 18.88$ ft/sec
$V_u = 30.1$ ft/sec

At $r = 1.50$,

$u = \frac{240}{60} \times 2\pi \times 1.50 = 37.76$ ft/sec
$V_u = 15.05$ ft/sec

At $r = 2.00$,

$u = \frac{240}{60} \times 2\pi \times 2.00 = 50.2$ ft/sec
$V_u = 11.3$ ft/sec

The discharge through the turbine is, from section 1,

$Q = 2 \times 4\pi \times 2 \times 8 \cos 45° = 284.5$ cfs

Hence, the axial velocity at section 2 is

$$V_a = \frac{284.5}{\pi[2^2 - (0.75)^2]} = 26.3 \text{ ft/sec}$$

Figure 9.19 shows the initial vane angle for the three positions.

**Fig. 9.19**  Velocity diagrams for angle of leading edge of a propeller turbine blade.

Moody[1] has developed a formula to estimate the efficiency of a unit of a homologous series of turbines when the efficiency of one of the series is known:

$$e = 1 - (1 - e_1)\left(\frac{D_1}{D}\right)^{1/4} \tag{9.5.2}$$

in which $e_1$ and $D_1$ are usually efficiency and diameter of a model.

### 9.6   pumps and blowers

Pumps add energy to liquids and blowers to gases.   The procedure for designing them is the same for both, except for those cases in which the density is appreciably increased.   Turbopumps and -blowers are *radial-flow*, *axial-flow*, or a combination of the two, called *mixed-flow*.   For high heads the radial (centrifugal) pump, frequently with two or more stages (two or more impellers in series), is best adapted.   A double-suction general-service centrifugal pump is shown in Fig. 9.20.   For large flows under

---

[1] Lewis F. Moody, The Propeller Type Turbine, *Trans. ASCE*, vol. 89, p. 628, 1926.

**Fig. 9.20**   Cross section of a single-stage double-suction centrifugal pump.   (*Ingersoll-Rand Co.*)

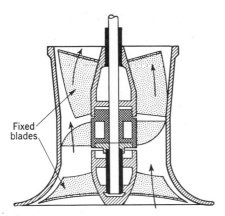

**Fig. 9.21** Axial-flow pump. (*Ingersoll-Rand Co.*)

small heads the axial-flow pump or blower (Fig. 9.21) is best suited.    The mixed-flow pump (Fig. 9.22) is used for medium head and medium discharge.

The equations developed in Sec. 9.2 apply just as well to pumps and blowers as to turbines.    The usual centrifugal pump has a suction, or inlet, pipe leading to the center of the impeller, a radial outward-flow runner, as in Fig. 9.23, and a collection pipe or spiral casing that guides the fluid to the discharge pipe.    Ordinarily, no fixed vanes are used, except for multistage units in which the flow is relatively small and the additional fluid friction is less than the additional gain in conversion of kinetic energy to pressure energy upon leaving the impeller.

**Fig. 9.22** Mixed-flow pump. (*Ingersoll-Rand Co.*)

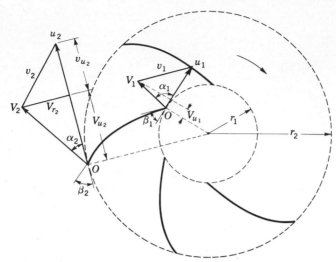

**Fig. 9.23**  Velocity relationships for flow through a centrifugal pump impeller.

**Fig. 9.24**  Sectional elevation of Eagle Mountain and Hayfield pumps, Colorado River Aqueduct.  (*Worthington Corp.*)

**Fig. 9.25**  Impeller types used in pumps and blowers.  (*Worthington Corp.*)

Figure 9.24 shows a sectional elevation of a large centrifugal pump. For lower heads and greater discharges (relatively) the impellers vary as shown in Fig. 9.25, from high head at left to low head at right with the axial-flow impeller.  The specific speed increases from left to right.  A chart for determining the types of pump for best efficiency is given in Fig. 9.26 for water.

Centrifugal and mixed-flow pumps are designed in the specific speed range 500 to 6500 and axial pumps from 5000 to 11,000; speed is expressed in revolutions per minute, discharge in gallons per minute, and head in feet.

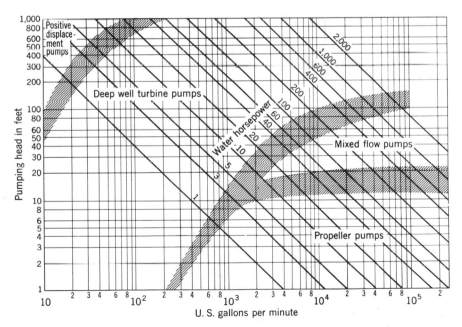

**Fig. 9.26**  Chart for selection of type of pump.  (*Fairbanks, Morse & Co.*)

**Fig. 9.27** Characteristic curves for typical centrifugal pump. 10-in. impeller, 1750 rpm. (*Ingersoll-Rand Co.*)

Characteristic curves showing head, efficiency, and brake horsepower as a function of discharge for a typical centrifugal pump with backward-curved vanes are given in Fig. 9.27. Pumps are not so efficient as turbines, in general, owing to the inherently high losses that result from conversion of kinetic energy into flow energy.

*theoretical head-discharge curve*

A theoretical head-discharge curve may be obtained by use of Eq. (9.3.8) and the vector diagrams of Fig. 9.8. From the exit diagram of Fig. 9.8

$$V_2 \cos \alpha_2 = V_{u2} = u_2 - V_{r2} \cot \beta_2$$

From the discharge, if $b_2$ is the width of the impeller at $r_2$ and vane thickness is neglected,

$$Q = 2\pi r_2 b_2 V_{r2}$$

By eliminating $V_{r2}$ and substituting these last two equations into Eq. (9.3.8),

$$H = \frac{u_2{}^2}{g} - \frac{u_2 Q \cot \beta_2}{2\pi r_2 b_2 g} \tag{9.6.1}$$

For a given pump and speed, $H$ varies linearly with $Q$, as shown in Fig. 9.28. The usual design of centrifugal pump has $\beta_2 < 90°$, which gives

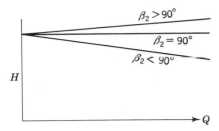

**Fig. 9.28** Theoretical head-discharge curves.

decreasing head with increasing discharge.  For blades radial at the exit, $\beta_2 = 90°$ and the theoretical head is independent of discharge.  For blades curved forward, $\beta_2 > 90°$ and the head rises with discharge.

*actual head-discharge curve*

By subtracting head losses from the theoretical head-discharge curve, the actual head-discharge curve is obtained.  The most important subtraction is not an actual loss, but a failure of the finite number of blades to impart the relative velocity with angle $\beta_2$ of the blades.  Without perfect guidance (infinite number of blades) the fluid actually is discharged as if the blades had an angle $\beta_2'$ which is less than $\beta_2$ (Fig. 9.29) for the same discharge. This inability of the blades to impart proper guidance reduces $V_{u2}$ and hence decreases the actual head produced.  This is called *circulatory flow* and is shown in Fig. 9.30.  Fluid friction in flow through the fixed and moving passages causes losses that are proportional to the square of the discharge.  They are shown in Fig. 9.30.  The final head loss to consider is that of turbulence, the loss due to improper relative-velocity angle at the blade inlet.  The pump can be designed for one discharge (at a given speed) at which the relative velocity is tangent to the blade at the inlet. This is the point of best efficiency, and shock or turbulence losses are negligible.  For other discharges the loss varies about as the square of

**Fig. 9.29** Effect of circulatory flow.

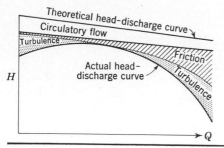

**Fig. 9.30**  Head-discharge relationships.

the discrepancy in approach angle, as shown in Fig. 9.30.   The final lower line then represents the actual head-discharge curve.   Shutoff head is usually about $u_2^2/2g$, or half of the theoretical shutoff head.

In addition to the head losses and reductions, pumps and blowers have torque losses due to bearing and packing friction and disk friction losses from the fluid between the moving impeller and housing.   Internal leakage is also an important power loss, in that fluid which has passed through the impeller, with its energy increased, escapes through clearances and flows back to the suction side of the impeller.

**example 9.8**   A centrifugal water pump has an impeller (Fig. 9.23) with $r_2 = 12$ in., $r_1 = 4$ in., $\beta_1 = 20°$, $\beta_2 = 10°$.   The impeller is 2 in. wide at $r = r_1$ and $\frac{3}{4}$ in. wide at $r = r_2$.   For 1800 rpm, neglecting losses and vane thickness, determine ($a$) the discharge for shockless entrance when $\alpha_1 = 90°$; ($b$) $\alpha_2$ and the theoretical head $H$; ($c$) the hosepower required; and ($d$) the pressure rise through the impeller.

($a$)   The peripheral speeds are

$$u_1 = \tfrac{1800}{60} \times 2\pi \times \tfrac{1}{3} = 62.8 \text{ ft/sec} \qquad u_2 = 3u_1 = 188.5 \text{ ft/sec}$$

The vector diagrams are shown in Fig. 9.31.   With $u_1$ and the angles $\alpha_1, \beta_1$ known, the entrance diagram is determined, $V_1 = u_1 \tan 20° = 22.85$

**Fig. 9.31**  Vector diagrams for entrance and exit of pump impeller.

ft/sec; hence

$$Q = 22.85 \times \pi \times \tfrac{2}{3} \times \tfrac{2}{12} = 7.97 \text{ cfs}$$

(b)   At the exit the radial velocity $V_{r2}$ is

$$V_{r2} = \frac{7.97 \times 12}{2\pi \times 0.75} = 20.3 \text{ ft/sec}$$

By drawing $u_2$ (Fig. 9.31) and a parallel line, distance $V_{r2}$ from it, the vector triangle is determined when $\beta_2$ is laid off.   Thus

$$v_{u2} = 20.3 \cot 10° = 115 \qquad V_{u2} = 188.5 - 115 = 73.5$$

$$\alpha_2 = \tan^{-1} \frac{20.3}{73.5} = 15°26' \qquad V_2 = 20.3 \csc 15°26' = 76.2$$

From Eq. (9.3.8)

$$H = \frac{u_2 V_2 \cos \alpha_2}{g} = \frac{u_2 V_{u2}}{g} = \frac{188.5 \times 73.5}{32.2} = 430 \text{ ft}$$

(c)   $\text{hp} = \dfrac{Q\gamma H}{550} = \dfrac{7.97 \times 62.4 \times 430}{550} = 388$

(d)   By applying the energy equation from entrance to exit of the impeller, including the energy $H$ added (elevation change across impeller may be neglected),

$$H + \frac{V_1{}^2}{2g} + \frac{p_1}{\gamma} = \frac{V_2{}^2}{2g} + \frac{p_2}{\gamma}$$

and

$$\frac{p_2 - p_1}{\gamma} = 430 + \frac{(22.85)^2}{64.4} - \frac{(76.2)^2}{64.4} = 348 \text{ ft}$$

or

$$p_2 - p_1 = 348 \times 0.433 = 151 \text{ psi}$$

## 9.7  centrifugal compressors

Centrifugal compressors operate according to the same principles as turbomachines for liquids.  It is important for the fluid to enter the impeller without shock, i.e., with the relative velocity tangent to the blade. Work is done on the gas by rotation of the vanes, the moment-of-momentum equation relating torque to production of tangential velocity.   At the impeller exit the high-velocity gas must have its kinetic energy converted in part to flow energy by suitable expanding flow passages. For adiabatic compression (no cooling of the gas) the actual work $w_a$ of compression per unit mass is compared with the work $w_{th}$ per unit mass to compress the gas to the same pressure isentropically. For cooled compressors the work $w_{th}$ is based on the isothermal work of compression to the same pressure as the actual case. Hence

$$\eta = \frac{w_{th}}{w_a} \tag{9.7.1}$$

is the formula for efficiency of a compressor.

The efficiency formula for compression of a perfect gas is developed for the adiabatic compressor, assuming no internal leakage in the machine, i.e., no "short-circuiting" of high-pressure fluid back to the low-pressure end of the impeller. Centrifugal compressors are usually multistage, with pressure ratios up to 3 across a single stage. From the moment-of-momentum equation (9.3.2) with inlet absolute velocity radial, $\alpha_1 = 90°$, the theoretical torque $T_{th}$ is

$$T_{th} = \dot{m} V_{u2} u_2 \tag{9.7.2}$$

in which $\dot{m}$ is the mass per unit time being compressed, $V_{u2}$ is the tangential component of the absolute velocity leaving the impeller, and $r_2$ is the impeller radius at exit. The actual applied torque $T_a$ is greater than the theoretical torque by the torque losses due to bearing and packing friction plus disk friction; hence

$$T_{th} = T_a \eta_m \tag{9.7.3}$$

if $\eta_m$ is the mechanical efficiency of the compressor.

In addition to the torque losses, there are irreversibilities due to flow through the machine. The actual work of compression through the adiabatic machine is obtained from the steady-flow energy equation (3.7.1), neglecting elevation changes and replacing $u + p/\rho$ by $h$,

$$-w_a = \frac{V_{2a}^2 - V_1^2}{2} + h_2 - h_1 \tag{9.7.4}$$

The isentropic work of compression may be obtained from Eq. (3.7.1) in differential form, neglecting the $z$-terms,

$$-dw_{th} = V\,dV + d\frac{p}{\rho} + du$$

$$= V\,dV + \frac{dp}{\rho} + p\,d\frac{1}{\rho} + du$$

The last two terms are equal to $T\,ds$ from Eq. (3.7.6), which is zero for isentropic flow, so that

$$-dw_{th} = V\,dV + \frac{dp}{\rho} \tag{9.7.5}$$

By integrating for $p/\rho^k = $ const between sections 1 and 2,

$$-w_{th} = \frac{V_{2th}{}^2 - V_1{}^2}{2} + \frac{k}{k-1}\frac{p_2}{\rho_{2th}} - \frac{p_1}{\rho_1} = \frac{V_{2th}{}^2 - V_1{}^2}{2}$$
$$+ c_p T_1\left[\left(\frac{p_2}{p_1}\right)^{(k-1)/k} - 1\right] \tag{9.7.6}$$

The efficiency may now be written as

$$\eta = \frac{-w_{th}}{-w_a} = \frac{[(V_{2th}{}^2 - V_1{}^2)/2] + c_p T_1[(p_2/p_1)^{(k-1)/k} - 1]}{[(V_{2a}{}^2 - V_1{}^2)/2] + c_p(T_{2a} - T_1)} \tag{9.7.7}$$

since $h = c_p T$. In terms of Eqs. (9.7.2) and (9.7.3)

$$-w_a = \frac{T_a\omega}{\dot{m}} = \frac{T_{th}\omega}{\eta_m \dot{m}} = \frac{V_{u2}r_2\omega}{\eta_m} = \frac{V_{u2}u_2}{\eta_m} \tag{9.7.8}$$

then

$$\eta = \frac{\eta_m}{V_{u2}u_2}\left\{ c_p T_1\left[\left(\frac{p_2}{p_1}\right)^{(k-1)/k} - 1\right] + \frac{V_{2th}{}^2 - V_1{}^2}{2}\right\} \tag{9.7.9}$$

Use of this equation is made in the following example.

**example 9.9** An adiabatic turbocompressor has blades that are radial at the exit of its 6.0-in.-diameter impeller. It is compressing 1.0 $lb_m$/sec air at 14.0 psia, $t = 60°F$, to 42.0 psia. The entrance area is 0.07 ft², and the exit area 0.04 ft². $\eta = 0.75$; $\eta_m = 0.90$. Determine the rotational speed of the impeller and the actual temperature of air at the exit.

The density at the inlet is

$$\rho_1 = \frac{p_1}{RT_1} = \frac{14.0 \times 144}{53.3 \times 32.17(460 + 60)} = 0.00226 \text{ slug/ft}^3$$

and the velocity at the entrance is

$$V_1 = \frac{\dot{m}}{\rho_1 A_1} = \frac{1.0}{32.17} \times \frac{1}{0.00226} \times \frac{1}{0.07} = 196.4 \text{ ft/sec}$$

The theoretical density at the exit is

$$\rho_{2th} = \rho_1\left(\frac{p_2}{p_1}\right)^{1/k} = 0.00226 \times 3^{1/1.4} = 0.00496 \text{ slug/ft}^3$$

and the theoretical velocity at the exit is

$$V_{2th} = \frac{\dot{m}}{\rho_{2th}A_2} = \frac{1}{32.17} \times \frac{1}{0.00496} \times \frac{1}{0.04} = 156.5 \text{ ft/sec}$$

For radial vanes at the exit, $V_{u2} = u_2 = \omega r_2$.   From Eq. (9.7.9)

$$u_2{}^2 = \frac{\eta_m}{\eta} \left\{ c_p T_1 \left[ \left(\frac{p_2}{p_1}\right)^{(k-1)/k} - 1 \right] + \frac{V_{2th}{}^2 - V_1{}^2}{2} \right\}$$

$$= \frac{0.90}{0.75} \left[ 0.24 \times 778 \times 32.17(460 + 60)(3^{(1.4-1)/1.4} - 1) \right.$$

$$\left. + \frac{(156.5)^2 - (196.4)^2}{2} \right]$$

and $u_2 = 1173$ ft/sec.   Then

$$\omega = \frac{u_2}{r_2} = \frac{1173}{\frac{3}{12}} = 4692 \text{ rad/sec}$$

and

$$N = \frac{\omega}{2\pi} 60 = \frac{4692}{2\pi} 60 = 44,800 \text{ rpm}$$

The theoretical work $w_{th}$ is the term in the brackets in the expression for $u_2{}^2$.   It is $-w_{th} = 1.147 \times 10^6$ ft-lb/slug.   Then from Eq. (9.7.1)

$$w_a = \frac{w_{th}}{\eta} = -\frac{1.147 \times 10^6}{0.75} = -1.53 \times 10^6 \text{ ft-lb/slug}$$

Since the kinetic-energy term is small, Eq. (9.7.4) may be solved for $h_2 - h_1$ and a trial solution effected,

$$h_2 - h_1 = c_p(T_{2a} - T_1) = 1.53 \times 10^6 + \frac{(196.4)^2 - V_{2a}{}^2}{2}$$

As a first approximation, let $V_{2a} = V_{2th} = 156.5$, then

$$T_{2a} = 520 + \frac{1}{0.24 \times 778 \times 32.17} \left[ 1.53 \times 10^6 + \frac{(196.4)^2 - (156.5)^2}{2} \right]$$

$$= 776°R$$

For this temperature the density at the exit is 0.00454 slug/ft³ and the velocity is 171 ft/sec.   Insertion of this value in place of 156.5 reduces the temperature by about 1°; hence $T_{2a} = 775°R$.

## 9.8  fluid couplings and fluid torque converters

The *fluid coupling* is a centrifugal pump and a turbine built together into a single housing to avoid losses by eliminating piping or channels that would otherwise be needed to connect them.    There is no solid connection between the pump and the turbine (Fig. 9.32); the liquid, usually oil, transmits the torque by carrying moment of momentum across from pump to turbine.    The coupling has two principal advantages: (*a*) smoothness of operation, since torsional vibrations are not transmitted through it; and (*b*) the full torque is not developed until the unit is up to speed, which is desirable for both electric motors and internal-combustion engines with heavy inertial loads.

Application of the moment-of-momentum equation [Eq. (9.3.1)] produces the relation between torque developed and change in moment of momentum for either the pump or the turbine.    The torque must be the same for both when the operating conditions are steady, since there are no stationary members to absorb torque and no angular acceleration. When the coupling and a portion of the driven and driving shafts are considered as a free body, the angular acceleration is zero for steady conditions; hence, the summation of torques acting on the free body must be zero, and the torque in the driven shaft is exactly the same as the torque in the driving shaft.

In the operation of the coupling, consider that the driven member is

**Fig. 9.32** Fluid coupling, Foettinger type.  (*David Taylor Model Basin, U.S. Navy Dept.*)

first stationary and the driving member is rotating at its design speed. Liquid enters the pump near the shaft and is given moment of momentum as it traverses radially outward and flows into the turbine at its outer edge. The moment of momentum of the fluid is reduced to zero in the stationary turbine and the fluid exerts the torque supplied by the driving shaft. As the driven shaft comes up to speed, centrifugal action in the turbine creates a resistance to flow that reduces the amount of liquid pumped. No pumping takes place when both shafts rotate at the same speed and, hence, no torque is transmitted. Since the unit is symmetrical, the driven shaft when turning at greater speed than the driving shaft transmits a torque to the driving shaft that in effect provides a braking action. For normal steady operation there must always be a difference in speed, or *slip*, if torque is to be transmitted. The efficiency $e$ is work out divided by work in, or

$$e = \frac{T\omega_t}{T\omega_p} = \frac{\omega_t}{\omega_p} = 1 - s \tag{9.8.1}$$

in which $T$ is the torque, $\omega_p$ the driving-shaft speed, $\omega_t$ the driven-shaft speed, and $s$ the slip, or $(\omega_p - \omega_t)/\omega_p$.

The larger the diameter of coupling, the less the slip required to transmit a given torque and, hence, the greater the efficiency of the coupling. Since efficiency can thus be increased by simply increasing diameter, no effort is made to curve the vanes or round their leading edges to decrease turbulence or fluid shock upon entering the vanes. Efficiencies are above 95 per cent.

In some applications in which variable torque transmission is desired, the amount of oil in the coupling is varied.

The *fluid torque converter* (Fig. 9.33) is in many ways similar to a fluid coupling. It has a *fixed* vane system, however, that transmits torque to the earth, and it always operates completely filled with liquid.

For steady conditions of operation there is no angular acceleration, and the summation of all torques acting on the unit must be zero. Since there is a stationary vane system that requires an outside torque $T_f$ to hold it fixed, the torques in the driving and driven shafts are no longer equal. For example, if the stationary vanes are curved so that the liquid acts to rotate them in the sense opposite to that of the driving shaft, there is a torque multiplication with the torque in the driven shaft equal to the sum of torque in driving shaft and torque on the fixed vanes, and with a corresponding decrease in speed of driven shaft.

By the proper designing of the fixed vane system there may be either a torque multiplication or a torque division. Since no work is done on the fixed vanes, the work output to the driven shaft must equal the work input

Stationary reaction vanes

Turbine

Stationary casing

Pump

Driving shaft

Driven shaft

**Fig. 9.33** Torque converter.

to the driving shaft less the losses. A single-stage torque converter is shown in Fig. 9.33. Maximum efficiency is less than for a fluid coupling, usually between 80 and 90 per cent.

As in the case of a reaction turbine, where fixed guide vanes create moment of momentum that is reduced by moving vanes to create torque on a rotating shaft, the fixed vanes of a torque converter are curved to give the liquid moment of momentum. The pump adds to this moment of momentum, and the turbine, by proper design and a speed much less than the pump, takes the moment of momentum out of the liquid and thus has a large torque exerted on it. When large torque multiplication is desired, the torque converter usually is designed with two or more sets of turbine vanes with fixed vanes or pump vanes between them, as in Fig. 9.34.

By use of a *freewheeling* arrangement on the fixed guide vanes that permit them to rotate in one direction when torque is applied in that direction, the torque converter becomes a fluid coupling. When there is a large difference in speed of pump and turbine, torque conversion is required and the reaction (fixed) vanes have a torque exerted on them that holds them stationary. As the pump and turbine speeds become nearly the same, the turbine moves so that the fluid discharged from it causes the reaction

**Fig. 9.34** Torque converter with two-stage turbine. $(a_1)$ First-stage turbine; $(a_2)$ second-stage turbine; $(b)$ pump; $(c)$ stationary guide vanes; $(d)$ maximum diameter of circuit. (*David Taylor Model Basin, U.S. Navy Dept.*)

vanes to freewheel, or take no part in the process, resulting in a fluid coupling with better efficiency than that of the torque converter.

### 9.9 cavitation

When a liquid flows into a region where its pressure is reduced to vapor pressure, it boils and vapor pockets develop in the liquid. The vapor bubbles are carried along with the liquid until a region of higher pressure is reached, where they suddenly collapse. This process is called *cavitation*. If the vapor bubbles are near to (or in contact with) a solid boundary when they collapse, the forces exerted by the liquid rushing into the cavities create very high localized pressures that cause pitting of the solid surface. The phenomenon is accompanied by noise and vibrations that have been described as similar to gravel going through a centrifugal pump.

In a flowing liquid, the *cavitation parameter* $\sigma$ is useful in characterizing the susceptibility of the system to cavitate. It is defined by

$$\sigma = \frac{p - p_v}{\rho V^2/2} \tag{9.9.1}$$

in which $p$ is the absolute pressure at the point of interest, $p_v$ is the vapor pressure of the liquid, $\rho$ is the density of the liquid, and $V$ is the undisturbed, or reference, velocity.   The cavitation parameter is a form of pressure coefficient.   In two geometrically similar systems, they would be equally likely to cavitate or would have the same degree of cavitation for the same value of $\sigma$.   When $\sigma = 0$, the pressure is reduced to vapor pressure and boiling should occur.

Tests made on chemically pure liquids show that they will sustain high tensile stresses, of the order of thousands of pounds per square inch, which is in contradiction to the concept of cavities forming when pressure is reduced to vapor pressure.   Since there is generally spontaneous boiling when vapor pressure is reached with commercial or technical liquids, it is generally accepted that nuclei must be present around which the vapor bubbles form and grow.   The nature of the nuclei is not thoroughly understood, but they may be microscopic dust particles or other contaminants, which are widely dispersed through technical liquids.

Cavitation bubbles may form on nuclei, grow, then move into an area of higher pressure and collapse, all in a few thousandths of a second in flow within a turbomachine.   In aerated water the bubbles have been photographed as they move through several oscillations, but this phenomenon does not seem to occur in nonaerated liquids.   Surface tension of the vapor bubbles appears to be an important property accounting for the high-pressure pulses resulting from collapse of a vapor bubble.   Recent experiments indicate pressures of the order of 200,000 psi based on the analysis of strain waves in a photoelastic specimen exposed to cavitation.[1]   Pressures of this magnitude appear to be reasonable, in line with the observed mechanical damage caused by cavitation.

The formation and collapse of great numbers of bubbles on a surface subject that surface to intense local stressing, which appears to damage the surface by fatigue.   Some ductile materials withstand battering for a period, called the incubation period, before damage is noticeable, while brittle materials may lose weight immediately.   There may be certain electrochemical, corrosive, and thermal effects which hasten the deterioration of exposed surfaces.   Rheingans[2] has collected a series of measurements made by magnetostriction-oscillator tests, showing weight losses of various metals used in hydraulic machines (see Table 9.1).

Protection against cavitation should start with the hydraulic design of the system in order to avoid the low pressures if practicable.   Otherwise, use of special cavitation-resistant materials or coatings may be effective.

---

[1] G. W. Sutton, A Photoelastic Study of Strain Waves Caused by Cavitation, *J. Appl. Mech.*, vol. 24, part 3, pp. 340–348, 1957.

[2] W. J. Rheingans, Selecting Materials to Avoid Cavitation Damage, *Mater. Design Eng.*, pp. 102–106, 1958.

**Table 9.1   Weight loss in materials used in hydraulic machines**

| Alloy | Weight loss after 2 hr, mg |
|---|---|
| Rolled stellite† | 0.6 |
| Welded aluminum bronze‡ | 3.2 |
| Cast aluminum bronze§ | 5.8 |
| Welded stainless steel (two layers, 17% Cr, 7% Ni) | 6.0 |
| Hot-rolled stainless steel (26% Cr, 13% Ni) | 8.0 |
| Tempered, rolled stainless steel (12% Cr) | 9.0 |
| Cast stainless steel (18% Cr, 8% Ni) | 13.0 |
| Cast stainless steel (12% Cr) | 20.0 |
| Cast manganese bronze | 80.0 |
| Welded mild steel | 97.0 |
| Plate steel | 98.0 |
| Cast steel | 105.0 |
| Aluminum | 124.0 |
| Brass | 156.0 |
| Cast iron | 224.0 |

† This material is not suitable for ordinary use, in spite of its high resistance, because of its high cost and difficulty in machining.

‡ Ampco-Trode 200: 83% Cu, 10.3% Al, 5.8% Fe.

§ Ampco 20: 83.1% Cu, 12.4% Al, 4.1% Fe.

Small amounts of air entrained into water systems have markedly reduced cavitation damage, and recent studies indicate that cathodic protection is helpful.

The formation of vapor cavities decreases the useful channel space for liquid and thus decreases the efficiency of a fluid machine.   Cavitation causes three undesirable conditions: lowered efficiency, damage to flow passages, and noise and vibrations.   Curved vanes are particularly susceptible to cavitation on their convex sides and may have localized areas where cavitation causes pitting or failure, as in Fig. 9.35.   All turbomachinery, ship propellers, and many hydraulic structures are subject to cavitation; hence, attention must be given to it in the designing of all of these.

A *cavitation index σ′* is useful in the proper selection of turbomachinery, and in its location with respect to suction or tailwater elevation.   The minimum pressure in a pump or turbine generally occurs along the convex side of vanes near the suction side of the impeller.   In Fig. 9.36, if $e$ be the point of minimum pressure, Bernoulli's equation applied between $e$ and the downstream liquid surface, neglecting losses between the two points, may

**Fig. 9.35** Cavitation damage to a Francis runner. (*Ingersoll-Rand Co.*)

be written

$$\frac{p_e}{\gamma} + \frac{V_e{}^2}{2g} + H_s = \frac{p_a}{\gamma} + 0 + 0$$

in which $p_a$ is the atmospheric pressure and $p_e$ the absolute pressure. For cavitation to occur at $e$, the pressure must be equal to or less than $p_v$, the vapor pressure. If $p_e = p_v$,

$$\sigma' = \frac{V_e{}^2}{2gH} = \frac{p_a - p_v - \gamma H_s}{\gamma H} \tag{9.9.2}$$

**Fig. 9.36** Turbine or pump setting.

is the ratio of energy available at $e$ to total energy $H$, since the only energy is kinetic energy. The ratio $\sigma'$ is a cavitation index or number. The critical value $\sigma_c$ may be determined by a test on a model of the homologous series. For cavitationless performance, the suction setting $H_s$ for an impeller installation must be so fixed that the resulting value of $\sigma'$ is greater than that of $\sigma_c$.

**example 9.10**    Tests on a pump model indicate a $\sigma_c = 0.10$. A homologous unit is to be installed at a location where $p_a = 13$ psi and $p_v = 0.50$ psi and is to pump water against a head of 80 ft. What is the maximum permissible suction head?

By solving Eq. (9.9.2) for $H_s$, and after substituting the values of $\sigma_c$, $H$, $p_a$, and $p_v$,

$$H_s = \frac{p_a - p_v}{\gamma} - \sigma'H = \frac{13 - 0.50}{0.433} - 0.10 \times 80 = 20.8 \text{ ft}$$

The less the value of $H_s$, the greater the value of the plant $\sigma'$, and the greater the assurance against cavitation.

The *net positive suction head (NPSH)* is frequently used in the specification of minimum suction conditions for a turbomachine. It is

$$NPSH = \frac{V_e^2}{2g} = \frac{p_a - p_v - \gamma H_s}{\gamma} \qquad (9.9.3)$$

A test is run on the machine to determine the maximum value of $H_s$ for operation of the machine with no impairment of efficiency and without objectionable noise or damage. Then, from this test $NPSH$ is calculated from Eq. (9.9.3). Any setting of this machine where the suction lift is less than $H_s$, as found from Eq. (9.9.3), is then acceptable. Note that $H_s$ is positive when the suction reservoir is below the turbomachine, as in Fig. 9.36.

A *suction specific speed* $S$ for homologous units may be formulated. By elimination of $D_e$ in the two equations

$$NPSH = \frac{V_e^2}{2g} \sim \frac{Q^2}{D_4} \qquad \frac{Q^2}{ND_e^3} = \text{const}$$

$S$ is obtained,

$$S = \frac{N\sqrt{Q}}{(NPSH)^{3/4}} \qquad (9.9.4)$$

When different units of a series are operating under cavitating conditions, equal values of $S$ indicate a similar degree of cavitation. When cavitation is not present, the equation is not valid.

**problems**

**9.1**  By use of Eqs. (9.1.1) and (9.1.3) together with $P = \gamma Q H$ for power, develop the homologous relationship for $P$ in terms of speed and diameter.

**9.2**  A centrifugal pump is driven by an induction motor that reduces in speed as the pump load increases.  A test determines several sets of values of $N, Q, H$ for the pump.  How is a characteristic curve of the pump for a constant speed determined from these data?

**9.3**  What is the specific speed of the pump of Example 9.1 at its point of best efficiency?

**9.4**  Plot the dimensionless characteristic curve of the pump of Example 9.1.  On this same curve plot several points from the characteristics of the new (52-in.) pump.  Why are they not exactly on the same curve?

**9.5**  Determine the size and synchronous speed of a pump homologous to the 72-in. pump of Example 9.1 that will produce 120 cfs at 300 ft head at its point of best efficiency.

**9.6**  Develop the characteristic curve for a homologous pump of the series of Example 9.1 for 18-in. discharge and 1800 rpm.

**9.7**  A pump with an 8-in.-diameter impeller discharges 2000 gpm at 1140 rpm and 30 ft head at its point of best efficiency.  What is its specific speed?

**9.8**  A hydroelectric site has a head of 300 ft and an average discharge of 400 cfs.  For a generator speed of 200 rpm, what specific speed turbine is needed?  Assume an efficiency of 92 per cent.

**9.9**  A model turbine, $N_s = 36$, with a 14-in.-diameter impeller develops 27 hp at a head of 44 ft and an efficiency of 86 per cent.  What are the discharge and speed of the model?

**9.10**  What size and synchronous speed of homologous unit of Prob. 9.9 would be needed to discharge 600 cfs at 260 ft of head?

**9.11**  800 cfs water flowing through the fixed vanes of a turbine has a tangential component of 6 ft/sec at a radius of 4 ft.  The impeller, turning at 180 rpm, discharges in an axial direction.  What torque is exerted on the impeller?

**9.12**  In Prob. 9.11, neglecting losses, what is the head on the turbine?

**9.13**  A generator with speed $N = 240$ rpm is to be used with a turbine at a site where $H = 400$ ft and $Q = 300$ cfs.  Neglecting losses, what tangential component must be given to the water at $r = 3$ ft by the fixed vanes?  What torque is exerted on the impeller?  How much horsepower is produced?

**9.14** A site for a Pelton wheel has a steady flow of 2 cfs with a nozzle velocity of 240 ft/sec. With a blade angle of 174°, and $C_v = 0.98$, for 60-cycle power, determine (a) the diameter of wheel, (b) the speed, (c) the horsepower, (d) the energy remaining in the water. Neglect losses.

**9.15** An impulse wheel is to be used to develop 50 cycle/sec power at a site where $H = 400$ ft and $Q = 2.7$ cfs. Determine the diameter of the wheel and its speed. $C_v = 0.97$; $e = 82$ per cent.

**9.16** At what angle should the wicket gates of a turbine be set to extract 12,000 hp from a flow of 900 cfs? The diameter of the opening just inside the wicket gates is 12 ft, and the height is 3 ft. The turbine runs at 200 rpm, and flow leaves the runner in an axial direction.

**9.17** For a given setting of wicket gates how does the moment of momentum vary with the discharge?

**9.18** Assuming constant axial velocity just above the runner of the propeller turbine of Prob. 9.16, calculate the tangential velocity components if the hub radius is 1 ft and the outer radius is 3 ft.

**9.19** Determine the vane angles $\beta_1$, $\beta_2$ for entrance and exit from the propeller turbine of Prob. 9.18 so that no angular momentum remains in the flow. (Compute the angles for inner radius, outer radius, and midpoint.)

**9.20** Neglecting losses, what is the head on the turbine of Prob. 9.16?

**9.21** The hydraulic efficiency of a turbine is 95 per cent, and its theoretical head is 290 ft. What is the actual head required?

**9.22** A turbine model test with 10-in.-diameter impeller showed an efficiency of 90 per cent. What efficiency could be expected from a 48-in.-diameter impeller?

**9.23** A turbine draft tube (Fig. 9.37) expands from 6 to 18 ft diameter. At section 1 the velocity is 30 ft/sec for vapor pressure of 1 ft and barometric pressure of 32 ft of water. Determine $h_s$ for incipient cavitation (pressure equal to vapor pressure at section 1).

**9.24** Construct a theoretical head-discharge curve for the following specifications of a centrifugal pump: $r_1 = 2$ in., $r_2 = 4$ in., $b_1 = 1$ in., $b_2 = \frac{3}{4}$ in., $N = 1200$ rpm, and $\beta_2 = 30°$.

**9.25** A centrifugal water pump (Fig. 9.23) has an impeller $r_1 = 2.5$ in., $b_1 = 1\frac{3}{8}$ in., $r_2 = 4.5$ in., $b_2 = \frac{3}{4}$ in., $\beta_1 = 30°$, $\beta_2 = 45°$ ($b_1$, $b_2$ are impeller width at $r_1$ and $r_2$, respectively). Neglect thickness of vanes. For 1800 rpm, calculate (a) the design discharge for no prerotation of entering fluid, (b) $\alpha_2$ and the theoretical head at point of best efficiency, and (c) for hydraulic efficiency of 85 per cent and over-all efficiency of 78 per cent, the

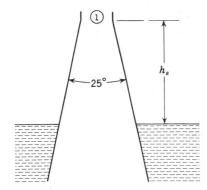

**Fig. 9.37**

actual head produced, losses in foot-pounds per pound, and brake horse-power.

**9.26** A centrifugal pump has an impeller with dimensions $r_1 = 3$ in., $r_2 = 6$ in., $b_1 = 2.0$ in., $b_2 = 1.25$ in., $\beta_1 = \beta_2 = 30°$. For a discharge of 2 cfs and shockless entry to vanes compute (a) the speed, (b) the head, (c) the torque, (d) the horsepower, and (e) the pressure rise across impeller. Neglect losses. $\alpha_1 = 90°$.

**9.27** A centrifugal water pump with impeller dimensions $r_1 = 2$ in., $r_2 = 5$ in., $b_1 = 3.0$ in., $b_2 = 1$ in., $\beta_2 = 60°$ is to pump 5 cfs at 64 ft head. Determine (a) $\beta_1$, (b) the speed, (c) the horsepower, and (d) the pressure rise across the impeller. Neglect losses, and assume no shock at the entrance. $\alpha_1 = 90°$.

**9.28** Select values of $r_1$, $r_2$, $\beta_1$, $\beta_2$, $b_1$, and $b_2$ of a centrifugal impeller to take 1 cfs water from a 4-in.-diameter suction line and increase its energy by 40 ft-lb/lb. $N = 1200$ rpm; $\alpha_1 = 90°$. Neglect losses.

**9.29** A pump has blade angles $\beta_1 = \beta_2$; $b_1 = 2b_2 = 1.0$ in.; $r_1 = r_2/3 = 2$ in. For a theoretical head of 95.2 ft at a discharge at best efficiency of 1.052 cfs, determine the blade angles and speed of the pump. Neglect thickness of vanes and assume perfect guidance. (*Hint:* Write down every relation you know connecting $\beta_1$, $\beta_2$, $b_1$, $b_2$, $r_1$, $r_2$, $u_1$, $u_2$, $H_{th}$, $Q$, $V_{r2}$, $V_{u2}$, $V_1$, $\omega$, and $N$ from the two velocity vector diagrams, and by substitution reduce to one unknown.)

**9.30** A mercury-water differential manometer, $R' = 26$ in., is connected from the 4-in.-diameter suction pipe to the 3-in.-diameter discharge pipe of a pump. The center line of the suction pipe is 1 ft below the discharge pipe. For $Q = 900$ gpm water, calculate the head developed by the pump.

**Fig. 9.38**

**9.31**  The impeller for a blower (Fig. 9.38) is 18 in. wide.   It has straight blades and turns at 1200 rpm.   For 10,000 ft³/min air, $\gamma = 0.08$ lb/ft³, calculate ($a$) entrance and exit blade angles ($\alpha_1 = 90°$), ($b$) the head produced in inches of water, and ($c$) the theoretical horsepower required.

**9.32**  An air blower is to be designed to produce 4 in. water pressure when operating at 3600 rpm.   $\gamma = 0.07$ lb/ft³; $r_2 = 1.1r_1$; $\beta_2 = \beta_1$; width of impeller is 4 in.; $\alpha_1 = 90°$.   Find $r_1$.

**9.33**  In Prob. 9.32 when $\beta_1 = 30°$, calculate the discharge in cubic feet per minute.

**9.34**  Develop the equation for efficiency of a cooled compressor,

$$\eta = \frac{\eta_m}{V_{u2}u_2}\left(\frac{V_{2th}{}^2 - V_1{}^2}{2} + \frac{p_1}{\rho_1}\ln\frac{p_2}{\rho_1}\right)$$

**9.35**  Find the rotational speed in Example 9.9 for a cooled compressor, using results of Prob. 9.34, with the actual air temperature at exit 60°F.

**9.36**  A fluid coupling transmits 60 hp when the driving shaft turns 1200 rpm, and the driven shaft speed is 1160 rpm.   What is the torque in each shaft, and how efficient is the coupling?

**9.37**  What is the cavitation parameter at a point in flowing water where $t = 68°F$, $p = 2$ psia, and the velocity is 40 ft/sec?

**9.38**  A turbine with $\sigma_c = 0.08$ is to be installed at a site where $H = 200$ ft and a water barometer stands at 27.6 ft.   What is the maximum permissible impeller setting above tailwater?

**9.39**  Two units are homologous when they are geometrically similar and have

(a)  similar streamlines
(b)  the same Reynolds number
(c)  the same efficiency
(d)  the same Froude number
(e)  none of these answers

**9.40**  The following two relationships are necessary for homologous units:

(a)  $H/ND^3 = \text{const}; Q/N^2D^2 = \text{const}$
(b)  $Q/D^2\sqrt{H} = \text{const}; H/N^3D = \text{const}$
(c)  $P/QH = \text{const}; H/N^2D^2 = \text{const}$
(d)  $N\sqrt{Q}/H^{3/2} = \text{const}; N\sqrt{P}/H^{3/4} = \text{const}$
(e)  none of these answers

**9.41**  The specific speed of a pump is defined as the speed of a unit

(a)  of unit size with unit discharge at unit head
(b)  of such a size that it requires unit power for unit head
(c)  of such a size that it delivers unit discharge at unit head
(d)  of such a size that it delivers unit discharge at unit power
(e)  none of these answers

**9.42**  An impulse turbine

(a)  always operates submerged
(b)  makes use of a draft tube
(c)  is most suited for low-head installations
(d)  converts pressure head into velocity head throughout the vanes
(e)  operates by initial complete conversion to kinetic energy

**9.43**  A Pelton wheel 24 in. in diameter turns at 400 rpm.  Select from the following the head, in feet, best suited for this wheel:

(a) 7     (b) 30     (c) 120     (d) 170     (e) 480

**9.44**  A shaft transmits 200 hp at 600 rpm.  The torque in pound-feet is

(a) 19.2     (b) 183     (c) 1750     (d) 3500     (e) none of these answers

**9.45**  What torque is required to give 100 cfs water a moment of momentum so that it has a tangential velocity of 10 ft/sec at a distance of 6 ft from the axis?

(a)  116 lb-ft     (b)  1935 lb-ft     (c)  6000 lb-ft
(d)  11,610 lb-ft     (e)  none of these answers

**9.46** The moment of momentum of water is reduced by 20,000 lb-ft in flowing through vanes on a shaft turning 400 rpm. The horsepower developed on the shaft is

(a) 242    (b) 1522    (c) 14,500    (d) not determinable; insufficient data    (e) none of these answers

**9.47** Liquid moving with constant angular momentum has a tangential velocity of 4.0 ft/sec 10 ft from the axis of rotation. The tangential velocity 5 ft from the axis is, in feet per second,

(a) 2    (b) 4    (c) 8    (d) 16    (e) none of these answers

**9.48** A reaction-type turbine discharges 1200 cfs under a head of 26 ft and with an over-all efficiency of 91 per cent. The horsepower developed is

(a) 3890    (b) 3540    (c) 3220    (d) 100    (e) none of these answers

**9.49** The head developed by a pump with hydraulic efficiency of 80 per cent, for $u_2 = 100$ ft/sec, $V_2 = 60$ ft/sec, $\alpha_2 = 45°$, $\alpha_1 = 90°$, is

(a) 52.6    (b) 105.3    (c) 132    (d) 165    (e) none of these answers

**9.50** Select the correct relationship for pump vector diagrams.

(a) $\alpha_1 = 90°$; $v_1 = u_1 \cot \beta_1$
(b) $V_{u2} = u_2 - V_{r2} \cot \beta_2$
(c) $\omega_2 = r_2/u_2$
(d) $r_1 V_1 = r_2 V_{r2}$
(e) none of these answers

**9.51** The cavitation parameter is defined by

(a) $\dfrac{p_v - p}{\rho V^2/2}$    (b) $\dfrac{p_{\text{atm}} - p_v}{\rho V^2/2}$    (c) $\dfrac{p - p_v}{\gamma V^2/2}$    (d) $\dfrac{p - p_v}{\rho V^2/2}$

(e) none of these answers

**9.52** Cavitation is caused by

(a) high velocity    (b) low barometric pressure    (c) high pressure
(d) low pressure    (e) low velocity

**references**

Church, A. H.: "Centrifugal Pumps and Blowers," John Wiley & Sons, Inc., New York, 1944.

Daily, J. W.: Hydraulic Machinery, in "Engineering Hydraulics," ed. by H. Rouse, John Wiley & Sons, Inc., New York, 1950.

Eisenberg, P., and M. P. Tulin: Cavitation, sec. 12 of "Handbook of Fluid Dynamics," ed. by V. L. Streeter, McGraw-Hill Book Company, New York, 1961.

Hunsaker, J. G., and B. C. Rightmire: "Engineering Applications of Fluid Mechanics," McGraw-Hill Book Company, New York, 1947.

Moody, L. F.: Hydraulic Machinery, in "Handbook of Applied Hydraulics," 2d ed., ed. by C. V. Davis, McGraw-Hill Book Company, New York, 1952.

Spannhake, W.: "Centrifugal Pumps, Turbines and Propellers," The Technology Press of the Massachusetts Institute of Technology, Cambridge, Mass., 1934.

Stepanoff, A. J.: "Centrifugal and Axial Flow Pumps," John Wiley & Sons, Inc., New York, 1948.

Wislicenus, G. F.: "Fluid Mechanics of Turbomachinery," McGraw-Hill Book Company, New York, 1947.

# 10

# steady closed-conduit flow

The basic procedures for solving problems in incompressible steady flow in closed conduits are presented in Sec. 5.10, where simple pipe-flow situations are discussed, including losses due to change in cross section or direction of flow.   Compressible flow in ducts is treated in Secs. 6.6 to 6.8. Velocity distributions in turbulent flow are discussed in Sec. 5.4.   This chapter deals with flow situations and applications more complex than those in Chap. 5.

## 10.1  hydraulic and energy grade lines

The concepts of *hydraulic* and *energy* grade lines are useful in analyzing more complex flow problems.   If, at each point along a pipe system, the term $p/\gamma$ is determined and plotted as a vertical distance above the center of the pipe, the locus of end points is the hydraulic grade line.   More generally, the plot of the two terms

$$\frac{p}{\gamma} + z$$

for the flow, as ordinates, against length along the pipe as abscissas, produces the hydraulic grade line.   The hydraulic grade line is the locus of heights to which liquid would rise in vertical glass tubes connected to piezometer openings in the line.   When the pressure in the line is less than atmospheric, $p/\gamma$ is negative and the hydraulic grade line is below the pipeline.

The energy grade line is a line joining a series of points marking the available energy in foot-pounds per pound for each point along the pipe as ordinate, plotted against distance along the pipe as the abscissa.    It consists of the plot of

$$\frac{V^2}{2g} + \frac{p}{\gamma} + z$$

for each point along the line.    By definition, the energy grade line is always vertically above the hydraulic grade line a distance of $V^2/2g$, neglecting the kinetic-energy correction factor.

The hydraulic and energy grade lines are shown in Fig. 10.1 for a simple pipeline containing a square-edged entrance, a valve, and a nozzle at the end of the line.    To construct these lines when the reservoir surface is given, it is necessary first to apply the energy equation from the reservoir to the exit, including all minor losses as well as pipe friction, and to solve for the velocity head $V^2/2g$.    Then, to find the elevation of hydraulic grade line at any point, the energy equation is applied from the reservoir to that point, including all losses between the two points.    The equation is solved for $(p/\gamma) + z$, which is plotted above the arbitrary datum.    To find the energy grade line at the same point the equation is solved for $(V^2/2g) + (p/\gamma) + z$, which is plotted above the arbitrary datum.

The reservoir surface is the hydraulic grade line and is also the energy grade line.    At the square-edged entrance the energy grade line drops by $0.5V^2/2g$ because of the loss there, and the hydraulic grade line drops $1.5V^2/2g$.    This is made obvious by applying the energy equation between

**Fig. 10.1**  Hydraulic and energy grade lines.

the reservoir surface and a point just downstream from the pipe entrance:

$$H + 0 + 0 = \frac{V^2}{2g} + z + \frac{p}{\gamma} + 0.5 \frac{V^2}{2g}$$

Solving for $z + p/\gamma$,

$$z + \frac{p}{\gamma} = H - 1.5 \frac{V^2}{2g}$$

shows the drop of $1.5V^2/2g$. The head loss due to the sudden entrance does not actually occur at the entrance itself, but over a distance of 10 or more diameters of pipe downstream. It is customary to show it at the fitting.

**example 10.1** Determine the elevation of hydraulic and energy grade lines at points $A$, $B$, $C$, $D$, and $E$ of Fig. 10.1.

If the arbitrary datum is selected as center line of the pipe, both grade lines start at elevation 60 ft. First, solving for the velocity head is accomplished by applying the energy equation from the reservoir to $E$,

$$60 + 0 + 0 = \frac{V_E^2}{2g} + 0 + 0 + \frac{1}{2}\frac{V^2}{2g} + 0.020 \times \frac{200}{0.50}\frac{V^2}{2g} + 10 \frac{V^2}{2g}$$

$$+ 0.10 \frac{V_E^2}{2g}$$

From the continuity equation, $V_E = 4V$. After simplifying,

$$60 = \frac{V^2}{2g}(16 + \tfrac{1}{2} + 8 + 10 + 16 \times 0.1) = 36.1 \frac{V^2}{2g}$$

and $V^2/2g = 1.66$ ft. By applying the energy equation for the portion from the reservoir to $A$,

$$60 + 0 + 0 = \frac{V^2}{2g} + \frac{p}{\gamma} + z + 0.5 \frac{V^2}{2g}$$

Hence the hydraulic grade line at $A$ is

$$\frac{p}{\gamma} + z \Big|_A = 60 - 1.5 \frac{V^2}{2g} = 60 - 1.5 \times 1.66 = 57.51 \text{ ft}$$

The energy grade line for $A$ is

$$\frac{V^2}{2g} + z + \frac{p}{\gamma} = 57.51 + 1.66 = 59.17 \text{ ft}$$

For $B$,

$$60 + 0 + 0 = \frac{V^2}{2g} + \frac{p}{\gamma} + z + 0.5 \frac{V^2}{2g} + 0.02 \times \frac{80}{8.5} \frac{V^2}{2g}$$

and

$$\frac{p}{\gamma} + z \Big|_B = 60 - (1.5 + 3.2)1.66 = 52.19 \text{ ft}$$

the energy grade line is at $52.19 + 1.66 = 53.85$ ft.

Across the valve the hydraulic grade line drops by $10V^2/2g$, or 16.6 ft. Hence, at $C$ the energy and hydraulic grade lines are at 37.25 ft and 35.59 ft, respectively.

At point $D$,

$$60 = \frac{V^2}{2g} + \frac{p}{\gamma} + z + \left(10.5 + 0.02 \times \frac{200}{0.50}\right) \frac{V^2}{2g}$$

and

$$\frac{p}{\gamma} + z \Big|_D = 60 - 19.5 \times 1.66 = 27.6 \text{ ft}$$

with the energy grade line at $27.6 + 1.66 = 29.96$ ft.

At point $E$ the hydraulic grade line is at zero elevation, and the energy grade line is

$$\frac{V_E^2}{2g} = 16 \frac{V^2}{2g} = 16 \times 1.66 = 26.6 \text{ ft}$$

The *hydraulic gradient* is the slope of the hydraulic grade line if the conduit is horizontal; otherwise, it is

$$\frac{d(z + p/\gamma)}{dL}$$

The *energy gradient* is the slope of the energy grade line if the conduit is horizontal; otherwise, it is

$$\frac{d(z + p/\gamma + V^2/2g)}{dL}$$

In many situations involving long pipelines the minor losses may be neglected (when less than 5 per cent of the pipe friction losses) or they may be included as equivalent lengths of pipe which are added to actual length in solving the problem.   For these situations the value of the velocity head

**Fig. 10.2** Hydraulic grade line for long pipelines where minor losses are neglected or included as equivalent lengths of pipe.

$V^2/2g$ is small compared with $f(L/D)V^2/2g$ and is neglected. The hydraulic grade line is then utilized, as shown in Fig. 10.2. No change in hydraulic grade line is shown for minor losses. For these situations with long pipe the hydraulic gradient becomes $h_f/L$, with $h_f$ given by the Darcy-Weisbach equation,

$$h_f = f\frac{L}{D}\frac{V^2}{2g} \tag{10.1.1}$$

Flow (except through a pump) is always in the direction of decreasing energy grade line.

Pumps add energy to the flow, a fact which may be expressed in the energy equation either by including a *negative loss* or by stating the energy per unit weight added as a positive term on the upstream side of the equation. The hydraulic grade line rises sharply at a pump. Figure 10.3 shows the hydraulic and energy grade lines for a system with a pump and a siphon. The true slope of the grade lines can be shown only for horizontal lines.

**example 10.2**   A pump with a shaft input of 10 hp and an efficiency of 70 per cent is connected in a water line carrying 3 cfs. The pump has a 6-in.-diameter suction line and a 4-in.-diameter discharge line. The suction line enters the pump 3 ft below the discharge line. For a suction pressure of 10 psi, calculate the pressure at the discharge flange and the rise in the hydraulic grade line across the pump.

The energy added in foot-pounds per pound is symbolized by $E$,

$$\frac{Q\gamma E}{550} = 10 \times 0.7$$

or

$$E = \frac{550 \times 7}{3 \times 62.4} = 20.6 \text{ ft}$$

**Fig. 10.3**  Hydraulic and energy grade lines for a system with pump and siphon.

By applying the energy equation from suction flange to discharge flange,

$$\frac{V_s^2}{2g} + \frac{p_s}{\gamma} + 0 + 20.6 = \frac{V_d^2}{2g} + \frac{p_d}{\gamma} + 3$$

in which the subscripts $s$ and $d$ refer to the suction and discharge conditions, respectively. From the continuity equation $V_s = 3 \times 16/\pi = 15.3$ ft/sec, $V_d = 3 \times 36/\pi = 34.4$ ft/sec. By solving for $p_d$,

$$\frac{p_d}{\gamma} = \frac{(15.3)^2}{64.4} + \frac{10}{0.433} + 20.6 - \frac{(34.4)^2}{64.4} - 3 = 25.94 \text{ ft}$$

and $p_d = 11.21$ psi. The rise in hydraulic grade line is

$$\left(\frac{p_d}{\gamma} + 3\right) - \frac{p_s}{\gamma} = 25.94 + 3 - \frac{10}{0.433} = 5.84 \text{ ft}$$

In this example almost all the energy was added in the form of kinetic energy, and the hydraulic grade line rises only 5.84 ft for a rise of energy grade line of 20.6 ft.

A turbine takes energy from the flow and causes a sharp drop in both the energy and the hydraulic grade lines.   The energy removed per unit weight of fluid may be treated as a loss in computing grade lines.

## 10.2   the siphon

A closed conduit, arranged as in Fig. 10.4, which lifts the liquid to an elevation higher than its free surface and then discharges it at a lower elevation is a *siphon*.   It has certain limitations to its performance due to the low pressures that occur near the summit $s$.

Assuming that the siphon flows full, with a continuous liquid column throughout the siphon, the application of the energy equation for the portion from 1 to 2 produces the equation

$$H = \frac{V^2}{2g} + K\frac{V^2}{2g} + f\frac{L}{D}\frac{V^2}{2g}$$

in which $K$ is the sum of all the minor-loss coefficients.   After factoring out the velocity head,

$$H = \frac{V^2}{2g}\left(1 + K + \frac{fL}{D}\right) \tag{10.2.1}$$

which is solved in the same fashion as the simple pipe problems of the first or second type.   With the discharge known, the solution for $H$ is straightforward, but the solution for velocity with $H$ given is a trial solution started by assuming an $f$.

The pressure at the summit $s$ is found by applying the energy equation for the portion between 1 and $s$ after Eq. (10.2.1) is solved.   It is

$$0 = \frac{V^2}{2g} + \frac{p_s}{\gamma} + y_s + K'\frac{V^2}{2g} + f\frac{L'}{D}\frac{V^2}{2g}$$

**Fig. 10.4**  Siphon.

in which $K'$ is the sum of the minor-loss coefficients between the two points and $L'$ is the length of conduit upstream from $s$.   By solving for the pressure,

$$\frac{p_s}{\gamma} = -y_s - \frac{V^2}{2g}\left(1 + K' + \frac{fL'}{D}\right) \tag{10.2.2}$$

which shows that the pressure is negative and that it decreases with $y_s$ and $V^2/2g$.   If the solution of the equation should be a value of $p_s/\gamma$ equal to or less than the vapor pressure[1] of the liquid, then Eq. (10.2.1) is not valid because the vaporization of portions of the fluid column invalidates the incompressibility assumption used in deriving the energy equation.

Although Eq. (10.2.1) is not valid for this case theoretically there will be a discharge so long as $y_s$ plus the vapor pressure is less than local atmospheric pressure expressed in length of the fluid column.   When Eq. (10.2.2) yields a pressure less than vapor pressure at $s$, the pressure at $s$ may be taken as vapor pressure.   Then, with this pressure known, Eq. (10.2.2) is solved for $V^2/2g$, and the discharge is obtained therefrom.   It is assumed that air does not enter the siphon at 2 and break at $s$ the vacuum that produces the flow.

Practically a siphon does not work satisfactorily when the pressure intensity at the summit is close to vapor pressure.   Air and other gases come out of solution at the low pressures and collect at the summit, thus reducing the length of the right-hand column of liquid that produces the low pressure at the summit.   Large siphons that operate continuously have at the summits vacuum pumps to remove the gases.

The lowest pressure may not occur at the summit, but somewhere downstream from that point, because friction and minor losses may reduce the pressure more than the decrease in elevation increases pressure.

**example 10.3**   Neglecting minor losses and considering the length of pipe equal to its horizontal distance, determine the point of minimum pressure in the siphon of Fig. 10.5.

---

[1] A liquid boils when its pressure is reduced to its vapor pressure.   The vapor pressure is a function of temperature for a particular liquid.   Water has a vapor pressure of 0.203 ft of water abs at 32°F, 0.773 ft of water abs at 68°F, 6.630 ft of water abs at 140°F, and 33.91 ft of water abs at 212°F.   See Sec. 1.8.

**Fig. 10.5**   Siphon connecting two reservoirs.

When minor losses are neglected the kinetic-energy term $V^2/2g$ is usually neglected also. Then the hydraulic grade line is a straight line connecting the two liquid surfaces. Coordinates of two points on the line are $x = -100$ ft, $y = 10$ ft; $x = 141.4$ ft, $y = 20$ ft. The equation of the line is, by substitution into $y = mx + b$,

$$y = 0.0415x + 14.15 \text{ ft}$$

The minimum pressure occurs where the distance between hydraulic grade line and pipe is a maximum,

$$\frac{p}{\gamma} = 0.001x^2 - 0.0415x - 14.15$$

To find minimum $p/\gamma$, set $d(p/\gamma)/dx = 0$, which yields $x = 20.75$, and $p/\gamma = -14.58$ ft of fluid flowing. The minimum point occurs where the slopes of the pipe and of the hydraulic grade line are equal.

## 10.3 pipes in series

When two pipes of different sizes or roughnesses are connected so that fluid flows through one pipe and then through the other pipe, they are said to be connected in series. A typical series-pipe problem, in which the head $H$ may be desired for a given discharge or the discharge wanted for a given $H$, is illustrated in Fig. 10.6. By applying the energy equation from $A$ to $B$, including all losses,

$$H + 0 + 0 = 0 + 0 + 0 + K_e \frac{V_1^2}{2g} + f_1 \frac{L_1}{D_1} \frac{V_1^2}{2g} + \frac{(V_1 - V_2)^2}{2g}$$
$$+ f_2 \frac{L_2}{D_2} \frac{V_2^2}{2g} + \frac{V_2^2}{2g}$$

in which the subscripts refer to the two pipes. The last item is the head

**Fig. 10.6** Pipes connected in series.

loss at exit from pipe 2. With the continuity equation

$$V_1 D_1{}^2 = V_2 D_2{}^2$$

$V_2$ is eliminated from the equations, so that

$$H = \frac{V_1{}^2}{2g} \left\{ K_e + \frac{f_1 L_1}{D_1} + \left[ 1 - \left(\frac{D_1}{D_2}\right)^2 \right]^2 + \frac{f_2 L_2}{D_2} \left(\frac{D_1}{D_2}\right)^4 + \left(\frac{D_1}{D_2}\right)^4 \right\}$$

For known lengths and sizes of pipes this reduces to

$$H = \frac{V_1{}^2}{2g} (C_1 + C_2 f_1 + C_3 f_2) \tag{10.3.1}$$

in which $C_1$, $C_2$, $C_3$ are known. With the discharge given, the Reynolds number is readily computed, and the $f$'s may be looked up in the Moody diagram. Then $H$ is found by direct substitution. With $H$ given, $V_1, f_1, f_2$ are unknowns in Eq. (10.3.1). By assuming values of $f_1$ and $f_2$ (they may be assumed equal), a trial $V_1$ is found from which trial Reynolds numbers are determined and values of $f_1, f_2$ looked up. Using these new values, a better $V_1$ is computed from Eq. (10.3.1). Since $f$ varies so slightly with the Reynolds number, the trial solution converges very rapidly. The same procedures apply for more than two pipes in series.

In place of the assumption of $f_1$ and $f_2$ when $H$ is given, a graphical solution may be utilized in which several values of $Q$ are assumed, in turn, and the corresponding values of $H$ are calculated and plotted against $Q$, as in Fig. 10.7. By connecting the points with a smooth curve, it is easy to read off the proper $Q$ for the given value of $H$.

**example 10.4** In Fig. 10.6, $K_e = 0.5$, $L_1 = 1000$ ft, $D_1 = 2$ ft, $\epsilon_1 = 0.005$ ft, $L_2 = 800$ ft, $D_2 = 3$ ft, $\epsilon_2 = 0.001$ ft, $\nu = 0.00001$ ft²/sec, and $H = 20$ ft. Determine the discharge through the system.

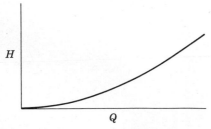

**Fig. 10.7** Plot of calculated $H$ for selected values of $Q$.

From the energy equation,

$$20 = \frac{V_1{}^2}{2g} \left\{ 0.5 + f_1 \frac{1000}{2} + \left[ 1 - \left(\frac{2}{3}\right)^2 \right]^2 + f_2 \frac{800}{3} \left(\frac{2}{3}\right)^4 + \left(\frac{2}{3}\right)^4 \right\}$$

After simplifying,

$$20 = \frac{V_1{}^2}{2g} (1.01 + 500f_1 + 52.6f_2)$$

From $\epsilon_1/D_1 = 0.0025$, $\epsilon_2/D_2 = 0.00033$, and Fig. 5.32 values of $f$'s are assumed for the complete turbulence range,

$$f_1 = 0.025 \qquad f_2 = 0.015$$

By solving for $V_1$, with these values, $V_1 = 9.49$ ft/sec, $V_2 = 4.21$ ft/sec,

$$\mathbf{R}_1 = \frac{9.49 \times 2}{0.00001} = 1{,}898{,}000 \qquad \mathbf{R}_2 = \frac{4.21 \times 3}{0.00001} = 1{,}263{,}000$$

and from Fig. 5.32, $f_1 = 0.025$, $f_2 = 0.016$.   By solving for $V_1$ again, $V_1 = 9.46$, and $Q = 9.46\pi = 29.8$ cfs.

*equivalent pipes*

Series pipes may be solved by the method of equivalent lengths.   Two pipe systems are said to be equivalent when the same head loss produces the same discharge in both systems.   From Eq. (10.1.1)

$$h_{f1} = f_1 \frac{L_1}{D_1} \frac{Q_1{}^2}{(D_1{}^2\pi/4)^2 2g} = \frac{f_1 L_1}{D_1{}^5} \frac{8Q_1{}^2}{\pi^2 g}$$

and for a second pipe

$$h_{f2} = \frac{f_2 L_2}{D_2{}^5} \frac{8Q_2{}^2}{\pi^2 g}$$

For the two pipes to be equivalent,

$$h_{f1} = h_{f2} \qquad Q_1 = Q_2$$

After equating $h_{f1} = h_{f2}$ and simplifying,

$$\frac{f_1 L_1}{D_1{}^5} = \frac{f_2 L_2}{D_2{}^5}$$

By solving for $L_2$,

$$L_2 = L_1 \frac{f_1}{f_2} \left(\frac{D_2}{D_1}\right)^5 \tag{10.3.2}$$

which determines the length of a second pipe to be equivalent to that of the first pipe. For example, to replace 1000 ft of 8-in. pipe with an equivalent length of 6-in. pipe, the values of $f_1, f_2$ must be approximated by selecting a discharge within the range intended for the pipes. Say $f_1 = 0.020$, $f_2 = 0.018$; then

$$L_2 = 1000 \frac{0.020}{0.018} \left(\frac{6}{8}\right)^5 = 264 \text{ ft}$$

For these assumed conditions 264 ft of 6-in. pipe is equivalent to 1000 ft of 8-in. pipe.

Hypothetically two or more pipes composing a system may also be replaced by a pipe which has the same discharge for the same over-all head loss.

**example 10.5**  Solve Example 10.4 by means of equivalent pipes.

First, by expressing the minor losses in terms of equivalent lengths, for pipe 1,

$$K_1 = 0.5 + [1 - (\tfrac{2}{3})^2]^2 = 0.809$$

$$L_{e1} = \frac{K_1 D_1}{f_1} = \frac{0.809 \times 2}{0.025} = 65 \text{ ft}$$

and for pipe 2,

$$K_2 = 1$$

$$L_{e2} = \frac{K_2 D_2}{f_2} = \frac{1 \times 3}{0.015} = 200 \text{ ft}$$

The values of $f_1, f_2$ are selected for the fully turbulent range as an approximation. The problem is now reduced to 1065 ft of 2-ft pipe and 1000 ft of 3-ft pipe. By expressing the 3-ft pipe in terms of an equivalent length of 2-ft pipe, by Eq. (10.3.2),

$$L_e = 1000 \times \frac{0.015}{0.025} \left(\frac{2}{3}\right)^5 = 79 \text{ ft}$$

By adding to the 2-ft pipe, the problem is reduced to the simple pipe problem of finding the discharge through $1065 + 79 = 1144$ ft of 2-ft diameter pipe, $\epsilon = 0.005$ ft, for a head loss of 20 ft,

$$20 = f\frac{1144}{2}\frac{V^2}{2g}$$

With $f = 0.025$, $V = 9.5$ ft/sec and $\mathbf{R} = 9.5 \times 2/0.00001 = 1,900,000$. For $\epsilon/D = 0.0025, f = 0.025$ and $Q = 9.5\pi = 29.9$ cfs.

### 10.4   pipes in parallel

A combination of two or more pipes connected as in Fig. 10.8, so that the flow is divided among the pipes and then is joined again, is a *parallel-pipe* system.   In series pipes the same fluid flows through all the pipes, and the head losses are cumulative; however, in parallel pipes the head losses are the same in any of the lines, and the discharges are cumulative.

In analyzing parallel-pipe systems, it is assumed that the minor losses are added into the lengths of each pipe as equivalent lengths.   From Fig. 10.8 the conditions to be satisfied are

$$h_{f1} = h_{f2} = h_{f3} = \frac{p_A}{\gamma} + z_A - \left(\frac{p_B}{\gamma} + z_B\right) \qquad (10.4.1)$$

$$Q = Q_1 + Q_2 + Q_3$$

in which $z_A$, $z_B$ are elevations of points $A$ and $B$, and $Q$ is the discharge through the approach pipe or the exit pipe.

Two types of problems occur: (1) with elevation of hydraulic grade line at $A$ and $B$ known, to find the discharge $Q$; (2) with $Q$ known, to find the distribution of flow and the head loss.   Sizes of pipe, fluid properties, and roughnesses are assumed to be known.

The first type is, in effect, the solution of simple pipe problems for discharge since the head loss is the drop in hydraulic grade line.   These discharges are added to determine the total discharge.

**Fig. 10.8**   Parallel-pipe system.

The second type of problem is more complex, as neither the head loss nor the discharge for any one pipe is known. The recommended procedure is as follows:

1. Assume a discharge $Q_1'$ through pipe 1.
2. Solve for $h_f'$, using the assumed discharge.
3. Using $h_{f1}'$, find $Q_2'$, $Q_3'$.
4. With the three discharges for a common head loss, now assume that the given $Q$ is split up among the pipes in the same proportion as $Q_1'$, $Q_2'$, $Q_3'$; thus

$$Q_1 = \frac{Q_1'}{\Sigma Q'} Q \qquad Q_2 = \frac{Q_2'}{\Sigma Q'} Q \qquad Q_3 = \frac{Q_3'}{\Sigma Q'} Q \qquad (10.4.2)$$

5. Check the correctness of these discharges by computing $h_{f1}$, $h_{f2}$, $h_{f3}$ for the computed $Q_1$, $Q_2$, $Q_3$.

This procedure works for any number of pipes. By judicious choice of $Q_1'$, obtained by estimating the per cent of the total flow through the system that should pass through pipe 1 (based on diameter, length, and roughness), Eq. (10.4.2) produces values that check within a few per cent, which is well within the range of accuracy of the friction factors.

**example 10.6** In Fig. 10.8, $L_1 = 3000$ ft, $D_1 = 1$ ft, $\epsilon_1 = 0.001$ ft; $L_2 = 2000$ ft, $D_2 = 8$ in., $\epsilon_2 = 0.0001$ ft; $L_3 = 4000$ ft, $D_3 = 16$ in., $\epsilon_3 = 0.0008$ ft; $\rho = 2.00$ slugs/ft$^3$, $\nu = 0.00003$ ft$^2$/sec, $p_A = 80$ psi, $z_A = 100$ ft, $z_B = 80$ ft. For a total flow of 12 cfs, determine flow through each pipe and the pressure at $B$.

Assume $Q_1' = 3$ cfs; then $V_1' = 3.82$, $\mathbf{R}_1' = 3.82 \times 1/0.00003 = 127,000$, $\epsilon_1/D_1 = 0.001$, $f_1' = 0.022$, and

$$h_{f1}' = 0.022 \times \frac{3000}{1.0} \frac{(3.82)^2}{64.4} = 14.97 \text{ ft}$$

For pipe 2

$$14.97 = f_2' \frac{2000}{0.667} \frac{V_2'^2}{2g}$$

Then $\epsilon_2/D_2 = 0.00015$. Assume $f_2' = 0.020$; then $V_2' = 4.01$ ft/sec, $\mathbf{R}_2' = 4.01 \times \frac{2}{3} \times 1/0.00003 = 89,000$, $f_2' = 0.019$, $V_2' = 4.11$ ft/sec, $Q_2' = 1.44$ cfs.

For pipe 3

$$14.97 = f_3' \frac{4000}{1.333} \frac{V_3'^2}{2g}$$

Then $\epsilon_3/D_3 = 0.0006$.    Assume $f_3' = 0.020$; then $V_3' = 4.01$ ft/sec, $\mathbf{R}_3' = 4.01 \times 1.333/0.00003 = 178,000$, $f_3' = 0.020$, $Q_3' = 5.60$ cfs.

The total discharge for the assumed conditions is

$$\Sigma Q' = 3.00 + 1.44 + 5.60 = 10.04 \text{ cfs}$$

Hence

$$Q_1 = \frac{3.00}{10.04} \times 12 = 3.58 \text{ cfs} \qquad Q_2 = \frac{1.44}{10.04} \times 12 = 1.72 \text{ cfs}$$

$$Q_3 = \frac{5.60}{10.04} \times 12 = 6.70 \text{ cfs}$$

Checking the values of $h_1, h_2, h_3$,

$$V_1 = \frac{3.58}{\pi/4} = 4.46 \qquad \mathbf{R}_1 = 152,000 \qquad f_1 = 0.021 \qquad h_{f1} = 20.4 \text{ ft}$$

$$V_2 = \frac{1.72}{\pi/9} = 4.93 \qquad \mathbf{R}_2 = 109,200 \qquad f_2 = 0.019 \qquad h_{f2} = 21.6 \text{ ft}$$

$$V_3 = \frac{6.70}{4\pi/9} = 4.80 \qquad \mathbf{R}_3 = 213,000 \qquad f_3 = 0.019 \qquad h_{f3} = 20.4 \text{ ft}$$

$f_2$ is about midway between 0.018 and 0.019.    If 0.018 had been selected, $h_2$ would be 20.4 ft.

To find $p_B$,

$$\frac{p_A}{\gamma} + z_A = \frac{p_B}{\gamma} + z_B + h_f$$

or

$$\frac{p_B}{\gamma} = \frac{80 \times 144}{62.4} + 100 - 80 - 20.8 = 183.5$$

in which the average head loss was taken.    Then

$$p_B = \frac{183.5 \times 2 \times 32.2}{144} = 81.8 \text{ psi}$$

## 10.5  branching pipes

A simple *branching-pipe* system is shown in Fig. 10.9.    In this situation the flow through each pipe is wanted when the reservoir elevations are given. The sizes and types of pipes and fluid properties are assumed known.    The

**Fig. 10.9** Three interconnected reservoirs.

Darcy-Weisbach equation must be satisfied for each pipe, and the continuity equation must be satisfied. It takes the form that the flow into the junction $J$ must just equal the flow out of the junction. Flow must be out of the highest reservoir and into the lowest; hence, the continuity equation may be either of the following,

$$Q_1 = Q_2 + Q_3 \qquad Q_1 + Q_2 = Q_3$$

If the elevation of hydraulic grade line at the junction is above the elevation of the intermediate reservoir, flow is *into* it; but if the elevation of hydraulic grade line at $J$ is below the intermediate reservoir, the flow is *out* of it. Minor losses may be expressed as equivalent lengths and added to the actual lengths of pipe.

The solution is effected by assuming an elevation of hydraulic grade line at the junction, then computing $Q_1$, $Q_2$, $Q_3$ and substituting into the continuity equation. If the flow into the junction is too great, a higher grade-line elevation, which will reduce the inflow and increase the outflow, is assumed.

**example 10.7** In Fig. 10.9, find the discharges for water at 60°F and with the following pipe data and reservoir elevations: $L_1 = 10{,}000$ ft, $D_1 = 3$ ft, $\epsilon_1/D_1 = 0.0002$; $L_2 = 2000$ ft, $D_2 = 1.5$ ft, $\epsilon_2/D_2 = 0.002$; $L_3 = 4000$ ft, $D_3 = 2$ ft, $\epsilon_3/D_3 = 0.001$; $z_1 = 100$ ft, $z_2 = 60$ ft, $z_3 = 30$ ft.

Assume $z_J + p_J/\gamma = 65$ ft; then

$$35 = f_1 \frac{10{,}000}{3} \frac{V_1{}^2}{2g} \qquad f_1 = 0.014 \qquad V_1 = 6.95 \text{ ft/sec} \qquad Q_1 = 49.1 \text{ cfs}$$

$$5 = f_2 \frac{2000}{1.5} \frac{V_2{}^2}{2g} \qquad f_2 = 0.024 \qquad V_2 = 3.17 \qquad Q_2 = 5.60$$

$$35 = f_3 \frac{4000}{2} \frac{V_3{}^2}{2g} \qquad f_3 = 0.020 \qquad V_3 = 7.51 \qquad Q_3 = 23.6$$

so that the inflow is greater than the outflow by

$49.1 - 5.60 - 23.6 = 19.9$ cfs

Assume $z_J + p_J/\gamma = 80$ ft; then

$$20 = f_1 \frac{10,000}{3} \frac{V_1^2}{2g} \qquad f_1 = 0.015 \qquad V_1 = 5.07 \qquad Q_1 = 35.8$$

$$20 = f_2 \frac{2000}{1.5} \frac{V_2^2}{2g} \qquad f_2 = 0.024 \qquad V_2 = 6.35 \qquad Q_2 = 11.33$$

$$50 = f_3 \frac{4000}{2} \frac{V_3^2}{2g} \qquad f_3 = 0.020 \qquad V_3 = 8.98 \qquad Q_3 = 28.2$$

The outflow is now greater by 3.73 cfs. Taking a straight-line interpolation, $z_J + p_J/\gamma = 77.6$ ft, and

$$22.4 = f_1 \frac{10,000}{3} \frac{V_1^2}{2g} \qquad f_1 = 0.015 \qquad V_1 = 5.36 \qquad Q_1 = 37.83$$

$$17.6 = f_2 \frac{2000}{1.5} \frac{V_2^2}{2g} \qquad f_2 = 0.024 \qquad V_2 = 5.96 \qquad Q_2 = 10.65$$

$$47.6 = f_3 \frac{4000}{2} \frac{V_3^2}{2g} \qquad f_3 = 0.020 \qquad V_3 = 8.75 \qquad Q_3 = 27.50$$

and the outflow is 0.32 cfs greater. By extrapolating from the last two values, $z_J + p_J/\gamma = 77.4$, $Q_1 = 38.05$, $Q_2 = 10.60$, $Q_3 = 27.45$.

More complex branching-pipe problems are solved by a similar method of taking a trial solution. It is important that only one independent assumption be made; otherwise convergence of the solution would be haphazard. Figure 10.10 illustrates a four-reservoir problem with two junctions. By assuming the elevation of hydraulic grade line at one junction point, e.g., $J_1$, the flow through pipes 1 and 2 can be determined. Thus, by continuity, the flow between junctions is obtained, and the elevation of hydraulic grade line at $J_2$ is computed. The check on the assumption is to see whether the flows in pipes 3 and 4 satisfy continuity at $J_2$. If not, a

**Fig. 10.10** Four reservoirs with two junctions.

**Fig. 10.11** Portion of graphical solution of reservoir problem of Fig. 10.10.

new assumption at $J_1$ is made, and the process is repeated. The direction in which the shift is made is usually obvious.

It is convenient to use a graphical solution with any of the branching-pipe problems. By preparing the curve of elevation of hydraulic grade line at the junction against flow through the pipe from an individual reservoir, no trial solutions of type II are required. If two reservoirs are joined to the same junction, the discharge curves are added horizontally, as shown in Fig. 10.11, which refers to reservoirs 1 and 2 of Fig. 10.10 and the elevation of hydraulic grade line at $J_1$. The next step would be the calculation of elevation of hydraulic grade line at $J_2$, also shown on the figure. By now plotting flow into $J_2$ from reservoirs 3 and 4, combined, on the right-hand side of Fig. 10.11, and flow out of reservoirs 3 and 4 on the left-hand side,

**Fig. 10.12** Pumping from one reservoir to two other reservoirs.

the intersection with the $J_2$ curve shown yields the elevation of hydraulic grade line at $J_2$, from which all other flows may be found.

In pumping from one reservoir to two or more other reservoirs, as in Fig. 10.12, the characteristics of the pump must be known.   Assuming that the pump runs at constant speed, its head depends upon the discharge. A suitable procedure is as follows:

1.   Assume a discharge through the pump.
2.   Compute the hydraulic-grade-line elevation at the suction side of the pump.
3.   From the pump characteristic curve find the head produced, and add it to suction hydraulic grade line.
4.   Compute drop in hydraulic grade line to the junction $J$, and determine elevation of hydraulic grade line there.
5.   For this elevation, compute flow into reservoirs 2 and 3.
6.   If flow into $J$ equals flow out of $J$, the problem is solved.   If flow into $J$ is too great, assume less flow through the pump and repeat the procedure.

This procedure is easily plotted on a graph, so that the intersection of two elevations vs. flow curves yields the answer.

## 10.6   networks of pipes

Interconnected pipes through which the flow to a given outlet may come from several circuits are called a *network of pipes*, in many ways analogous to flow through electric networks.   Problems on these in general are complicated and require trial solutions in which the elementary circuits are balanced in turn until all conditions for the flow are satisfied.

The following conditions must be satisfied in a network of pipes:

1.   The algebraic sum of the pressure drops around each circuit must be zero.
2.   Flow into each junction must equal flow out of the junction.
3.   The Darcy-Weisbach equation must be satisfied for each pipe; i.e., the proper relation between head loss and discharge must be maintained for each pipe.

The first condition states that the pressure drop between any two points in the circuit, e.g., $A$ and $G$ (Fig. 10.13), must be the same whether through the pipe $AG$ or through $AFEDG$.   The second condition is the continuity equation.

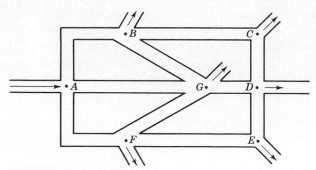

**Fig. 10.13** Pipe network.

An exponential equation is usually developed to replace the Darcy-Weisbach equation. By expressing $f$ as a function of $V$ for a given pipe and a given fluid, the Darcy-Weisbach equation may be reduced to

$$h_f = rQ^n \qquad (10.6.1)$$

**example 10.8** Determine the exponential formula for flow of water at 60°F through a 6-in.-diameter clean cast-iron pipe for the velocity range 2 to 6 ft/sec.

First, $f$ is determined for 2 ft/sec and for 6 ft/sec. Using the Moody diagram, $\epsilon/D = 0.0017$. For 2 ft/sec, $f = 0.025$, and for 6 ft/sec, $f = 0.023$. Hence

$$f = 0.025 \qquad Q = \frac{2\pi}{16} = 0.392 \text{ cfs} \qquad f = 0.023 \qquad Q = \frac{6\pi}{16} = 1.180 \text{ cfs}$$

Substituting into

$$f = aQ^b$$

produces

$$0.025 = a(0.392)^b \qquad 0.023 = a(1.180)^b$$

By taking the ratio of the two equations,

$$\frac{0.025}{0.023} = \left(\frac{0.392}{1.180}\right)^b \qquad b = -0.076 \qquad a = 0.0233$$

Hence

$$f = 0.0233Q^{-0.076}$$

Substituting into the Darcy-Weisbach equation produces

$$\frac{h_f}{L} = \frac{fQ^2}{2gD^5(\pi/4)^2} = \frac{0.0233}{64.4(0.5)^5(0.7854)^2}Q^{1.924} = 0.0188Q^{1.924}$$

If the pipe is 1000 ft long, $h_f = 18.8Q^{1.924}$.

Since it is impractical to solve network problems analytically, methods of successive approximations are utilized. The Hardy Cross method[1] is one in which flows are assumed for each pipe so that continuity is satisfied at every junction. A correction to the flow in each circuit is then computed in turn and applied to bring the circuits into closer balance.

Minor losses are included as equivalent lengths in each pipe. With the head loss equation $h_f = rQ^n$, in which $r$ and $n$ are determined for each pipe, the method is applied as follows:

1.  Assume the best distribution of flows that satisfies continuity by careful examination of the network.
2.  Compute the head loss $h = rQ^n$ in each pipe. Compute the net head loss around each elementary circuit: $\Sigma h = \Sigma rQ^n$ (should be zero for a balanced circuit).
3.  Compute for each circuit: $\Sigma|nrQ^{n-1}|$ (all terms are considered positive).
4.  Set up in each circuit a corrective flow $\Delta Q$ to balance the head in that circuit (for $\Sigma rQ^n = 0$):

$$\Delta Q = \frac{\Sigma rQ^n}{\Sigma|nrQ^{n-1}|} \tag{10.6.2}$$

5.  Compute the revised flows in each pipe, and repeat the procedure until the desired accuracy is obtained.

The solution is known to be correct when all the conditions are satisfied for each circuit. The source of the corrective term is obtained as follows:
For any pipe,

$$Q = Q_0 + \Delta Q$$

in which $Q$ is the correct discharge, $Q_0$ the assumed discharge, and $\Delta Q$ the correction. Then, for each pipe,

$$h = rQ^n = r(Q_0 + \Delta Q)^n = r(Q_0^n + nQ_0^{n-1}\Delta Q + \cdots)$$

If $\Delta Q$ is small compared with $Q_0$, all terms of the series after the second one may be dropped. Now for a circuit,

$$\Sigma h = \Sigma rQ^n = \Sigma rQ_0^n + \Delta Q\Sigma rnQ_0^{n-1} = 0$$

[1] Hardy Cross, Analysis of Flow in Networks of Conduits or Conductors, *Univ. Illinois Bull.* 286, November, 1946.

in which $\Delta Q$ has been taken out of the summation as it is the same for all pipes in the circuit. After solving for $\Delta Q$,

$$\Delta Q = \frac{\Sigma r Q_0{}^n}{\Sigma |r n Q_0{}^{n-1}|}$$

When $\Delta Q$ is applied to a circuit, it has the same sense in every pipe; i.e., it adds to flows in the counterclockwise direction and subtracts from flows in the clockwise direction. Since the $\Delta Q$ contains the sign change, the denominator of the correction term is the sum of the absolute terms.

The values of $r$ occur in both numerator and denominator; hence, values proportional to the actual $r$ may be used to find the distribution. Similarly, the apportionment of flows may be expressed as a per cent of the actual flows. To find a particular head loss, the actual values of $r$ and $Q$ must be used after the distribution has been determined.

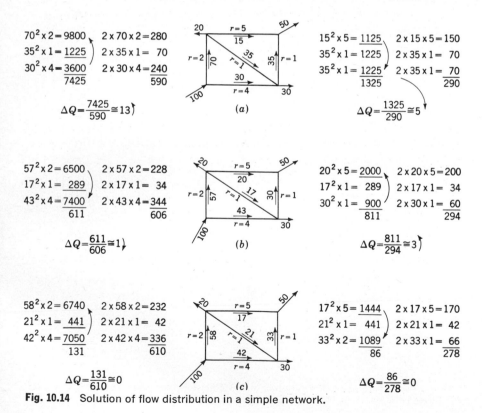

$$
\begin{array}{ll}
70^2 \times 2 = 9800 & 2 \times 70 \times 2 = 280 \\
35^2 \times 1 = \underline{1225} & 2 \times 35 \times 1 = \phantom{0}70 \\
30^2 \times 4 = \underline{3600} & 2 \times 30 \times 4 = \underline{240} \\
\phantom{30^2 \times 4 = }7425 & \phantom{2 \times 30 \times 4 = }590
\end{array}
$$

$$\Delta Q = \frac{7425}{590} \cong 13$$

$$
\begin{array}{ll}
15^2 \times 5 = \underline{1125} & 2 \times 15 \times 5 = 150 \\
35^2 \times 1 = 1225 & 2 \times 35 \times 1 = \phantom{0}70 \\
35^2 \times 1 = \underline{1225} & 2 \times 35 \times 1 = \underline{\phantom{0}70} \\
\phantom{35^2 \times 1 = }1325 & \phantom{2 \times 35 \times 1 = }290
\end{array}
$$

$$\Delta Q = \frac{1325}{290} \cong 5$$

(a)

$$
\begin{array}{ll}
57^2 \times 2 = 6500 & 2 \times 57 \times 2 = 228 \\
17^2 \times 1 = \underline{\phantom{0}289} & 2 \times 17 \times 1 = \phantom{0}34 \\
43^2 \times 4 = \underline{7400} & 2 \times 43 \times 4 = \underline{344} \\
\phantom{43^2 \times 4 = }611 & \phantom{2 \times 43 \times 4 = }606
\end{array}
$$

$$\Delta Q = \frac{611}{606} \cong 1$$

$$
\begin{array}{ll}
20^2 \times 5 = \underline{2000} & 2 \times 20 \times 5 = 200 \\
17^2 \times 1 = \underline{\phantom{0}289} & 2 \times 17 \times 1 = \phantom{0}34 \\
30^2 \times 1 = \underline{\phantom{0}900} & 2 \times 30 \times 1 = \underline{\phantom{0}60} \\
\phantom{30^2 \times 1 = }811 & \phantom{2 \times 30 \times 1 = }294
\end{array}
$$

$$\Delta Q = \frac{811}{294} \cong 3$$

(b)

$$
\begin{array}{ll}
58^2 \times 2 = 6740 & 2 \times 58 \times 2 = 232 \\
21^2 \times 1 = \underline{\phantom{0}441} & 2 \times 21 \times 1 = \phantom{0}42 \\
42^2 \times 4 = \underline{7050} & 2 \times 42 \times 4 = \underline{336} \\
\phantom{42^2 \times 4 = }131 & \phantom{2 \times 42 \times 4 = }610
\end{array}
$$

$$\Delta Q = \frac{131}{610} \cong 0$$

$$
\begin{array}{ll}
17^2 \times 5 = \underline{1444} & 2 \times 17 \times 5 = 170 \\
21^2 \times 1 = \underline{\phantom{0}441} & 2 \times 21 \times 1 = \phantom{0}42 \\
33^2 \times 2 = \underline{1089} & 2 \times 33 \times 1 = \underline{\phantom{0}66} \\
\phantom{33^2 \times 2 = }86 & \phantom{2 \times 33 \times 1 = }278
\end{array}
$$

$$\Delta Q = \frac{86}{278} \cong 0$$

(c)

**Fig. 10.14** Solution of flow distribution in a simple network.

**example 10.9** The distribution of flow through the network of Fig. 10.14 is desired for the inflows and outflows as given. For simplicity $n$ has been given the value 2.0.

The assumed distribution is shown in diagram $a$. At the upper left the terms $\Sigma r Q^n$ are computed for the lower circuit. By listing the clockwise terms first, an arrow at the right drawn to the larger terms shows the direction of the counterbalancing $\Delta Q$. Next to the diagram on the left is the computation of $\Sigma |nrQ^{n-1}|$. Diagram $b$ gives the distribution after both circuits have been corrected once. Diagram $c$ shows the values correct to within about 1 per cent of the distribution, which is more accurate than the exponential equations for head loss.

The Hardy Cross method is easily programmed for the digital computer and converges rapidly; the method given, that of balancing heads around circuits, is limited to the case of having only one head specified. Many new methods have been developed that take advantage of the computer. Shamir and Howard[1] have developed a method of balancing networks that is quite general, in that the unknowns may be junction pressures, junction outflows or inflows, or pipe sizes. It is based on the Newton-Raphson method of solving simultaneous nonlinear equations, one for each junction of the system.

## 10.7 conduits with noncircular cross sections

In this chapter so far, only circular pipes have been considered. For cross sections that are noncircular, the Darcy-Weisbach equation may be applied if the term $D$ can be interpreted in terms of the section. The concept of the *hydraulic radius* $R$ permits circular and noncircular sections to be treated in the same manner. The hydraulic radius is defined as the cross-sectional area divided by the *wetted perimeter*. Hence, for a circular section,

$$R = \frac{\text{area}}{\text{perimeter}} = \frac{\pi D^2/4}{\pi D} = \frac{D}{4} \tag{10.7.1}$$

and the diameter is equivalent to $4R$. Assuming that the diameter may be replaced by $4R$ in the Darcy-Weisbach equation, in the Reynolds number, and in the relative roughness,

$$h_f = f \frac{L}{4R} \frac{V^2}{2g} \qquad \mathbf{R} = \frac{V 4 R \rho}{\mu} \qquad \frac{\epsilon}{D} = \frac{\epsilon}{4R} \tag{10.7.2}$$

[1] Uri Shamir and C. D. D. Howard, Water Distribution Systems Analysis, *J. Hydraulics Div. ASCE*, No. HY1, paper No. 5758, pp. 219–234, January, 1968.

Noncircular sections may be handled in a similar manner. The Moody diagram applies as before. The assumptions in Eqs. (10.7.2) cannot be expected to hold for odd-shaped sections but should give reasonable values for square, oval, triangular, and similar types of sections.

**example 10.10**   Determine the head loss in inches of water required for flow of 10,000 ft³/min of air at 60°F and 14.7 psia through a rectangular galvanized-iron section 2 ft wide, 1 ft high, and 200 ft long.

$$R = \frac{2}{6} = 0.333 \text{ ft} \qquad \frac{\epsilon}{4R} = 0.00038$$

$$V = \frac{10,000}{60 \times 2} = 83.3 \text{ ft/sec} \qquad V4R'' = 83.3 \times 4 \times 4 = 1330$$

$$f = 0.017$$

Then

$$h_f = f \frac{L}{4R} \frac{V^2}{2g} = \frac{0.017 \times 200}{4 \times 0.333} \frac{(83.3)^2}{64.4} = 275 \text{ ft}$$

The specific weight of air is $\gamma = (14.7 \times 144)/(53.3 \times 520) = 0.0762 \text{ lb/ft}^3$. In inches of water the head loss is

$$\frac{275 \times 0.0762 \times 12}{62.4} = 4.04 \text{ in.}$$

## 10.8   aging of pipes

The Moody diagram, with the values of absolute roughness shown there, is for new, clean pipe. With use, pipes become rougher, owing to corrosion, incrustations, and deposition of material on the pipe walls. The speed with which the friction factor changes with time depends greatly on the fluid being handled. Colebrook and White[1] found that the absolute roughness $\epsilon$ increases linearly with time,

$$\epsilon = \epsilon_0 + \alpha t \tag{10.8.1}$$

in which $\epsilon_0$ is the absolute roughness of the new surface. Tests on a pipe are required to determine $\alpha$.

---

[1] C. F. Colebrook and C. M. White, The Reduction of Carrying Capacity of Pipes with Age, *J. Inst. Civil Engrs. London*, 1937.

**example 10.11**   An 18-in.-diameter wrought-iron pipe 12 years old has a pressure drop of 1.365 psi/1000 ft when carrying 7.08 cfs water at 60°F. Estimate the loss per thousand feet for 10 cfs water when the pipe is 20 years old.

When new, $\epsilon_0 = 0.00015$ from Fig. 5.32.   At 12 years

$$V = \frac{7.08}{\pi(0.75)^2} = 4 \text{ ft/sec} \qquad h_f = \frac{1.365}{0.433} = 3.145$$

and

$$f = \frac{h_f}{(L/D)\,V^2/2g} = \frac{3.145}{(1000/1.5)(16/64.4)} = 0.019$$

From Fig. 5.32, $\epsilon/D = 0.00075$, $\epsilon = 0.00075 \times 1.5 = 0.00112$ ft.   Then

$$\alpha = \frac{\epsilon - \epsilon_0}{t} = \frac{0.00112 - 0.00015}{12} = 0.000081 \text{ ft/year}$$

When 20 years old

$$\epsilon = 0.00015 + 20 \times 0.000081 = 0.0018 \text{ ft}$$

For 10 cfs, $V = 5.65$, $VD'' = 102$, $\epsilon/D = 0.0012$, $f = 0.021$, and

$$\Delta p = 0.021 \times \frac{1000}{1.5}\frac{(5.65)^2}{64.4} \times 0.433 = 3.00 \text{ psi/1000 ft}$$

**problems**

**10.1**   Sketch the hydraulic and energy grade lines for Fig. 10.15.   $H = 24$ ft.

**Fig. 10.15**

**Fig. 10.16**

**10.2** Calculate the value of $K$ for the valve of Fig. 10.15 so that the discharge of Prob. 10.1 is reduced by one-half. Sketch the hydraulic and energy grade lines.

**10.3** Compute the discharge of the system in Fig. 10.16. Draw the hydraulic and energy grade lines.

**10.4** What head is needed in Fig. 10.16 to produce a discharge of 10 cfs?

**10.5** Calculate the discharge through the siphon of Fig. 10.17 with the conical diffuser removed. $H = 4$ ft.

**10.6** Calculate the discharge in the siphon of Fig. 10.17 for $H = 8$ ft. What is the minimum pressure in the system?

**10.7** Find the discharge through the siphon of Fig. 10.18. What is the pressure at $A$? Estimate the minimum pressure in the system.

**10.8** Neglecting minor losses other than the valve, sketch the hydraulic grade line for Fig. 10.19. The globe valve has a loss coefficient $K = 4.5$.

**10.9** What is the maximum height of point $A$ (Fig. 10.19) for no cavitation? Barometer reading is 29.5 in. mercury.

**Fig. 10.17**

**Fig. 10.18**

**10.10**  Two reservoirs are connected by three commercial steel pipes in series, $L_1 = 1000$ ft, $D_1 = 8$ in.; $L_2 = 1200$ ft, $D_2 = 1$ ft; $L_3 = 4000$ ft, $D_3 = 18$ in.  When $Q = 3$ cfs water at 70°F, determine the difference in elevation of the reservoirs.

**10.11**  Solve Prob. 10.10 by the method of equivalent lengths.

**10.12**  For a difference in elevation of 30 ft in Prob. 10.10, find the discharge by determining the friction factors.

**10.13**  For a difference in elevation of 40 ft in Prob. 10.10, determine the discharge by the method of equivalent lengths.

**10.14**  What diameter smooth pipe is required to convey 100 gpm kerosene at 90°F 500 ft with a head of 16 ft?  There are a valve and other minor losses with total $K$ of 7.6.

**10.15**  Air at atmospheric pressure and 60°F is carried through two horizontal pipes ($\epsilon = 0.06$) in series.  The upstream pipe is 400 ft of 24 in. diameter, and the downstream pipe is 100 ft of 36 in. diameter.  Estimate the equivalent length of 18-in. smooth pipe.  Neglect minor losses.

**Fig. 10.19**

**10.16** What pressure drop, in inches of water, is required for flow of 6000 cfm in Prob. 10.15? Include losses due to sudden expansion.

**10.17** Two pipes are connected in parallel between two reservoirs: $L_1 = 8000$ ft, $D_1 = 48$-in.-diameter old cast-iron pipe, $f_1 = 0.026$; $L_2 = 8000$ ft, $D_2 = 42$ in., $\epsilon_2 = 0.003$. For a difference in elevation of 12 ft, determine the total flow of water at 70°F.

**10.18** For 160 cfs flow in the system of Prob. 10.17, determine the difference in elevation of reservoir surfaces.

**10.19** Three smooth tubes are connected in parallel: $L_1 = 40$ ft, $D_1 = \frac{1}{2}$ in.; $L_2 = 60$ ft, $D_2 = 1$ in.; $L_3 = 50$ ft, $D_3 = \frac{3}{4}$ in. For total flow of 30 gpm oil, $\gamma = 55$ lb/ft³, $\mu = 0.65$ poise, what is the drop in hydraulic grade line between junctions?

**10.20** Determine the discharge of the system of Fig. 10.20 for $L = 2000$ ft, $D = 18$ in., $\epsilon = 0.0015$, and $H = 25$ ft, with the pump $A$ characteristics given.

**10.21** Determine the discharge through the system of Fig. 10.20 for $L = 4000$ ft, $D = 24$-in. smooth pipe, $H = 40$ ft, with pump $B$ characteristics.

**10.22** Construct a head-discharge-efficiency table for pumps $A$ and $B$ (Fig. 10.20) connected in series.

$H$

$P$ Water 60° F

| Pump $A$ | | | | Pump $B$ | | |
|---|---|---|---|---|---|---|
| $H_{ft}$ | $Q_{cfs}$ | $e\ \%$ | | $H_{ft}$ | $Q_{cfs}$ | $e\ \%$ |
| 70 | 0 | 0 | | 80 | 0 | 0 |
| 60 | 2.00 | 59 | | 70 | 2.60 | 54 |
| 55 | 2.56 | 70 | | 60 | 3.94 | 70 |
| 50 | 3.03 | 76 | | 50 | 4.96 | 80 |
| 45 | 3.45 | 78 | | 40 | 5.70 | 73 |
| 40 | 3.82 | 76.3 | | 30 | 6.14 | 60 |
| 35 | 4.11 | 72 | | 20 | 6.24 | 40 |
| 30 | 4.38 | 65 | | | | |
| 25 | 4.59 | 56.5 | | | | |
| 20 | 4.73 | 42 | | | | |

**Fig. 10.20**

**Fig. 10.21**

**10.23**   Construct a head-discharge-efficiency table for pumps $A$ and $B$ (Fig. 10.20) connected in parallel.

**10.24**   Find the discharge through the system of Fig. 10.20 for pumps $A$ and $B$ in series; 5000 ft of 12-in. clean cast-iron pipe, $H = 100$ ft.

**10.25**   Determine the horsepower needed to drive pumps $A$ and $B$ in Prob. 10.24.

**10.26**   Find the discharge through the system of Fig. 10.20 for pumps $A$ and $B$ in parallel; 5000 ft of 18-in. steel pipe, $H = 30$ ft.

**10.27**   Determine the horsepower needed to drive the pumps in Prob. 10.26.

**10.28**   For $H = 40$ ft in Fig. 10.21, find the discharge through each pipe. $\mu = 0.08$ poise; $\gamma = 60$ lb/ft$^3$.

**10.29**   Find $H$ in Fig. 10.21 for 1 cfs flowing.   $\mu = 0.05$ poise; $\rho = 1.8$ slugs/ft$^3$.

**10.30**   Find the equivalent length of 12-in.-diameter clean cast-iron pipe to replace the system of Fig. 10.22.   For $H = 30$ ft, what is the discharge?

**10.31**   With velocity of 4 ft/sec in the 8-in.-diameter pipe of Fig. 10.22, calculate the flow through the system and the head $H$ required.

**Fig. 10.22**

**Fig. 10.23**

**10.32**   In Fig. 10.23 find the flow through the system when the pump is removed.

**10.33**   If the pump of Fig. 10.23 is delivering 3 cfs toward $J$, find the flow into $A$ and $B$ and the elevation of the hydraulic grade line at $J$.

**10.34**   The pump is adding 10 fluid horsepower to the flow (toward $J$) in Fig. 10.23.   Find $Q_A$ and $Q_B$.

**10.35**   With pump $A$ of Fig. 10.20 in the system of Fig. 10.23, find $Q_A$, $Q_B$, and the elevation of the hydraulic grade line at $J$.

**10.36**   With pump $B$ of Fig. 10.20 in the system of Fig. 10.23, find the flow into $B$ and the elevation of the hydraulic grade line at $J$.

**10.37**   For flow of 1 cfs into $B$ of Fig. 10.23, what head is produced by the pump?   For pump efficiency of 70 per cent, how much power is required?

**10.38**   Find the flow through the system of Fig. 10.24 for no pump in the system.

**10.39**   With pumps $A$ and $B$ of Fig. 10.20 in parallel in the system of Fig. 10.24, find the flow into $B$, $C$, and $D$ and the elevation of the hydraulic grade line at $J_1$ and $J_2$.

**Fig. 10.24**

**Fig. 10.25**

**10.40**   Calculate the flow through each of the pipes of the network shown in Fig. 10.25.   $n = 2$.

**10.41**   Determine the flow through each line of Fig. 10.26.   $n = 2$.

**10.42**   Find the distribution through the network of Fig. 10.25 for $n = 1$.

**10.43**   Find the distribution through the network of Fig. 10.26 tor $n = 1$.

**10.44**   Determine the slope of the hydraulic grade line for flow of atmospheric air at 80°F through a rectangular 18- by 6-in. galvanized-iron conduit. $V = 30$ ft/sec.

**10.45**   What size square conduit is needed to convey 10 cfs water at 60°F with slope of hydraulic grade line of 0.001?   $\epsilon - 0.003$.

**10.46**   Calculate the discharge of oil, sp gr 0.85, $\mu = 0.04$ poise, through 100 ft of 2- by 4-in. sheet-metal conduit when the head loss is 2 ft.   $\epsilon = 0.0005$.

**10.47**   A duct, with cross section an equilateral triangle 1 ft on a side, conveys 6 cfs water at 60°F.   $\epsilon = 0.003$.   Calculate the slope of the hydraulic grade line.

**10.48**   A clean cast-iron water pipe 24 in. in diameter has its absolute roughness doubled in 5 years of service.   Estimate the head loss per 1000 ft for a flow of 15 cfs when the pipe is 25 years old.

**Fig. 10.26**

**10.49**  An 18-in.-diameter pipe has an $f$ of 0.020 when new for 5 ft/sec water flow of 60°F.  In 10 years $f = 0.029$ for $V = 3$ ft/sec.  Find $f$ for 4 ft/sec at end of 20 years.

**10.50**  The hydraulic grade line is

($a$)  always above the energy grade line
($b$)  always above the closed conduit
($c$)  always sloping downward in the direction of flow
($d$)  the velocity head below the energy grade line
($e$)  upward in direction of flow when pipe is inclined downward

**10.51**  In solving a series-pipe problem for discharge, the energy equation is used along with the continuity equation to obtain an expression that contains a $V^2/2g$ and $f_1, f_2$, etc.  The next step in the solution is to assume

($a$) $Q$     ($b$) $V$     ($c$) **R**     ($d$) $f_1, f_2, \ldots$     ($e$) none of these quantities

**10.52**  One pipe system is said to be equivalent to another pipe system when the following two quantities are the same:

($a$) $h, Q$     ($b$) $L, Q$     ($c$) $L, D$     ($d$) $f, D$     ($e$) $V, D$

**10.53**  In parallel-pipe problems

($a$)  the head losses through each pipe are added to obtain the total head loss
($b$)  the discharge is the same through all the pipes
($c$)  the head loss is the same through each pipe
($d$)  a direct solution gives the flow through each pipe when the total flow is known
($e$)  a trial solution is not needed

**10.54**  Branching-pipe problems are solved

($a$)  analytically by using as many equations as unknowns
($b$)  by the Hardy Cross method of correcting assumed flows
($c$)  by equivalent lengths
($d$)  by assuming a distribution which satisfies continuity and computing a correction
($e$)  by assuming the elevation of hydraulic grade line at the junction point and trying to satisfy continuity

**10.55**  In networks of pipes

($a$)  the head loss around each elementary circuit must be zero
($b$)  the (horsepower) loss in all circuits is the same
($c$)  the elevation of hydraulic grade line is assumed for each junction
($d$)  elementary circuits are replaced by equivalent pipes
($e$)  friction factors are assumed for each pipe

**10.56**   The following quantities are computed by using $4R$ in place of diameter, for noncircular sections:

($a$)  velocity, relative roughness
($b$)  velocity, head loss
($c$)  Reynolds number, relative roughness, head loss
($d$)  velocity, Reynolds number, friction factor
($e$)  none of these answers

**10.57**   Experiments show that in the aging of pipes

($a$)  the friction factor increases linearly with time
($b$)  a pipe becomes smoother with use
($c$)  the absolute roughness increases linearly with time
($d$)  no appreciable trends can be found
($e$)  the absolute roughness decreases with time

# 11

# steady flow in open channels

A broad coverage of topics in open-channel flow has been selected for this chapter. Steady uniform flow was discussed in Sec. 5.9, and application of the momentum equation to the hydraulic jump in Sec. 3.11. Weirs were introduced in Sec. 8.6. In this chapter open-channel flow is first classified and then the *shape* of optimum canal cross sections is discussed followed by a section on flow through a floodway. The hydraulic jump and its application to stilling basins is then treated, followed by a discussion of specific energy and critical depth which leads into gradually varied flow. Water-surface profiles are classified and related to channel control sections. Transitions are next discussed, with one special application to the critical-depth meter.

The mechanics of flow in open channels is more complicated than closed-conduit flow owing to the presence of a free surface. The hydraulic grade line coincides with the free surface, and, in general, its position is unknown.

For laminar flow to occur, the cross section must be extremely small, the velocity very small, or the kinematic viscosity extremely high. One example of laminar flow is given by a thin film of liquid flowing down an inclined or vertical plane. This case is treated by the methods developed in Chap. 5 (see Prob. 5.10). Pipe flow has a lower critical Reynolds number of 2000, and this same value may be applied to an open channel when the diameter $D$ is replaced by $4R$. $R$ is the hydraulic radius, which is defined as the cross-sectional area of the channel divided by the wetted perimeter. In the range of the Reynolds number, based on $R$ in place of $D$, $\mathbf{R} = VR/\nu$ $< 500$ flow is laminar, $500 < \mathbf{R} < 2000$ flow is *transitional* and may be either laminar or turbulent, and $\mathbf{R} > 2000$ flow is generally turbulent.

Most open-channel flows are turbulent, usually with water as the liquid. The methods for analyzing open-channel flow are not developed to the extent of those for closed conduits. The equations in use assume complete turbulence, with the head loss proportional to the square of the velocity. Although practically all data on open-channel flow have been obtained from experiments on the flow of water, the equations should yield reasonable values for other liquids of low viscosity. The material in this chapter applies to turbulent flow only.

## 11.1 classification of flow

Open-channel flow occurs in a large variety of forms, from flow of water over the surface of a plowed field during a hard rain to the flow at constant depth through a large prismatic channel. It may be classified as steady or unsteady, uniform or nonuniform. *Steady uniform flow* occurs in very long inclined channels of constant cross section, in those regions where "terminal velocity" has been reached, i.e., where the head loss due to turbulent flow is exactly supplied by the reduction in potential energy due to the uniform decrease in elevation of the bottom of the channel. The depth for steady uniform flow is called the *normal depth*. In steady uniform flow the discharge is constant, and the depth is everywhere constant along the length of the channel. Several equations are in common use for determining the relations among the average velocity, the shape of the cross section, its size and roughness, and the slope, or inclination, of the channel bottom (Sec. 5.9).

*Steady nonuniform flow* occurs in any irregular channel in which the discharge does not change with the time; it also occurs in regular channels when the flow depth and, hence, the average velocity change from one cross section to another. For gradual changes in depth or section, called *gradually varied flow*, methods are available, by numerical integration or step-by-step means, for computing flow depths for known discharge, channel dimensions and roughness, and given conditions at one cross section. For those reaches of a channel where pronounced changes in velocity and depth occur in a short distance, as in a transition from one cross section to another, model studies are frequently made. The *hydraulic jump* is one example of steady nonuniform flow; it is discussed in Secs. 3.11 and 11.4.

*Unsteady uniform flow* rarely occurs in open-channel flow. *Unsteady nonuniform flow* is common but is extremely difficult to analyze. Wave motion is an example of this type of flow, and its analysis is complex when friction is taken into account. Positive and negative *surge waves* in a rectangular channel are analyzed, neglecting effects of friction, in Secs. 12.9 and 12.10.

Flow is also classfied as *tranquil* or *rapid*.  When flow occurs at low velocities so that a small disturbance can travel upstream and thus change upstream conditions, it is said to be tranquil flow[1] (**F** < 1).  Conditions upstream are affected by downstream conditions, and the flow is controlled by the downstream conditions.  When flow occurs at such high velocities that a small disturbance, such as an elementary wave, is swept downstream, the flow is described as *shooting* or *rapid* (**F** > 1).  Small changes in downstream conditions do not effect any change in upstream conditions; hence, the flow is controlled by upstream conditions.  When flow is such that its velocity is just equal to the velocity of an elementary wave, the flow is said to be critical (**F** = 1).

*velocity distribution*

The velocity at a solid boundary must be zero, and in open-channel flow it generally increases with distance from the boundaries.  The maximum velocity does not occur at the free surface but is usually below the free surface a distance of 0.05 to 0.25 of the depth.  The average velocity along a vertical line is sometimes determined by measuring the velocity at 0.6 of the depth, but a more reliable method is to take the average of the velocities at 0.2 and 0.8 of the depth, according to measurements of the U.S. Geological Survey.

## 11.2  best hydraulic channel cross sections

For the cross section of channel for conveying a given discharge for given slope and roughness factor, some shapes are more efficient than others. In general, when a channel is constructed, the excavation, and possibly the lining, must be paid for.  Based on the Manning formula it is shown that when the area of cross section is a minimum, the wetted perimeter is also a minimum, and so both lining and excavation approach their minimum value for the same dimensions of channel.  The *best hydraulic section* is one that has the least wetted perimeter, or its equivalent, the least area for the type of section.  The Manning formula is

$$Q = \frac{1.49}{n} AR^{2/3}S^{1/2} \tag{11.2.1}$$

[1] See Sec. 4.4 for definition and discussion of the Froude number **F**.

**Fig. 11.1** Rectangular cross section.

in which $Q$ is the discharge (cubic feet per second), $A$ the cross-sectional flow area (square feet), $R$ (area divided by wetted perimeter $P$) the hydraulic radius (feet), $S$ the slope of energy grade line, and $n$ the Manning roughness factor (Table 5.2, Sec. 5.9). With $Q$, $n$, and $S$ known, Eq. (11.2.1) may be written

$$A = cP^{2/5} \qquad (11.2.2)$$

in which $c$ is known. This equation shows that $P$ is a minimum when $A$ is a minimum. To find the best hydraulic section for a *rectangular* channel (Fig. 11.1) $P = b + 2y$, and $A = by$. Then

$$A = (P - 2y)y = cP^{2/5}$$

by elimination of $b$. The value of $y$ is sought for which $P$ is a minimum. Differentiating with respect to $y$,

$$\left(\frac{dP}{dy} - 2\right)y + P - 2y = \frac{2}{5}cP^{-3/5}\frac{dP}{dy}$$

After setting $dP/dy = 0$, $P = 4y$, or since $P = b + 2y$,

$$b = 2y \qquad (11.2.3)$$

Therefore, the depth is one-half the bottom width, independent of the size of rectangular section.

To find the best hydraulic *trapezoidal* section (Fig. 11.2) $A = by + my^2$,

**Fig. 11.2** Trapezoidal cross section.

$P = b + 2y \sqrt{1 + m^2}$.   After eliminating $b$ and $A$ in these equations and Eq. (11.2.2),

$$A = by + my^2 = (P - 2y \sqrt{1 + m^2})y + my^2 - cP^{2/5} \qquad (11.2.4)$$

By holding $m$ constant and by differentiating with respect to $y$, $\partial P / \partial y$ is set equal to zero; thus

$$P = 4y \sqrt{1 + m^2} - 2my \qquad (11.2.5)$$

Again, by holding $y$ constant, Eq. (11.2.4) is differentiated with respect to $m$, and $\partial P / \partial m$ is set equal to zero, producing

$$\frac{2m}{\sqrt{1 + m^2}} = 1$$

After solving for $m$,

$$m = \frac{\sqrt{3}}{3}$$

and after substituting for $m$ in Eq. (11.2.5),

$$P = 2\sqrt{3}\, y \qquad b = 2\frac{\sqrt{3}}{3}\, y \qquad A = \sqrt{3}\, y^2 \qquad (11.2.6)$$

which shows that $b = P/3$ and, hence, the sloping sides have the same length as the bottom.   As $\tan^{-1} m = 30°$, the best hydraulic section is one-half a hexagon.   For trapezoidal sections with $m$ specified (maximum slope at which wet earth will stand) Eq. (11.2.5) is used to find the best bottom-width-to-depth ratio.

The semicircle is the best hydraulic section of all possible open-channel cross sections.

**example 11.1**   Determine the dimensions of the most economical trapezoidal brick-lined channel to carry 8000 cfs with a slope of 0.0004.

With Eq. (11.2.6),

$$R = \frac{A}{P} = \frac{y}{2}$$

and by substituting into Eq. (11.2.1),

$$8000 = \frac{1.49}{0.016} \sqrt{3}\, y^2 \left(\frac{y}{2}\right)^{2/3} \sqrt{0.0004}$$

or

$$y^{8/3} = 3930 \qquad y = 22.3 \text{ ft}$$

and from Eq. (11.2.6), $b = 25.8$ ft.

## 11.3 steady uniform flow in a floodway

A practical open-channel problem of importance is the computation of discharge through a floodway (Fig. 11.3). In general the floodway is much rougher than the river channel, and its depth (and hydraulic radius) is much less. The slope of energy grade line must be the same for both portions. The discharge for each portion is determined separately, using the dashed line of Fig. 11.3 as the separation line for the two sections (but not as solid boundary), and then the discharges are added to determine the total capacity of the system.

Since both portions have the same slope, the discharge may be expressed as

$$Q_1 = K_1 \sqrt{S} \qquad Q_2 = K_2 \sqrt{S}$$

or

$$Q = (K_1 + K_2) \sqrt{S} \tag{11.3.1}$$

in which the value of $K$ is

$$K = \frac{1.49}{n} AR^{2/3}$$

from Manning's formula and is a function of depth only for a given channel with fixed roughness. By computing $K_1$ and $K_2$ for different elevations of water surface, their sum may be taken and plotted against elevation. From this plot it is easy to determine the slope of energy grade line for a given depth and discharge from Eq. (11.3.1).

**Fig. 11.3** Floodway cross section.

## 11.4 hydraulic jump. stilling basins

The relations among the variables $V_1$, $y_1$, $V_2$, $y_2$ for a hydraulic jump to occur in a horizontal rectangular channel are developed in Sec. 3.12. Another way of determining the conjugate depths for a given discharge is the $F + M$-method. The momentum equation applied to the free body of liquid between $y_1$ and $y_2$ (Fig. 11.4) is, for unit width $(V_1y_1 = V_2y_2 = q)$,

$$\frac{\gamma y_1^2}{2} - \frac{\gamma y_2^2}{2} = \rho q(V_2 - V_1) = \rho V_2^2 y_2 - \rho V_1^2 y_1$$

By rearranging,

$$\frac{\gamma y_1^2}{2} + \rho V_1^2 y_1 = \frac{\gamma y_2^2}{2} + \rho V_2^2 y_2 \tag{11.4.1}$$

or

$$F_1 + M_1 = F_2 + M_2 \tag{11.4.2}$$

in which $F$ is the hydrostatic force at the section and $M$ is the momentum per second passing the section. By writing $F + M$ for a given discharge $q$ per unit width

$$F + M = \frac{\gamma y^2}{2} + \frac{\rho q^2}{y} \tag{11.4.3}$$

a plot is made of $F + M$ as abscissa against $y$ as ordinate, Fig. 11.5, for $q = 10$ cfs/ft. Any vertical line intersecting the curve cuts it at two points having the same value of $F + M$; hence, they are conjugate depths. The value of $y$ for minimum $F + M$ [by differentiation of Eq. (11.4.3) with respect to $y$ and setting $d(F + M)/dy$ equal to zero] is

$$y_c = \left(\frac{q^2}{g}\right)^{1/3} \tag{11.4.4}$$

The jump must always occur from a depth less than this value to a depth greater than this value. This depth is the *critical* depth, which is shown in

**Fig. 11.4** Hydraulic jump in horizontal rectangular channel.

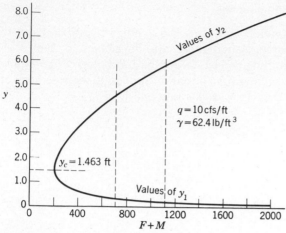

**Fig. 11.5** $F + M$ curve for hydraulic jump.

the following section to be the depth of minimum energy. Therefore, the jump always occurs from rapid flow to tranquil flow. The fact that available energy is lost in the jump prevents any possibility that it could suddenly change from the higher conjugate depth to the lower conjugate depth.

The conjugate depths are directly related to the Froude numbers before and after the jump,

$$\mathbf{F}_1 = \frac{V_1{}^2}{gy_1} \qquad \mathbf{F}_2 = \frac{V_2{}^2}{gy_2} \tag{11.4.5}$$

From the continuity equation

$$V_1{}^2y_1{}^2 = g\mathbf{F}_1y_1{}^3 = V_2{}^2y_2{}^2 = \mathbf{F}_2y_2{}^3$$

or

$$\mathbf{F}_1y_1{}^3 = \mathbf{F}_2y_2{}^3 \tag{11.4.6}$$

From Eq. (11.4.1)

$$y_1{}^2\left(1 + 2\frac{V_1{}^2}{gy_1}\right) = y_2{}^2\left(1 + 2\frac{V_2{}^2}{gy_2}\right)$$

After substituting from Eqs. (11.4.5) and (11.4.6)

$$(1 + 2\mathbf{F}_1)\mathbf{F}_1{}^{-2/3} = (1 + 2\mathbf{F}_2)\mathbf{F}_2{}^{-2/3} \tag{11.4.7}$$

The value of $F_2$ in terms of $F_1$ is obtained from the hydraulic jump equation (3.11.23),

$$y_2 = -\frac{y_1}{2} + \sqrt{\left(\frac{y_1}{2}\right)^2 + 2\frac{V_1{}^2 y_1}{g}}$$

or

$$2\frac{y_2}{y_1} = -1 + \sqrt{1 + 8\frac{V_1{}^2}{gy_1}}$$

By using Eqs. (11.4.5) and (11.4.6)

$$F_2 = \frac{8F_1}{(\sqrt{1 + 8F_1} - 1)^3} \tag{11.4.8}$$

The Froude number before the jump is always greater than unity, and after the jump it is always less than unity.

*stilling basins*

A stilling basin is a structure for dissipating available energy of flow below a spillway, outlet works, chute, or canal structure.   In the majority of existing installations a hydraulic jump is housed within the stilling basin and is used as the energy dissipator.   This discussion is limited to rectangular basins with horizontal floors although sloping floors are used in some cases to save excavation.   An authoritative and comprehensive work[1] by personnel of the Bureau of Reclamation classified the hydraulic jump as an effective energy dissipator in terms of the Froude number $F_1(V_1{}^2/gy_1)$ entering the basin as follows:

At $F_1 = 1$ to 3.   Standing wave.   There is only a slight difference in conjugate depths.   Near $F_1 = 3$ a series of small rollers develops.

At $F_1 = 3$ to 6.   Pre-jump.   The water surface is quite smooth, the velocity is fairly uniform, and the head loss is low.   No baffles required if proper length of pool is provided.

At $F_1 = 6$ to 20.   Transition.   Oscillating action of entering jet, from bottom of basin to surface.   Each oscillation produces a large wave of irregular period that can travel downstream for miles and damage earth banks and riprap.   If possible, it is advantageous to avoid this range of Froude numbers in stilling-basin design.

---

[1] *Hydraulic Lab. Rept.* no. Hyd-399, Research Study on Stilling Basins, Energy Dissipators, and Associated Appurtenances, progress report II, U.S. Bur. Reclamation, Denver, June 1, 1955. In this report the Froude number was defined as $V/\sqrt{gy}$.

At $F_1 = 20$ to $80$.   Range of good jumps.   The jump is well-balanced and the action is at its best.   Energy absorption (irreversibilities) ranges from 45 to 70 per cent.   Baffles and sills may be utilized to reduce length of basin.

At $F_1 = 80$ upward.   Effective but rough.   Energy dissipation up to 85 per cent.   Other types of stilling basins may be more economical.

Baffle blocks are frequently used at entrance to a basin to corrugate the flow.   They are usually regularly spaced with gaps about equal to block widths.   Sills, either triangular or dentated, are frequently employed at the downstream end of a basin to aid in holding the jump within the basin and to permit some shortening of the basin.

The basin should be paved with high-quality concrete to prevent erosion and cavitation damage.   No irregularities in floor or training walls should be permitted.   The length of the jump, about $6y_2$, should be within the paved basin, with good riprap downstream if the material is easily eroded.

**example 11.2**   A hydraulic jump occurs downstream from a 50-ft-wide sluice gate.   The depth is 5.0 ft and the velocity is 60 ft/sec.   Determine (a) the Froude number and the Froude number corresponding to the conjugate depth; (b) the depth and velocity after the jump; and (c) the horsepower dissipated by the jump.

(a)   $$\mathbf{F}_1 = \frac{V_1^2}{gy_1} = \frac{60^2}{32.2 \times 5} = 22.35$$

From Eq. (11.4.8)

$$\mathbf{F}_2 = \frac{8 \times 22.35}{(\sqrt{1 + 8 \times 22.35} - 1)^3} = 0.0938$$

(b)   $$\mathbf{F}_2 = \frac{V_2^2}{gy_2} = 0.0938 \qquad V_2y_2 = 5 \times 60 = 300$$

then

$$V_2^3 = 300 \times 32.2 \times 0.0938$$

and $V_2 = 9.67$, $y_2 = 31.0$ ft.

(c)   From Eq. (3.11.24), the head loss in the jump, $h_j$, is

$$h_j = \frac{(y_2 - y_1)^3}{4y_1y_2} = \frac{(31.0 - 5)^3}{4 \times 5 \times 31.0} = 28.32 \text{ ft-lb/lb}$$

The horsepower dissipated is

$$\text{hp} = \frac{Q\gamma h_j}{550} = 50 \times 300 \times 62.4 \times \frac{28.32}{550} = 48,200$$

## 11.5  specific energy, critical depth

The energy per unit weight, $E$, with elevation datum taken as the bottom of the channel, is called the *specific energy*.   It is a convenient quantity to use in studying open-channel flow and was introduced by Bakhmeteff in 1911. It is plotted vertically above the channel floor,

$$E = y + \frac{V^2}{2g} \tag{11.5.1}$$

A plot of specific energy for a particular case is shown in Fig. 11.6.   In a rectangular channel, in which $q$ is the discharge per unit width, with $Vy = q$,

$$E = y + \frac{q^2}{2gy^2} \tag{11.5.2}$$

It is of interest to note how the specific energy varies with the depth for a constant discharge (Fig. 11.7).   For small values of $y$ the curve goes to infinity along the $E$-axis, while for large values of $y$ the velocity-head term is negligible and the curve approaches the 45° line $E = y$ asymptotically. The specific energy has a minimum value below which the given $q$ cannot occur.   The value of $y$ for minimum $E$ is obtained by setting $dE/dy$ equal to zero, from Eq. (11.5.2), holding $q$ constant,

$$\frac{dE}{dy} = 0 = 1 - \frac{q^2}{gy^3}$$

or

$$y_c = \left(\frac{q^2}{g}\right)^{1/3} \tag{11.5.3}$$

The depth for minimum energy $y_c$ is called *critical depth*.   By eliminating $q^2$ in Eqs. (11.5.2) and (11.5.3),

$$E_{\min} = \tfrac{3}{2}y_c \tag{11.5.4}$$

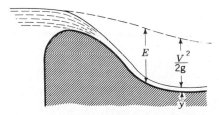

**Fig. 11.6**  Example of specific energy.

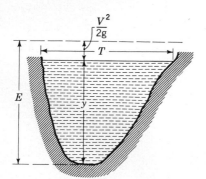

**Fig. 11.7**  Specific energy required for flow of a given discharge at various depths.

showing that the critical depth is two-thirds of the specific energy.   By eliminating $E$ in Eqs. (11.5.1) and (11.5.4),

$$V_c = \sqrt{gy_c} \qquad\qquad (11.5.5)$$

The velocity of flow at critical condition $V_c$ is $\sqrt{gy_c}$, which was used in Sec. 8.6 in connection with the broad-crested weir.   Another method of arriving at the critical condition is to determine the maximum discharge $q$ that could occur for a given specific energy.   The resulting equations are the same as Eqs. (11.5.3) to (11.5.5).

For nonrectangular cross sections, as illustrated in Fig. 11.8, the specific-

**Fig. 11.8**  Specific energy for a non-rectangular section.

energy equation takes the form

$$E = y + \frac{Q^2}{2gA^2} \tag{11.5.6}$$

in which $A$ is the cross-sectional area.   To find the critical depth,

$$\frac{dE}{dy} = 0 = 1 - \frac{Q^2}{gA^3}\frac{dA}{dy}$$

From Fig. 11.8, the relation between $dA$ and $dy$ is expressed by

$$dA = T\,dy$$

in which $T$ is the width of the cross section at the liquid surface.   With this relation,

$$\frac{Q^2}{gA_c^3}T_c = 1 \tag{11.5.7}$$

The critical depth must satisfy this equation.   By eliminating $Q$ in Eqs. (11.5.6) and (11.5.7),

$$E = y_c + \frac{A_c}{2T_c} \tag{11.5.8}$$

This equation shows that the minimum energy occurs when the velocity head is one-half the average depth $A/T$.   Equation (11.5.7) may be solved by trial for irregular sections, by plotting

$$f(y) = \frac{Q^2 T}{gA^3}$$

Critical depth occurs for that value of $y$ which makes $f(y) = 1$.

**example 11.3**   Determine the critical depth for 300 cfs flowing in a trapezoidal channel with bottom width 8 ft and side slopes one horizontal to two vertical (1 on 2).

$$A = 8y + \frac{y^2}{2} \qquad T = 8 + y$$

Hence

$$f(y) = \frac{(300)^2(8 + y)}{32.2(8y + y^2/2)^3} = \frac{2795(8 + y)}{(8y + 0.5y^2)^3}$$

By trial

| $y = 2$ | 4 | 3 | 3.2 | 3.24 | 3.26 | 3.30 | 3.28 |
|---------|------|------|------|------|------|-------|-------|
| $f(y) = 4.8$ | 0.52 | 1.33 | 1.08 | 1.03 | 1.02 | 0.975 | 0.997 |

The critical depth is 3.28 ft.

In uniform flow in an open channel, the energy grade line slopes downward parallel to the bottom of the channel, thus showing a steady decrease in available energy. The specific energy, however, remains constant along the channel, since $y + V^2/2g$ does not change. In nonuniform flow, the energy grade line always slopes downward, or the available energy is decreased. The specific energy may either increase or decrease, depending upon the slope of the channel bottom, the discharge, the depth of flow, properties of the cross section, and channel roughness. In Fig. 11.6 the specific energy increases during flow down the steep portion of the channel and decreases along the horizontal channel floor.

The specific-energy and critical-depth relationships are essential in studying gradually varied flow and in determining control sections in open-channel flow.

By comparing Figs. 11.5 and 11.7, which are both drawn for $q = 10$ cfs, it is easy to show the head loss that results from the hydraulic jump. Taking the two values of $y$ on a vertical line from the momentum curve and plotting these points on the specific-energy curve shows that the jump is always to a depth of less available energy.

### 11.6  gradually varied flow

Gradually varied flow is steady nonuniform flow of a special class. The depth, area, roughness, bottom slope, and hydraulic radius change very slowly (if at all) along the channel. The basic assumption required is that the head-loss rate at a given section is given by the Manning formula for the same depth and discharge, regardless of trends in the depth. Solving Eq. (11.2.1) for the head loss per unit length of channel produces

$$S = -\frac{\Delta E}{\Delta L} = \frac{n^2 Q^2}{2.22 A^2 R^{4/3}} \tag{11.6.1}$$

in which $S$ is now the slope of the energy grade line, or, more specifically, the sine of the angle the energy grade line makes with the horizontal. In gradually varied flow the slopes of energy grade line, hydraulic grade line, and bottom are all different.   Computations of gradually varied flow may be carried out either by the *standard step method* or by *numerical integration*. Horizontal channels of great width are treated as a special case that may be integrated.

*standard step method*

By applying the energy equation between two sections a finite distance apart, $\Delta L$, Fig. 11.9, including the loss term,

$$\frac{V_1{}^2}{2g} + S_0 \, \Delta L + y_1 = \frac{V_2{}^2}{2g} + y_2 + S \, \Delta L \qquad (11.6.2)$$

After solving for the length of reach,

$$\Delta L = \frac{(V_1{}^2 - V_2{}^2)/2g + y_1 - y_2}{S - S_0} \qquad (11.6.3)$$

If conditions are known at one section, e.g., section 1, and the depth $y_2$ is wanted a distance $\Delta L$ away, a trial solution is required.   The procedure is

1.   Assume a depth $y_2$; then compute $A_2$, $V_2$.
2.   For the assumed $y_2$ find an average $y$, $P$, and $A$ for the reach [for prismatic channels $y = (y_1 + y_2)/2$ with $A$ and $R$ computed for this depth] and compute $S$.
3.   Substitute in Eq. (11.6.3) to compute $\Delta L$.
4.   If $\Delta L$ is not correct, assume a new $y_2$ and repeat the procedure.

**example 11.4**   At section 1 of a canal the cross section is trapezoidal, $b_1 = 40$ ft, $m_1 = 2$, $y_1 = 20$ ft, $V_1 = 3$ ft/sec and at section 2, downstream

**Fig. 11.9**  Gradually varied flow.

500 ft, the bottom is 0.20 ft higher than at section 1, $b_2 = 50$ ft, and $m_2 = 3$, $n = 0.035$. Determine the depth of water at section 2.

$$A_1 = b_1 y_1 + m_1 y_1{}^2 = 40 \times 20 + 2 \times (20)^2 = 1600 \text{ ft}^2$$
$$P_1 = b_1 + 2y_1 \sqrt{m_1{}^2 + 1} = 40 + 2 \times 20 \sqrt{2^2 + 1} = 129.6 \text{ ft}$$
$$S_0 = -\frac{0.20}{500} = -0.0004$$
$$Q = V_1 A_1 = 3 \times 1600 = 4800 \text{ cfs}$$

Since the bottom has an adverse slope, i.e., it is rising in the downstream direction, and since section 2 is larger than section 1, $y_2$ is probably less than $y_1$ for $\Delta L$ to be positive. Assume $y_2 = 19.8$; then

$$A_2 = 19.8 \times 50 + 3 \times (19.8)^2 = 2166 \text{ ft}^2$$

and

$$P_2 = 50 + 2 \times 19.8 \sqrt{10} = 175 \text{ ft}$$

The average area $A = 1883$ and average wetted perimeter $P = 152.3$ are used to find an average hydraulic radius for the reach, $R = 12.36$. Then

$$S = \frac{n^2 Q^2}{2.22 A^2 R^{4/3}} = \left(\frac{0.035 \times 4800}{1883}\right)^2 \frac{1}{2.22 \times (12.36)^{4/3}} = 0.000125$$

and

$$V_2 = \frac{4800}{2166} = 2.22$$

By substituting into Eq. (11.6.3)

$$\Delta L = \frac{[3^2 - (2.22)^2]/64.4 + 20 - 19.8}{0.000125 + 0.00040} = 514 \text{ ft}$$

The value of $y_2$ should be slightly greater, e.g., 19.81 ft.

*numerical integration method*

A more satisfactory procedure, particularly for flow through channels having a constant shape of cross section and constant bottom slope, is to obtain a differential equation in terms of $y$ and $L$ and then to perform the integration numerically. Considering $\Delta L$ an infinitesimal in Fig. 11.9, the rate of change of available energy is equal to the rate of head loss $-\Delta E/\Delta L$

given by Eq. (11.6.1), or

$$\frac{d}{dL}\left(\frac{V^2}{2g} + z_0 - S_0L + y\right) = -\frac{n^2Q^2}{2.22A^2R^{4/3}}$$    (11.6.4)

in which $z_0 - S_0L$ is the elevation of bottom of channel at $L$, $z_0$ is the elevation of bottom at $L = 0$, and $L$ is measured positive in the downstream direction.    After performing the differentiation,

$$-\frac{V}{g}\frac{dV}{dL} + S_0 - \frac{dy}{dL} = \frac{n^2Q^2}{2.22A^2R^{4/3}}$$    (11.6.5)

By using the continuity equation $VA = Q$ to eliminate $V$,

$$\frac{dV}{dL}A + V\frac{dA}{dL} = 0$$

After expressing $dA = T\,dy$, in which $T$ is the liquid-surface width of the cross section,

$$\frac{dV}{dL} = -\frac{VT}{A}\frac{dy}{dL} = -\frac{QT}{A^2}\frac{dy}{dL}$$

By substituting for $V$ in Eq. (11.6.5)

$$\frac{Q^2}{yA^3}T\frac{dy}{dL} + S_0 - \frac{dy}{dL} = \frac{n^2Q^2}{2.22A^2R^{4/3}}$$

and by solving for $dL$,

$$dL = \frac{1 - Q^2T/gA^3}{S_0 - n^2Q^2/2.22A^2R^{4/3}}\,dy$$    (11.6.6)

After integrating,

$$L = \int_{y_1}^{y_2}\frac{1 - Q^2T/gA^3}{S_0 - n^2Q^2/2.22A^2R^{4/3}}\,dy$$    (11.6.7)

in which $L$ is the distance between the two sections having depths $y_1$ and $y_2$.

When the numerator of the integrand is zero, critical flow prevails; there is no change in $L$ for a change in $y$ (neglecting curvature of the flow and nonhydrostatic pressure distribution at this section).    This is not a case of gradual change in depth, and, hence, the equations are not accurate near critical depth.    When the denominator of the integrand is zero, uniform flow prevails, and there is no change in depth along the channel.    The flow is at *normal depth*.

**Fig. 11.10** Numerical integration of gradually varied flow equation.

For a channel of prismatic cross section, constant $n$ and $S_0$, the integrand becomes a function of $y$ only,

$$F(y) = \frac{1 - Q^2 T/g A^3}{S_0 - n^2 Q^2/2.22 A^2 R^{4/3}}$$

and the equation may be integrated numerically by plotting $F(y)$ as ordinate against $y$ as abscissa. The area under the curve (Fig. 11.10) between two values of $y$ is the length $L$ between the sections, since

$$L = \int_{y_1}^{y_2} F(y)\, dy$$

has exactly the same form as the area integral $\int y\, dx$.

**example 11.5**  A trapezoidal channel, $b = 10$ ft, $m = 1$, $n = 0.014$, $S_0 = 0.001$, carries 1000 cfs.  If the depth is 10 ft at section 1, determine the water-surface profile for the next 2000 ft downstream.

To determine whether the depth increases or decreases, the slope of energy grade line at section 1 is computed, Eq. (11.6.1):

$$A = by + my^2 = 10 \times 10 + 1 \times (10)^2 = 200\,\text{ft}^2$$
$$P = b + 2y\sqrt{m^2 + 1} = 38.2\text{ ft}$$

and

$$R = \frac{200}{38.2} = 5.24\text{ ft}$$

Then

$$S = \frac{1}{2.22}\left(\frac{0.014 \times 1000}{200}\right)^2 \frac{1}{(5.24)^{4/3}} = 0.000243$$

The depth is greater than critical and $S < S_0$, hence, the specific energy is increasing and this can be accomplished only by increasing the depth downstream.   After substituting into Eq. (11.6.7),

$$L = \int_{10}^{y} \frac{1 - 3.105 \times 10^{4} T / A^{3}}{0.001 - 88.3 / A^{2} R^{4/3}} \, dy$$

The following table evaluates the terms in the integrand:

| $y$ | $A$ | $P$ | $R$ | $T$ | $Num.$ | $10^{3} \times$ $Den.$ | $F(y)$ | $L$ |
|------|-------|------|------|----|--------|------|------|------|
| 10.0 | 200   | 38.2 | 5.24 | 30 | 0.8836 | 757  | 1167 | 0    |
| 10.5 | 215.2 | 39.8 | 5.41 | 31 | 0.9037 | 800  | 1129 | 574  |
| 11.0 | 232   | 41.1 | 5.64 | 32 | 0.9204 | 836  | 1101 | 1131 |
| 11.5 | 247.2 | 42.5 | 5.82 | 33 | 0.9323 | 862  | 1082 | 1677 |
| 12.0 | 264   | 43.9 | 6.01 | 34 | 0.9426 | 884  | 1067 | 2214 |

The integral $\int F(y) \, dy$ may be evaluated by plotting the curve and taking the area under it between $y = 10$ and the following values of $y$.   As $F(y)$ does not vary greatly in this example, the average of $F(y)$ may be used for each reach and, when multiplied by $\Delta y$, the length of reach is obtained. Between $y = 10$ and $y = 10.5$

$$\frac{1167 + 1129}{2} \times 0.50 = 574$$

Between $y = 10.5$ and $y = 11.0$

$$\frac{1129 + 1101}{2} \times 0.50 = 557$$

and so on.   Five points on the water surface are known so that it may be plotted.

*horizontal channels of great width*

For channels of great width the hydraulic radius equals the depth; and for horizontal channel floors $S_0 = 0$; hence, Eq. (11.6.7) may be simplified. The width may be considered as unity, i.e., $T = 1$, $Q = q$ and $A = y$, $R = y$; thus

$$L = - \int_{y_1}^{y} \frac{1 - q^2/gy^3}{n^2 q^2 / 2.22 y^{10/3}} \, dy \tag{11.6.8}$$

or, after performing the integration,

$$L = - \frac{0.512}{n^2 q^2} (y^{13/3} - y_1^{13/3}) + \frac{0.0517}{n^2} (y^{4/3} - y_1^{4/3}) \qquad (11.6.9)$$

**example 11.6**   After contracting below a sluice gate water flows onto a wide horizontal floor with a velocity of 40 ft/sec and a depth of 2.0 ft.   Find the equation for water-surface profile, $n = 0.015$.

From Eq. (11.6.9), with $x$ replacing $L$ as distance from section 1, where $y_1 = 2$,

$$x = - \frac{0.512}{(0.015 \times 80)^2} (y^{13/3} - 2^{13/3}) + \frac{0.0517}{(0.015)^2} (y^{4/3} - 2^{4/3})$$

$$= -572 - 0.3556 y^{13/3} + 229.6 y^{4/3}$$

Critical depth occurs at [Eq. (11.5.3)]

$$y_1 = \left( \frac{q^2}{g} \right)^{1/3} = \left[ \frac{(80)^2}{32.2} \right]^{1/3} = 5.84 \text{ ft}$$

The depth must increase downstream, since the specific energy decreases, and the depth must move toward the critical value for less specific energy. The equation does not hold near the critical depth because of vertical accelerations that have been neglected in the derivation of gradually varied flow.   If critical depth is attained before the end of the channel, the high-velocity flow downstream from the gate is drowned by the backwater.   The calculation must then start with critical depth at the downstream end of the channel.   A jump may occur, as discussed in Sec. 11.9.

The various types of water-surface profile obtained in gradually varied flow are discussed in Sec. 11.8.

## 11.7   computer calculation of gradually varied flow

In the previous section the standard-step method and the numerical integration method were introduced.   For prismatic sections the rather tedious calculations in the numerical integration method are conveniently handled by digital computer.   Appendix E.1 illustrates the use of Simpson's rule by computer.   Use of the computer for a gradually varied flow problem is illustrated by the following example.

**example 11.7**   A trapezoidal channel, $B = 8$ ft, $M = 0.8$, has two slopes. The upstream portion is 2000 ft long, $S_0 = 0.04$, and the downstream portion, 1800 ft long, $S_0 = 0.0002$, $n = 0.012$.   At the upstream end a reservoir

```
C     COMPUTATION FOR WATER SURFACE PROFILE IN TRAPEZOIDAL CHANNEL WITH
C     ONE SLOPE CHANGE
      REAL M,N,LEN,L,L1,L2
      DIMENSION S0(2),YN(2),Y(200),L(200),FM(200)
    1 FORMAT('1    CRITICAL DEPTH YC=',F5.2,'UPSTREAM NORMAL DEPTH=',F5.2
     2,'DOWNSTREAM NORMAL DEPTH=',F5.2,'DISCHARGE=',F7.1)
    2 FORMAT('0           DEPTH          LENGTH          F + M')
    3 FORMAT(10X,F5.2,10X,F7.1,9X,F8.0)
      NAMELIST/DIN/YR1,YR2,N,B,M,S0,L1,L2,G/DN2/YJ,J1,DY
      A(Y1)=Y1*(B+M*Y1)
      P(Y2)=B+2.*Y2*SQRT(1.+M*M)
      T(Y3)=B+2.*M*Y3
      YNORM(Y4,SS)=1.-(Q*N)**2*P(Y4)**1.333/(2.22*SS*A(Y4)**3.333)
      LEN(Y5,S1)=(1.-Q*Q*T(Y5)/(G*A(Y5)**3))/(S1*YNORM(Y5,S1))
   10 READ(5,DIN,END=99)
      WRITE(6,DIN)
C     CRITICAL DEPTH AND DISCHARGE DETERMINATION
      BB=3.*B-4.*M*YR1
      YC=(-BB+SQRT(BB**2+40.*M*B*YR1))/(10.*M)
      Q=A(YC)*SQRT(2.*G*(YR1-YC))
C     DETERMINATION OF NORMAL DEPTH
      DO 12 J=1,2
      UP=100.
      DN=.0
      DO 12 K=1,19
      YN(J)=.5*(UP+DN)
      IF(YNORM(YN(J),S0(J)).GT..0) GO TO 11
      DN=YN(J)
      GO TO 12
   11 UP=YN(J)
   12 CONTINUE
      WRITE(6,1) YC,YN(1),YN(2),Q
      WRITE(6,2)
      IF(YN(1).GT.YC) GO TO 10
C     DETERMINATION OF PROFILES AND F+M
      L(1)=.0
      DY=(YN(1)+.01-YC)/80.
      DO 13 J=1,41
      Y(J)=YC+2.*(J-1)*DY
      L(J+1)=L(J)+(LEN(Y(J),S0(1))+4.*LEN(Y(J)+DY,S0(1))+LEN(Y(J)+2.*DY,
     2S0(1)))*DY/3.
      WRITE(6,3) Y(J),L(J)
      IF(L(J+1).LT.L1) GO TO 13
      YJ=Y(J)+2.*DY*(1.-(L(J+1)-L1)/(L(J+1)-L(J)))
      J1=J+1
      L(J1)=L1
      WRITE(6,DN2)
      GO TO 15
   13 CONTINUE
      IF(L(42).LT.L1) GO TO 14
      GO TO 15
   14 L(42)=L1
      J1=42
      YJ=YN(1)
      WRITE(6,DN2)
      DO 16 J=1,42
   15 L(1)=L1
      Y(J)=YJ-2.*DY*(J-1)
      IF(Y(J)-DY.GT.YC) GO TO 17
      L(J+1)=L(J)-(LEN(Y(J),S0(2))+4.*LEN(Y(J)-DY,S0(2))+LEN(Y(J)-2.*DY,
     2S0(2)))*DY/3.
      FM(J)=62.4*(Y(J)**2*(2.*B+T(Y(J)))/6.+Q*Q/(G*A(Y(J))))
   16 WRITE(6,3) Y(J),L(J),FM(J)
   17 L(1)=L1+L2
      Y(1)=YR2
      DY=(YN(2)-YR2)/80.
      DO 18 J=1,26
      L(J+1)=L(J)+(LEN(Y(J),S0(2))+4.*LEN(Y(J)+DY,S0(2))+LEN(Y(J)+2.*DY,
     2S0(2)))*DY/3.
      FM(J)=62.4*(Y(J)**2*(2.*B+T(Y(J)))/6.+Q*Q/(G*A(Y(J))))
      Y(J+1)=Y(J)+2.*DY
   18 WRITE(6,3) Y(J),L(J),FM(J)
      GO TO 10
   99 CALL SYSTEM
      END
```

**Fig. 11.11** Computer program for solution of Example 11.7.

**Fig. 11.12** Solution to Example 11.7 as obtained from computer.

has a level 8 ft above the bottom of the channel, and at the downstream end of the system the water depth is 6 ft. Neglecting losses at the entrance to the system, determine (a) the discharge, critical depth, and normal depths, (b) the $F + M$ data for location of a possible jump, and (c) the water-surface profiles throughout the system, including jump location.

Critical depth occurs at entrance to the system, and so the discharge and critical depth can be found by writing Bernoulli's equation from the reservoir surface to the upstream end of channel. Normal depths are found by using the bisection method of solving the Manning formula. Simpson's rule is used in calculating the water-surface profile. The computer program, which uses several one-statement internal functions (Fig. 11.11), solves for all information needed for this problem. From its output, Fig. 11.12 is prepared, which gives the solution to the problem. The location of hydraulic jump is discussed in Sec. 11.9.

## 11.8 classification of surface profiles

A study of Eq. (11.6.7) reveals many types of surface profiles, each of which has its definite characteristics. The bottom slope is classified as *adverse, horizontal, mild, critical,* and *steep;* and, in general, the flow can be above the normal depth or below the normal depth, and it can be above critical depth or below critical depth.

The various profiles are plotted in Fig. 11.13; the procedures used are discussed for the various classifications in the following paragraphs. A very wide channel is assumed in the reduced equations which follow, with $R = y$.

*adverse-slope profiles*

When the channel bottom rises in the direction of flow, the resulting surface profiles are said to be adverse. There is no normal depth, but the

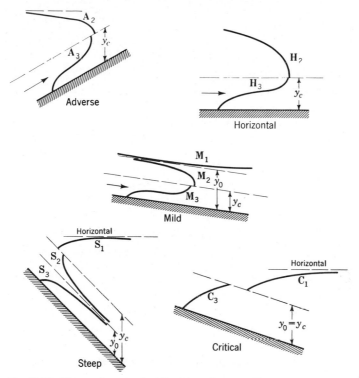

**Fig. 11.13** The various typical liquid-surface profiles.

flow may be either below critical depth or above critical depth.   Thus, $S_0$ is negative.    Below critical depth the numerator is negative, and Eq. (11.6.6) has the form

$$dL = \frac{1 - C_1/y^3}{S_0 - C_2/y^{10/3}} \, dy$$

Here, $F(y)$ is positive, and the depth increases downstream.   This curve is labeled **A₃** and shown in Fig. 11.13.   For depths greater than critical depth, the numerator is positive, and $F(y)$ is negative, i.e., the depth decreases in the downstream direction.   For $y$ very large, $dL/dy = 1/S_0$, which is a horizontal asymptote for the curve.   At $y = y_c$, $dL/dy$ is 0, and the curve is perpendicular to the critical-depth line.   This curve is labeled **A₂**.

*horizontal-slope profiles*

For a horizontal channel $S_0 = 0$, the normal depth is infinite and flow may be either below critical depth or above critical depth. The equation has the form

$$dL = -Cy^{1/3}(y^3 - C_1)\, dy$$

For $y$ less than critical, $dL/dy$ is positive, and the depth increases down-stream. It is labeled **H**$_3$. For $y$ greater than critical (**H**$_2$-curve), $dL/dy$ is negative, and the depth decreases downstream. These equations are integrable analytically for very wide channels.

*mild-slope profiles*

A mild slope is one on which the normal flow is tranquil, i.e., where normal depth $y_0$ is greater than critical depth. Three profiles may occur, **M**$_1$, **M**$_2$, **M**$_3$, for depth above normal, below normal and above critical, and below critical, respectively. For the **M**$_1$-curve, $dL/dy$ is positive and approaches $1/S_0$ for very large $y$; hence, the **M**$_1$-curve has a horizontal asymptote downstream. As the denominator approaches zero as $y$ approaches $y_0$, the normal depth is an asymptote at the upstream end of the curve. Thus, $dL/dy$ is negative for the **M**$_2$-curve, with the upstream asymptote the nor-mal depth, and $dL/dy = 0$ at critical. The **M**$_3$-curve has an increasing depth downstream, as shown.

*critical-slope profiles*

When the normal depth and the critical depth are equal, the resulting pro-files are labeled **C**$_1$ and **C**$_3$ for depth above and below critical, respectively. The equation has the form

$$dL = \frac{1}{S_0}\frac{1 - b/y^3}{1 - b_1/y^{10/3}}\, dy$$

with both numerator and denominator positive for **C**$_1$ and negative for **C**$_3$. Therefore the depth increases downstream for both. For large $y$, $dL/dy$ approaches $1/S_0$; hence, a horizontal line is an asymptote. The value of $dL/dy$ at critical depth is $0.9/S_0$; hence, curve **C**$_1$ is convex upward. Curve **C**$_3$ is also convex upward, as shown.

*steep-slope profiles*

When the normal flow is rapid in a channel (normal depth less than critical depth), the resulting profiles **S**$_1$, **S**$_2$, **S**$_3$ are referred to as steep profiles: **S**$_1$

is above the normal and critical, **S**$_2$ between critical and normal, and **S**$_3$ below normal depth.    For curve **S**$_1$ both numerator and denominator are positive, and the depth increases downstream approaching a horizontal asymptote.    For curve **S**$_2$ the numerator is negative, and the denominator positive but approaching zero at $y = y_0$.    The curve approaches the normal depth asymptotically.    The **S**$_3$-curve has a positive $dL/dy$ as both numerator and denominator are negative.    It plots as shown on Fig. 11.13.

It should be noted that a given channel may be classified as mild for one discharge, critical for another discharge, and steep for a third discharge, since normal depth and critical depth depend upon different functions of the discharge.    The use of the various surface profiles is discussed in the next section.

### 11.9  control sections

A small change in downstream conditions cannot be relayed upstream when the depth is critical or less than critical; hence, downstream conditions do not control the flow.    All rapid flows are controlled by upstream conditions, and computations of surface profiles must be started at the upstream end of a channel.

Tranquil flows are affected by small changes in downstream conditions and, therefore, are controlled by them.    Tranquil-flow computations must start at the downstream end of a reach and be carried upstream.

Control sections occur at entrances and exits to channels and at changes in channel slopes, under certain conditions.    A gate in a channel can be a control for both the upstream and downstream reaches.    Three control sections are illustrated in Fig. 11.14.    In $a$ the flow passes through critical

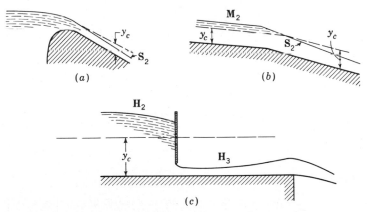

**Fig. 11.14**  Channel control sections.

**Fig. 11.15** Hydraulic jump between two control sections.

at the entrance to a channel, and depth can be computed there for a given discharge. The channel is steep; therefore, computations proceed downstream. In $b$ a change in channel slope from mild to steep causes the flow to pass through critical at the break in grade. Computations proceed both upstream and downstream from the control section at the break in grade. In $c$ a gate in a horizontal channel provides controls both upstream and downstream from it. The various curves are labeled according to the classification in Fig. 11.13.

The hydraulic jump occurs whenever the conditions required by the momentum equation are satisfied. In Fig. 11.15, liquid issues from under a gate in rapid flow along a horizontal channel. If the channel were short enough, the flow could discharge over the end of the channel as an $H_3$-curve. With a longer channel, however, the jump occurs and the resulting profile consists of pieces of $H_3$- and $H_2$-curves with the jump in between. In computing these profiles for a known discharge, the $H_3$-curve is computed, starting at the gate (contraction coefficient must be known) and proceeding downstream until it is clear that the depth will reach critical before the end of the channel is reached. Then the $H_2$-curve is computed, starting with critical depth at the end of the channel and proceeding upstream. The depths conjugate to those along $H_3$ are computed and plotted as shown. The intersection of the conjugate depth curve and the $H_2$-curve locates the position of the jump. The channel may be so long that the $H_2$-curve is everywhere greater than the depth conjugate to $H_3$. A "drowned jump" then occurs, with $H_2$ extending to the gate.

All sketches are drawn to a greatly exaggerated vertical scale, since usual channels have small bottom slopes.

## 11.10 transitions

At entrances to channels and at changes in cross section and bottom slope, the structure that conducts the liquid from the upstream section to the

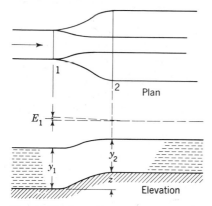

**Fig. 11.16** Transition from rectangular channel to trapezoidal channel for tranquil flow.

new section is a *transition*.   Its purpose is to change the shape of flow and surface profile in such a manner that minimum losses result.   A transition for tranquil flow from a rectangular channel to a trapezoidal channel is illustrated in Fig. 11.16.   By applying the energy equation from section 1 to section 2,

$$\frac{V_1^2}{2g} + y_1 = \frac{V_2^2}{2g} + y_2 + z + E_1 \tag{11.10.1}$$

In general, the sections and depths are determined by other considerations, and $z$ must be determined for the expected available energy loss $E_1$.   By good design, i.e., with slowly tapering walls and flooring with no sudden changes in cross-sectional area, the losses can be held to about one-tenth of the difference between velocity heads for accelerated flow and to about three-tenths of the difference between velocity heads for retarded flow. For rapid flow, wave mechanics is required in designing the transitions.[1]

**example 11.8**   In Fig. 11.16, 400 cfs flows through the transition; the rectangular section is 8 ft wide; and $y_1 = 8$ ft.   The trapezoidal section is 6 ft wide at the bottom with side slopes 1:1, and $y_2 = 7.5$ ft.   Determine the rise $z$ in the bottom through the transition.

$$V_1 = \frac{400}{64} = 6.25 \qquad \frac{V_1^2}{2g} = 0.61 \qquad A_2 = 101.25 \text{ ft}^2$$

$$V_2 = \frac{400}{101.25} = 3.95 \qquad \frac{V_2^2}{2g} = 0.24 \qquad E_1 = 0.3\left(\frac{V_1^2}{2g} - \frac{V_2^2}{2g}\right) = 0.11$$

---

[1] A. T. Ippen, Channel Transitions and Controls, in "Engineering Hydraulics," ed. by H. Rouse, John Wiley & Sons, Inc., New York, 1950.

After substituting into Eq. (11.10.1)

$$z = 0.61 + 8 - 0.24 - 7.5 - 0.11 = 0.76 \text{ ft}$$

The *critical-depth meter*[1] is an excellent device for measuring discharge in an open channel. The relationships for determination of discharge are worked out for a rectangular channel of constant width, Fig. 11.17, with a raised floor over a reach of channel about $3y_c$ long. The raised floor is of such height that the restricted section becomes a control section with critical velocity occurring over it. By measuring only the upstream depth $y_1$, the discharge per foot of width is accurately determined. By applying the energy equation from section 1 to the critical section (exact location unimportant), including the transition loss term,

$$\frac{V_1{}^2}{2g} + y_1 = z + y_c + \frac{V_c{}^2}{2g} + \frac{1}{10}\left(\frac{V_c{}^2}{2g} - \frac{V_1{}^2}{2g}\right)$$

Since

$$y_c + \frac{V_c{}^2}{2g} = E_c \qquad \frac{V_c{}^2}{2g} = \frac{E_c}{3}$$

in which $E_c$ is the specific energy at critical depth,

$$y_1 + 1.1\frac{V_1{}^2}{2g} = z + 1.033E_c \tag{11.10.2}$$

From Eq. (11.5.3)

$$y_c = \frac{2}{3}E_c = \left(\frac{q^2}{g}\right)^{1/3}$$

or

$$q = 3.087E_c{}^{3/2} \tag{11.10.3}$$

---

[1] H. W. King and E. F. Brater, "Handbook of Hydraulics," 5th ed., pp. 8-14 to 8-16, McGraw-Hill Book Company, New York, 1963.

**Fig. 11.17**  Critical-depth meter.

In Eqs. (11.10.2) and (11.10.3) $E_c$ is eliminated and the resulting equation solved for $q$,

$$q = 2.94 \left( y_1 - z + 1.1 \frac{V_1^2}{2g} \right)^{3/2}$$

Since $q = V_1 y_1$, $V_1$ may be eliminated,

$$q = 2.94 \left( y_1 - z + \frac{0.0171}{y_1^2} q^2 \right)^{3/2} \qquad\qquad (11.10.4)$$

The equation is solved by trial.   As $y_1$ and $z$ are known, and the right-hand term containing $q$ is small, it may first be neglected for an approximate $q$. A value a little larger than the approximate $q$ may be substituted on the right-hand side.   When the two $q$'s are the same the equation is solved. Once $z$ and the width of channel are known, a chart or table may be prepared yielding $Q$ for any $y_1$.   Experiments indicate that accuracy within 2 to 3 per cent may be expected.

With tranquil flow a jump occurs downstream from the meter and with rapid flow a jump occurs upstream from the meter.

**example 11.9**   In a critical-depth meter 6 ft wide with $z = 1.0$ ft the depth $y_1$ is measured to be 2.40 ft.   Find the discharge.

In Eq. (11.10.4), as a first approximation,

$$q = 2.94(1.4)^{3/2} = 4.87$$

As a second approximation let $q$ be 5.00,

$$q = 2.94(1.4 + 0.00297 \times 5^2)^{3/2} = 5.26$$

and as a third approximation 5.32,

$$q = 2.94[1.4 + 0.00297 \times (5.32)^2]^{3/2} = 5.32$$

Then

$$Q = 6 \times 5.32 = 31.92 \text{ cfs}$$

**problems**

**11.1**   Show that for laminar flow to be ensured down an inclined surface, the discharge per unit width cannot be greater than $500\nu$.   (See Prob. 5.10.)

**11.2**   Calculate the depth of laminar flow of water at 70°F down a plane surface making an angle of 30° with the horizontal for the lower critical Reynolds number.   (See Prob. 5.10.)

**11.3**   Calculate the depth of turbulent flow at $\mathbf{R} = VR/\nu = 500$ for flow of water at 70°F down a plane surface making an angle $\theta$ of 30° with the horizontal.   Use Manning's formula.   $n = 0.01$; $S = \sin \theta$.

**11.4**   A rectangular channel is to carry 40 cfs at a slope of 0.009.   If the channel is lined with galvanized iron, $n = 0.011$, what is the minimum number of square feet of metal needed for each 100 ft of channel?   Neglect freeboard.

**11.5**   A trapezoidal channel, with side slopes 2 on 1 (2 horizontal to 1 vertical), is to carry 600 cfs with a bottom slope of 0.0009.   Determine the bottom, width, depth, and velocity for the best hydraulic section.   $n = 0.025$.

**11.6**   A trapezoidal channel made out of brick, with bottom width 6 ft and with bottom slope 0.001, is to carry 600 cfs.   What should the side slopes and depth of channel be for the least number of bricks?

**11.7**   What radius semicircular corrugated-metal channel is needed to convey 90 cfs 1 mile with a head loss of 7 ft?   Can you find another cross section that requires less perimeter?

**11.8**   Determine the best hydraulic trapezoidal section to convey 3000 cfs with a bottom slope of 0.001.   The lining is finished concrete.

**11.9**   Calculate the discharge through the channel and floodway of Fig. 11.18 for steady uniform flow, with $S = 0.0009$ and $y = 8$ ft.

**11.10**   For 7000 cfs flow in the section of Fig. 11.18 when the depth over the floodway is 4 ft, calculate the energy gradient.

**11.11**   For 25,000 cfs flow through the section of Fig. 11.18, find the depth of flow in the floodway when the slope of the energy grade line is 0.0004.

**11.12**   Draw an $F + M$-curve for 80 cfs/ft of width.

**11.13**   Draw the specific-energy curve for 80 cfs/ft of width on the same chart as Prob. 11.12.

**11.14**   Prepare a plot of Eq. (11.4.7).

**11.15**   With $q = 100$ cfs/ft and $\mathbf{F}_1 = 12$, determine $v_1$, $y_1$, and the conjugate depth $y_2$.

**11.16**   Determine the two depths having a specific energy of 6 ft for 30 cfs/ft.

**Fig. 11.18**

**Fig. 11.19**

**11.17**   What is the critical depth for flow of 18 cfs/ft of width?

**11.18**   What is the critical depth for flow of 10 cfs through the cross section of Fig. 5.49?

**11.19**   Determine the critical depth for flow of 300 cfs through a trapezoidal channel with a bottom width of 8 ft and side slopes of 1 on 1.

**11.20**   An unfinished concrete rectangular channel 12 ft wide has a slope of 0.0009.   It carries 480 cfs and has a depth of 7 ft at one section.   By using the step method and taking one step only, compute the depth 1000 ft downstream.

**11.21**   Solve Prob. 11.20 by taking two equal steps.   What is the classification of this water-surface profile?

**11.22**   A very wide gate (Fig. 11.19) admits water to a horizontal channel. Considering the pressure distribution hydrostatic at section $O$, compute the depth at section $O$ and the discharge per foot of width, when $y = 3.0$ ft.

**11.23**   If the depth at section $O$ of Fig. 11.19 is 2 ft and the discharge per foot of width is 65.2 cfs, compute the water-surface curve downstream from the gate.

**11.24**   Draw the curve of conjugate depths for the surface profile of Prob. 11.23.

**11.25**   If the very wide channel in Fig. 11.19 extends downstream 2000 ft and then has a sudden drop off, compute the flow profile upstream from the end of the channel for $q = 65.2$ cfs/ft by integrating the equation for gradually varied flow.

**11.26**   Using the results of Probs 11.24 and 11.25, determine the position of a hydraulic jump in the channel.

**11.27**   In Fig. 11.20 the depth downstream from the gate is 2 ft, and the velocity is 40 ft/sec.   For a very wide channel, compute the depth at the downstream end of the adverse slope.

**Fig. 11.20**

**11.28**    Sketch (without computation) and label all the liquid-surface profiles that can be obtained from Fig. 11.21 by varying $z_1$, $z_2$, and the lengths of
the channels, for $z_2 < z_1$ and with a steep, inclined channel.

**11.29**    In Fig. 11.21 determine the possible combinations of control sections
for various values of $z_1$, $z_2$ and various channel lengths, for $z_1 > z_2$ and with
the inclined channel always steep.

**11.30**    Sketch the various liquid-surface profiles and control sections for
Fig. 11.21 obtained by varying channel length for $z_2 > z_1$.

**11.31**    Show an example of a channel that is mild for one discharge and
steep for another discharge.    What discharge is required for it to be
critical?

**11.32**    Sketch the various combinations of liquid profiles obtainable from
the channel profile of Fig. 11.22 for various values of $z_1$, $z_2$.

**Fig. 11.21**

**Fig. 11.22**

**11.33**   Design a transition from a trapezoidal section, 8 ft bottom width and side slopes 1 on 1, depth 4 ft, to a rectangular section, 6 ft wide and 6 ft deep, for a flow of 250 cfs.   The transition is to be 20 ft long, and the loss is one-tenth of the difference between velocity heads.   Show the bottom profile, and do not make any sudden changes in cross-sectional area.

**11.34**   A transition from a rectangular channel, 8 ft wide and 6 ft deep, to a trapezoidal channel, bottom width 12 ft and side slopes 2 on 1, with depth 4 ft, has a loss of four-tenths of the difference between velocity heads.   The discharge is 200 cfs.   Determine the difference between elevations of channel bottoms.

**11.35**   A critical-depth meter 20 ft wide has a rise in bottom of 2.0 ft.   For an upstream depth of 3.52 ft determine the flow through the meter.

**11.36**   With flow approaching a critical-depth meter site at 20 ft/sec and a Froude number of 10, what is the minimum amount the floor must be raised?

**11.37**   In open-channel flow

($a$)   the hydraulic grade line is always parallel to the energy grade line
($b$)   the energy grade line coincides with the free surface
($c$)   the energy and hydraulic grade lines coincide
($d$)   the hydraulic grade line can never rise
($e$)   the hydraulic grade line and free surface coincide

**11.38**   Gradually varied flow is

($a$) steady uniform flow          ($b$)  steady nonuniform flow
($c$) unsteady uniform flow       ($d$)  unsteady nonuniform flow
($e$) none of these answers

**11.39**   Tranquil flow must always occur

($a$) above normal depth          ($b$) below normal depth
($c$) above critical depth         ($d$) below critical depth
($e$) on adverse slopes

**11.40**   Shooting flow can never occur

($a$) directly after a hydraulic jump
($b$) in a mild channel
($c$) in an adverse channel
($d$) in a horizontal channel
($e$) in a steep channel

**11.41**   Flow at critical depth occurs when

($a$) changes in upstream resistance alter downstream conditions
($b$) the specific energy is a maximum for a given discharge

(c) any change in depth requires more specific energy
(d) the normal depth and critical depth coincide for a channel
(e) the velocity is given by $\sqrt{2gy}$

**11.42**  The best hydraulic rectangular cross section occurs when ($b =$ bottom width, $y =$ depth)

(a) $y = 2b$    (b) $y = b$    (c) $y = b/2$    (d) $y = b^2$
(e) $y = b/5$

**11.43**  The best hydraulic canal cross section is defined as

(a) the least expensive canal cross section
(b) the section with minimum roughness coefficient
(c) the section that has a maximum area for a given flow
(d) the one that has a minimum perimeter
(e) none of these answers

**11.44**  The hydraulic jump always occurs from

(a) an $\mathbf{M}_3$-curve to an $\mathbf{M}_1$-curve
(b) an $\mathbf{H}_3$-curve to an $\mathbf{H}_2$-curve
(c) an $\mathbf{S}_3$-curve to an $\mathbf{S}_1$-curve
(d) below normal depth to above normal depth
(e) below critical depth to above critical depth

**11.45**  Critical depth in a rectangular channel is expressed by

(a) $\sqrt{Vy}$    (b) $\sqrt{2gy}$    (c) $\sqrt{gy}$    (d) $\sqrt{q/g}$    (e) $(q^2/g)^{1/3}$

**11.46**  Critical depth in a nonrectangular channel is expressed by

(a) $Q^2T/gA^3 = 1$    (b) $QT^2/gA^2 = 1$    (c) $Q^2A^3/gT^2 = 1$
(d) $Q^2/gA^3 = 1$    (e) none of these answers

**11.47**  The specific energy for the flow expressed by $V = 8.02$ ft/sec, $y = 2$ ft is, in foot-pounds per pound,

(a) 3    (b) 4    (c) 6.02    (d) 10.02    (e) none of these answers

**Fig. 11.23**

**Fig. 11.24**

**11.48**   The minimum possible specific energy for a flow is 2.475 ft-lb/lb. The discharge per foot of width, in cubic feet per second, is

(*a*) 4.26     (*b*) 12.02     (*c*) 17     (*d*) 22.15     (*e*) none of these answers

**11.49**   The profile resulting from flow under the gate in Fig. 11.23 is classified as

(*a*) **H**$_1$     (*b*) **H**$_2$     (*c*) **H**$_3$     (*d*) **A**$_2$     (*e*) **A**$_3$

**11.50**   The number of different possible surface profiles that can occur for any variations of $z_1$, $z_2$, and length of channel in Fig. 11.24 is ($z_1 \neq z_2$)

(*a*) 2     (*b*) 3     (*c*) 4     (*d*) 5     (*e*) 6

**11.51**   The loss through a diverging transition is about

(*a*) $0.1 \dfrac{(V_1 - V_2)^2}{2g}$     (*b*) $0.1 \dfrac{(V_1^2 - V_2^2)}{2g}$     (*c*) $0.3 \dfrac{(V_1 - V_2)^2}{2g}$

(*d*) $0.3 \dfrac{V_1^2 - V_2^2}{2g}$     (*e*) none of these answers

**11.52**   A critical-depth meter

(*a*) measures the depth at the critical section
(*b*) is always preceded by a hydraulic jump
(*c*) must have a tranquil flow immediately upstream
(*d*) always has a hydraulic jump downstream
(*e*) always has a hydraulic jump associated with it

**references**

Bakhmeteff, B. A.: "Hydraulics of Open Channels," McGraw-Hill Book Company, New York, 1932.

Chow, V. T.: "Open-channel Hydraulics," McGraw-Hill Book Company, New York, 1959.

Henderson, F. M.: "Open Channel Flow," The Macmillan Company, New York, 1966.

Hinds, J.: The Hydraulic Design of Flume and Siphon Transitions, *Trans. ASCE*, vol. 92, 1928.

Keulegan, G. H.: Laws of Turbulent Flow in Open Channels, Research Paper 1151, *J. Res. Nat. Bur. Std.*, vol. 21, 1938.

Kindsvater, C. E.: The Hydraulic Jump in Sloping Channels, *Trans. ASCE*, vol. 109, 1944.

Woodward, S. M., and C. J. Posey: "The Hydraulics of Steady Flow in Open Channels," John Wiley & Sons, Inc., New York, 1941.

# 12

# unsteady flow

Up to this point practically all flow cases examined have been for steady flow or have been reducible to a steady-flow situation. As technology advances, and larger equipment is constructed or higher speeds employed, the problems of hydraulic transients become increasingly more important. The hydraulic transients not only cause dangerously high pressures but produce excessive noise, fatigue, pitting due to cavitation, and disruption of normal control of circuits. Owing to the inherent period of certain systems of pipes, resonant vibrations may be incurred which can be destructive.

Hydraulic-transient analysis deals with the pressures and velocities resulting from a change from one steady state to another steady state, e.g., by adjustment of a valve in a piping system or by the starting or stopping of a pump.

The analysis of unsteady flow is much more complex than that of steady flow. Another independent variable enters, the time, and equations may be partial differential equations rather than ordinary differential equations. The digital computer is ideally suited to the solution of such problems because of its large storage capacity and its ability to operate at very high computing rates. This chapter is in two parts: the first part dealing with closed-conduit transients, and the second part with open-channel unsteady flow.

First, oscillation of a U-tube is studied, followed by its application to pipelines and reservoirs, the use of surge tanks, and the establishment of flow in a system. Equations are next developed for cases with more severe changes in velocity that require consideration of liquid compressibility and pipe-wall elasticity (usually called waterhammer).   The open-channel cases are the positive and negative surge waves in a frictionless prismatic channel with instantaneous gate changes, the more general case of flood routing through a prismatic channel with friction, and flow over plane inclined surfaces due to rainfall.

## flow in closed conduits

In general, unsteady-flow situations are much more difficult to analyze than steady-flow situations.   The equation of motion or the unsteady linear momentum equation is used, and the unsteady continuity equation takes special forms.   With nonlinear resistance terms for friction and other effects, the differential equations are frequently solved by numerical methods, usually by means of a digital computer.

### 12.1   oscillation of liquid in a U-tube

Three cases of oscillations of liquid in a simple U-tube are of interest: (1) frictionless liquid, (2) laminar resistance, and (3) turbulent resistance.

*frictionless liquid*

For the frictionless case, Euler's equation of motion in unsteady form [Eq. (3.5.2)] may be applied.   It is

$$\frac{1}{\rho}\frac{\partial p}{\partial s} + g\frac{\partial z}{\partial s} + v\frac{\partial v}{\partial s} + \frac{\partial v}{\partial t} = 0$$

By designating sections 1 and 2 (Fig. 12.1) and by integrating the equation from 1 to 2, for incompressible flow

$$\frac{p_2 - p_1}{\rho} + g(z_2 - z_1) + v_2{}^2 - v_1{}^2 + \int_1^2 \frac{\partial v}{\partial t}\,ds = 0 \tag{12.1.1}$$

But $p_1 = p_2$ and $v_1 = v_2$; also $\partial v/\partial t$ is independent of $s$, hence

$$g(z_2 - z_1) = -L\frac{\partial v}{\partial t} \tag{12.1.2}$$

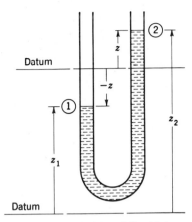

**Fig. 12.1** Oscillation of liquid in a U-tube.

in which $L$ is the length of liquid column.    By changing the elevation datum to the equilibrium position through the menisci, $g(z_2 - z_1) = 2gz$; since $v$ is a function of $t$ only, $\partial v/\partial t$ may be written $dv/dt$, or $d^2z/dt^2$,

$$\frac{d^2z}{dt^2} = \frac{dv}{dt} = -\frac{2g}{L}z \qquad\qquad (12.1.3)$$

The general solution of this equation is

$$z = C_1 \cos \sqrt{\frac{2g}{L}}\,t + C_2 \sin \sqrt{\frac{2g}{L}}\,t$$

in which $C_1$ and $C_2$ are arbitrary constants of integration.    The solution is readily checked by differentiating twice and substituting into the differential equation.    To evaluate the constants, if $z = Z$ and $dz/dt = 0$ when $t = 0$, then $C_1 = Z$ and $C_2 = 0$, or

$$z = Z \cos \sqrt{\frac{2g}{L}}\,t \qquad\qquad (12.1.4)$$

This equation defines a simple harmonic motion of a meniscus, with a period for a complete oscillation of $2\pi \sqrt{L/2g}$.    Velocity of the column may be obtained by differentiating $z$ with respect to $t$.

**example 12.1**    A frictionless fluid column 4.025 ft long has a speed of 4 ft/sec when $z = 1$ ft.    Find ($a$) the maximum value of $z$, ($b$) the maximum speed, and ($c$) the period.

(a)   By differentiating Eq. (12.1.4), after substituting for $L$,

$$\frac{dz}{dt} = -4Z \sin 4t$$

If $t_1$ is the time when $z = 1$ and $dz/dt = 4$,

$$1 = Z \cos 4t_1$$
$$-4 = -4Z \sin 4t_1$$

Dividing the second equation by the first equation,

$$\tan 4t_1 = 1$$

or $4t_1 = 0.785$ radian, $t_1 = 0.196$ sec, $\sin 4t_1 = 0.707$, and $\cos 4t_1 = 0.707$. Then $Z = 1/\cos 4t_1 = 1/0.707 = 1.41$ ft, the maximum value of $z$.

(b)   The maximum speed occurs when $\sin 4t = 1$, or $4Z = 4 \times 1.41 = 5.64$ ft/sec.

(c)   The period is

$$2\pi \sqrt{\frac{L}{2g}} = 1.571 \text{ sec}$$

*laminar resistance*

When a shear stress $\tau_0$ at the wall of the tube resists motion of the liquid column, it may be introduced into the Euler equation of motion along a streamline (Fig. 3.8).   The resistance in length $\delta s$ is $\tau_0 \pi D \, \delta s$.   After dividing through by the mass of the particle $\rho A \, \delta s$, it is $4\tau_0/D$, and Eq. (12.1.1) becomes

$$\frac{1}{\rho}\frac{\partial p}{\partial s} + g\frac{\partial z}{\partial s} + v\frac{\partial v}{\partial s} + \frac{\partial v}{\partial t} + \frac{4\tau_0}{\rho D} = 0 \tag{12.1.5}$$

This equation is good for either laminar or turbulent resistance.   The assumption is made that the frictional resistance in unsteady flow is the same as for the steady flow at the same velocity.   From the Poiseuille equation the shear stress at the wall of a tube is

$$\tau_0 = \frac{8\mu v}{D} \tag{12.1.6}$$

After making the substitution for $\tau_0$ in Eq. (12.1.5) and integrating with respect to $s$ as before,

$$g(z_2 - z_1) + L\frac{\partial v}{\partial t} + \frac{32\nu v}{D^2} = 0$$

By setting $2gz = g(z_2 - z_1)$, changing to total derivatives, and replacing $v$ by $dz/dt$,

$$\frac{d^2z}{dt^2} + \frac{32\nu}{D^2}\frac{dz}{dt} + \frac{2g}{L}z = 0 \tag{12.1.7}$$

In effect, the column is assumed to have the average velocity $dz/dt$ at any cross section.

By substitution

$$z = C_1 e^{at} + C_2 e^{bt}$$

can be shown to be the general solution of Eq. (12.1.7) provided that

$$a^2 + \frac{32\nu}{D^2}a + \frac{2g}{L} = 0$$

and

$$b^2 + \frac{32\nu}{D^2}b + \frac{2g}{L} = 0$$

$C_1$ and $C_2$ are arbitrary constants of integration that are determined by given values of $z$ and $dz/dt$ at a given time.   To keep $a$ and $b$ distinct, since the equations defining them are identical, they are taken with opposite signs before the radical term in solution of the quadratics; thus

$$a = -\frac{16\nu}{D^2} + \sqrt{\left(\frac{16\nu}{D^2}\right)^2 - \frac{2g}{L}}$$

and

$$b = -\frac{16\nu}{D^2} - \sqrt{\left(\frac{16\nu}{D^2}\right)^2 - \frac{2g}{L}}$$

To simplify the formulas, if

$$m = \frac{16\nu}{D^2} \qquad n = \sqrt{\left(\frac{16\nu}{D^2}\right)^2 - \frac{2g}{L}}$$

then

$$z = C_1 \exp\left(-mt + nt\right) + C_2 \exp\left(-mt - nt\right)$$

When the initial condition is taken that $t = 0$, $z = 0$, $dz/dt = V_0$, then by substitution $C_1 = -C_2$, and

$$z = C_1 e^{-mt}(e^{nt} - e^{-nt}) \tag{12.1.8}$$

Since

$$\frac{e^{nt} - e^{-nt}}{2} = \sinh nt$$

Eq. (12.1.8) becomes

$$z = 2C_1 e^{-mt} \sinh nt$$

By differentiating with respect to $t$,

$$\frac{dz}{dt} = 2C_1(-me^{-mt} \sinh nt + ne^{-mt} \cosh nt)$$

and after setting $dz/dt = V_0$ for $t = 0$,

$$V_0 = 2C_1 n$$

since $\sinh 0 = 0$ and $\cosh 0 = 1$.   Then

$$z = \frac{V_0}{n} e^{-mt} \sinh nt \tag{12.1.9}$$

This equation gives the displacement $z$ of one meniscus of the column as a function of time, starting with the meniscus at $z = 0$ when $t = 0$, and rising with velocity $V_0$.

Two principal cases[1] are to be considered.   When

$$\frac{16\nu}{D^2} > \sqrt{\frac{2g}{L}}$$

$n$ is a real number and the viscosity is so great that the motion is damped out in a partial cycle with $z$ never becoming negative, Fig. 12.2 $(m/n = 2)$. The time $t_0$ for maximum $z$ to occur is found by differentiating $z$ [Eq. (12.1.9)] with respect to $t$ and equating to zero,

$$\frac{dz}{dt} = 0 = \frac{V_0}{n} (-me^{-mt} \sinh nt + ne^{-mt} \cosh nt)$$

or

$$\tanh nt_0 = \frac{n}{m} \tag{12.1.10}$$

---

[1] A third case, $16\nu/D^2 = \sqrt{2g/L}$, must be treated separately, yielding $z = V_0 t e^{-mt}$. The resulting oscillation is for a partial cycle only and is a limiting case of $16\nu/D^2 > \sqrt{2g/L}$.

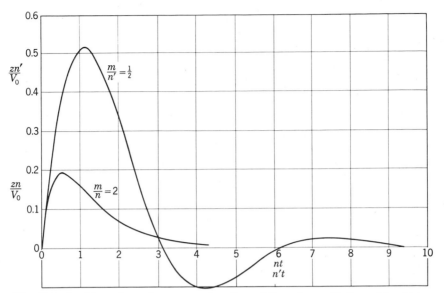

**Fig. 12.2**   Position of meniscus as a function of time for oscillation of liquid in a U-tube with laminar resistance.

Substitution of this value of $t$ into Eq. (12.1.9) yields the maximum displacement $Z$.

$$Z = \frac{V_0}{\sqrt{m^2 - n^2}} \left(\frac{m - n}{m + n}\right)^{m/2n} = V_0 \sqrt{\frac{L}{2g}} \left(\frac{m - n}{m + n}\right)^{m/2n} \qquad (12.1.11)$$

The second case, when

$$\frac{16\nu}{D^2} < \sqrt{\frac{2g}{L}}$$

results in a negative term within the radical,

$$n = \sqrt{-1 \left[\frac{2g}{L} - \left(\frac{16\nu}{D^2}\right)^2\right]} = i \sqrt{\frac{2g}{L} - \left(\frac{16\nu}{D^2}\right)^2} = in'$$

in which $i = \sqrt{-1}$ and $n'$ is a real number.   Replacing $n$ by $in'$ in Eq. (12.1.9) produces the real function

$$z = \frac{V_0}{in'} e^{-mt} \sinh in't = \frac{V_0}{n'} e^{-mt} \sin n't \qquad (12.1.12)$$

since

$$\sin n't = \frac{1}{i} \sinh in't$$

The resulting motion of $z$ is an oscillation about $z = 0$ with decreasing amplitude, as shown in Fig. 12.2 for the case $m/n' = \frac{1}{2}$. The time $t_0$ of maximum or minimum displacement is obtained from Eq. (12.1.12) by equating $dz/dt = 0$, producing

$$\tan n't_0 = \frac{n'}{m} \tag{12.1.13}$$

There are an indefinite number of values of $t_0$ satisfying this expression, corresponding with all the maximum and minimum positions of a meniscus. By substitution of $t_0$ into Eq. (12.1.12)

$$Z = \frac{V_0}{\sqrt{n'^2 + m^2}} \exp\left[-\left(\frac{m}{n'}\right)\tan^{-1}\left(\frac{n'}{m}\right)\right]$$

$$= V_0 \sqrt{\frac{L}{2g}} \exp\left[-\left(\frac{m}{n'}\right)\tan^{-1}\left(\frac{n'}{m}\right)\right] \tag{12.1.14}$$

**example 12.2**  A 1.0-in.-diameter U-tube contains oil, $\nu = 1 \times 10^{-4}$ ft²/sec, with a total column length of 120 in.  Applying air pressure to one of the tubes makes the gage difference 16 in.  By quickly releasing the air pressure the oil column is free to oscillate.  Find the maximum velocity, the maximum Reynolds number, and the equation for position of one meniscus $z$, in terms of time.

The assumption is made that the flow is laminar, and the Reynolds number will be computed on this basis.  The constants $m$ and $n$ are

$$m = \frac{16\nu}{D^2} = \frac{16 \times 10^{-4}}{(\frac{1}{12})^2} = 0.2302$$

$$n = \sqrt{\left(\frac{16\nu}{D^2}\right)^2 - \frac{2g}{L}} = \sqrt{(0.2302)^2 - \frac{2 \times 32.2}{10}} = \sqrt{-1}\,2.527 = i2.527$$

or

$$n' = 2.527$$

Equations (12.1.12), (12.1.13), and (12.1.14) apply to this case, as the liquid will oscillate above and below $z = 0$.  The oscillation starts from the maximum position, i.e., $Z = 0.667$ ft.  By use of Eq. (12.1.14) the velocity (fictitious) when $z = 0$ at time $t_0$ before the maximum is determined to be

$$V_0 = Z \sqrt{\frac{2g}{L}} \exp\left(\frac{m}{n'} \tan^{-1} \frac{n'}{m}\right) = 0.667 \sqrt{\frac{64.4}{10}} \exp\left(\frac{0.2302}{2.527} \tan^{-1} \frac{2.527}{0.2302}\right)$$

$$= 1.935 \text{ ft/sec}$$

and

$$\tan n't_0 = \frac{n'}{m} \qquad t_0 = \frac{1}{2.527} \tan^{-1} \frac{2.527}{0.2302} = 0.586 \text{ sec}$$

Hence by substitution into Eq. (12.1.12)

$$z = 0.766 \exp\left[-0.2302(t + 0.586)\right] \sin 2.527(t + 0.586)$$

in which $z = Z$ at $t = 0$. The maximum velocity (actual) occurs for $t > 0$. Differentiating with respect to $t$ to obtain the expression for velocity,

$$V = \frac{dz}{dt} = -0.1763 \exp\left[-0.2302(t + 0.586)\right] \sin 2.57(t + 0.586)$$
$$+ 1.935 \exp\left[-0.2302(t + 0.586)\right] \cos 2.527(t + 0.586)$$

Differentiating again with respect to $t$ and equating to zero to obtain maximum $V$ produces

$$\tan 2.527(t + 0.586) = -0.1837$$

The solution in the second quadrant should produce the desired maximum, $t = 0.584$ sec. Substituting this time into the expression for $V$ produces $V = -1.48$ ft/sec. The corresponding Reynolds number is

$$\mathbf{R} = \frac{VD}{\nu} = 1.48 \times \frac{1}{12} \times 10^4 = 1234$$

hence the assumption of laminar resistance is justified.

### *turbulent resistance*

In the majority of practical cases of oscillation, or surge, in pipe systems there is turbulent resistance. With large pipes and tunnels the Reynolds number is large except for those time periods when the velocity is very near to zero. The assumption of fluid resistance proportional to the square of the average velocity is made (constant $f$). It closely approximates true conditions, although it yields too small a resistance for slow motions, in which case resistance is almost negligible.   The equations will be developed for $f$ = const for oscillation within a simple U-tube.   This case will then be extended to include oscillation of flow within a pipe or tunnel between two reservoirs, taking into account the minor losses.   The assumption is again made that resistance in unsteady flow is given by steady-flow resistance at the same velocity.

By using Eq. (5.10.2) to substitute for $\tau_0$ in Eq. (12.1.5),

$$\frac{1}{\rho}\frac{\partial p}{\partial s} + g\frac{\partial z}{\partial s} + v\frac{\partial v}{\partial s} + \frac{\partial v}{\partial t} + \frac{fv^2}{2D} = 0 \tag{12.1.15}$$

When integrating this equation from section 1 to section 2 (Fig. 12.1), the first term drops out as the limits are $p = 0$ in each case; the third term drops out as $\partial v/\partial s \equiv 0$; the fourth and fifth terms are independent of $s$, hence

$$g(z_2 - z_1) + \frac{\partial v}{\partial t}L + \frac{fv^2}{2D}L = 0$$

Since $v$ is a function of $t$ only the partial may be replaced with the total derivative,

$$\frac{dv}{dt} + \frac{f}{2D}v|v| + \frac{2g}{L}z = 0 \tag{12.1.16}$$

The absolute-value sign on the velocity term is needed so that the resistance opposes the velocity, whether positive or negative.   By expressing $v = dz/dt$,

$$\frac{d^2z}{dt^2} + \frac{f}{2D}\frac{dz}{dt}\left|\frac{dz}{dt}\right| + \frac{2g}{L}z = 0 \tag{12.1.17}$$

This is a nonlinear differential equation because of the $v$-squared term. It can be integrated once with respect to $t$, but no closed solution is known for the second integration.   It is easily handled by the Runge-Kutta methods (Appendix E) with the digital computer when initial conditions are known: $t = t_0$, $z = z_0$, $dz/dt = 0$.   Much can be learned from Eq. (12.1.17), however, by restricting the motion to the $-z$-direction; thus

$$\frac{d^2z}{dt^2} - \frac{f}{2D}\left(\frac{dz}{dt}\right)^2 + \frac{2g}{L}z = 0 \tag{12.1.18}$$

The equation may be integrated once,[1] producing

$$\left(\frac{dz}{dt}\right)^2 = \frac{4gD^2}{f^2L}\left(1+\frac{fz}{D}\right) + Ce^{fz/D} \tag{12.1.19}$$

in which $C$ is the constant of integration.  To evaluate the constant, if $z = z_m$ for $dz/dt = 0$,

$$C = -\frac{4gD^2}{f^2L}\left(1+\frac{fz_m}{D}\right)\exp\left(-\frac{fz_m}{D}\right)$$

and

$$\left(\frac{dz}{dt}\right)^2 = \frac{4gD^2}{f^2L}\left[1+\frac{fz}{D}-\left(1+\frac{fz_m}{D}\right)\exp\left(\frac{f(z-z_m)}{D}\right)\right] \tag{12.1.20}$$

Although this equation cannot be integrated again, numerical integration of particular situations yields $z$ as a function of $t$.  The equation, however, may be used to determine the magnitude of successive oscillations.  At the instants of maximum or minimum $z$, say $z_m$ and $z_{m+1}$, respectively, $dz/dt = 0$ and Eq. (12.1.20) simplifies to

$$\left(1+\frac{fz_m}{D}\right)\exp\left(-\frac{fz_m}{D}\right) = \left(1+\frac{fz_{m+1}}{D}\right)\exp\left(-\frac{fz_{m+1}}{D}\right) \tag{12.1.21}$$

Since the original equation, Eq. (12.1.18), holds only for decreasing $z$, $z_m$ must be positive and $z_{m+1}$ negative.  To find $z_{m+2}$ the other meniscus could be considered and $z_{m+1}$ as a positive number substituted into the left-hand side of the equation to determine a minus $z_{m+2}$ in place of $z_{m+1}$ on the right-hand side of the equation

**example 12.3**  A U-tube consisting of 2.0-ft-diameter pipe with $f = 0.03$ has a maximum oscillation (Fig. 12.1) of $z_m = 20$ ft.  Find the minimum position of the surface and the following maximum.

----

[1] By substitution of

$$p = \frac{dz}{dt} \qquad \frac{d^2z}{dt^2} = \frac{dp}{dt} = \frac{dp}{dz}\frac{dz}{dt} = p\frac{dp}{dz}$$

then

$$p\frac{dp}{dz} - \frac{f}{2D}p^2 \times \frac{2gz}{L} = 0$$

This equation may be made exact by multiplying by the integrating factor $e^{-fz/D}$.  For the detailed method see Earl D. Rainville, "Elementary Differential Equations," 3d ed., The Macmillan Company, New York, 1964.

From Eq. (12.1.21)

$$\left(1 + \frac{0.03 \times 20}{2}\right) \exp\left(\frac{-0.03 \times 20}{2}\right) = (1 + 0.015z_{m+1}) \exp\left(-0.015z_{m+1}\right)$$

or

$$(1 + 0.015z_{m+1}) \exp\left(-0.015z_{m+1}\right) = 0.9603$$

which is satisfied by $z_{m+1} = -16.6$ ft. Using $z_m = 16.6$ in Eq. (12.2.21),

$$(1 + 0.015z_{m+1}) \exp\left(-0.015z_{m+1}\right)$$
$$= (1 + 0.015 \times 16.6) \exp\left(-0.015 \times 16.6\right)$$
$$= 0.974$$

which is satisfied by $z_{m+1} = -14.2$ ft. Hence, the minimum water surface is $z = -16.6$ ft and the next maximum is $z = 14.2$ ft.

Equation (12.1.21) may be solved graphically: If $\phi = fz/D$, then

$$F(\phi) = (1 + \phi)e^{-\phi} \tag{12.1.22}$$

which is conveniently plotted with $F(\phi)$ as ordinate and both $-\phi$ and $+\phi$ on the same abscissa scale (Fig. 12.3). Successive values of $\phi$ are found as indicated by the dashed stepped line.

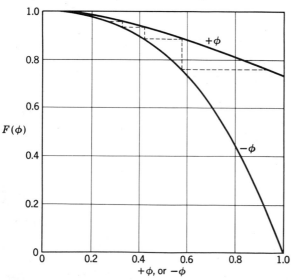

**Fig. 12.3** Graphical solution of $F(\phi) = (1 + \phi)e^{-\phi}$, yielding successive maximum and minimum displacements.

Although $z$ cannot be found as a function of $t$ from Eq. (12.1.20), $V$ is given as a function of $z$, since $V = dz/dt$. The maximum value of $V$ is found by equating $dV^2/dz = 0$ to find its position $z'$; thus

$$\frac{dV^2}{dz} = 0 = \frac{f}{D} - \left(1 + \frac{fz_m}{D}\right) \exp\left(\frac{f(z' - z_m)}{D}\right) \frac{f}{D}$$

After solving for $z'$,

$$z' = z_m - \frac{D}{f} \ln\left(1 + \frac{fz_m}{D}\right)$$

and after substituting back into Eq. (12.1.20),

$$V_m{}^2 = \frac{4gD^2}{f^2L}\left[\frac{fz_m}{D} - \ln\left(1 + \frac{fz_m}{D}\right)\right] \tag{12.1.23}$$

*oscillation of two reservoirs*

The equation for oscillation of two reservoirs connected by a pipeline is the same as that for oscillation of a U-tube, except for value of constant terms. If $z_1$ and $z_2$ represent displacements of the reservoir surfaces from their equilibrium positions (Fig. 12.4) and if $z$ represents displacement of a water particle within the connecting pipe from its equilibrium position,

$$zA = z_1 A_1 = z_2 A_2$$

in which $A_1$ and $A_2$ are the reservoir areas, assumed to be constant in this derivation. Taking into account minor losses in the system by using the equivalent length $L_e$ of pipe and fittings plus other minor losses, the

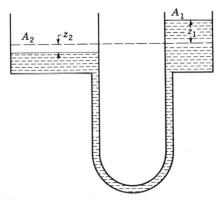

**Fig. 12.4**  Oscillation of two reservoirs.

equation of motion is

$$-\gamma A(z_1 + z_2) + \frac{\gamma A f L_e}{2gD}\left(\frac{dz}{dt}\right)^2 = \frac{\gamma A L}{g}\frac{d^2z}{dt^2}$$

for $z$ decreasing.   After simplifying

$$\frac{d^2z}{dt^2} - \frac{f}{2D}\frac{L_e}{L}\left(\frac{dz}{dt}\right)^2 + \frac{gA}{L}\left(\frac{1}{A_1} + \frac{1}{A_2}\right)z = 0 \qquad (12.1.24)$$

After comparing with Eq. (12.1.18), $f$ is replaced by $fL_e/L$, and $2g/L$ by $gA(1/A_1 + 1/A_2)/L$.   In Eq. (12.1.22)

$$\phi = f\frac{L_e}{L}\frac{z}{D}$$

**example 12.4**   In Fig. 12.4 a valve is opened suddenly in the pipeline when $z_1 = 40$ ft.   $L = 2000$ ft, $A_1 = 200$ ft$^2$, $A_2 = 300$ ft$^2$, $D = 3.0$ ft, $f = 0.024$, and minor losses are $3.50V^2/2g$.   Determine the subsequent maximum negative and positive surges in the reservoir $A_1$.
   The equivalent length of minor losses is

$$\frac{KD}{f} = \frac{3.5 \times 3}{0.024} = 438 \text{ ft}$$

Then $L_e = 2000 + 438 = 2438$ and

$$z_m = \frac{z_1 A_1}{A} = \frac{40 \times 200}{2.25\pi} = 1132 \text{ ft}$$

The corresponding $\phi$ is

$$\phi = f\frac{L_e}{L}\frac{z_m}{D} = 0.024 \times \frac{2438}{2000} \times \frac{1132}{3} = 11.04$$

and

$$F(\phi) = (1 + \phi)e^{-\phi} = (1 + 11.04)e^{-11.04} = 0.000193$$

which is satisfied by $\phi \cong -1.0$.   Then

$$F(\phi) = (1 + 1)e^{-1} = 0.736 = (1 + \phi)e^{-\phi}$$

which is satisfied by $\phi = -0.593$.   The values of $z_m$ are, for $\phi = -1$,

$$z_m = \frac{\phi L D}{f L_e} = \frac{-1 \times 2000 \times 3}{0.024 \times 2438} = -102.6$$

and for $\phi = 0.593$,

$$z_m = \frac{0.593 \times 2000 \times 3}{0.024 \times 2438} = 60.9$$

The corresponding values of $z_1$ are

$$z_1 = z_m \frac{A}{A_1} = -102.6 \times \frac{2.25\pi}{200} = -3.63 \text{ ft}$$

and

$$z_1 = 60.9 \times \frac{2.25\pi}{200} = 2.15 \text{ ft}$$

In this example it should be noted that the subsequent oscillations are almost independent of the original $z_1$, so long as $z_1$ is greater than about 20 ft.


## 12.2   establishment of flow

The problem of determination of time for flow to become established in a pipeline when a valve is suddenly opened is easily handled when friction and minor losses are taken into account.   After a valve is opened (Fig. 12.5), the head $H$ is available to accelerate the flow in the first instants, but as the velocity increases the accelerating head is reduced by friction and minor losses.   If $L_e$ is the equivalent length of the pipe system, the final

**Fig. 12.5**   Notation for establishment of flow.

velocity $V_0$ is given by application of the energy equation

$$H = f \frac{L_e}{D} \frac{V_0{}^2}{2g} \tag{12.2.1}$$

The equation of motion is

$$\gamma A \left( H - f \frac{L_e}{D} \frac{V^2}{2g} \right) = \frac{\gamma A L}{g} \frac{dV}{dt}$$

By solving for $dt$ and rearranging, with Eq. (12.2.1),

$$\int_0^t dt = \frac{L V_0{}^2}{gH} \int_0^V \frac{dV}{V_0{}^2 - V^2}$$

After performing the integration,

$$t = \frac{L V_0}{2gH} \ln \frac{V_0 + V}{V_0 - V} \tag{12.2.2}$$

The velocity $V$ approaches $V_0$ asymptotically; i.e., mathematically it takes infinite time for $V$ to attain the value $V_0$. Practically, for $V$ to reach 0.99 $V_0$ takes

$$t = \frac{L V_0}{gH} \frac{1}{2} \ln \frac{1.99}{0.01} = 2.646 \frac{L V_0}{gH}$$

$V_0$ must be determined by taking minor losses into account, but Eq. (12.2.2) does not contain $L_e$.

**example 12.5** In Fig. 12.5 the minor losses are $16 V^2/2g$, $f = 0.030$, $L = 10,000$ ft, $D = 8.0$ ft, and $H = 60$ ft. Determine the time, after the sudden opening of a valve, for velocity to attain nine-tenths of the final velocity.

$$L_e = 10,000 + \frac{16 \times 8}{0.03} = 14,270 \text{ ft}$$

From Eq. (12.2.1)

$$V_0 = \sqrt{\frac{2gHD}{fL_e}} = \sqrt{\frac{64.4 \times 60 \times 8}{0.030 \times 14,270}} = 8.5 \text{ ft/sec}$$

After substituting $V = 0.9 V_0$ into Eq. (12.2.2),

$$t = \frac{10,000 \times 8.5}{64.4 \times 60} \ln \frac{1.90}{0.10} = 64.8 \text{ sec}$$

## 12.3 surge control

The oscillation of flow in pipelines, when compressibility effects are not important, is referred to as *surge*. For sudden deceleration of flow due to closure of the flow passage, compressibility of the liquid and elasticity of the pipe walls must be considered; this phenomenon, known as *water-hammer*, is discussed in Secs. 12.4–12.8. Oscillations in a U-tube are special cases of surge. As one means of eliminating waterhammer, provision is made to permit the liquid to surge into a tank (Fig. 12.6). The valve at the end of a pipeline may be controlled by a turbine governor, and may rapidly stop the flow if the generator loses its load. To quickly destroy all momentum in the long pipe system would require high pressure which in turn would require a very costly pipeline. With a surge tank as near the valve as feasible, although surge will occur between the reservoir and surge tank, the developing of high pressure in this reach is prevented. It is still necessary to design the pipeline between surge tank and valve to withstand waterhammer.

Surge tanks may be classified as *simple, orifice,* and *differential*. The simple surge tank has an unrestricted opening into it, and must be of adequate size so that it will not overflow (unless a spillway is provided) and so that it will not be emptied and air permitted to enter the pipeline. It must also be of such size that it will not fluctuate in resonance with the governor action on the valve. The period of oscillation of a simple surge tank is relatively long.

The orifice surge tank has a restricted opening or orifice between pipe line and tank and, hence, allows more rapid pressure changes in the pipeline than the simple surge tank. The more rapid pressure change causes a more rapid adjustment of flow to the new valve setting and losses through the orifice aid in dissipating excess available energy resulting from valve closure.

The differential surge tank (Fig. 12.7) is in effect a combination of an orifice surge tank and a simple surge tank of small cross-sectional area. In case of rapid valve opening a limited amount of liquid is directly available from the central riser and flow from the large tank supplements this flow

**Fig. 12.6** Surge tank on a long pipeline.

**Fig. 12.7** Differential surge tank.

For sudden valve closures the central riser may be designed so that it over-flows into the outside tank.

Surge tanks operating under air pressure are utilized in certain circum-stances, such as after a reciprocating pump. They are generally uneco-nomical for large pipelines.

Detailed analysis of surge tanks entails a numerical integration of the equation of motion for the liquid in the pipeline, taking into account the particular rate of valve closure, together with the continuity equation. The particular type of surge tank to be selected for a given situation is dependent upon a detailed study of the economics of the pipeline system. High-speed digital computers are most helpful in their design.

Another means of controlling surge and waterhammer is to supply a quick-opening bypass valve that opens when the control valve closes. The quick-opening valve has a controlled slow closure at such a rate that excessive pressure is not developed in the line. The bypass valve wastes liquid, however, and does not provide relief from surge due to opening of the control valve or starting of a pump.

The following sections on closed-conduit flow take compressibility of the liquid and elasticity of the pipe walls into account. Waterhammer calcu-lations may be accomplished in several ways; three methods are given: graphical, characteristics method, and algebraic method.

## 12.4 description of the waterhammer phenomenon

Waterhammer may occur in a closed conduit flowing full when there is either a retardation or acceleration of the flow, such as with the change in opening of a valve in the line. If the changes are gradual, the calculations may be carried out by surge methods, considering the liquid incompressible and the conduit rigid. When a valve is rapidly closed in a pipeline during flow, the flow through the valve is reduced. This increases the head on the upstream side of the valve and causes a pulse of high pressure to be propagated upstream. The action of this pressure pulse is to decrease the velocity of flow. On the downstream side of the valve the pressure is reduced and a wave of lowered pressure travels downstream, which also reduces the velocity. If the closure is rapid enough and the steady pressure low enough, a vapor pocket may be formed downstream from the valve. When this occurs, the cavity will eventually collapse and produce a high-pressure wave downstream.

Before undertaking the derivation of equations for solution of water-hammer, a description of the sequence of events following sudden closure of a valve at the downstream end of a pipe leading from a reservoir (Fig. 12.8) is given. Friction is neglected in this case. At the instant of valve closure $(t = 0)$ the fluid nearest the valve is compressed, brought to rest, and the pipe wall stretched (Fig. 12.8a). As soon as the first layer is compressed the process is repeated for the next layer. The fluid upstream from the valve continues to move downstream with undiminished speed until successive layers have been compressed back to the source. The high pressure moves upstream as a wave, bringing the fluid to rest as it

**Fig. 12.8** Sequence of events for one cycle of sudden closure of a valve.

passes, compressing it, and expanding the pipe. When the wave reaches the upstream end of the pipe ($t = L/a$ sec), all the fluid is under the extra head $h$, all the momentum has been lost, and all the kinetic energy has been converted into elastic energy.

There is an unbalanced condition at the upstream (reservoir) end at the instant of arrival of the pressure wave, as the reservoir pressure is unchanged. The fluid starts to flow backward, beginning at the upstream end. This flow returns the pressure to the value which was normal before closure, the pipe wall returns to normal, and the fluid has a velocity $V_0$ in the backward sense. This process of conversion travels downstream toward the valve at the speed of sound $a$ in the pipe. At the instant $2L/a$ the wave arrives at the valve, pressures are back to normal along the pipe, and the velocity is everywhere $V_0$ in the backward direction.

Since the valve is closed no fluid is available to maintain the flow at the valve and a low pressure develops $(-h)$ such that the fluid is brought to rest. This low-pressure wave travels upstream at speed $a$ and everywhere brings the fluid to rest, causes it to expand because of the lower pressure, and allows the pipe walls to contract. (If the static pressure in the pipe is not sufficiently high to sustain head, $-h$, above vapor pressure, the liquid vaporizes in part and continues to move backward over a longer period of time.)

At the instant the negative pressure wave arrives at the upstream end of the pipe, $3L/a$ sec after closure, the fluid is at rest, but uniformly at head $-h$ less than before closure. This leaves an unbalanced condition at the reservoir, and fluid flows into the pipe, acquiring a velocity $V_0$ forward and returning the pipe and fluid to normal conditions as the wave progresses downstream at speed $a$. At the instant this wave reaches the valve, conditions are exactly the same as at the instant of closure, $4L/a$ sec earlier.

This process is then repeated every $4L/a$ sec. The action of fluid friction and imperfect elasticity of fluid and pipe wall, neglected heretofore, is to damp out the vibration and eventually cause the fluid to come permanently to rest. Closure of a valve in less than $2L/a$ is called *rapid closure; slow closure* refers to times of closure greater than $2L/a$.

The sequence of events taking place in a pipe may be compared with the sudden stopping of a freight train by the engine hitting an immovable object. The car behind the engine compresses the spring in its forward coupling and stops as it exerts a force against the engine, and each car in turn keeps moving at its original speed until the preceding one suddenly comes to rest. When the caboose is at rest all the energy is stored in compressing the coupling springs (neglecting losses). The caboose has an unbalanced force exerted on it, and starts to move backward, which in turn causes an unbalanced force on the next car setting it in backward motion.

This action proceeds as a wave toward the engine, causing each car to move at its original speed in a backward direction.   If the engine is immovable, the car next to it is stopped by a tensile force in the coupling between it and the engine, analogous to the low-pressure wave in waterhammer. The process repeats itself car by car until the train is again at rest, with all couplings in tension.   The caboose is then acted upon by the unbalanced tensile force in its coupling and is set into forward motion, followed in turn by the rest of the cars.   When this wave reaches the engine all cars are in motion as before the original impact.   Then the whole cycle is repeated again.   Friction acts to reduce the energy to zero in a very few cycles.

## 12.5   differential equations for calculation of waterhammer

Two basic mechanics equations are applied to a short segment of fluid in a pipe to obtain the differential equations for transient flow: Newton's second law of motion and the continuity equation.   The dependent variables are the elevation of hydraulic grade line $H$ above a fixed datum and the average velocity $V$ at a cross section.   The independent variables are distance $x$ along the pipe measured from the upstream end and time $t$; hence, $H = H(x,t)$, $V = V(x,t)$.   Poisson's ratio effect is not taken into account in this derivation.   For pipelines with expansion joints it does not enter into the derivation.   Friction is considered to be proportional to the square of the velocity.

*equation of motion*

The fluid element between two parallel planes $\delta x$ apart, normal to the pipe axis, is taken as a free body for application of Newton's second law of motion in the axial direction (Fig. 12.9).   In equation form

$$pA - \left[ pA + \frac{\partial}{\partial x} (pA) \, \delta x \right] + p \, \frac{\partial A}{\partial x} \, \delta x + \gamma A \, \delta x \sin \theta - \tau_0 \pi D \, \delta x$$

$$= \rho A \, \delta x \, \frac{dV}{dt}$$

By dividing through by the mass of the element $\rho A \, \delta x$ and simplifying,

$$-\frac{1}{\rho} \frac{\partial p}{\partial x} + g \sin \theta - \frac{4\tau_0}{\rho D} = \frac{dV}{dt} \qquad (12.5.1)$$

**Fig. 12.9** Free-body diagram for derivation of equation of motion.

After introducing the hydraulic grade-line elevation, from $p = \rho g(H - z)$,

$$\frac{\partial p}{\partial x} \cong \rho g \left( \frac{\partial H}{\partial x} - \frac{\partial z}{\partial x} \right) \qquad (12.5.2)$$

But

$$\frac{\partial z}{\partial x} = - \sin \theta$$

and

$$g \frac{\partial H}{\partial x} + \frac{4\tau_0}{\rho D} + \frac{dV}{dt} = 0 \qquad (12.5.3)$$

For steady turbulent flow, $\tau_0 = \rho f V^2/8$ [Eq. (5.10.2)]. The assumption is made that the friction factor in unsteady flow is the same as in steady flow. Hence, the equation of motion becomes

$$g \frac{\partial H}{\partial x} + \frac{dV}{dt} + \frac{fV^2}{2D} = 0 \qquad (12.5.4)$$

Since friction must oppose the motion, $V^2$ is written as $V|V|$ to provide the proper sign.    After expanding the acceleration term,

$$L_2 = g \frac{\partial H}{\partial x} + V \frac{\partial V}{\partial x} + \frac{\partial V}{\partial t} + \frac{fV|V|}{2D} = 0 \qquad (12.5.5)$$

The equation is indicated by $L_2$ to distinguish it from the equation of continuity $L_1$, which is next derived.

### *equaton of continuity*

The unsteady continuity equation (3.2.1) is applied to the control volume of Fig. 12.10,

$$-\frac{\partial}{\partial x} (\rho A V) \, \delta x = \frac{\partial}{\partial t} (\rho A \, \delta x) \qquad (12.5.6)$$

in which $\delta x$ is not a function of $t$.    After expanding the equation and by dividing through by the mass $\rho A \, \delta x$,

$$\frac{V}{A}\frac{\partial A}{\partial x} + \frac{1}{A}\frac{\partial A}{\partial t} + \frac{V}{\rho}\frac{\partial \rho}{\partial x} + \frac{1}{\rho}\frac{\partial \rho}{\partial t} + \frac{\partial V}{\partial x} = 0 \qquad (12.5.7)$$

The first two terms are the total derivative[1] $(1/A) \, dA/dt$, and the next two terms the total derivative $(1/\rho) \, d\rho/dt$, yielding

$$\frac{1}{A}\frac{dA}{dt} + \frac{1}{\rho}\frac{d\rho}{dt} + \frac{\partial V}{\partial x} = 0 \qquad (12.5.8)$$

[1] See Appendix B, and equations following Eq. (12.6.3).

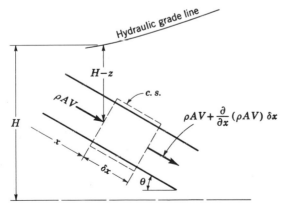

**Fig. 12.10**   Control volume for derivation of continuity equation.

The first term deals with the elasticity of the pipe wall and its rate of deformation with pressure; the second term takes into account the compressibility of the liquid. For the wall elasticity the rate of change of tensile force per unit length (Fig. 12.11) is $(D/2)\,dp/dt$; when divided by the wall thickness $t'$, it is the rate of change of unit stress $(D/2t')\,dp/dt$; when this is divided by Young's modulus of elasticity for the wall material, the rate of increase of unit strain is obtained, $(D/2t'E)\,dp/dt$. After multiplying this by the radius $D/2$, the rate of radial extension is obtained; finally, by multiplying by the perimeter $\pi D$ the rate of area increase is obtained:

$$\frac{dA}{dt} = \frac{D}{2t'E}\frac{dp}{dt}\frac{D}{2}\,\pi D$$

and hence

$$\frac{1}{A}\frac{dA}{dt} = \frac{D}{t'E}\frac{dp}{dt} \tag{12.5.9}$$

From the definition of bulk modulus of elasticity of fluid (Chap. 1),

$$K = -\frac{dp}{d\upsilon/\upsilon} = \frac{dp}{d\rho/\rho}$$

and the rate of change of density divided by density yields

$$\frac{1}{\rho}\frac{d\rho}{dt} = \frac{1}{K}\frac{dp}{dt} \tag{12.5.10}$$

By use of Eqs. (12.5.9) and (12.5.10), Eq. (12.5.8) becomes

$$\frac{1}{K}\frac{dp}{dt}\left(1 + \frac{K}{E}\frac{D}{t'}\right) + \frac{\partial V}{\partial x} = 0 \tag{12.5.11}$$

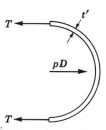

**Fig. 12.11** Tensile force in pipe wall.

It is convenient to express the constants in this equation in the form

$$a^2 = \frac{K/\rho}{1 + (K/E)(D/t')c_1} \tag{12.5.12}$$

in which $c_1$ is unity for the pipeline with expansion joints.   Equation (12.5.11) now becomes

$$\frac{1}{\rho}\frac{dp}{dt} + a^2\frac{\partial V}{\partial x} = 0 \tag{12.5.13}$$

Now, since $p = \rho g(H - z)$ (Fig. 12.10),

$$\frac{dp}{dt} = V\frac{\partial p}{\partial x} + \frac{\partial p}{\partial t}$$

$$= V\rho g\left(\frac{\partial H}{\partial x} - \frac{\partial z}{\partial x}\right) + \rho g\left(\frac{\partial H}{\partial t} - \frac{\partial z}{\partial t}\right)$$

The change of $\rho$ with respect to $x$ or $t$ is very much less than the change of $H$ with respect to $x$ or $t$, and so $\rho$ was considered constant in the preceding equation.   If the pipe is at rest, $\partial z/\partial t = 0$, and $\partial z/\partial x = -\sin\theta$; hence

$$\frac{1}{\rho}\frac{dp}{\partial t} = Vg\left(\frac{\partial H}{\partial x} + \sin\theta\right) + g\frac{\partial H}{dt}$$

and Eq. (12.5.13) becomes

$$L_1 = \frac{a^2}{g}\frac{\partial V}{\partial x} + V\frac{\partial H}{\partial x} + \frac{\partial H}{\partial t} + V\sin\theta = 0 \tag{12.5.14}$$

which is the continuity equation for a compressible liquid in an elastic pipe. $L_1$ and $L_2$ provide two nonlinear partial differential equations in $V$ and $H$ in terms of the independent variables $x$ and $t$.   No general solution to these equations is known, but they may be solved by the method of characteristics for a convenient finite-difference solution with the digital computer. Then by omitting terms of lesser importance, equations suitable to graphical and arithmetic solutions are obtained.

## 12.6   the method of characteristics solution

Equations $L_1$ and $L_2$ in the preceding section contain two unknowns. These equations may be combined with an unknown multiplier as $L = L_1 + \lambda L_2$.   Any two real, distinct values of $\lambda$ yield two equations in $V$ and $H$ that contain all the physics of the original two equations $L_1$ and $L_2$ and may replace them in any solution.   It may happen that great simplification will result if two particular values of $\lambda$ are found. $L_1$ and $L_2$ are substituted into the equation for $L$, with some rearrangement.

$$L = \left[\frac{\partial H}{\partial x}(V + \lambda g) + \frac{\partial H}{\partial t}\right] + \lambda\left[\frac{\partial V}{\partial x}\left(V + \frac{a^2}{g\lambda}\right) + \frac{\partial V}{\partial t}\right]$$

$$+ V \sin\theta + \lambda\frac{fV|V|}{2D} = 0 \quad (12.6.1)$$

This expression is arranged so that the first term in brackets would be the total derivative $dH/dt$ if

$$\frac{dx}{dt} = V + \lambda g \qquad (12.6.2)$$

and the second term in brackets would be $dV/dt$ if

$$\frac{dx}{dt} = V + \frac{a^2}{g\lambda} \qquad (12.6.3)$$

since

$$\frac{dH}{dt} = \frac{\partial H}{\partial x}\frac{dx}{dt} + \frac{\partial H}{\partial t} \qquad \frac{dV}{dt} = \frac{\partial V}{\partial x}\frac{dx}{dt} + \frac{\partial V}{\partial t}$$

from calculus. Equations (12.6.2) and (12.6.3) must be equivalent,

$$V + \lambda g = V + \frac{a^2}{g\lambda} \qquad (12.6.4)$$

After solving for $\lambda$,

$$\lambda = \pm\frac{a}{g} \qquad (12.6.5)$$

Therefore, two real, distinct values of $\lambda$ have been found that convert the two partial differential equations into a pair of total differential equations restricted by Eqs. (12.6.2) and (12.6.3).

These equations, with $\lambda$ substituted, become

$$\frac{dH}{dt} + \frac{a}{g}\frac{dV}{dt} + V \sin\theta + \frac{afV|V|}{2gD} = 0 \qquad \left.\right\} \quad (12.6.6)$$

$$\left.\frac{dx}{dt} = V + a\right\} C^+ \qquad (12.6.7)$$

$$\frac{dH}{dt} - \frac{a}{g}\frac{dV}{dt} + V \sin\theta - \frac{afV|V|}{2gD} = 0 \qquad \left.\right\} \quad (12.6.8)$$

$$\left.\frac{dx}{dt} = V - a\right\} C^- \qquad (12.6.9)$$

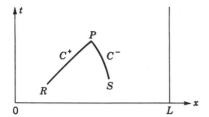

**Fig. 12.12**  $xt$ plot of characteristics along which solution is obtained.

To understand the significance of these four equations, it is convenient to consider the solution being carried out on an $xt$ plot (Fig. 12.12).   Consider that $V$ and $H$ are known at the two known locations $R$ and $S$ in the figure.   The curve labeled $C^+$ is a plot of Eq. (12.6.7); Eq. (12.6.6) is valid only along a $C^+$ characteristic.   The curve labeled $C^-$ is a plot of Eq. (12.6.9); Eq. (12.6.8) is valid only along a $C^-$ characteristic.   Each equation, (12.6.6) and (12.6.8), contains two unknowns for a known point on its characteristic, but at the intersection of $C^+$ and $C^-$ at $P$ both equations may be solved to yield $VP$ and $HP$.   At this point Eqs. (12.6.7) and (12.6.9) may also be solved for $x$ and $t$.   Hence the solution is carried out along the characteristics, starting from known conditions and by finding new intersections so that heads and velocities are found for later times.

In waterhammer calculations in metal pipes, the subject of this treatment, $V$ is very small compared with $a$, and may be dropped from Eqs. (12.6.7) and (12.6.9).   The characteristic lines are now straight, with slopes $\pm a$.   $a$ is the speed with which the pressure-pulse wave is transmitted along the pipe.   The pipe is considered to be made up of $N$ equal reaches (Fig. 12.13), and $H$ and $V$ are initially known at each of the dividing sections.   The solution to the waterhammer problem can then be carried out at the intersections of the characteristic lines, as shown by the solid dots.   It is to be noted that the solution can be carried over only a limited region,

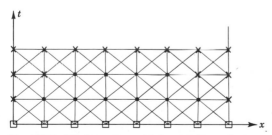

**Fig. 12.13**  Rectangular grid for solution of characteristics equations.

**Fig. 12.14** Finite-difference notation.

unless information is given at $x = 0$ and $x = L$, of some external condition as a function of time. (See under "Boundary conditions.")

From the grid of Fig. 12.13, it is seen that the time step of the calculation is $\Delta t = \Delta x/a$. By using the grid, $x$ and $t$ are known at each intersection, and Eqs. (12.6.7) and (12.6.9) need be considered no further. By writing Eqs. (12.6.6) and (12.6.8) in difference notation (Fig. 12.14), for Eq. (12.6.6)

$$dH = HP(I) - H(I - 1) \qquad dV = VP(I) - V(I - 1) \qquad dt = \Delta t$$

then

$$HP(I) - H(I - 1) + \frac{a}{g}(VP(I) - V(I - 1)) + V(I - 1) \sin \theta \, \Delta t$$

$$+ \frac{af \, \Delta t}{2gD} V(I - 1)|V(I - 1)| = 0 \quad (12.6.10)$$

and similarly for Eq. (12.6.8)

$$HP(I) - H(I + 1) - \frac{a}{g}(VP(I) - V(I + 1)) + V(I + 1) \sin \theta \, \Delta t$$

$$- \frac{af \, \Delta t}{2gD} V(I + 1)|V(I + 1)| = 0 \quad (12.6.11)$$

By adding the last two equations, $VP(I)$ is eliminated:

$$HP(I) = 0.5(H(I - 1) + H(I + 1) + \frac{a}{g}(V(I - 1) - V(I + 1))$$

$$- \sin \theta \, \Delta t \, (V(I - 1) + V(I + 1))$$

$$- \frac{a}{2gD} f \, \Delta t \, (V(I - 1)|V(I - 1)|$$

$$- V(I + 1)|V(I + 1)|)) \quad (12.6.12)$$

Similarly, by subtraction, VP(I) is obtained:

$$VP(I) = 0.5(V(I-1) + V(I+1) + \frac{g}{a}(H(I-1) - H(I+1)$$
$$- \sin \theta \, \Delta t \, (V(I-1) - V(I+1)))$$
$$- \frac{f}{2D} \Delta t \, (V(I-1)|V(I-1)|$$
$$+ V(I+1)|V(I+1)|)) \quad (12.6.13)$$

With $N$ reaches there are $N1 = N + 1$ sections along the pipe. These last two equations are used in an iteration loop to solve for $VP$ and $HP$ for $I = 2$ to $N$. The boundary conditions are then utilized to solve for $HP(1)$, $VP(1)$ and $HP(N1)$, $VP(N1)$. After these are obtained the results may be printed out, and then the values of $V(I)$ and $H(I)$ are replaced by the values of $VP(I)$ and $HP(I)$, the time incremented, and the procedure repeated.

### boundary conditions

At the upstream, or left, end of a pipe, Eq. (12.6.11) for the $C^-$ characteristic (for $I - 1$) provides one equation in the two unknowns $VP(1)$ and $HP(1)$ (Fig. 12.15a). One condition is needed exterior of the pipe to solve the equation. For example, consider a reservoir to be located at the upstream end, with elevation $HR$ above the center line of the pipe. Neglecting the minor loss at the entrance (Fig. 12.16), the unsteady Euler's equation may be applied [Eq. (12.1.1)]. The last term $\partial v / \partial t \, ds$ is zero except at the mouth, and for this very short distance $ds$ may be considered small, so that the term drops completely out, yielding

$$HR = HP(1) + \frac{(VP(1))^2}{2g} \qquad (12.6.14)$$

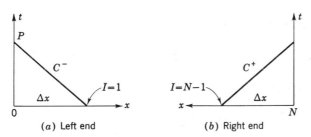

(a) Left end          (b) Right end

**Fig. 12.15**  Boundary conditions.

**Fig. 12.16** Entrance to a pipe from a reservoir.

However, for reverse flow, $HR = HP(1)$. Solving this equation with Eq. (12.6.11) gives $HP(1)$ and $VP(1)$. As another example of an upstream boundary condition, the discharge could be given as a function of time, which permits an easy solution.

At the downstream end, or right end, of the pipe (Fig. 12.15$b$), the $C^+$ characteristic is given by Eq. (12.6.10) for $I = N1$. One external condition is needed; for the purposes of this section a valve is selected (Fig. 12.17). For steady-state flow through the valve, considered as an orifice,

$$A V_0 = (C_d A_v)_0 \sqrt{2gH_0} \tag{12.6.15}$$

with $A$ the pipe area, $H_0$ the head across the valve, $(C_d A_v)_0$ the area of opening times the discharge coefficient, and $V_0$ the steady-state velocity in the pipe. For another opening, in general,

$$A\, VP(N1) = C_d A_v \sqrt{2gHP(N1)} \tag{12.6.16}$$

By dividing the second equation by the first equation,

$$\frac{VP(N1)}{V_0} = \tau \sqrt{\frac{HP(N1)}{H_0}} \tag{12.6.17}$$

**Fig. 12.17** Valve at downstream end of a pipe.

```
C       BASIC WATERHAMMER IN FORTRAN IV.  RESERVOIR AT UPSTREAM END OF
C       PIPE AND VALVE AT DOWNSTREAM END.    TAU=(1.-T/TC).P.M
        REAL L,M
        INTEGER U
        DIMENSION V(11),VP(11),H(11),HP(11)
      1 FORMAT('0                              HEADS AND VELOCITIES AT
     2TENTH POINTS ALONG THE PIPE')
      2 FORMAT('0    TIME  TAU   X/L=    .0       .1      .2       .3       .4
     2    .5      .6      .7       .8       .9      1.')
      3 FORMAT(1H0,2F7.3,3X,2HH=,F7.2,10F8.2/18X,2HV=,F7.2,10F8.2)
      4 FORMAT('1   L=',F6.1,3H A=,F5.0,3H N=,I2,3H D=,F2.0,4H V0=,F3.1,4H
     2TC=,F3.1,6H TMAX=,F4.1,4H H0=,F5.1,3H J=,I1,3H G=,F4.1,3H M=,F3.1,
     33H F=,F5.3)
        NAMELIST/DIN/L,A,N,D,V0,TC,TMAX,H0,J,G,M,F
     10 READ(5,DIN,END=99)
        WRITE(6,4) L,A,N,D,V0,TC,TMAX,H0,J,G,M,F
C       STEADY-STATE CALCULATIONS
        DHF=F*L*V0**2/(2.*G*D*N)
        HR=H0+N*DHF+V0**2/(2.*G)
        N1=N+1
        DO 11 I=1,N1
        V(I)=V0
     11 H(I)=H0+(N1-I)*DHF
        C2=G/A
        C4=V0**2/(C2*H0)
        TAU=1.
        T=.0
        DT=L/(A*N)
        FF=F*DT/(2.*D)
        U=0
        WRITE(6,1)
        WRITE(6,2)
     12 WRITE(6,3) T,TAU,(H(I),I=1,N1),(V(I),I=1,N1)
     13 T=T+DT
        U=U+1
        IF(T.GT.TMAX) GO TO 10
C       COMPUTATION OF INTERIOR POINTS
        DO 14 I=2,N
        VP(I)=.5*(V(I-1)+V(I+1)+C2*(H(I-1)-H(I+1))-FF*(V(I-1)*ABS(V(I-1))+
     2V(I+1)*ABS(V(I+1))))
     14 HP(I)=H(I-1)-(VP(I)-V(I-1)*(1.-FF*ABS(V(I-1))))/C2
C       UPSTREAM BOUNDARY CONDITION
        C5=H(2)-(V(2)-FF*V(2)*ABS(V(2)))/C2
        IF(V(1).GT..0) GO TO 15
        HP(1)=HR
        VP(1)=C2*(HP(1)-C5)
        GO TO 16
     15 VP(1)=A*(SQRT(1.+2.*G*(HR-C5)/(A*A))-1.)
        HP(1)=HR-VP(1)**2/(2.*G)
C       DOWNSTREAM BOUNDARY CONDITION
     16 C1=V(N)+C2*H(N)-FF*V(N)*ABS(V(N))
        IF(T.GT.TC) GO TO 17
        TAU=(1.-T/TC)**M
        GO TO 18
     17 TAU=.0
        VP(N1)=.0
        HP(N1)=C1/C2
        GO TO 19
     18 C3=TAU**2*C4
        VP(N1)=SQRT(.25*C3*C3+C3*C1)-.5*C3
        HP(N1)=(C1-VP(N1))/C2
     19 DO 20 I=1,N1
        V(I)=VP(I)
     20 H(I)=HP(I)
        IF(U/J*J.EQ.U) GO TO 12
        GO TO 13
     99 CALL SYSTEM
        END
```

**Fig. 12.18**   Basic waterhammer program in FORTRAN IV.

L=5743.5 A=3927. N=10 D=4. V0=3.6 TC=6.2 TMAX= 7.5 H0=300.0 J=2 G=32.2 M=3.2 F=0.019

HEADS AND VELOCITIES AT TENTH POINTS ALONG THE PIPE

| TIME | TAU | X/L= | .0 | .1 | .2 | .3 | .4 | .5 | .6 | .7 | .8 | .9 | 1. |
|---|---|---|---|---|---|---|---|---|---|---|---|---|---|
| 0.0 | 1.000 | H= | 305.49 | 304.94 | 304.39 | 303.84 | 303.29 | 302.74 | 302.20 | 301.65 | 301.10 | 300.55 | 300.00 |
|  |  | V= | 3.60 | 3.60 | 3.60 | 3.60 | 3.60 | 3.60 | 3.60 | 3.60 | 3.60 | 3.60 | 3.60 |
| 0.293 | 0.857 | H= | 305.49 | 304.88 | 304.39 | 303.84 | 303.29 | 302.74 | 302.20 | 301.65 | 301.10 | 319.89 | 339.13 |
|  |  | V= | 3.60 | 3.60 | 3.60 | 3.60 | 3.60 | 3.60 | 3.60 | 3.60 | 3.60 | 3.44 | 3.28 |
| 0.585 | 0.728 | H= | 305.49 | 304.88 | 304.33 | 303.78 | 303.29 | 302.74 | 302.20 | 320.94 | 340.13 | 359.71 | 379.53 |
|  |  | V= | 3.60 | 3.60 | 3.60 | 3.60 | 3.60 | 3.60 | 3.60 | 3.44 | 3.28 | 3.12 | 2.95 |
| 0.878 | 0.614 | H= | 305.49 | 304.88 | 304.33 | 303.78 | 303.23 | 321.93 | 341.14 | 360.67 | 380.45 | 400.40 | 420.40 |
|  |  | V= | 3.60 | 3.60 | 3.60 | 3.60 | 3.60 | 3.44 | 3.28 | 3.12 | 2.95 | 2.78 | 2.62 |
| 1.170 | 0.512 | H= | 305.49 | 304.88 | 304.33 | 322.99 | 342.09 | 361.57 | 381.30 | 401.22 | 421.23 | 441.15 | 460.90 |
|  |  | V= | 3.60 | 3.60 | 3.60 | 3.44 | 3.28 | 3.12 | 2.95 | 2.78 | 2.62 | 2.45 | 2.29 |
| 1.463 | 0.423 | H= | 305.49 | 324.04 | 343.09 | 362.55 | 382.22 | 402.10 | 422.01 | 441.90 | 461.61 | 481.08 | 500.23 |
|  |  | V= | 3.60 | 3.44 | 3.28 | 3.12 | 2.95 | 2.79 | 2.62 | 2.45 | 2.29 | 2.12 | 1.97 |
| 1.755 | 0.345 | H= | 305.55 | 344.35 | 383.14 | 402.98 | 422.85 | 442.70 | 462.38 | 481.82 | 500.88 | 519.48 | 537.55 |
|  |  | V= | 2.96 | 2.96 | 2.95 | 2.79 | 2.62 | 2.45 | 2.29 | 2.13 | 1.97 | 1.81 | 1.66 |
| 2.048 | 0.277 | H= | 305.61 | 345.45 | 384.98 | 424.40 | 463.15 | 482.56 | 501.60 | 520.17 | 538.22 | 555.68 | 572.44 |
|  |  | V= | 2.31 | 2.31 | 2.31 | 2.30 | 2.29 | 2.13 | 1.97 | 1.82 | 1.66 | 1.52 | 1.38 |
| 2.340 | 0.219 | H= | 305.65 | 345.66 | 385.48 | 425.00 | 463.66 | 501.78 | 538.88 | 556.33 | 573.07 | 589.09 | 604.30 |
|  |  | V= | 1.65 | 1.65 | 1.65 | 1.66 | 1.66 | 1.66 | 1.67 | 1.52 | 1.38 | 1.25 | 1.12 |
| 2.633 | 0.171 | H= | 305.68 | 344.83 | 384.08 | 423.03 | 461.22 | 498.75 | 535.09 | 570.65 | 604.90 | 619.30 | 632.80 |
|  |  | V= | 0.99 | 1.00 | 1.00 | 1.02 | 1.03 | 1.05 | 1.07 | 1.10 | 1.13 | 1.01 | 0.89 |
| 2.925 | 0.130 | H= | 305.69 | 343.56 | 381.16 | 418.58 | 455.52 | 491.91 | 527.25 | 561.71 | 594.81 | 626.98 | 657.75 |
|  |  | V= | 0.36 | 0.36 | 0.37 | 0.39 | 0.42 | 0.45 | 0.49 | 0.53 | 0.58 | 0.63 | 0.69 |
| 3.218 | 0.096 | H= | 305.69 | 341.48 | 377.11 | 412.44 | 447.19 | 481.55 | 515.24 | 548.25 | 580.10 | 593.99 | 605.51 |
|  |  | V= | -0.25 | -0.24 | -0.23 | -0.20 | -0.17 | -0.13 | -0.07 | -0.01 | 0.05 | 0.27 | 0.49 |
| 3.510 | 0.069 | H= | 305.69 | 338.76 | 371.72 | 404.45 | 436.83 | 468.79 | 500.05 | 513.83 | 525.95 | 536.88 | 545.83 |
|  |  | V= | -0.81 | -0.81 | -0.79 | -0.76 | -0.72 | -0.66 | -0.60 | -0.39 | -0.16 | 0.08 | 0.34 |
| 3.803 | 0.048 | H= | 305.69 | 335.59 | 365.42 | 395.12 | 424.58 | 436.75 | 447.57 | 457.44 | 465.79 | 473.37 | 479.81 |
|  |  | V= | -1.33 | -1.32 | -1.30 | -1.27 | -1.22 | -1.02 | -0.80 | -0.57 | -0.32 | -0.06 | 0.22 |
| 4.095 | 0.032 | H= | 305.69 | 332.15 | 358.57 | 367.93 | 376.21 | 383.82 | 390.39 | 396.33 | 401.46 | 406.22 | 410.49 |
|  |  | V= | -1.79 | -1.78 | -1.76 | -1.58 | -1.39 | -1.17 | -0.94 | -0.69 | -0.42 | -0.15 | 0.13 |
| 4.388 | 0.020 | H= | 305.69 | 311.60 | 316.53 | 320.93 | 324.47 | 327.59 | 330.17 | 332.66 | 335.12 | 337.81 | 340.52 |
|  |  | V= | -2.19 | -2.04 | -1.88 | -1.69 | -1.48 | -1.25 | -1.01 | -0.75 | -0.49 | -0.21 | 0.07 |
| 4.680 | 0.011 | H= | 305.69 | 288.62 | 271.70 | 271.37 | 270.60 | 269.87 | 269.29 | 269.13 | 269.27 | 269.96 | 271.32 |
|  |  | V= | -1.96 | -1.95 | -1.91 | -1.71 | -1.50 | -1.27 | -1.02 | -0.77 | -0.51 | -0.24 | 0.04 |
| 4.973 | 0.006 | H= | 305.69 | 282.57 | 259.83 | 237.66 | 216.63 | 213.01 | 209.79 | 207.23 | 205.53 | 204.78 | 205.14 |
|  |  | V= | -1.63 | -1.62 | -1.58 | -1.53 | -1.46 | -1.23 | -1.00 | -0.75 | -0.50 | -0.24 | 0.02 |
| 5.265 | 0.002 | H= | 305.69 | 277.85 | 250.64 | 224.26 | 199.09 | 175.10 | 152.95 | 148.72 | 145.70 | 143.97 | 143.68 |
|  |  | V= | -1.21 | -1.20 | -1.18 | -1.14 | -1.08 | -1.02 | -0.93 | -0.70 | -0.47 | -0.23 | 0.01 |
| 5.558 | 0.001 | H= | 305.69 | 275.22 | 244.96 | 215.32 | 186.98 | 160.01 | 135.04 | 111.88 | 91.14 | 88.82 | 88.14 |
|  |  | V= | -0.72 | -0.72 | -0.71 | -0.69 | -0.65 | -0.61 | -0.56 | -0.50 | -0.42 | -0.21 | 0.00 |
| 5.850 | 0.000 | H= | 305.69 | 273.62 | 242.03 | 210.98 | 180.93 | 152.11 | 125.19 | 100.11 | 77.50 | 57.04 | 39.31 |
|  |  | V= | -0.21 | -0.21 | -0.20 | -0.19 | -0.18 | -0.17 | -0.15 | -0.12 | -0.09 | -0.05 | 0.00 |
| 6.143 | 0.000 | H= | 305.69 | 273.51 | 241.66 | 210.42 | 180.24 | 151.09 | 123.38 | 97.27 | 73.36 | 68.40 | 67.03 |
|  |  | V= | 0.32 | 0.32 | 0.32 | 0.31 | 0.31 | 0.30 | 0.29 | 0.28 | 0.28 | 0.14 | 0.00 |
| 6.435 | 0.0 | H= | 305.68 | 274.47 | 243.73 | 213.62 | 184.12 | 155.58 | 128.41 | 119.37 | 112.90 | 108.63 | 107.42 |
|  |  | V= | 0.84 | 0.84 | 0.83 | 0.81 | 0.79 | 0.76 | 0.73 | 0.56 | 0.38 | 0.19 | 0.0 |
| 6.728 | 0.0 | H= | 305.66 | 276.68 | 247.99 | 219.63 | 191.89 | 181.89 | 173.61 | 166.91 | 162.44 | 159.58 | 158.77 |
|  |  | V= | 1.33 | 1.33 | 1.31 | 1.29 | 1.25 | 1.07 | 0.87 | 0.67 | 0.45 | 0.23 | 0.0 |
| 7.020 | 0.0 | H= | 305.64 | 279.52 | 253.58 | 244.92 | 237.44 | 230.90 | 225.87 | 222.06 | 219.45 | 217.85 | 217.46 |
|  |  | V= | 1.78 | 1.78 | 1.76 | 1.59 | 1.40 | 1.19 | 0.97 | 0.74 | 0.50 | 0.25 | 0.0 |
| 7.313 | 0.0 | H= | 305.62 | 299.63 | 294.81 | 290.72 | 287.47 | 285.00 | 283.20 | 281.78 | 280.85 | 280.30 | 280.11 |
|  |  | V= | 2.18 | 2.03 | 1.87 | 1.68 | 1.48 | 1.26 | 1.02 | 0.77 | 0.52 | 0.26 | 0.0 |

**Fig. 12.19**  Computer solution to Example 12.6.

in which $\tau$ is the dimensionless valve opening.   $\tau = 1$ for steady flow and reduces to zero as the valve closes.   By solving Eq. (12.6.17) simultaneously with Eq. (12.6.10), $VP(N1)$ and $HP(N1)$ are obtained.   $\tau$ is generally given as a function of time $t$.   The solution involves a quadratic; it is important that the proper sign be taken.

A computer program is given for solution of the basic waterhammer problem of closing a valve at the downstream end of a pipeline, with a reservoir at the upstream end.   In Fig. 12.18 the program is listed.   In this program the valve closure is given by the equation

$$\tau = \left(1 - \frac{t}{t_C}\right)^m \qquad\qquad (12.6.18)$$

in which $t_C$ is the time of closure.   The pipe is taken as horizontal, so that $\theta = 0$.

**example 12.6**   Obtain the solution to the waterhammer problem of closure of a valve at the downstream end of a pipe for the following conditions: $L = 5743.5$ ft, $a = 3927$ ft/sec, $D = 4$ ft, $f = 0.019$, $V_0 = 3.6$ ft/sec, $T_C = 6.2$ sec, $T_{\max} = 10$ sec, $H_0 = 300$ ft, for the valve closure of Eq. (12.6.18) with $m = 3.2$.

The computer program of Fig. 12.18 is utilized for the data of the problem, for $N = 10$, with $J = 2$, which prints out every other calculation. The solution is shown (Fig. 12.19).   It is of interest to follow the wave of the pressure pulse through the pipe.

The methods for computer solution of waterhammer may be extended easily to more complex systems.   References at the end of the chapter include many special solutions.

## 12.7   graphical solution of simple waterhammer cases

Although the computer is the most satisfactory method of solving waterhammer problems, in some situations lack of availability of a computer or the simplicity of the problem makes it expedient to use other methods. In the graphical solution friction is neglected, as well as the angle of inclination of pipe.   Equations (12.6.10) and (12.6.11) are applied over the whole reach of pipe from section 1 upstream to section 2 downstream.

$$H_2 - H_1 = -\frac{a}{g}(V_2 - V_1) \qquad\qquad (12.7.1)$$

for a pulse wave traveling from section 1 to section 2.   In using this equation it must be remembered that if $H_2$ is for time $t$, then $H_1$ is the head at section 1 at time $t - L/a$, and similarly for $V_2$ and $V_1$. This equation may be made dimensionless as follows:

$$\frac{H_2 - H_1}{H_0} = - \frac{aV_0}{gH_0} \frac{V_2 - V_1}{V_0} \tag{12.7.2}$$

By defining

$$\Delta h = \frac{H_2 - H_1}{H_0} \qquad \Delta v = \frac{V_2 - V_1}{V_0} \qquad 2\rho = \frac{aV_0}{gH_0} \tag{12.7.3}$$

$$\frac{\Delta h}{\Delta v} = -2\rho \tag{12.7.4}$$

Similarly, from Eq. (12.6.11),

$$\frac{\Delta h}{\Delta v} = 2\rho \tag{12.7.5}$$

These last two equations embody all the physics of the wave translation along the pipe. In Fig. 12.20 each of these equations plots as a straight line on the $hv$ plot. The first equation is for the wave traveling downstream, and the second equation for the wave traveling upstream. Conditions at the ends of the pipe are now needed to carry out a meaningful solution of a waterhammer situation in a simple pipe.

Consider the case of sudden closure of a valve (Fig. 12.21) on the pipeline, with the values given.

$$2\rho = \frac{aV_0}{gH_0} = \frac{4000 \times 3.22}{32.2 \times 400} = 1$$

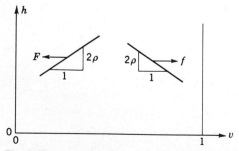

**Fig. 12.20** Dimensionless dependent-variable plot used in solution of waterhammer by graphical method.

**Fig. 12.21**  Closure of a valve at $A$.

Steady-state flow is portrayed on the graphical solution (Fig. 12.22) at $v = 1$, $h = 1$ for the complete pipe.   If the valve closes at $t = 1$, then the solution may start at $B_0$ (the subscript refers to the time and the letter to the location).   This is an $f$ wave (Fig. 12.20), starting at $B_0$ with slope $-2\rho$, and conditions at $A_1$ must fall on this line.   At $A_1$, however, it is known that $V = 0$, as the valve is closed, and this makes $v = 0$, which is the ordinate axis.   Hence $A_1$ occurs as shown.   Now proceeding from $A_1$ to $B_2$, the $B_2$ condition must lie on the $F$ wave through $A_1$.   At the reservoir (neglecting the velocity head) the head is $h = 1$; hence the intersection of $h = 1$ and the $F$ wave through $A_1$ yields the location of $B_2$.   Continuing this procedure, $A_3$ and $B_4$ are located.   Then $A_5$, $B_6$, $A_7$, and $B_8$ would be a repetition of the first cycle, etc.

For a gradual valve closure, Eq. (12.6.17), in dimensionless form, becomes

$$v = \tau \sqrt{h} \qquad\qquad\qquad (12.7.6)$$

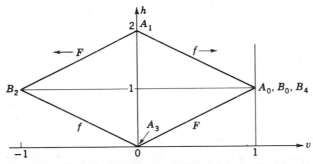

**Fig. 12.22**   Graphical solution for sudden closure of a valve at downstream end of pipe.

**Fig. 12.23** $\tau t$-curve for valve closure.

Taking a valve closure as given by Fig. 12.23, in place of the smooth closure, it will be assumed that the valve closes each $L/a$ by a sudden increment. The value of $\tau$ for each $L/a$ increment is read from the $\tau t$ curve. Then on the $vh$ plot Eq. (12.7.6) becomes a parabola (Fig. 12.24). At each time shown on the parabola, the $h$ and $v$ values at the valve must occur; i.e., $A_1$ must be on the $t = 1$ parabola, etc. At the other end of the pipe (Fig. 12.21) $h = 1$ due to the reservoir. To start the solution, begin at the steady condition $B_0$ and construct the $f$-line through $B_0$. On this line $A_1$ must be found, which is also on the parabola $t = 1$. Proceeding from $A_1$ to $B_2$ on an $F$-line, its intersection with $h = 1$ yields $B_2$. Then draw an

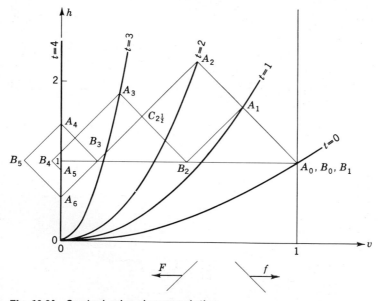

**Fig. 12.24** Gradual-valve-closure solution.

$f$-line from $B_2$ to $A_3$, and an $F$-line from $A_3$ to $B_4$.   At all times after $t = 4$ the gate is closed, so that $A$ is on the ordinate axis $v = 0$, and $B$ is on $h = 1$.   To provide extra detail, start with $B_1$ (undisturbed, as the first valve movement is at $t = 1$), proceed on an $f$-line to the $t = 2$ parabola $A_2$, then to $B_3$, $A_4$, etc., as shown.

The graphical method is the most visual of all methods.   The reflections at the reservoir are handled by satisfying the head condition, and similarly any reflections at the valve are taken care of by handling boundary conditions—a great simplification.   If one wished to know the values of $h$ and $v$ at the pipe mid-point $C$, a wave leaving $A_2$ on an $F$-line would arrive at $C_{2\frac{1}{4}}$, and similarly a wave leaving $B_2$ on an $f$-line would find $C_{2\frac{1}{4}}$.   Hence the intersection of these two lines yields $C_{2\frac{1}{4}}$.   By taking more detail in the $\tau t$ curve, say for each $L/2a$, intersections of the $f$ and $F$ lines can be interpreted to yield values of $v$ and $h$ at the quarter points.

**example 12.7**   Consider the pipe liquid at rest in the dead-end pipe of Fig. 12.25 when waves on the reservoir, 4 ft high (trough to crest), start. Determine the head variation at $A$ for a few cycles.

Since there is no velocity for steady state, any $V_0$ may be assumed in computing $2\rho$, say $V_0 = 2$ ft/sec,

$$2\rho = \frac{aV_0}{gH_0} = \frac{3220}{32.2}\frac{2}{20} = 10$$

As a slope of 10:1 is unhandy graphically, the ordinate scale may be made one-tenth the abscissa scale.   Start the solution at $A_0$ ($v = 0$, $h = 1$) and assume the wave crests occur at $t = \frac{1}{2}$, $2\frac{1}{2}$, $4\frac{1}{2}$, etc.   The $B$ intersections are on $H = 22$ ft or $h = \frac{22}{20} = 1.1$ for $t = \frac{1}{2}$, $2\frac{1}{2}$, $4\frac{1}{2}$, etc., and are on $h = \frac{18}{20} = 0.9$ for $t = 1\frac{1}{2}$, $3\frac{1}{2}$, $5\frac{1}{2}$, etc.   Since $A$ is a dead end, $v = 0$ always, and the solution develops as shown in Fig. 12.26.   When the head at $A$

**Fig. 12.25**  Waves on a reservoir having same period as the waterhammer cycle $4L/a$.

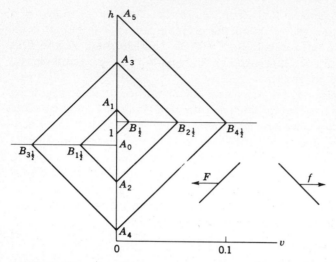

**Fig. 12.26**  Graphical solution of resonance problem of Fig. 12.25.

reaches vapor pressure, the cycle will be broken by a change in timing due to expansion and collapse of the vapor cavity.

Quite complicated problems have been solved by the graphical method, including branching pipes, series pipes, pump power failures, etc.   It is very widely used in hydraulic-transient analysis.   A correction for friction can also be included in the method.   In the following section, another method of solution is available, based on the characteristic equations, which includes friction and which can be solved by slide rule or desk calculation if a computer is not available.

## 12.8   algebraic waterhammer

In the graphical method, discussed in the preceding section, Eqs. (12.6.10) and (12.6.11) were applied for the case $\theta = 0$ and no friction.   The sin $\theta$ term, in general, is small and may be neglected.   These same equations, with the friction term included, are now handled as simultaneous algebraic equations, which may be solved by several means: slide rule, desk calculator, or digital computer.

First consider a single pipe (Fig. 12.27) divided into $P$ equal reaches such that $L/a = P \, \Delta t$, $\Delta t$ being the time step for waterhammer calculations.   In general the time is given by $J \, \Delta t$, or the integer $J$ is an index to the time.   In Eq. (12.6.10) for $\theta = 0$, by applying the equation

**Fig. 12.27** Pipe divided into $P$ equal reaches $L/a = P\,\Delta t$.

over the whole length of pipe,

$$H_B(J) - H_C(J - P) + \frac{a}{g}(V_B(J) - V_C(J - P))$$
$$+ \frac{f}{2Dg}\, a\, \frac{L}{a}\, V_C(J - P)|V_C(J - P)| = 0$$

After dividing through by $H_0$, the steady-state head at some point in the system, and nondimensionalizing,

$$h_B(J) - h_C(J - P) + B(v_B(J) - v_C(J - P))$$
$$+ Hv_C(J - P)|v_C(J - P)| = 0 \quad (12.8.1)$$

in which $H$ is the steady-state friction drop across the pipe divided by $H_0$ and $B = aV_0/gH_0$. Similarly by applying Eq. (12.6.11) over the length of pipe,

$$h_C(J) - h_B(J - P) - B(v_C(J) - v_B(J - P))$$
$$- Hv_B(J - P)|v_B(J - P)| = 0 \quad (12.8.2)$$

To apply these equations to a valve closure in a simple pipe (Fig. 12.28), let $H_0$ be the steady state head at the valve; then

$$HR = H_0 + f\frac{L}{D}\frac{V_0^2}{2g}$$

**Fig. 12.28** Closure of a valve with friction included.

neglecting the velocity head at the entrance.  In dimensionless form

$$h_r = h_C(J) = 1 + H \tag{12.8.3}$$

which is constant.  Let $\tau(J)$ be the known valve position for each time
. $J \, \Delta t$.  By solving the valve equation $v_B(J) = \tau(J) \sqrt{h_B(J)}$ simultaneously
with Eq. (12.8.1),

$$v_B(J) = -\frac{B\tau^2}{2}$$

$$+ \sqrt{\left(\frac{B\tau^2}{2}\right)^2 + (h_C(J - P) + Bv_C(J - P) - Hv_C(J - P)|v_C(J - P)|)\tau^2} \tag{12.8.4}$$

From Eq. (12.8.1)

$$h_B(J) = h_C(J - P) - B(v_B(J) - v_C(J - P)) \\ - Hv_C(J - P)|v_C(J - P)| \tag{12.8.5}$$

At the reservoir, from Eq. (12.8.2),

$$v_C(J) = v_B(J - P) + \frac{1}{B}(h_r - h_B(J - P) \\ - Hv_B(J - P)|v_B(J - P)|) \tag{12.8.6}$$

The solution is started by listing the steady-state values which occur at
$P \, \Delta t$ seconds if the first closure occurs at $J = P + 1$.  All previous values
are the same as the steady-state values.

**example 12.8**  Determine the head and velocity at the valve of Fig. 12.28 by
algebraic  waterhammer  for  the  following  conditions:  $L = 12,000$  ft,
$D = 4$ ft, $f = 0.02$, $V_0 = 4.01$ ft/sec, $a = 4000$ ft/sec, $H_0 = 200$ ft,
$t_C = 10$ sec, $P = 6$, and $\tau = 1 - (t/t_C)^{1/3}$.
First the constants in Eqs. (12.8.4) and (12.8.6) are evaluated,

$$B = \frac{aV_0}{gH_0} = \frac{4000 \times 4.01}{32.2 \times 200} = 2.495 \qquad \Delta t = \frac{L}{Pa} = \frac{12,000}{6 \times 4000} = 0.5 \text{ sec}$$

$$H = \frac{fL}{D}\frac{V_0^2}{2gH_0} = \frac{0.02 \times 12,000 \times (4.01)^2}{4 \times 64.4 \times 200} = 0.075$$

$$h_r = h_C = 1 + H = 1.075 \qquad T = (J - P)\Delta t = 0.5(J - 6)$$

The equations reduce to

$$v_B(J) = 1.2475\tau$$

$$\times\left(\sqrt{\tau^2 + \frac{1.075 + 2.495v_C\,(J-P) - 0.075v_C\,(J-P)|v_C\,(J-P)|}{1.556}} - \tau\right)$$

$$v_C(J) = v_B(J-P) + 0.401(1.075 - h_B(J-P)$$
$$- 0.075v_B(J-P)|v_B(J-P)|)$$

and from Eq. (12.8.1)

$$h_B(J) = 1.075 - 2.495(v_B(J) - v_C(J-P)) + 0.075v_C(J-P)|v_C(J-P)|$$

```
C      ALGEBRAIC WATERHAMMER IN A SINGLE PIPE
       INTEGER P,P1
       REAL L,MM
       DIMENSION HB(500),VB(500),VC(500)
     1 FORMAT('0        J              TIME           TAU          HB(J)
     2        VB(J)        VC(J)           HB          VB')
     2 FORMAT(1H ,I8,1X,7F15.3)
     3 FORMAT('1 GIVEN L=',F6.0,3H A=,F5.0,3H F=,F4.2,4H V0=,F4.2,3H G=,
     2 2F4.1,4H H0=,F4.0,4H TC=,F3.0,3H P=,I1,6H TMAX=,F3.0,3H D=,F3.1,
     3 4H MM=,F6.4)
     4 FORMAT('0 CALCULATED DATA DT=',F3.1,3H M=,I2,3H B=,F6.4,3H H=,F7.
     2 5,4H HR=,F6.4)
       NAMELIST/DIN/L,A,F,V0,G,H0,TC,P,TMAX,D,MM/DN1/DT,M,B,H,HR
    10 READ(5,DIN,END=99)
       WRITE(6,3) L,A,F,V0,G,H0,TC,P,TMAX,D,MM
       P1=P+1
       DT=L/(A*P)
       M=TMAX/DT+P1
       B=A*V0/(G*H0)
       H=F*L*V0**2/(2.*G*D*H0)
       HR=1.+H
       DO 11 J=1,P1
       VC(J)=1.
       VB(J)=1.
    11 HB(J)=1.
       WRITE(6,4) DT,M,B,H,HR
       WRITE(6,1)
       DO 14 J=P1,M
       T=(J-P1)*DT
       IF(T.LT.TC) GO TO 12
       TAU=.0
       VB(J)=.0
       GO TO 13
    12 TAU=1.-(T/TC)**MM
       VB(J)=.5*B*TAU*(SQRT(TAU**2+4.*(HR+VC(J-P)*(B-H*ABS(VC(J-P))))/(B*
     2 B))-TAU)
    13 HB(J)=HR-B*(VB(J)-VC(J-P))-H*VC(J-P)*ABS(VC(J-P))
       VC(J)=VB(J-P)+(HR-HB(J-P)-H*VB(J-P)*ABS(VB(J-P)))/B
       HBB=HB(J)*H0
       VBB=VB(J)*V0
    14 WRITE(6,2) J,T,TAU,HB(J),VB(J),VC(J),HBB,VBB
       GO TO 10
    99 CALL SYSTEM
       END
```

**Fig. 12.29**  FORTRAN IV listing for algebraic waterhammer in single pipe.

The last three equations are solved in succession for each $J$, starting with $J = 7$. This solution is most conveniently handled by computer, but desk calculator or slide rule can be used. The computer program and solution are shown in Figs. 12.29 and 12.30.

**example 12.9** The series pipe system of Fig. 12.31 has the valve closure

| $\tau$ | 1.0 | 0.86 | 0.73 | 0.61 | 0.5 | 0.4 | 0.31 | 0.23 | 0.16 | 0.1 | 0.05 | 0 |
|---|---|---|---|---|---|---|---|---|---|---|---|---|
| $t$, sec | 0 | 0.5 | 1 | 1.5 | 2 | 2.5 | 3 | 3.5 | 4 | 4.5 | 5 | 5.5 |

By use of the algebraic method find the dimensionless head at $A$ and $B$ and the dimensionless velocity at $A$, $B$, and $C$.

Let $\Delta t = 0.15$ sec, and let $P$ be the number of $\Delta t$'s for wave travel time from $C$ to $B$, and let $Q$ be the number of $\Delta t$'s for wave travel time from $B$ to $A$. Then

$$V_{02} = V_{01} \frac{D_1^2}{D_2^2} = 2.2 \left(\frac{4}{3}\right)^2 = 3.9111$$

$$P = \frac{L_1}{a_1 \Delta t} = \frac{3600}{4000 \times 0.15} = 6 \qquad Q = \frac{2250}{3000 \times \Delta t} = 5$$

$$B_1 = \frac{a_1 V_{01}}{g H_0} = \frac{4000 \times 2.2}{32.2 \times 200} = 1.3665$$

$$B_2 = \frac{a_2 V_{02}}{g H_0} = \frac{3000 \times 3.9111}{32.2 \times 200} = 1.8219$$

$$H_1 = f_1 \frac{L_1}{D_1} \frac{V_{01}^2}{2 g H_0} = \frac{0.02 \times 3600(2.2)^2}{4 \times 64.4 \times 200} = 0.006764$$

$$H_2 = f_2 \frac{L_2}{D_2} \frac{V_{02}^2}{2 g H_0} = \frac{0.024 \times 2250(3.9111)^2}{3 \times 64.4 \times 200} = 0.02138$$

$$h_{B0} = 1.02138 \qquad h_R = 1.02814$$

Equations (12.8.1) and (12.8.2) are written for each pipe:

$$h_{A_i} - h_{B_{i-Q}} = -B_2(v_{A_i} - v_{B_{i-Q}}) - H_2 v_{B_{i-Q}}|v_{B_{i-Q}}| \tag{1}$$

$$h_{B_i} - h_{A_{i-Q}} = B_2(v_{B_i} - v_{A_{i-Q}}) + H_2 v_{A_{i-Q}}|v_{A_{i-Q}}| \tag{2}$$

$$h_{B_i} - h_R = -B_1(v_{B_i} - v_{C_{i-P}}) - H_1 v_{C_{i-P}}|v_{C_{i-P}}| \tag{3}$$

$$h_R - h_{B_{i-P}} = B_1(v_{C_i} - v_{B_{i-P}}) + H_1 v_{B_{i-P}}|v_{B_{i-P}}| \tag{4}$$

SCOPY V10

GIVEN L=12000. A=4000. F=0.02 VO=4.01 G=32.2 HO=200. TC=10. P=6 TMAX=24. D=4.0 MM=0.3333

CALCULATED DATA DT=0.5 N=55 B=2.4907 H=0.07491 HR=1.0749

| J | TIME | TAU | HB(J) | VB(J) | VC(J) | HB | VB |
|---|------|-----|-------|-------|-------|-----|-----|
| 7 | 0.0 | 1.000 | 1.000 | 1.000 | 1.000 | 200.000 | 4.010 |
| 8 | 0.500 | 0.632 | 1.539 | 0.784 | 1.000 | 307.832 | 3.142 |
| 9 | 1.000 | 0.536 | 1.734 | 0.705 | 1.000 | 346.716 | 2.829 |
| 10 | 1.500 | 0.469 | 1.887 | 0.644 | 1.000 | 377.440 | 2.582 |
| 11 | 2.000 | 0.415 | 2.021 | 0.590 | 1.000 | 404.151 | 2.367 |
| 12 | 2.500 | 0.370 | 2.142 | 0.542 | 1.000 | 428.385 | 2.171 |
| 13 | 3.000 | 0.331 | 2.255 | 0.496 | 1.000 | 450.907 | 1.990 |
| 14 | 3.500 | 0.295 | 2.361 | 0.454 | 0.579 | 472.161 | 1.819 |
| 15 | 4.000 | 0.263 | 2.462 | 0.413 | 0.426 | 492.432 | 1.656 |
| 16 | 4.500 | 0.234 | 2.560 | 0.374 | 0.305 | 511.913 | 1.499 |
| 17 | 5.000 | 0.206 | 2.654 | 0.336 | 0.200 | 530.744 | 1.348 |
| 18 | 5.500 | 0.181 | 2.745 | 0.299 | 0.104 | 549.030 | 1.200 |
| 19 | 6.000 | 0.157 | 2.834 | 0.264 | 0.015 | 566.847 | 1.057 |
| 20 | 6.500 | 0.134 | 2.018 | 0.190 | -0.069 | 403.579 | 0.762 |
| 21 | 7.000 | 0.112 | 1.753 | 0.148 | -0.149 | 350.570 | 0.595 |
| 22 | 7.500 | 0.091 | 1.545 | 0.114 | -0.226 | 309.002 | 0.456 |
| 23 | 8.000 | 0.072 | 1.362 | 0.084 | -0.301 | 272.318 | 0.335 |
| 24 | 8.500 | 0.053 | 1.191 | 0.058 | -0.374 | 238.115 | 0.231 |
| 25 | 9.000 | 0.035 | 1.026 | 0.035 | -0.445 | 205.181 | 0.140 |
| 26 | 9.500 | 0.017 | 0.865 | 0.016 | -0.190 | 172.914 | 0.063 |
| 27 | 10.000 | 0.0 | 0.705 | 0.0 | -0.124 | 141.014 | 0.0 |
| 28 | 10.500 | 0.0 | 0.515 | 0.0 | -0.075 | 102.948 | 0.0 |
| 29 | 11.000 | 0.0 | 0.331 | 0.0 | -0.032 | 66.278 | 0.0 |
| 30 | 11.500 | 0.0 | 0.154 | 0.0 | 0.011 | 30.793 | 0.0 |
| 31 | 12.000 | 0.0 | -0.018 | 0.0 | 0.055 | -3.671 | 0.0 |
| 32 | 12.500 | 0.0 | 0.605 | 0.0 | 0.100 | 121.024 | 0.0 |
| 33 | 13.000 | 0.0 | 0.766 | 0.0 | 0.148 | 153.216 | 0.0 |
| 34 | 13.500 | 0.0 | 0.887 | 0.0 | 0.225 | 177.465 | 0.0 |
| 35 | 14.000 | 0.0 | 0.996 | 0.0 | 0.299 | 199.217 | 0.0 |
| 36 | 14.500 | 0.0 | 1.102 | 0.0 | 0.370 | 220.456 | 0.0 |
| 37 | 15.000 | 0.0 | 1.211 | 0.0 | 0.439 | 242.129 | 0.0 |
| 38 | 15.500 | 0.0 | 1.324 | 0.0 | 0.189 | 264.746 | 0.0 |
| 39 | 16.000 | 0.0 | 1.443 | 0.0 | 0.124 | 288.618 | 0.0 |
| 40 | 16.500 | 0.0 | 1.631 | 0.0 | 0.075 | 326.257 | 0.0 |
| 41 | 17.000 | 0.0 | 1.812 | 0.0 | 0.032 | 362.349 | 0.0 |
| 42 | 17.500 | 0.0 | 1.966 | 0.0 | -0.011 | 397.121 | 0.0 |
| 43 | 18.000 | 0.0 | 2.154 | 0.0 | -0.054 | 430.747 | 0.0 |
| 44 | 18.500 | 0.0 | 1.542 | 0.0 | -0.100 | 308.405 | 0.0 |
| 45 | 19.000 | 0.0 | 1.383 | 0.0 | -0.148 | 276.516 | 0.0 |
| 46 | 19.500 | 0.0 | 1.262 | 0.0 | -0.223 | 252.413 | 0.0 |
| 47 | 20.000 | 0.0 | 1.154 | 0.0 | -0.296 | 230.730 | 0.0 |
| 48 | 20.500 | 0.0 | 1.048 | 0.0 | -0.366 | 209.509 | 0.0 |
| 49 | 21.000 | 0.0 | 0.939 | 0.0 | -0.433 | 187.878 | 0.0 |
| 50 | 21.500 | 0.0 | 0.827 | 0.0 | -0.188 | 165.366 | 0.0 |
| 51 | 22.000 | 0.0 | 0.708 | 0.0 | -0.124 | 141.672 | 0.0 |
| 52 | 22.500 | 0.0 | 0.522 | 0.0 | -0.075 | 104.453 | 0.0 |
| 53 | 23.000 | 0.0 | 0.345 | 0.0 | -0.032 | 68.925 | 0.0 |
| 54 | 23.500 | 0.0 | 0.174 | 0.0 | 0.011 | 34.845 | 0.0 |
| 55 | 24.000 | 0.0 | 0.010 | 0.0 | 0.054 | 2.027 | 0.0 |

**Fig. 12.30**  Computer results for Example 12.8.

**Fig. 12.31**  Series pipe system to be solved for arbitrary closure by algebraic method.

```
C      PROGRAM FOR SOLUTION OF WATERHAMMER IN TWO PIPES IN SERIES WITH
C      RESERVOIR UPSTREAM AND VALVE DOWNSTREAM.
C      L1/(A1*DT)=P, L2/(A2*DT)=Q.  ARBITRARY VALVE CLOSURE.
       REAL L1,L2
       INTEGER P,Q,U
       DIMENSION HA(200),HB(200),VA(200),VB(200),VC(200),TA(12)
     1 FORMAT('1                              RESULTS OF ALGEBRAIC WATERH
     2AMMER FOR TWO PIPES IN SERIES')
     2 FORMAT(4H0L1=,F6.1,4H L2=,F6.1,4H D1=,F3.1,4H D2=,F3.1,4H A1=,F6.0
     2,4H A2=,F6.0,4H F1=,F5.3,4H F2=,F5.3,5H V01=,F3.1,4H H0=,F5.1,5H D
     3TA=,F3.1,4H TC=,F3.1/3H G=,F4.1,3H M=,I2,4H DT=,F4.2,3H U=,I1,4H T
     4A=,12F5.2)
     3 FORMAT('0      TIME            TAU            HA(J)            HB(J
     2)          VA(J)           VB(J)           VC(J)'/)
     4 FORMAT(1H ,F11.3,F15.3,5F16.3)
       NAMELIST/DIN/L1,L2,D1,D2,A1,A2,F1,F2,V01,H0,DTA,TC,G,M,DT,U,TA
    10 READ(5,DIN,END=99)
       V02=V01*(D1/D2)**2
       B1=A1*V01/(G*H0)
       B2=A2*V02/(G*H0)
       P=L1/(A1*DT)
       Q=L2/(A2*DT)
       H1=F1*L1*V01**2/(2.*G*D1*H0)
       H2=F2*L2*V02**2/(2.*G*D2*H0)
       HBB=1.+H2
       HR=HBB+H1
       N1=P+Q+1
       DO 11 J=1,N1
       VA(J)=1.
       VB(J)=1.
       VC(J)=1.
       HA(J)=1.
    11 HB(J)=HBB
       WRITE(6,1)
       WRITE(6,2) L1,L2,D1,D2,A1,A2,F1,F2,V01,H0,DTA,TC,G,M,DT,U,(TA(I),I
     2=1,12)
       WRITE(6,3)
       DO 16 J=N1,M
       T=(J-N1)*DT
C      PARABOLIC INTERPOLATION FOR DETERMINATION OF TAU
       IF(T.GT.TC) GO TO 13
       I=T/DTA+1
       TH=(T-(I-1)*DTA)/DTA
       IF(I.GT.1) GO TO 12
       I=2
       TH=TH-1.
    12 TAU=TA(I)+.5*TH*(TA(I+1)-TA(I-1)+TH*(TA(I+1)+TA(I-1)-2.*TA(I)))
       IF(TAU.LT..0) TAU=.0
       GO TO 14
    13 TAU=.0
       VA(J)=.0
       GO TO 15
    14 VA(J)=.5*TAU*B2*(SQRT(TAU**2+4.*(HB(J-Q)+VB(J-Q)*(B2-H2*ABS(VB(J-Q
     2))))/(B2**2))-TAU)
    15 HA(J)=HB(J-Q)-B2*(VA(J)-VB(J-Q))-H2*VB(J-Q)*ABS(VB(J-Q))
       VB(J)=(HR-HA(J-Q)+B2*VA(J-Q)+B1*VC(J-P)-H2*VA(J-Q)*ABS(VA(J-Q))
     2-H1*VC(J-P)*ABS(VC(J-P)))/(B1+B2)
       HB(J)=HA(J-Q)+B2*(VB(J)-VA(J-Q))+H2*VA(J-Q)*ABS(VA(J-Q))
       VC(J)=VB(J-P)+(HR-HB(J-P)-H1*VB(J-P)*ABS(VB(J-P)))/B1
    16 IF(J/U*U.EQ.J) WRITE(6,4) T,TAU,HA(J),HB(J),VA(J),VB(J),VC(J)
       GO TO 10
    99 CALL SYSTEM
       END
```

**Fig. 12.32**   FORTRAN IV program for solution of algebraic waterhammer equations for series pipes.   Parabolic interpolation of valve-closure data.

RESULTS OF ALGEBRAIC WATERHAMMER FOR TWO PIPES IN SERIES

L1=3600.1 L2=2250.1 D1=4.0 D2=3.0 A1= 4000. A2= 3000. F1=0.020 F2=0.024 V01=2.2 H0=200.0 DTA=0.5 TC=5.5
G=32.2 M=60 DT=0.15 U=1 TA= 1.00 0.86 0.73 0.61 0.50 0.40 0.31 0.23 0.16 0.10 0.05 0.0

| TIME | TAU | HA(J) | HB(J) | VA(J) | VB(J) | VC(J) |
|------|-----|-------|-------|-------|-------|-------|
| 0.0 | 1.000 | 1.000 | 1.021 | 1.000 | 1.000 | 1.000 |
| 0.150 | 0.957 | 1.042 | 1.021 | 0.977 | 1.000 | 1.000 |
| 0.300 | 0.915 | 1.085 | 1.021 | 0.953 | 1.000 | 1.000 |
| 0.450 | 0.874 | 1.130 | 1.021 | 0.929 | 1.000 | 1.000 |
| 0.600 | 0.833 | 1.176 | 1.021 | 0.903 | 1.000 | 1.000 |
| 0.750 | 0.794 | 1.223 | 1.021 | 0.878 | 1.000 | 1.000 |
| 0.900 | 0.755 | 1.271 | 1.057 | 0.851 | 0.974 | 1.000 |
| 1.050 | 0.718 | 1.320 | 1.094 | 0.824 | 0.947 | 1.000 |
| 1.200 | 0.681 | 1.370 | 1.132 | 0.797 | 0.919 | 1.000 |
| 1.350 | 0.645 | 1.421 | 1.170 | 0.769 | 0.891 | 1.000 |
| 1.500 | 0.610 | 1.473 | 1.210 | 0.740 | 0.862 | 1.000 |
| 1.650 | 0.576 | 1.518 | 1.251 | 0.710 | 0.832 | 1.000 |
| 1.800 | 0.543 | 1.563 | 1.293 | 0.679 | 0.801 | 0.948 |
| 1.950 | 0.511 | 1.609 | 1.335 | 0.648 | 0.770 | 0.895 |
| 2.100 | 0.479 | 1.654 | 1.379 | 0.616 | 0.739 | 0.839 |
| 2.250 | 0.449 | 1.699 | 1.423 | 0.585 | 0.706 | 0.783 |
| 2.400 | 0.419 | 1.743 | 1.466 | 0.554 | 0.675 | 0.725 |
| 2.550 | 0.391 | 1.788 | 1.509 | 0.522 | 0.643 | 0.665 |
| 2.700 | 0.363 | 1.831 | 1.512 | 0.491 | 0.590 | 0.605 |
| 2.850 | 0.336 | 1.875 | 1.514 | 0.460 | 0.535 | 0.543 |
| 3.000 | 0.310 | 1.917 | 1.515 | 0.429 | 0.480 | 0.479 |
| 3.150 | 0.285 | 1.959 | 1.514 | 0.399 | 0.424 | 0.415 |
| 3.300 | 0.261 | 2.000 | 1.512 | 0.369 | 0.368 | 0.352 |
| 3.450 | 0.238 | 1.971 | 1.509 | 0.334 | 0.311 | 0.290 |
| 3.600 | 0.215 | 1.937 | 1.504 | 0.300 | 0.254 | 0.234 |
| 3.750 | 0.194 | 1.898 | 1.498 | 0.267 | 0.197 | 0.178 |
| 3.900 | 0.173 | 1.853 | 1.491 | 0.236 | 0.140 | 0.123 |
| 4.050 | 0.154 | 1.804 | 1.481 | 0.206 | 0.083 | 0.067 |
| 4.200 | 0.135 | 1.749 | 1.448 | 0.178 | 0.045 | 0.013 |
| 4.350 | 0.117 | 1.689 | 1.410 | 0.152 | 0.009 | -0.041 |
| 4.500 | 0.100 | 1.624 | 1.375 | 0.127 | -0.021 | -0.095 |
| 4.650 | 0.084 | 1.554 | 1.337 | 0.105 | -0.048 | -0.147 |
| 4.800 | 0.069 | 1.479 | 1.296 | 0.084 | -0.073 | -0.199 |
| 4.950 | 0.055 | 1.411 | 1.251 | 0.065 | -0.096 | -0.249 |
| 5.100 | 0.040 | 1.343 | 1.203 | 0.046 | -0.115 | -0.262 |
| 5.250 | 0.025 | 1.286 | 1.152 | 0.028 | -0.132 | -0.270 |
| 5.400 | 0.010 | 1.229 | 1.098 | 0.011 | -0.146 | -0.275 |
| 5.550 | 0.0 | 1.162 | 1.041 | 0.0 | -0.157 | -0.274 |
| 5.700 | 0.0 | 1.077 | 0.987 | 0.0 | -0.168 | -0.269 |
| 5.850 | 0.0 | 0.993 | 0.933 | 0.0 | -0.179 | -0.259 |
| 6.000 | 0.0 | 0.912 | 0.912 | 0.0 | -0.177 | -0.243 |
| 6.150 | 0.0 | 0.833 | 0.895 | 0.0 | -0.172 | -0.223 |
| 6.300 | 0.0 | 0.757 | 0.871 | 0.0 | -0.160 | -0.197 |
| 6.450 | 0.0 | 0.681 | 0.835 | 0.0 | -0.133 | -0.166 |

**Fig. 12.33**  Computer solution of Example 12.9.

In dimensionless form, neglecting velocity head changes, the continuity equation at the junction is $h_{B_1} = h_{B_2}$, $v_{B_1} = v_{B_2}$, which has been used in the equations as written.  By solving the first of the equations simultaneously with $v_{A_j} = \tau \sqrt{h_{A_j}}$,

$$v_{A_j} = -0.5B_2\tau^2 + \sqrt{(0.5B_2\tau^2)^2 + \tau^2(h_{B_{j-Q}} - v_{B_{j-Q}}(H_2|v_{B_{j-Q}}| - B_2))} \qquad (5)$$

With $v_{A_j}$ solved, $h_{A_j}$ is found from Eq. (1).  Equations (2) and (3) yield

$$h_{B_j} = 0.5(h_{A_{j-Q}} + h_R + B_1v_{C_{j-P}} - B_2v_{A_{j-P}} + H_2v_{A_{j-Q}}|v_{A_{j-Q}}| - H_1v_{C_{j-P}}|v_{C_{j-P}}|)$$

$$v_{B_j} = v_{C_{j-P}} + \frac{h_R - h_{B_j} - H_1v_{C_{j-P}}|v_{C_{j-P}}|}{B_1}$$

$$v_{C_j} = v_{B_{j-P}} + \frac{h_R - h_{B_{j-P}} - H_1v_{B_{j-P}}|v_{B_{j-P}}|}{B_1}$$

The program for solution of these equations is given in Fig. 12.32. Parabolic interpolation of the $\tau$-values has been used (see Appendix E). Figure 12.33 is the solution to the problem.

The algebraic and characteristics methods may be applied to such complex problems as parallel and branching pipes, as well as to networks. They are also very useful in studying special valve-closing relations that control waterhammer.

## open-channel flow

In general, open-channel transients are more complex to handle than closed-conduit transients. Surface-wave motion is an example of open-channel and unsteady flow. The subject is too vast to attempt to cover as part of a chapter. A few special topics are discussed that use about the same approach as the waterhammer equations: frictionless positive and negative surge waves, flood routing, and a case of rainfall and runoff from a plane area.

### 12.9 frictionless positive surge wave in a rectangular channel

In this section the surge wave resulting from a sudden change in flow (due to a gate or other mechanism) that increases the depth is studied. A rectangular channel is assumed, and friction is neglected. Such a situation is shown in Fig. 12.34 shortly after a sudden, partial closure of a gate. The problem is analyzed by reducing it to a steady-state problem, as in Fig. 12.35. The continuity equation yields, per unit width,

$$(V_1 + c)y_1 = (V_2 + c)y_2 \tag{12.9.1}$$

and the momentum equation for the control volume $1 - 2$, neglecting shear stress on the floor, per unit width, is

$$\frac{\gamma}{2}(y_1{}^2 - y_2{}^2) = \frac{\gamma}{g} y_1(V_1 + c)(V_2 + c - V_1 - c) \tag{12.9.2}$$

**Fig. 12.34** Positive surge wave in a rectangular channel.

**Fig. 12.35** Surge problem reduced to a steady-state problem by superposition of surge velocity.

By elimination of $V_2$ in the last two equations,

$$V_1 + c = \sqrt{gy_1} \left[ \frac{y_2}{2y_1} \left( 1 + \frac{y_2}{y_1} \right) \right]^{1/2} \tag{12.9.3}$$

In this form the speed of an elementary wave is obtained by letting $y_2$ approach $y_1$, yielding

$$V_1 + c = \sqrt{gy} \tag{12.9.4}$$

For propagation through still liquid $V_1 \to 0$, and the wave speed is $c = \sqrt{gy}$ when the problem is converted back to the unsteady form by superposition of $V = -c$.

In general, Eqs. (12.9.1) and (12.9.2) have to be solved by trial. The hydraulic-jump formula results from setting $c = 0$ in the two equations (3.11.23).

**example 12.10**  A rectangular channel 10 ft wide and 6 ft deep, discharging 600 cfs, suddenly has the discharge reduced to 400 cfs at the downstream end.  Compute the height and speed of the surge wave.

$V_1 = 10$, $y_1 = 6$, $V_2 y_2 = 40$.  With Eqs. (12.9.1) and (12.9.2),

$$60 = 40 + c(y_2 - 6)$$

and

$$y_2{}^2 - 36 = \frac{2 \times 6}{32.2} (c + 10)(10 - V_2)$$

By eliminating $c$ and $V_2$,

$$y_2{}^2 - 36 = \frac{12}{32.2} \left( \frac{20}{y_2 - 6} + 10 \right) \left( 10 - \frac{40}{y_2} \right)$$

or

$$\left(\frac{y_2 - 6}{y_2 - 4}\right)^2 (y_2 + 6)y_2 = \frac{1200}{32.2} = 37.25$$

After solving for $y_2$ by trial, $y_2 = 8.47$ ft.   Hence $V_2 = 40/8.47 = 4.72$ ft/sec.   The height of surge wave is 2.47 ft, and the speed of the wave is

$$c = \frac{20}{y_2 - 6} = \frac{20}{2.47} = 8.1 \text{ ft/sec}$$

## 12.10   frictionless negative surge wave in a rectangular channel

The negative surge wave appears as a gradual flattening and lowering of a liquid surface.   It occurs, for example, in a channel downstream from a gate that is being closed, or upstream from a gate that is being opened. Its propagation is accomplished by a series of elementary negative waves superposed on the existing velocity, with each wave traveling at less speed than the one at next greater depth.   Application of the momentum equation and the continuity equation to a small depth change produces simple differential expressions relating wave speed $c$, velocity $V$, and depth $y$. Integration of the equations yields liquid-surface profile as a function of time, and velocity as a function of depth or as a function of position along the channel and time ($x$ and $t$).   The assumptions are made that the fluid is frictionless and that vertical accelerations are neglected.

In Fig. 12.36$a$ an elementary disturbance is indicated in which the flow

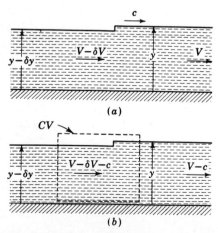

**Fig. 12.36**   Elementary wave.

upstream has been slightly reduced.   For application of the momentum and continuity equations it is convenient to reduce the motion to a steady one, as in Fig. 12.36b, by imposing a uniform velocity $c$ to the left.   The continuity equation is

$$(V - \delta V - c)(y - \delta y) = (V - c)y$$

or, by neglecting the product of small quantities,

$$(c - V)\,\delta y = y\,\delta V \tag{12.10.1}$$

The momentum equation produces

$$\frac{\gamma}{2}(y - \delta y)^2 - \frac{\gamma}{2}y_2 = \frac{\gamma}{g}(V - c)y\,[V - c - (V - \delta V - c)]$$

After simplifying,

$$\delta y = \frac{c - V}{g}\,\delta V \tag{12.10.2}$$

By equating $\delta V/\delta y$ in Eqs. (12.10.1) and (12.10.2),

$$c - V = \pm\sqrt{gy} \tag{12.10.3}$$

or

$$c = V \pm \sqrt{gy}$$

The speed of an elementary wave in still liquid at depth $y$ is $\sqrt{gy}$ and with

flow the wave travels at the speed $\sqrt{gy}$ *relative* to the flowing liquid.
By eliminating $c$ from Eqs. (12.10.1) and (12.10.2),

$$\frac{dV}{dy} = \pm\sqrt{\frac{g}{y}}$$

After integrating,

$$V = \pm 2\sqrt{gy} + \text{const}$$

For the case of a negative wave forming downstream from a gate, Fig. 12.37, by using the plus sign, after an instantaneous partial closure, $V = V_0$ when $y = y_0$, and

$$V_0 = 2\sqrt{gy_0} + \text{const}$$

After eliminating the constant,

$$V = V_0 - 2\sqrt{g}\,(\sqrt{y_0} - \sqrt{y}) \tag{12.10.4}$$

**Fig. 12.37**   Negative wave after gate closure.

The wave travels in the $+x$-direction, so that

$$c = V + \sqrt{gy} = V_0 - 2\sqrt{gy_0} + 3\sqrt{gy} \qquad (12.10.5)$$

If the gate motion occurs at $t = 0$, the liquid-surface position is expressed by $x = ct$, or

$$x = (V_0 - 2\sqrt{gy_0} + 3\sqrt{gy})t \qquad (12.10.6)$$

By eliminating $y$ from Eqs. (12.10.5) and (12.10.6),

$$V = \frac{V_0}{3} + \frac{2}{3}\frac{x}{t} - \frac{2}{3}\sqrt{gy_0} \qquad (12.10.7)$$

which is the velocity in terms of $x$ and $t$.

**example 12.11**   In Fig. 12.37 find the Froude number of the undisturbed flow such that the depth $y_1$ at the gate is just zero when the gate is suddenly closed.   For $V_0 = 20$ ft/sec, find the liquid-surface equation.

It is required that $V_1 = 0$ when $y_1 = 0$ at $x = 0$ for any time after $t = 0$. In Eq. (12.10.4), with $V = 0$, $y = 0$,

$$V_0 = 2\sqrt{gy_0}$$

or

$$\mathbf{F}_0 = \frac{V_0{}^2}{gy_0} = 4$$

For $V_0 = 20$,

$$y_0 = \frac{V_0{}^2}{4g} = \frac{(20)^2}{4g} = 3.11 \text{ ft}$$

By use of Eq. (12.10.6)

$$x = (20 - 2\sqrt{32.2 \times 3.11} + 3\sqrt{32.2y})t$$
$$= 17.04\sqrt{y}\,t$$

The liquid surface is a parabola with vertex at the origin and surface concave upward.

**example 12.12**  In Fig. 12.37 the gate is partially closed at the instant $t = 0$ so that the discharge is reduced by 50 per cent. $V_0 = 20$ ft/sec, $y_0 = 8$ ft. Find $V_1$, $y_1$, and the surface profile.

The new discharge is

$$q = \frac{20 \times 8}{2} = 80 = V_1 y_1$$

By use of Eq. (12.10.4)

$$V_1 = 20 - 2\sqrt{32.2}\,(\sqrt{8} - \sqrt{y_1})$$

Then $V_1$ and $y_1$ are found by trial from the last two equations, $V_1 = 14.5$ ft/sec, $y_1 = 5.52$ ft. The liquid-surface equation, from Eq. (12.10.6), is

$$x = (20 - 2\sqrt{8g} + 3\sqrt{gy})t$$

or

$$x = (17.04\sqrt{y} - 12.08)t$$

which holds for the range of values of $y$ between 5.52 and 8.0.

*dam break*

An idealized dam-break water-surface profile, Fig. 12.38, may be obtained from Eqs. (12.10.4) to (12.10.7). From a frictionless, horizontal channel with depth of water $y_0$ on one side of a gate and no water on the other side

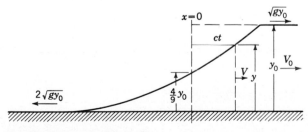

**Fig. 12.38**  Dam-break profile.

of the gate, the gate is suddenly removed. Vertical accelerations are neglected. $V_0 = 0$ in the equations and $y$ varies from $y_0$ to 0. The velocity at any section, from Eq. (12.10.4), is

$$V = -2\sqrt{g}\,(\sqrt{y_0} - \sqrt{y})\tag{12.10.8}$$

always in the downstream direction. The water-surface profile is, from Eq. (12.10.6),

$$x = (3\sqrt{gy} - 2\sqrt{gy_0})t\tag{12.10.9}$$

At $x = 0$, $y = 4y_0/9$, the depth remains constant and the velocity past the section $x = 0$ is, from Eq. (12.10.8),

$$V = -\tfrac{2}{3}\sqrt{gy_0}$$

also independent of time. The leading edge of the wave feathers out to zero height and moves downstream at $V = c = -2\sqrt{gy_0}$. The water surface is a parabola with vertex at the leading edge, concave upward.

With an actual dam break, ground roughness causes a positive surge, or wall of water, to move downstream; i.e., the feathered edge is retarded by friction.

## 12.11   flood routing in prismatic channels

In the two preceding sections instantaneous changes in frictionless rectangular channels were considered. In this section friction is taken into account, and conditions may change gradually at inlet or outlet sections. With prismatic channels the area is a function of depth of flow. The assumption is made that the channel slope $\alpha$ is small enough so that cos $\alpha \approx 1$ and that hydrostatic conditions prevail along any vertical line in the fluid. Any known flow as a function of time may be added to the flow or taken from it at the upstream or downstream section of the channel.

In Fig. 12.39 an element of the flow is taken as control volume, the

**Fig. 12.39** Control volume for application of unsteady-momentum equation.

$x$-direction is taken parallel to the bottom of the channel, and the depth $y$ is measured normal to the bottom.  The unsteady momentum equation (3.11.2) is applied,

$$-\frac{\partial y}{\partial x}\, \gamma\, \Delta x\, A - \tau_0 P\, \Delta x + \gamma A\, \Delta x \sin\alpha = \frac{\partial}{\partial x}\,(\rho V^2 A)\, \Delta x + \frac{\partial}{\partial t}\,(\rho A V\, \Delta x)$$

After expanding and dividing through by the mass of the element $\rho A\, \Delta x$,

$$g\frac{\partial y}{\partial x} + \frac{\tau_0}{\rho R} - g\sin\alpha + 2V\frac{\partial V}{\partial x} + \frac{V^2}{A}\frac{\partial A}{\partial x} + \frac{V}{A}\frac{\partial A}{\partial t} + \frac{\partial V}{\partial t} = 0 \qquad (12.11.1)$$

$P$ is the wetted perimeter of the cross section, and $R$ is the hydraulic radius.
   The continuity equation (3.2.1) applied to the control volume of Fig. 12.39 yields

$$-\frac{\partial}{\partial x}\,(\rho A V)\, \Delta x = \frac{\partial}{\partial t}\,(\rho A\, \Delta x)$$

After expanding and dividing by the mass of the element,

$$\frac{V}{A}\frac{\partial A}{\partial x} + \frac{1}{A}\frac{\partial A}{\partial t} + \frac{\partial V}{\partial x} = 0 \qquad (12.11.2)$$

Equation (12.11.1) may be simplified by subtracting Eq. (12.11.2), when multiplied by $V$, from it:

$$L_1 = g\frac{\partial y}{\partial x} + \frac{\tau_0}{\rho R} - g\sin\alpha + V\frac{\partial V}{\partial x} + \frac{\partial V}{\partial t} - 0 \qquad (12.11.3)$$

Equation (12.11.2) may be written

$$L_2 = \frac{A}{T}\frac{\partial V}{\partial x} + V\frac{\partial y}{\partial x} + \frac{\partial y}{\partial t} = 0 \qquad (12.11.4)$$

since

$$\frac{\partial A}{\partial x} = \frac{\partial A}{\partial y}\frac{\partial y}{\partial x} = T\frac{\partial y}{\partial x}$$

with $T$ the top width.   $L_1$ and $L_2$ are now in suitable form for solution by the method of characteristics.   Combining, as in Sec. 12.6,

$$L_1 + \lambda L_2 = \left[\frac{\partial V}{\partial x}\left(V + \frac{\lambda A}{T}\right) + \frac{\partial V}{\partial t}\right] + \lambda\left[\frac{\partial y}{\partial x}\left(V + \frac{g}{\lambda}\right) + \frac{\partial y}{\partial t}\right]$$

$$+ \frac{\tau_0}{\rho R} - g\sin\alpha = 0 \qquad (12.11.5)$$

For the term within the first pair of brackets to be a total derivative

$$\frac{dx}{dt} = V + \frac{\lambda A}{T}$$

and for the term within the second pair of brackets to be a total derivative

$$\frac{dx}{dt} = V + \frac{g}{\lambda}$$

After equating the two latter expressions and solving for $\lambda$,

$$\lambda = \pm \sqrt{\frac{gT}{A}} \tag{12.11.6}$$

and

$$\frac{dx}{dt} = V \pm \sqrt{\frac{gA}{T}} \tag{12.11.7}$$

For a rectangular cross section it should be noted that this expression for speed of a wave (surface wave) is given by

$$\frac{dx}{dt} = V \pm \sqrt{gy} \tag{12.11.8}$$

Equation (12.11.5) reduces to

$$\frac{dV}{dt} + \lambda \frac{dy}{dt} + \frac{\tau_0}{\rho R} - g \sin \alpha = 0 \tag{12.11.9}$$

subject to Eqs. (12.11.6) and (12.11.7).

After substituting into Eq. (12.11.9) the values for $\lambda$ and by writing in finite-difference form,

$$V_P - V_R + \lambda_C(y_P - y_R) + \frac{\tau_0 \, \Delta t}{\rho R} - g \sin \alpha \, \Delta t = 0 \tag{12.11.10}$$

$$x_P - x_R = \left( V_C + \lambda_C \frac{A_C}{T_C} \right) \Delta t \tag{12.11.11}$$

$C_+$

$$V_P - V_S - \lambda_C(y_P - y_S) + \frac{\tau_0 \, \Delta t}{\rho R} - g \sin \alpha \, \Delta t = 0 \tag{12.11.12}$$

$$x_P - x_S = \left( V_C - \lambda_C \frac{A_C}{T_C} \right) \Delta t \tag{12.11.13}$$

$C_-$

The subscript $C$ means evaluation of the quantity at point $C$ in Fig. 12.40. $\lambda_C$ is the positive root of Eq. (12.11.6).

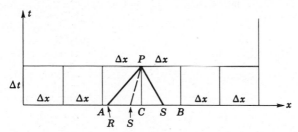

**Fig. 12.40**  Solution for specified time and distance intervals.

In Fig. 12.40 it is assumed that initially $y$ and $V$ are known at equidistant sections along the channel, $\Delta x$ apart. To find $y_P$ and $V_P$ at one of the sections at the new time $t + \Delta t$, $\lambda$ is evaluated at $C$, and $y_R$, $V_R$, $y_S$, and $V_S$ are found by linear interpolation from known values at $A$, $C$, and $B$. Then Eqs. (12.11.10) and (12.11.12) may be solved for $V_P$ and $y_P$. To find $V_R$, the proportion

$$\frac{V_C - V_R}{V_C - V_A} = \frac{x_C - x_R}{\Delta x} = \frac{x_P - x_R}{\Delta x} = \left(V_C + \frac{\lambda_C A_C}{T_C}\right)\frac{\Delta t}{\Delta x}$$

is utilized. By defining $\theta = \Delta t/\Delta x$ and after solving for $V_R$,

$$V_R = V_C + (V_A - V_C)\theta\left(V_C + \frac{\lambda_C A_C}{T_C}\right) \qquad (12.11.14)$$

and similarly

$$y_R = y_C + (y_A - y_C)\theta\left(V_C + \frac{\lambda_C A_C}{T_C}\right) \qquad (12.11.15)$$

The interpolation for $V_S$ and $y_S$ depends upon which is greater, $V_C$ or $\lambda_C A_C/T_C$. If $V_C > \lambda_C A_C/T_C$, shown by the dashed line in Fig. 12.40, then using proportions and Eq. (12.11.13),

$$\frac{V_C - V_S}{V_C - V_A} = \frac{x_P - x_S}{\Delta x} = \left(V_C - \frac{\lambda_C A_C}{T_C}\right)\frac{\Delta t}{\Delta x}$$

and

$$V_S = V_C + (V_A - V_C)\theta\left(V_C - \frac{\lambda_C A_C}{T_C}\right) \qquad V_C > \left(\frac{\lambda A}{T}\right)_C \qquad (12.11.16)$$

Also

$$y_S = y_C + (y_A - y_C)\theta\left(V_C - \frac{\lambda_C A_C}{T_C}\right) \qquad (12.11.17)$$

```
C      FLOOD ROUTING INTO A RECTANGULAR CHANNEL.  D.S. GAGE HEIGHT
C      DISCHARGE EQ.  Q=CW*(Y-Y00)**M.  LINEAR RISE AND FALL OF INTAKE
C      HYDROGRAPH.  FINAL STEADY FLOW Q1 AT T1,  QM AT T0, WIDTH B,
C      CHEZY C, NORMAL DEPTH YN GIVEN.  ALP = SLOPE.
       INTEGER U
       REAL K1,K2,L,M,LC
       DIMENSION V(100),VP(100),Y(100),YP(100)
       R(YY)=B*YY/(B+2.*YY)
     1 FORMAT('0                       VELOCITIES AND DEPTHS AT 500. FT INTE
     2RVALS    TIME IN MINUTES')
     2 FORMAT('0   X/L=.0     .05     .10     .15     .20     .25     .30     .35     .4
     20   .45     .50     .55     .60     .65     .70     .75     .80     .85     .90     .9
     25   1.')
     3 FORMAT(1H ,20X,2HT=,F7.2,25X,2HQ=,F7.1/2X,2HV=,21F6.2/2X,2HY=,21F6
     2.2)
     4 FORMAT('1 GIVEN T0=',F5.0,4H T1=,F5.0,4H K1=,F2.0,4H K2=,F3.1,3H B
     2=,F3.0,4H YN=,F2.0,3H C=,F4.0,3H L=,F6.0,3H N=,I2,5H ALP=,F6.4,6H
     3TMAX=,F5.0,3H G=,F4.1,3H M=,F3.1,3H J=,I1,4H CW=,F4.0)
     5 FORMAT('0 CALCULATED VALUES QM=',F7.2,4H QF=,F6.2,4H Q0=,F6.2,5H Y
     200=,F5.3,4H DX=,F4.0,4H DT=,F6.3)
       NAMELIST/DIN/T0,T1,K1,K2,B,YN,C,L,N,ALP,TMAX,G,M,J,CW
    10 READ(5,DIN,END=99)
       Q0=C*YN*B*SQRT(R(YN)*ALP)
       QM=K1*Q0
       QF=K2*Q0
       Q6=(QM-Q0)/T0
       Q7=(QF-QM)/(T1-T0)
       CB=CW/B
       C7=G/(C*C)
C      STEADY-STATE CONDITIONS
       V0=Q0/(B*YN)
       NS=N+1
       DO 11 I=1,NS
       V(I)=V0
    11 Y(I)=YN
       Y00=YN-(Q0/CW)**(1./M)
       SA=SIN(ALP)
       DX=L/N
       T=.0
       U=0
       DT=.9*DX/(V(1)+SQRT(G*YN))
       TH=DT/DX
       WRITE(6,4)T0,T1,K1,K2,B,YN,C,L,N,ALP,TMAX,G,M,J,CW
       WRITE(6,5) QM,QF,Q0,Y00,DX,DT
       WRITE(6,1)
       WRITE(6,2)
    12 T=T+DT
       U=U+1
       IF(T.GT.TMAX) GO TO 10
C      INTERIOR POINTS
    13 DXX=.0
       DO 17 I=2,N
       A=SQRT(G*Y(I))
       LC=A/Y(I)
       DXI=(V(I)+A)*DT
       IF(DXI.GT.DXX) DXX=DXI
       IF(DXI.LE.DX) GO TO 14
       T=T-.1*DT
       DT=.9*DT
       TH=DT/DX
       GO TO 13
```

**Fig. 12.41** FORTRAN IV program for flood routing in a rectangular channel.

```
   14  VR=V(I)+(V(I-1)-V(I))*TH*(V(I)+A)
       YR=Y(I)+(Y(I-1)-Y(I))*TH*(V(I)+A)
       IF(V(I).LT.A) GO TO 15
       VS=V(I)+(V(I-1)-V(I))*TH*(V(I)-A)
       YS=Y(I)+(Y(I-1)-Y(I))*TH*(V(I)-A)
       GO TO 16
   15  VS=V(I)+(V(I)-V(I+1))*TH*(V(I)-A)
       YS=Y(I)+(Y(I)-Y(I+1))*TH*(V(I)-A)
   16  VP(I)=.5*(VR+VS+LC*(YR-YS))-C7*V(I)*ABS(V(I))/R(Y(I))*DT+G*SA*DT
   17  YP(I)=.5*(YR+YS+(VR-VS)/LC)
C      UPSTREAM BOUNDARY CONDITION
       IF(T.LT.T0) QQ=Q0+Q6*T
       IF(T.GE.T0.AND.T.LT.T1) QQ=QM+Q7*(T-T0)
       IF(T.GT.T1) QQ=QF
       A=SQRT(G*Y(1))
       Q1=QQ/B
       LC=A/Y(1)
       IF(V(1).LE.A) GO TO 18
       YP(1)=(Q1**2/G)**.3333
       VP(1)=Q1/YP(1)
       GO TO 19
   18  VS=V(1)+(V(1)-V(2))*TH*(V(1)-A)
       YS=Y(1)+(Y(1)-Y(2))*TH*(V(1)-A)
       C11=VS-LC*YS-(C7*V(1)*ABS(V(1))/R(Y(1))-G*SA)*DT
       VP(1)=.5*C11*(1.-SQRT(1.+4.*LC*Q1/C11**2))
       YP(1)=Q1/VP(1)
C      DOWNSTREAM BOUNDARY CONDITION
   19  A=SQRT(G*Y(NS))
       LC=A/Y(NS)
       DXI=(V(NS)+A)*DT
       IF(DXI.GT.DX) GO TO 20
       GO TO 21
   20  T=T-.1*DT
       DT=.9*DT
       TH=DT/DX
       GO TO 13
   21  IF(DXI.GT.DXX) DXX=DXI
       VR=V(NS)+(V(N)-V(NS))*TH*(V(NS)+A)
       YR=Y(NS)+(Y(N)-Y(NS))*TH*(V(NS)+A)
       C11=VR+LC*YR-(C7*V(NS)*ABS(V(NS))/R(Y(NS))-G*SA)*DT
       YPMA=2.*YN
       YPMI=Y00
       YP1=.5*(YPMA+YPMI)
       DO 24 I=0,12
       IF(C11*YP1-LC*YP1**2-CB*(YP1-Y00)**M) 22,22,23
   22  YPMA=YP1
       GO TO 24
   23  YPMI=YP1
   24  YP1=.5*(YPMA+YPMI)
       YP(NS)=YP1
       VP(NS)=C11-LC*YP(NS)
       DO 25 I=1,NS
       V(I)=VP(I)
   25  Y(I)=YP(I)
       TM=T/60.
       IF(U/J*J.EQ.U) WRITE(6,3) TM,QQ,(V(I),I=1,NS),(Y(I),I=1,NS)
       IF(DXX.LT..8*DX) DT=1.15*DT
       GO TO 12
   99  CALL SYSTEM
       END
```

**Fig. 12.41**   *(Continued)*

GIVEN T0=1200. T1=1800. K1=2. K2=0.5 B=20. YN=6. C=100. L=10000. N=20 ALP=0.0016 TMAX=2400. G=32.2 M=1.5 J=5 CW=132.

CALCULATED VALUES QM=1859.03 QF=464.76 QU=929.52 Y00=2.326 Y00=929.52 DT=20.789

VELOCITIES AND DEPTHS AT 500. FT INTERVALS

TIME IN MINUTES

| X/L= | .0 | .05 | .10 | .15 | .20 | .25 | .30 | .35 | .40 | .45 | .50 | .55 | .60 | .65 | .70 | .75 | .80 | .85 | .90 | .95 | 1. |
|---|---|---|---|---|---|---|---|---|---|---|---|---|---|---|---|---|---|---|---|---|---|
| V= (T=1.73, Q=1010.0) | 8.11 | 8.02 | 7.94 | 7.86 | 7.80 | 7.75 | 7.75 | 7.75 | 7.75 | 7.75 | 7.75 | 7.75 | 7.75 | 7.75 | 7.75 | 7.75 | 7.75 | 7.75 | 7.75 | 7.75 | 7.75 |
| Y= | 6.22 | 6.16 | 6.10 | 6.06 | 6.02 | 6.00 | 6.00 | 6.00 | 6.00 | 6.00 | 6.00 | 6.00 | 6.00 | 6.00 | 6.00 | 6.00 | 6.00 | 6.00 | 6.00 | 6.00 | 6.00 |
| V= (T=3.46, Q=1090.5) | 8.38 | 8.29 | 8.21 | 8.12 | 8.05 | 7.98 | 7.91 | 7.86 | 7.81 | 7.78 | 7.75 | 7.75 | 7.75 | 7.75 | 7.75 | 7.75 | 7.75 | 7.75 | 7.75 | 7.75 | 7.75 |
| Y= | 6.51 | 6.41 | 6.33 | 6.26 | 6.19 | 6.14 | 6.09 | 6.06 | 6.03 | 6.01 | 6.00 | 6.00 | 6.00 | 6.00 | 6.00 | 6.00 | 6.00 | 6.00 | 6.00 | 6.00 | 6.00 |
| V= (T=5.20, Q=1171.1) | 8.59 | 8.51 | 8.43 | 8.35 | 8.27 | 8.19 | 8.12 | 8.06 | 7.99 | 7.94 | 7.89 | 7.85 | 7.81 | 7.78 | 7.77 | 7.75 | 7.75 | 7.75 | 7.75 | 7.75 | 7.75 |
| Y= | 6.82 | 6.71 | 6.61 | 6.51 | 6.42 | 6.35 | 6.28 | 6.21 | 6.16 | 6.12 | 6.08 | 6.06 | 6.03 | 6.02 | 6.01 | 6.00 | 6.00 | 6.00 | 6.00 | 6.00 | 6.00 |
| V= (T=6.93, Q=1251.6) | 8.76 | 8.69 | 8.62 | 8.54 | 8.47 | 8.40 | 8.32 | 8.25 | 8.18 | 8.12 | 8.06 | 8.00 | 7.95 | 7.91 | 7.87 | 7.83 | 7.81 | 7.78 | 7.77 | 7.76 | 7.75 |
| Y= | 7.15 | 7.03 | 6.91 | 6.80 | 6.70 | 6.60 | 6.51 | 6.43 | 6.35 | 6.29 | 6.23 | 6.18 | 6.14 | 6.10 | 6.07 | 6.05 | 6.03 | 6.02 | 6.01 | 6.01 | 6.00 |
| V= (T=8.63, Q=1330.5) | 8.90 | 8.84 | 8.77 | 8.71 | 8.64 | 8.57 | 8.50 | 8.43 | 8.36 | 8.30 | 8.23 | 8.17 | 8.11 | 8.05 | 8.00 | 7.95 | 7.91 | 7.88 | 7.85 | 7.82 | 7.80 |
| Y= | 7.47 | 7.35 | 7.22 | 7.10 | 6.99 | 6.88 | 6.77 | 6.68 | 6.59 | 6.50 | 6.42 | 6.35 | 6.29 | 6.24 | 6.19 | 6.15 | 6.11 | 6.09 | 6.06 | 6.04 | 6.03 |
| V= (T=10.19, Q=1403.0) | 9.02 | 8.96 | 8.90 | 8.84 | 8.78 | 8.72 | 8.65 | 8.59 | 8.52 | 8.45 | 8.39 | 8.32 | 8.26 | 8.20 | 8.14 | 8.08 | 8.03 | 7.99 | 7.95 | 7.91 | 7.89 |
| Y= | 7.78 | 7.65 | 7.52 | 7.39 | 7.27 | 7.15 | 7.04 | 6.93 | 6.83 | 6.73 | 6.64 | 6.55 | 6.47 | 6.40 | 6.34 | 6.28 | 6.23 | 6.19 | 6.15 | 6.11 | 6.00 |
| V= (T=11.75, Q=1475.4) | 9.13 | 9.07 | 9.02 | 8.97 | 8.91 | 8.85 | 8.79 | 8.73 | 8.67 | 8.60 | 8.54 | 8.47 | 8.41 | 8.35 | 8.29 | 8.23 | 8.17 | 8.12 | 8.07 | 8.04 | 8.05 |
| Y= | 8.08 | 7.95 | 7.82 | 7.69 | 7.56 | 7.44 | 7.32 | 7.20 | 7.09 | 6.98 | 6.88 | 6.78 | 6.69 | 6.60 | 6.52 | 6.45 | 6.38 | 6.32 | 6.27 | 6.21 | 6.15 |
| V= (T=13.31, Q=1547.9) | 9.22 | 9.18 | 9.13 | 9.08 | 9.03 | 8.97 | 8.92 | 8.86 | 8.80 | 8.74 | 8.68 | 8.62 | 8.56 | 8.49 | 8.43 | 8.37 | 8.31 | 8.26 | 8.22 | 8.19 | 8.19 |
| Y= | 8.39 | 8.26 | 8.12 | 7.99 | 7.86 | 7.73 | 7.60 | 7.48 | 7.36 | 7.24 | 7.13 | 7.03 | 6.92 | 6.83 | 6.73 | 6.65 | 6.57 | 6.49 | 6.41 | 6.33 | 6.24 |
| V= (T=14.86, Q=1620.3) | 9.32 | 9.27 | 9.23 | 9.18 | 9.14 | 9.09 | 9.03 | 8.98 | 8.93 | 8.87 | 8.81 | 8.75 | 8.69 | 8.63 | 8.57 | 8.51 | 8.46 | 8.41 | 8.37 | 8.36 | 8.39 |
| Y= | 8.70 | 8.56 | 8.43 | 8.16 | 8.16 | 8.03 | 7.90 | 7.77 | 7.65 | 7.52 | 7.40 | 7.29 | 7.18 | 7.07 | 6.97 | 6.87 | 6.77 | 6.68 | 6.58 | 6.48 | 6.35 |
| V= (T=16.42, Q=1692.8) | 9.40 | 9.36 | 9.32 | 9.28 | 9.24 | 9.19 | 9.14 | 9.09 | 9.04 | 8.99 | 8.94 | 8.88 | 8.82 | 8.77 | 8.71 | 8.66 | 8.60 | 8.56 | 8.54 | 8.54 | 8.64 |
| Y= | 9.00 | 8.87 | 8.73 | 8.59 | 8.46 | 8.33 | 8.20 | 8.07 | 7.94 | 7.81 | 7.69 | 7.57 | 7.45 | 7.33 | 7.22 | 7.11 | 7.00 | 6.89 | 6.78 | 6.64 | 6.47 |
| V= (T=17.98, Q=1765.3) | 9.48 | 9.45 | 9.41 | 9.37 | 9.33 | 9.29 | 9.24 | 9.20 | 9.15 | 9.10 | 9.05 | 9.00 | 8.95 | 8.89 | 8.84 | 8.79 | 8.75 | 8.72 | 8.71 | 8.73 | 8.84 |
| Y= | 9.31 | 9.17 | 9.03 | 8.90 | 8.76 | 8.63 | 8.50 | 8.36 | 8.23 | 8.10 | 7.98 | 7.85 | 7.73 | 7.60 | 7.48 | 7.37 | 7.24 | 7.12 | 6.98 | 6.82 | 6.60 |
| V= (T=19.45, Q=1833.4) | 9.56 | 9.52 | 9.49 | 9.45 | 9.41 | 9.37 | 9.33 | 9.29 | 9.24 | 9.20 | 9.15 | 9.10 | 9.06 | 9.01 | 8.96 | 8.92 | 8.88 | 8.86 | 8.87 | 8.92 | 9.06 |
| Y= | 9.59 | 9.46 | 9.32 | 9.18 | 9.05 | 8.91 | 8.78 | 8.65 | 8.51 | 8.38 | 8.25 | 8.12 | 8.00 | 7.87 | 7.74 | 7.61 | 7.48 | 7.34 | 7.18 | 6.99 | 6.73 |
| V= (T=20.85, Q=1740.3) | 9.12 | 9.28 | 9.41 | 9.52 | 9.49 | 9.45 | 9.41 | 9.37 | 9.33 | 9.24 | 9.24 | 9.20 | 9.15 | 9.11 | 9.07 | 9.03 | 9.01 | 9.00 | 9.02 | 9.10 | 9.29 |
| Y= | 9.54 | 9.54 | 9.51 | 9.46 | 9.32 | 9.19 | 9.05 | 8.92 | 8.79 | 8.65 | 8.52 | 8.39 | 8.26 | 8.13 | 7.99 | 7.86 | 7.72 | 7.56 | 7.38 | 7.16 | 6.86 |

**Fig. 12.42** Computer solution of Example 12.13.

However, if $V_C < (\lambda A/T)_C$, from Fig. 12.40 and Eq. (12.11.13),

$$\frac{V_S - V_C}{V_B - V_C} = \frac{x_S - x_P}{\Delta x} = -\left(V_C - \frac{\lambda_C A_C}{T_C}\right)\frac{\Delta t}{\Delta x}$$

and

$$V_S = V_C + (V_C - V_B)\theta\left(V_C - \frac{\lambda_C A_C}{T_C}\right) \tag{12.11.18}$$

$$y_S = y_C + (y_C - y_B)\theta\left(V_C - \frac{\lambda_C A_C}{T_C}\right) \tag{12.11.19}$$

After solving Eqs. (12.11.10) and (12.11.12) for $V_P$ and $y_P$,

$$V_P = \frac{V_R + V_S}{2} + \frac{\lambda_C}{2}(y_R - y_S) - \frac{\tau_0 \Delta t}{\rho R} + g\sin\alpha\,\Delta t \tag{12.11.20}$$

$$y_P = \frac{y_R + y_S}{2} + \frac{1}{2\lambda_C}(V_R - V_S) \tag{12.11.21}$$

For the end sections of the channel Eqs. (12.11.10) and (12.11.12) each yield one linear equation in two unknowns $V_P$, $y_P$, which, together with a known condition at the end, permits the solution to be carried forward.

In solving the equations, it is absolutely essential that $R$ and $S$ always stay within $AB$ (Fig. 12.40); otherwise the solution is unstable.

**example 12.13** A rectangular channel 20 ft wide and 10,000 ft long, $\alpha = 0.0016$, is discharging under steady uniform flow conditions at $y_n = 6.0$ ft. At time $t = 0$ the flow is increased at the upstream end linearly until it has doubled in 20 min. The flow then decreases linearly until it is one-half the original flow in 10 additional minutes. For Chézy $C = 100$, prepare a computer program to find the velocity and depth in the channel for the first 40 min flow. The gage-height discharge curve at the downstream end is $Q = 132(y - 2.34)^{3/2}$.

The steady uniform flow is

$$Q = CA\sqrt{RS} = 100 \times 20 \times 6\sqrt{\frac{20 \times 6}{20 + 12}} \times 0.0016 = 930 \text{ cfs}$$

Hence

$$Q = 930\left(1 + \frac{t}{1200}\right) \qquad 0 \le t \le 1200 \text{ sec}$$

and

$$Q = 4650 - 2.325t \qquad 1200 \leq t \leq 1800$$
$$Q = 465 \qquad\qquad t > 1800$$

The computer program for solution of this problem is given in Fig. 12.41, and a portion of the solution in Fig. 12.42.

Some caution should be used in applying the program of Fig. 12.41 to continually increasing flows or sudden flows, as no provision is made for the handling of hydraulic bores.

## 12.12  mechanics of rainfall-runoff relations for sloping plane areas

An interesting, simplified characteristics problem, worked out by Henderson,[1] is that of the relation between rainfall and runoff on a plane sloping surface.  Percolation rate may be subtracted from rainfall rate to yield more meaningful results.  One-dimensional flow is assumed (Fig. 12.43), with $R \sim y$, $\cos\theta \approx 1$, $\sin\theta \approx S_0$, with $C$ the Chézy coefficient.

The momentum equation yields

$$\gamma y\,\Delta x\,S_0 - \gamma y\,\frac{\partial y}{\partial x}\,\Delta x - \tau_0\,\Delta x = \rho\,\frac{\partial}{\partial x}\,(V^2 y)\,\Delta x + \rho\,\frac{\partial}{\partial t}\,(Vy)\,\Delta x$$

After replacing $\tau_0$ by $\gamma V^2/C^2$ and by simplifying,

$$gy\,\frac{\partial y}{\partial x} + \frac{gV^2}{C^2} - gyS_0 + V^2\,\frac{\partial y}{\partial x} + 2Vy\,\frac{\partial V}{\partial x} + y\,\frac{\partial V}{\partial t} + V\,\frac{\partial y}{\partial t} = 0 \quad (12.12.1)$$

[1] Personal communication from F. M. Henderson, Professor of Civil Engineering, Canterbury University, Christchurch, New Zealand.

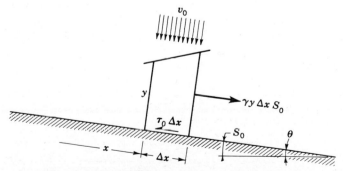

**Fig. 12.43**  Control volume for continuity and momentum equations for rainfall and runoff.

The continuity equation yields

$$\frac{\partial}{\partial x}(Vy)\,\Delta x = v_0\,\Delta x - \frac{\partial y}{\partial t}\,\Delta x$$

or

$$y\frac{\partial V}{\partial x} + V\frac{\partial y}{\partial x} + \frac{\partial y}{\partial t} - v_0 = 0 \qquad (12.12.2)$$

By multiplying Eq. (12.12.2) by $V$ and after subtracting from Eq. (12.12.1),

$$gy\frac{\partial y}{\partial x} + \frac{gV^2}{C^2} - gyS_0 + Vy\frac{\partial V}{\partial x} + y\frac{\partial V}{\partial t} + v_0 V = 0 \qquad (12.12.3)$$

After solving for $V$ in the $V^2$ term,

$$V = C\sqrt{y\left(S_0 - \frac{\partial y}{\partial x} - \frac{V}{g}\frac{\partial V}{\partial x} - \frac{1}{g}\frac{\partial V}{\partial t} - \frac{v_0 V}{gy}\right)} \qquad (12.12.4)$$

For one class of problems

$$\frac{\partial y}{\partial x}, \frac{V}{g}\frac{\partial V}{\partial x}, \frac{1}{g}\frac{\partial V}{\partial t} \ll S_0$$

and

$$V = C\sqrt{yS_0 - \frac{v_0 V}{g}} \qquad (12.12.5)$$

Since $v_0$ is very small for rainfall,

$$V \approx C\sqrt{yS_0} \qquad (12.12.6)$$

Now

$$q = Vy = C\sqrt{S_0}\,y^{3/2}$$

or, by generalizing, for other resistance formulas than Chezy,

$$q = \alpha y^n \qquad (12.12.7)$$

The continuity equation in terms of $q$ is

$$\frac{\partial q}{\partial x} + \frac{\partial y}{\partial t} = v_0 \qquad (12.12.8)$$

These last two equations, one algebraic, one differential, may be solved

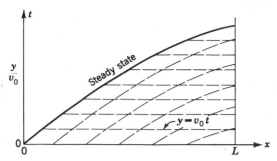

**Fig. 12.44** Liquid build-up on plane to steady-state position.

with steady-state discharge

$$q_{x=L} = Lv_0 = \alpha(v_0 t_s)^n \qquad (12.12.17)$$

For subsidence of the runoff, let $v_0 = 0$ from some time $t$ after $t_s$. Then

$$\frac{dy}{dt} = 0$$

along the characteristic

$$\frac{dx}{dt} = \alpha n y^{n-1}$$

or $y = $ const along the characteristic. Figure 12.45 shows the characteristics drawn from conditions for steady state, when $v_0$ then becomes zero.

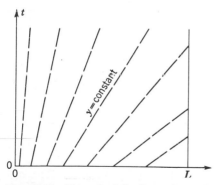

**Fig. 12.45** Characteristic lines for subsidence of liquid surface after termination of rainfall.

along a characteristic.   From Eq. (12.12.7)

$$\frac{\partial q}{\partial x} = \frac{dq}{dy}\frac{\partial y}{\partial x} = n\alpha y^{n-1}\frac{\partial y}{\partial x} \tag{12.12.9}$$

which, when combined with Eq. (12.12.8), yields

$$n\alpha y^{n-1}\frac{\partial y}{\partial x} + \frac{\partial y}{\partial t} = v_0 \tag{12.12.10}$$

Now, if

$$\frac{dx}{dt} = n\alpha y^{n-1} \tag{12.12.11}$$

then Eq. (12.12.10) becomes

$$\frac{dy}{dt} = v_0 \tag{12.12.12}$$

which is valid along the $xt$-path given by Eq. (12.12.11).
   For constant rate of rainfall starting from $t = 0$, Eq. (12.12.12) integrates to

$$y = v_0 t \tag{12.12.13}$$

which states that along any $xt$-characteristic the depth of liquid increases linearly.   By substituting Eq. (12.12.13) into Eq. (12.12.11) and integrating,

$$\frac{dx}{dt} = n\alpha(v_0 t)^{n-1}$$

or

$$x = x_0 + \alpha v_0^{n-1}t^n \tag{12.12.14}$$

with $x_0$ the starting point on the characteristic for $t = 0$.   For $x_0 = 0$, this line plots on the $xt$-plane of Fig. 12.44, as shown.   Since $t = y/v_0$, this characteristic represents the final depth after steady-state flow is attained. The build-up on the plane occurs with the surface parallel to the plane, as indicated.   This time $t_s$ required for steady state is given by Eq. (12.12.14) for $x = L$, $x_0 = 0$,

$$t_s = \left(\frac{L}{\alpha v_0^{n-1}}\right)^{1/n} \tag{12.12.15}$$

which is also the time for maximum depth and runoff to occur.   The discharge $x = L$ from the downstream end of the plane is

$$q_{x=L} = \alpha y^n = \alpha(v_0 t)^n \qquad 0 < t \le t_s \tag{12.12.16}$$

To find the equation for discharge at $x = L$, first for $x$,

$$x = x_0 + \alpha n y_0^{n-1} t \qquad (12.12.18)$$

for $t = 0$ at termination of steady-state conditions.   From the steady-state relations for the characteristic through $x = 0$ from Eq. (12.12.14),

$$x = \alpha v_0^{n-1} t^n = \frac{\alpha}{v_0} (v_0 t)^n = \frac{\alpha y^n}{v_0}$$

or

$$x_0 = \frac{\alpha y_0^n}{v_0}$$

is the liquid-surface profile for steady state.   By replacing $x_0$ in Eq. (12.12.18),

$$x = \frac{\alpha y_0^n}{v_0} + \alpha n y_0^{n-1} t$$

but $q = \alpha y_0^n$,

$$x = \frac{q}{v_0} + \alpha n \left(\frac{q}{\alpha}\right)^{(n-1)/n} t \qquad (12.12.19)$$

which yields the discharge $q$ at any $x$ during subsidence.   For $x = L$,

$$L = \frac{q}{v_0} + \alpha n \left(\frac{q}{\alpha}\right)^{(n-1)/n} t \qquad (12.12.20)$$

from which the subsidence hydrograph can be calculated.   The discharge hydrograph for the complete rainfall period is generally as shown in Fig. 12.46.

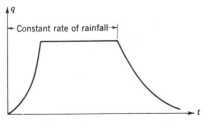

**Fig. 12.46**   Hydrograph for runoff from an inclined plane.

**Fig. 12.47** Runoff hydrograph for Example 12.14.

**example 12.14** A paved parking lot 200 yd square on a slope of 0.0016 is subjected to rain of 2 in./hr for 30 min. Resistance is given by Chézy $C = 60$. Determine the hydrograph for this storm from this area.

$$v_0 = \frac{2.0}{12 \times 3600} = \frac{1}{21,600} \text{ ft/sec}$$

$$\alpha = C \sqrt{S_0} = 60 \times \sqrt{0.0016} = 2.4$$

From Eq. (12.12.15), for $n = 1.5$,

$$t_s = \left(\frac{L}{\alpha v_0{}^{n-1}}\right)^{1/n} = \left(\frac{600}{2.4 \times \sqrt{0.0000463}}\right)^{2/3} = 1102 \text{ sec}$$

From Eq. (12.12.16)

$$Q = 600\alpha(v_0 t)^n = 600 \times 2.4(0.0000463t)^{1.5}$$
$$= 4.54 \times 10^{-4}t^{1.5} \quad 0 < t < 1105$$

From Eq. (12.12.20), for $q = Q/600$,

$$t = \frac{600 - 36Q}{0.3475Q^{1/3}}$$

For $t > 1800$ sec, $Q_{\max} = 16.67$ cfs, and the hydrograph is as plotted in Fig. 12.47.

## problems

**12.1** Determine the period of oscillation of a U-tube containing one pint of water. The cross-sectional area is 0.40 in.$^2$ Neglect friction.

**12.2** A U-tube containing alcohol is oscillating with maximum displacement from equilibrium position of 5.0 in. The total column length is 40 in.

Determine the maximum fluid velocity and the period of oscillation. Neglect friction.

**12.3**  A liquid, $\nu = 0.002$ ft²/sec, is in a U-tube 0.50 in. in diameter.  The total liquid column is 70 in. long.  If one meniscus is 15 in. above the other meniscus when the column is at rest, determine the time for one meniscus to move to within 1.0 in. of its equilibrium position.

**12.4**  Develop the equations for motion of a liquid in a U-tube for laminar resistance when $16\nu/D^2 = \sqrt{2g/L}$.  *Suggestion:* Try $z = e^{-mt}(c_1 + c_2 t)$.

**12.5**  A U-tube contains liquid oscillating with a velocity 6 ft/sec at the instant the menisci are at the same elevation.  Find the time to the instant the menisci are next at the same elevation, and determine the velocity then. $\nu = 1 \times 10^{-4}$ ft²/sec, $D = \frac{1}{4}$ in., $L = 30$ in.

**12.6**  A 10-ft-diameter horizontal tunnel has 10-ft-diameter vertical shafts spaced one mile apart.  When valves are closed isolating this reach of tunnel, the water surges to a depth of 50 ft in one shaft when it is 20 ft in the other shaft.  For $f = 0.022$ find the height of the next two surges.

**12.7**  Two standpipes 20 ft in diameter are connected by 3000 ft of 8.0-ft-diameter pipe, $f = 0.020$ and minor losses are 4.5 velocity heads.  One reservoir level is 30 ft above the other one when a valve is rapidly opened in the pipeline.  Find the maximum fluctuation in water level in the standpipe.

**12.8**  A valve is quickly opened in a pipe 4000 ft long, $D = 2.0$ ft, with a 1-ft-diameter nozzle on the downstream end.  Minor losses are $4V^2/2g$, with $V$ the velocity in the pipe, $f = 0.024$, $H = 30$ ft.  Find the time to attain 95 per cent of the steady-state discharge.

**12.9**  A globe valve ($K = 10$) at the end of a pipe 2000 ft long is rapidly opened.  $D = 3.0$ ft, $f = 0.018$, minor losses are $2V^2/2g$, and $H = 75$ ft. How long does it take for the discharge to attain 80 per cent of its steady-state value?

**12.10**  A steel pipeline with expansion joints is 36 in. in diameter and has a $\frac{3}{8}$-in. wall thickness.  When it is carrying water, determine the speed of a pressure wave.

**12.11**  Benzine ($K = 150,000$ psi, $S = 0.88$) flows through $\frac{3}{4}$-in. ID steel tubing with $\frac{1}{8}$-in. wall thickness.  Determine the speed of a pressure wave.

**12.12**  Determine the maximum time for rapid valve closure on the pipeline: $L = 3000$ ft, $D = 4$ ft, $t' = \frac{1}{2}$ in., steel pipe, $V_0 = 10$ ft/sec, water flowing.

**12.13**  A valve is closed in 5 sec at the downstream end of a 10,000-ft pipeline carrying water at 6 ft/sec.  $a = 3400$ ft/sec.  What is the peak pressure developed by the closure?

**12.14**   Determine the length of pipe in Prob. 12.13 subjected to the peak pressure.

**12.15**   A valve is closed at the downstream end of a pipeline in such a manner that only one-third of the line is subjected to maximum pressure. During what proportion of the time $2L/a$ is it closed?

**12.16**   A pipe, $L = 6000$ ft, $a = 3000$ ft/sec, has a valve on its downstream end, $V_0 = 8$ ft/sec and $h_0 = 60$ ft.   It closes in three increments, spaced 1 sec apart, each area reduction being one-third of the original opening.   Find the pressure at the gate and at the mid-point of the pipeline at 1-sec intervals for 5 sec after initial closure.

**12.17**   A pipeline, $L = 2000$ ft, $a = 4000$ ft/sec, has a valve at its downstream end, $V_0 = 6$ ft/sec and $h_0 = 100$ ft.   Determine the pressure at the valve for the closure:

| $A_v/A_{v0}$ | 1 | 0.75 | 0.60 | 0.45 | 0.30 | 0.15 | 0 |
|---|---|---|---|---|---|---|---|
| $t$, sec | 0 | 0.5 | 1.0 | 1.5 | 2.0 | 2.5 | 3.0 |

**12.18**   In Prob. 12.17 determine the peak pressure at the valve for uniform area reduction in 3.0 sec.

**12.19**   Find the maximum area reduction for $\frac{1}{2}$-sec intervals for the pipeline of Prob. 12.17 when the maximum head at the valve is not to exceed 160 ft.

**12.20**   Derive the characteristics-method solution for waterhammer with the pressure $p$ and the discharge $Q$ as dependent variables.

**12.21**   By use of the graphical method, determine $\tau$ vs. time to close a valve at the downstream end of a pipe: $L = 7000$ ft, $a = 3500$ ft/sec, $H_0 = 300$ ft, $V_0 = 3$ ft/sec without exceeding a head of 450 ft at the valve.

**12.22**   Solve Example 12.6 for uniform closure of the valve in the same time, and compare with the results from the example.   (Computer solution.)

**12.23**   Solve Example 12.6 by the algebraic method.

**12.24**   Solve Example 12.6 by the graphical method, neglecting friction and minor losses.

**12.25**   If the wave frequency in Example 12.7 is doubled, work out the graphical solution.

**12.26**   By computer, solve the series-pipe-system problem of Example 12.9 when the pipes are interchanged.

**12.27**   Work Example 12.8 by the graphical method, neglecting friction.

**12.28**   A rectangular channel is discharging 50 cfs per foot of width at a depth of 10 ft when the discharge upstream is suddenly increased to 70 cfs/ft.   Determine the speed and height of the surge wave.

**12.29**   In a rectangular channel with velocity 6 ft/sec flowing at a depth of 6 ft, a surge wave 1.0 ft high travels upstream.   What is the speed of the wave, and how much is the discharge reduced per foot of width?

**12.30**   A rectangular channel 10 ft wide and 6 ft deep discharges 1000 cfs when the flow is completely stopped downstream by closure of a gate. Compute the height and speed of the resulting positive surge wave.

**12.31**   Determine the depth downstream from the gate of Prob. 12.30 after it closes.

**12.32**   Find the downstream water surface of Prob. 12.30 3 sec after closure.

**12.33**   Determine the water surface 2 sec after an ideal dam breaks. Original depth is 100 ft.

**12.34**   Work Example 12.13, by computer, for linear increase in flow to 50 per cent more than steady flow in 15 min, then decreased to 75 per cent of steady flow in 20 min. $C = 80$; channel width is 10 ft.

**12.35**   Calculate the runoff hydrograph for a 1.5 in./hr rainfall for 40 min on an impervious flat surface 400 ft long and 200 ft wide.   The surface slopes downward 1 ft along the 400-ft length.   $C = 75$.

**12.36**   Neglecting friction, the maximum difference in elevation of the two menisci of an oscillating U-tube is 1.0 ft, $L = 3.0$ ft.   The period of oscillation is, in seconds,

($a$) 0.52      ($b$) 1.92      ($c$) 3.27      ($d$) 20.6      ($e$) none of
these answers

**12.37**   The maximum speed of the liquid column in Prob. 12.36, in feet per second, is

($a$) 0.15      ($b$) 0.31      ($c$) 1.64      ($d$) 3.28      ($e$) none of these
answers

**12.38**   In frictionless oscillation of a U-tube, $L = 4.0$ ft, $z = 0$, $V = 6$ ft/sec. The maximum value of $z$ is, in feet,

($a$) 0.75      ($b$) 1.50      ($c$) 6.00      ($d$) 24.0      ($e$) none of these
answers

**12.39**   In analyzing the oscillation of a U-tube with laminar resistance, the assumption is made that the

($a$) motion is steady
($b$) resistance is constant

(c) Darcy-Weisbach equation applies

(d) resistance is a linear function of the displacement

(e) resistance is the same at any instant as if the motion were steady

**12.40** When $16\nu/D^2 = 5$ and $2g/L = 12$ in oscillation of a U-tube with laminar resistance,

(a) the resistance is so small that it may be neglected

(b) the menisci oscillate about the $z = 0$ axis

(c) the velocity is a maximum when $z = 0$

(d) the velocity is zero when $z = 0$

(e) the speed of column is a linear function of $z$

**12.41** In laminar resistance to oscillation in a U-tube, $m = 1$, $n = \frac{1}{2}$, $V_0 = 3$ ft/sec when $t = 0$ and $z = 0$. The time of maximum displacement of meniscus is, in seconds,

(a) 0.46    (b) 0.55    (c) 0.93    (d) 1.1    (e) none of these answers

**12.42** In Prob. 12.41 the maximum displacement, in feet, is

(a) 0.53    (b) 1.06    (c) 1.16    (d) 6.80    (e) none of these answers

**12.43** In analyzing the oscillation of a U-tube with turbulent resistance, the assumption is made that

(a) the Darcy-Weisbach equation applies

(b) the Hagen-Poiseuille equation applies

(c) the motion is steady

(d) the resistance is a linear function of velocity

(e) the resistance varies as the square of the displacement

**12.44** The maximum displacement is $z_m = 20$ ft for $f = 0.020$, $D = 1.0$ ft in oscillation of a U-tube with turbulent flow. The minimum displacement $(-z_{m+1})$ of the same fluid column is

(a) $-13.3$    (b) $-15.7$    (c) $-16.5$    (d) $-20$

(e) none of these answers

**12.45** When a valve is suddenly opened at the downstream end of a long pipe connected at its upstream end with a water reservoir,

(a) the velocity attains its final value instantaneously if friction is neglected

(b) the time to attain nine-tenths of its final velocity is less with friction than without friction

(c) the value of $f$ does not affect the time to acquire a given velocity

(d) the velocity increases exponentially with time

(e) the final velocity is attained in less than $2L/a$ sec

**12.46**  Surge may be differentiated from waterhammer by

(a) the time for a pressure wave to traverse the pipe
(b) the presence of a reservoir at one end of the pipe
(c) the rate of deceleration of flow
(d) the relative compressibility of liquid to expansion of pipe walls
(e) the length-diameter ratio of pipe

**12.47**  Waterhammer occurs only when

(a) $2L/a > 1$    (b) $V_0 > a$    (c) $2L/a = 1$    (d) $K/E < 1$
(e) compressibility effects are important

**12.48**  Valve closure is *rapid* only when

(a) $2L/a \geq t_c$    (b) $L/a \geq t_c$    (c) $L/2a \geq t_c$    (d) $t_c = 0$
(e) none of these answers

**12.49**  The head rise at a valve due to sudden closure is

(a) $a^2/2g$    (b) $V_0a/g$    (c) $V_0a/2g$    (d) $V_0^2/2g$
(e) none of these answers

**12.50**  The speed of a pressure wave through a pipe depends upon

(a) the length of pipe
(b) the original head at the valve
(c) the viscosity of fluid
(d) the initial velocity
(e) none of these answers

**12.51**  When the velocity in a pipe is suddenly reduced from 10 ft/sec to 6 ft/sec by downstream valve closure, for $a = 3220$ ft/sec, the head rise in feet is

(a) 1000    (b) 600    (c) 400    (d) 300    (e) none of these
    answers

**12.52**  When $t_c = L/2a$ the proportion of pipe length subjected to maximum head is, in per cent,

(a) 25    (b) 50    (c) 75    (d) 100    (e) none of these answers

**12.53**  When the steady-state value of head at a valve is 120 ft the valve is given a sudden partial closure such that $\Delta h = 80$ ft.  The head at the valve at the instant this reflected wave returns is

(a) $-80$    (b) 40    (c) 80    (d) 200    (e) none of these answers

**12.54**  An elementary wave can travel upstream in a channel, $y = 4$ ft, $V = 8$ ft/sec, with a velocity of

(a) 3.35 ft/sec    (b) 11.35 ft/sec    (c) 16.04 ft/sec
(d) 19.35 ft/sec    (e) none of these answers

**12.55**  The speed of an elementary wave in a still liquid is given by

(a) $(gy^2)^{1/3}$    (b) $2y/3$    (c) $\sqrt{2gy}$    (d) $\sqrt{gy}$

(e)  none of these answers

**12.56**  A negative surge wave

(a)  is a positive surge wave moving backward
(b)  is an inverted positive surge wave
(c)  can never travel upstream
(d)  can never travel downstream
(e)  is none of the above

**12.57**  The algebraic solution for waterhammer

(a)  must neglect friction
(b)  can be accomplished only by use of a computer
(c)  is limited to single pipes
(d)  requires a calculation period $\Delta t$ that yields an integer when divided into $L/a$ for each pipe
(e)  is valid only for rapid valve closures

## references

Bergeron, L.: "Water Hammer in Hydraulics and Wave Surges in Electricity," translated under the sponsorship of the ASME, John Wiley & Sons, Inc., New York, 1961.

Halliwell, A. R.: Velocity of a Water-hammer Wave in an Elastic Pipe, *J. Hydraulics Div. ASCE*, vol. 89, no. HY4, pp. 1–21, July, 1963.

Parmakian, J.: "Waterhammer Analysis," Prentice-Hall, Inc., Englewood Cliffs, N.J., 1955 (also Dover Publications, Inc., New York).

Streeter, V. L., and E. B. Wylie: "Hydraulic Transients," McGraw-Hill Book Company, New York, 1967.

# appendixes

# A

# force systems, moments, and centroids

The material in this appendix has been assembled to aid in working with force systems. Simple force systems are briefly reviewed and first and second moments, including the product of inertia, are discussed. Centroids and centroidal axes are defined.

## simple force systems

A free-body diagram for an object or portion of an object shows the action of all other bodies on it. The action of the earth on the object is called a *body force* and is proportional to the mass of the object. In addition, forces and couples may act on the object by contact with its surface. When the free body is at rest or is moving in a straight line with uniform speed, it is said to be in *equilibrium*. By Newton's second law of motion, since there is no acceleration of the free body, the summation of all force components in any direction must be zero and the summation of all moments about any axis must be zero.

Two force systems are equivalent if they have the same value for summation of forces in every direction and the same value for summation of moments about every axis. The simplest equivalent force system is called the *resultant* of the force system. Equivalent force systems always cause the same motion (or lack of motion) of a free body.

In coplanar force systems the resultant is either a force or a couple. In noncoplanar parallel force systems the resultant is either a force or a couple. In general noncoplanar systems the resultant may be a force, a couple, or a force and a couple.

The action of a fluid on any surface may be replaced by the resultant force system that causes the same external motion or reaction as the distributed fluid force system. In this situation the fluid may be considered to be completely removed, the resultant acting in its place.

## first and second moments.    centroids

The moment of an area, volume, weight, or mass may be determined in a manner analogous to that of determining the moments of a force about an axis.

### *first moments*

The moment of an area $A$ about the $y$-axis (Fig. A.1) is expressed by

$$\int_A x \, dA$$

in which the integration is carried out over the area. To determine the moment about a parallel axis, e.g., $x = k$, the moment becomes

$$\int_A (x - k) \, dA = \int_A x \, dA - kA \tag{A.1}$$

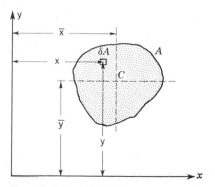

**Fig. A.1** Notation for first and second moments.

which shows that there will always be a parallel axis $x = k = \bar{x}$, about which the moment is zero.   This axis is called a *centroidal* axis and is obtained from Eq. (A.1) by setting it equal to zero and solving for $\bar{x}$,

$$\bar{x} = \frac{1}{A} \int_A x \, dA \qquad\qquad (A.2)$$

Another centroidal axis may be determined parallel to the $x$-axis,

$$\bar{y} = \frac{1}{A} \int_A y \, dA \qquad\qquad (A.3)$$

The point of intersection of centroidal axes is called the *centroid* of the area.   It may easily be shown, by rotation of axes, that the first moment of the area is zero about any axis through the centroid.   When an area has an axis of symmetry, it is a centroidal axis, because the moments of corresponding area elements on each side of the axis are equal in magnitude and opposite in sign.   When location of the centroid is known, the first moment for any axis may be obtained without integration by taking the product of area and distance from centroid to the axis,

$$\int_A z \, dA = \bar{z} A \qquad\qquad (A.4)$$

The centroidal axis of a triangle, parallel to one side, is one-third the altitude from that side; the centroid of a semicircle of radius $a$ is $4a/3\pi$ from the diameter.

By taking the first moment of a volume $\mathcal{U}$ about a plane, say the $yz$-plane, the distance to its centroid is similarly determined,

$$\bar{x} = \frac{1}{\mathcal{U}} \int_{\mathcal{U}} x \, d\mathcal{U} \qquad\qquad (A.5)$$

The mass center of a body is determined by the same procedure,

$$x_m = \frac{1}{M} \int_M x \, dm \qquad\qquad (A.6)$$

in which $dm$ is an element of mass and $M$ is the total mass of the body. For practical engineering purposes the *center of gravity* of a body is at its mass center.

*second moments*

The second moment of an area $A$ (Fig. A.1) about the $y$-axis is

$$I_y = \int_A x^2 \, dA \qquad\qquad (A.7)$$

$$I_c = \tfrac{1}{12} bh^3$$

$$I_c = \tfrac{1}{36} bh^3$$

$$I_{x-x} = \tfrac{1}{12} bh^3$$

$$I_c = \frac{\pi a^4}{4}$$

**Fig. A.2**  Moments of inertia of simple areas about centroidal axes.

It is called the *moment of inertia* of the area and is always positive since $dA$ is always considered positive. After transferring the axis to a parallel axis through the centroid $C$ of the area,

$$I_c = \int_A (x - \bar{x})^2 \, dA = \int_A x^2 \, dA - 2\bar{x} \int_A x \, dA + \bar{x}^2 \int_A dA$$

Since

$$\int_A x \, dA = \bar{x}A \qquad \int_A x^2 \, dA = I_y \qquad \int_A dA = A$$

therefore

$$I_c = I_y - \bar{x}^2 A \qquad \text{or} \qquad I_y = I_c + \bar{x}^2 A \tag{A.8}$$

In words, the moment of inertia of an area about any axis is the sum of the moment of inertia about a parallel axis through the centroid and the product of the area and square of distance between axes. Figure A.2 shows moments of inertia for three simple areas.

The *product of inertia* $I_{xy}$ of an area is expressed by

$$I_{xy} = \int_A xy \, dA \tag{A.9}$$

with the notation of Fig. A.1. It may be positive or negative. Writing the expression for product of inertia $\bar{I}_{xy}$ about centroidal axes parallel to the $xy$-axes produces

$$\bar{I}_{xy} = \int_A (x - \bar{x})(y - \bar{y}) \, dA = \int_A xy \, dA - \bar{x} \int_A y \, dA - \bar{y} \int_A x \, dA + \bar{x}\bar{y}A$$

After simplifying, and solving for $I_{xy}$,

$$I_{xy} = \bar{I}_{xy} + \bar{x}\bar{y}A \tag{A.10}$$

Whenever either axis is an axis of symmetry of the area, the product of inertia is zero. The product of inertia $I_{xy}$ of a triangle having two sides $b$ and $h$ along the positive coordinate axis is $b^2 h^2 / 24$.

# B

# partial derivatives and
# total differentials

## partial derivatives

A partial derivative is an expression of the rate of change of one variable with respect to another variable when all other variables are held constant. When one sees a partial derivative, he should determine which variables are considered constant. For example, the temperature $T$ at any point throughout a plane might be expressed as an equation containing space coordinates and time, $x$, $y$, and $t$. To determine how the temperature changes at some point, e.g., $x_0$, $y_0$, with the time, the actual numbers for coordinates are substituted, and the equation becomes a relation between $T$ and $t$ only. The rate of change of temperature with respect to time is $dT/dt$, which is written as a total differential because $T$ and $t$ are the only two variables in the equation. When one wants an expression for rate of change of temperature with time at any point, $x$, $y$, then these are considered to be constants and the derivative of the equation with respect to $t$ is taken. This is written $\partial T/\partial t$, to indicate that the other variables $x$, $y$ have been held constant. Substitution of particular values of $x$, $y$ into the expression yields $\partial T/\partial t$, in terms of $t$. As a specific case, if

$$T = x^2 + xyt + \sin t$$

then

$$\frac{\partial T}{\partial t} = xy + \cos t$$

For the point (1,2)

$$\frac{\partial T}{\partial t} = 2 + \cos t$$

which could have been obtained by first substituting (1,2) into the equation for $T$,

$$T = 1 + 2t + \sin t$$

and then by taking the total derivative,

$$\frac{dT}{dt} = 2 + \cos t$$

If one wants to know the variation of temperature along any line parallel to the $x$-axis at a given instant of time, then $\partial T/\partial x$ is taken and the specific $y$-coordinates of the line and the time are substituted later; thus

$$\frac{\partial T}{\partial x} = 2x + yt$$

in which $y$, $t$ have been considered constant.  For the line through $y = 2$, at time $t = 4$,

$$\frac{\partial T}{\partial x} = 2x + 8$$

and the rate of change of $T$ with respect to $x$ at this instant can be found at any point $x$ along the particular line.

In the function

$$u = f(x,y)$$

$x$ and $y$ are independent variables, and $u$ is the dependent variable.  If $y$ is held constant, $u$ becomes a function of $x$ alone, and its derivative may be determined as if $u$ were a function of one variable.  It is denoted by

$$\frac{\partial f}{\partial x} \quad \text{or} \quad \frac{\partial u}{\partial x}$$

and is called the partial derivative of $f$ with respect to $x$ or the partial derivative of $u$ with respect to $x$.  Similarly, if $x$ is held constant, $u$ becomes a function of $y$ alone and $\partial u/\partial y$ is the partial of $u$ with respect to $y$.  These partials are defined by

$$\frac{\partial u}{\partial x} = \frac{\partial f(x,y)}{\partial x} = \lim_{\Delta x \to 0} \frac{f(x + \Delta x, y) - f(x,y)}{\Delta x}$$

$$\frac{\partial u}{\partial y} = \frac{\partial f(x,y)}{\partial y} = \lim_{\Delta y \to 0} \frac{f(x,y + \Delta y) - f(x,y)}{\Delta y}$$

*Examples*

(a)    $u = x^3 + x^2y^3 + 3y^2$

$$\frac{\partial u}{\partial x} = 3x^2 + 2xy^3 \qquad \frac{\partial u}{\partial y} = 3x^2y^2 + 6y$$

(b)    $u = \sin (ax + by^2)$

$$\frac{\partial u}{\partial x} = a \cos (ax + by^2) \qquad \frac{\partial u}{\partial y} = 2by \cos (ax + by^2)$$

(c)    $u = x \ln y$

$$\frac{\partial u}{\partial x} = \ln y \qquad \frac{\partial u}{\partial y} = \frac{x}{y}$$

## total differentials

When $u$ is a function of one variable only, $u = f(x)$,

$$\frac{du}{dx} = \lim_{\Delta x \to 0} \frac{\Delta u}{\Delta x} = \lim_{\Delta x \to 0} \frac{f(x + \Delta x) - f(x)}{\Delta x} = f'(x)$$

and

$$\Delta u = f'(x)\, \Delta x + \epsilon\, \Delta x$$

in which

$$\lim_{\Delta x \to 0} \epsilon = 0$$

After applying the limiting process to $\Delta u$, then

$$du = f'(x)\, \Delta x \equiv f'(x)\, dx$$

is the differential $du$.

When $u = f(x,y)$, the differential $du$ is defined in a similar manner.    If $x$ and $y$ take on increments, $\Delta x$, $\Delta y$, then

$$\Delta u = f(x + \Delta x, y + \Delta y) - f(x,y)$$

in which $\Delta x$, $\Delta y$ may approach zero in any manner.    If $\Delta u$ approaches zero regardless of the way in which $\Delta x$ and $\Delta y$ approach zero, then $u = f(x,y)$ is called a *continuous* function of $x$ and $y$.    In the following it is assumed that $f(x,y)$ is continuous and that $\partial f/\partial x$ and $\partial f/\partial y$ are also continuous.

By adding and subtracting $f(x, y + \Delta y)$ to the expression for $\Delta u$,

$$\Delta u = f(x + \Delta x, y + \Delta y) - f(x, y + \Delta y) + f(x, y + \Delta y) - f(x,y)$$

Then

$$f(x + \Delta x, y + \Delta y) - f(x, y + \Delta y) = \frac{\partial f(x, y + \Delta y)}{\partial x} \Delta x + \epsilon_1 \Delta x$$

in which $\lim_{\Delta y \to 0} \epsilon_1 = 0$, because

$$\lim_{\Delta x \to 0} \frac{f(x + \Delta x, y + \Delta y) - f(x, y + \Delta y)}{\Delta x} = \frac{\partial f(x, y + \Delta y)}{\partial x}$$

Furthermore

$$\lim_{\Delta y \to 0} \frac{\partial f(x, y + \Delta y)}{\partial x} = \frac{\partial f(x,y)}{\partial x}$$

as the derivative is continuous, and

$$\frac{\partial f(x, y + \Delta y)}{\partial x} = \frac{\partial f(x,y)}{\partial x} + \epsilon_2$$

in which $\lim_{\Delta y \to 0} \epsilon_2 = 0$. Similarly

$$f(x, y + \Delta y) - f(x,y) = \frac{\partial f(x,y)}{\partial y} \Delta y + \epsilon_3 \Delta y$$

in which $\lim_{\Delta y \to 0} \epsilon_2 = 0$. By substituting into the expression for $\Delta u$,

$$\Delta u = \frac{\partial f(x,y)}{\partial x} \Delta x + \frac{\partial f(x,y)}{\partial y} \Delta y + (\epsilon_1 + \epsilon_2) \Delta x + \epsilon_3 \Delta y$$

If the limit is taken as $\Delta x$ and $\Delta y$ approach zero, the last two terms drop out since they are the product of two infinitesimals and, hence, are of a higher order of smallness. The total differential of $u$ is obtained,

$$du = \frac{\partial f}{\partial x} dx + \frac{\partial f}{\partial y} dy = \frac{\partial u}{\partial x} dx + \frac{\partial u}{\partial y} dy$$

If $x$ and $y$ in $u = f(x,y)$ are functions of one independent variable, e.g., $t$, then $u$ becomes a function of $t$ alone and has a derivative with respect to $t$ if the functions $x = f_1(t)$, $y = f_2(t)$ are assumed differentiable. An increment in $t$ results in increments $\Delta x$, $\Delta y$, $\Delta u$ which approach zero with $\Delta t$. By dividing the expression for $\Delta u$ by $\Delta t$,

$$\frac{\Delta u}{\Delta t} = \frac{\partial u}{\partial x} \frac{\Delta x}{\Delta t} + \frac{\partial u}{\partial y} \frac{\Delta y}{\Delta t} + (\epsilon_1 + \epsilon_2) \frac{\Delta x}{\Delta t} + \epsilon_3 \frac{\Delta y}{\Delta t}$$

and by taking the limit as $\Delta t$ approaches zero,

$$\frac{du}{dt} = \frac{\partial u}{\partial x}\frac{dx}{dt} + \frac{\partial u}{\partial y}\frac{dy}{dt}$$

The same general form results for additional variables, namely,

$$u = f(x,y,t)$$

in which $x$, $y$ are functions of $t$; then

$$\frac{du}{dt} = \frac{\partial u}{\partial x}\frac{dx}{dt} + \frac{\partial u}{\partial y}\frac{dy}{dt} + \frac{\partial u}{dt}$$

# C
# physical properties of fluids

**Table C.1  Physical properties of water†**

| Temp, °F | Specific weight $\gamma$, lb/ft³ | Density $\rho$, slugs/ft³ | Viscosity $\mu$, lb-sec/ft² $10^5 \mu =$ | Kine-matic viscosity $\nu$, ft²/sec $10^5 \nu =$ | Surface tension $\sigma$, lb/ft $100 \sigma =$ | Vapor pressure head $p_v/\gamma$, ft | Bulk modulus of elasticity $K$, lb/in² $10^{-3} K =$ |
|---|---|---|---|---|---|---|---|
| 32  | 62.42 | 1.940 | 3.746 | 1.931 | 0.518 | 0.20  | 293 |
| 40  | 62.43 | 1.940 | 3.229 | 1.664 | 0.514 | 0.28  | 294 |
| 50  | 62.41 | 1.940 | 2.735 | 1.410 | 0.509 | 0.41  | 305 |
| 60  | 62.37 | 1.938 | 2.359 | 1.217 | 0.504 | 0.59  | 311 |
| 70  | 62.30 | 1.936 | 2.050 | 1.059 | 0.500 | 0.84  | 320 |
| 80  | 62.22 | 1.934 | 1.799 | 0.930 | 0.492 | 1.17  | 322 |
| 90  | 62.11 | 1.931 | 1.595 | 0.826 | 0.486 | 1.61  | 323 |
| 100 | 62.00 | 1.927 | 1.424 | 0.739 | 0.480 | 2.19  | 327 |
| 110 | 61.86 | 1.923 | 1.284 | 0.667 | 0.473 | 2.95  | 331 |
| 120 | 61.71 | 1.918 | 1.168 | 0.609 | 0.465 | 3.91  | 333 |
| 130 | 61.55 | 1.913 | 1.069 | 0.558 | 0.460 | 5.13  | 334 |
| 140 | 61.38 | 1.908 | 0.981 | 0.514 | 0.454 | 6.67  | 330 |
| 150 | 61.20 | 1.902 | 0.905 | 0.476 | 0.447 | 8.58  | 328 |
| 160 | 61.00 | 1.896 | 0.838 | 0.442 | 0.441 | 10.95 | 326 |
| 170 | 60.80 | 1.890 | 0.780 | 0.413 | 0.433 | 13.83 | 322 |
| 180 | 60.58 | 1.883 | 0.726 | 0.385 | 0.426 | 17.33 | 318 |
| 190 | 60.36 | 1.876 | 0.678 | 0.362 | 0.419 | 21.55 | 313 |
| 200 | 60.12 | 1.868 | 0.637 | 0.341 | 0.412 | 26.59 | 308 |
| 212 | 59.83 | 1.860 | 0.593 | 0.319 | 0.404 | 33.90 | 300 |

† This table was compiled primarily from *ASCE Manual Eng. Pract.*, no. 25, Hydraulic Models, 1942.

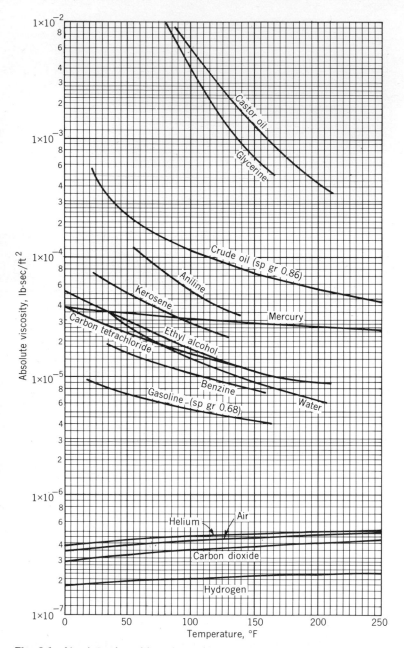

**Fig. C.1** Absolute viscosities of certain gases and liquids.

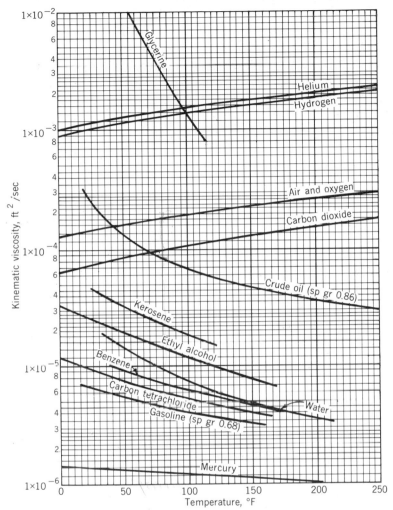

**Fig. C.2**  Kinematic viscosities of certain gases and liquids. The gases are at standard pressure.

**Table C.2  Properties of gases at low pressures and 80°F**

| Gas | Chemical formula | Molecular weight $M$ | Gas constant $R$ ft-lb/lb$_m$°R, | Specific heat, Btu/lb$_m$°R | | Specific-heat ratio $k$ |
|---|---|---|---|---|---|---|
| | | | | $c_p$ | $c_v$ | |
| Air | — | 29.0 | 53.3 | 0.240 | 0.171 | 1.40 |
| Carbon monoxide | CO | 28.0 | 55.2 | 0.249 | 0.178 | 1.40 |
| Helium | He | 4.00 | 386 | 1.25 | 0.753 | 1.66 |
| Hydrogen | $H_2$ | 2.02 | 766 | 3.43 | 2.44 | 1.40 |
| Nitrogen | $N_2$ | 28.0 | 55.2 | 0.248 | 0.177 | 1.40 |
| Oxygen | $O_2$ | 32.0 | 48.3 | 0.219 | 0.157 | 1.40 |
| Water vapor | $H_2O$ | 18.0 | 85.8 | 0.445 | 0.335 | 1.33 |

**Table C.3  One-dimensional isentropic relations (For a perfect gas with constant specific heat.  $k = 1.4$.)**[†]

| M | $A/A^*$ | $p/p_0$ | $\rho/\rho_0$ | $T/T_0$ | M | $A/A^*$ | $p/p_0$ | $\rho/\rho_0$ | $T/T_0$ |
|---|---|---|---|---|---|---|---|---|---|
| 0.00 | ..... | 1.000 | 1.000 | 1.000 | 0.78 | 1.05 | 0.669 | 0.750 | 0.891 |
| 0.01 | 57.87 | 0.9999 | 0.9999 | 0.9999 | 0.80 | 1.04 | 0.656 | 0.740 | 0.886 |
| 0.02 | 28.94 | 0.9997 | 0.9999 | 0.9999 | 0.82 | 1.03 | 0.643 | 0.729 | 0.881 |
| 0.04 | 14.48 | 0.999 | 0.999 | 0.9996 | 0.84 | 1.02 | 0.630 | 0.719 | 0.875 |
| 0.06 | 9.67 | 0.997 | 0.998 | 0.999 | 0.86 | 1.02 | 0.617 | 0.708 | 0.871 |
| 0.08 | 7.26 | 0.996 | 0.997 | 0.999 | 0.88 | 1.01 | 0.604 | 0.698 | 0.865 |
| 0.10 | 5.82 | 0.993 | 0.995 | 0.998 | 0.90 | 1.01 | 0.591 | 0.687 | 0.860 |
| 0.12 | 4.86 | 0.990 | 0.993 | 0.997 | 0.92 | 1.01 | 0.578 | 0.676 | 0.855 |
| 0.14 | 4.18 | 0.986 | 0.990 | 0.996 | 0.94 | 1.00 | 0.566 | 0.666 | 0.850 |
| 0.16 | 3.67 | 0.982 | 0.987 | 0.995 | 0.96 | 1.00 | 0.553 | 0.655 | 0.844 |
| 0.18 | 3.28 | 0.978 | 0.984 | 0.994 | 0.98 | 1.00 | 0.541 | 0.645 | 0.839 |
| 0.20 | 2.96 | 0.973 | 0.980 | 0.992 | 1.00 | 1.00 | 0.528 | 0.632 | 0.833 |
| 0.22 | 2.71 | 0.967 | 0.976 | 0.990 | 1.02 | 1.00 | 0.516 | 0.623 | 0.828 |
| 0.24 | 2.50 | 0.961 | 0.972 | 0.989 | 1.04 | 1.00 | 0.504 | 0.613 | 0.822 |
| 0.26 | 2.32 | 0.954 | 0.967 | 0.987 | 1.06 | 1.00 | 0.492 | 0.602 | 0.817 |
| 0.28 | 2.17 | 0.947 | 0.962 | 0.985 | 1.08 | 1.01 | 0.480 | 0.592 | 0.810 |
| 0.30 | 2.04 | 0.939 | 0.956 | 0.982 | 1.10 | 1.01 | 0.468 | 0.582 | 0.805 |
| 0.32 | 1.92 | 0.932 | 0.951 | 0.980 | 1.12 | 1.01 | 0.457 | 0.571 | 0.799 |
| 0.34 | 1.82 | 0.923 | 0.944 | 0.977 | 1.14 | 1.02 | 0.445 | 0.561 | 0.794 |
| 0.36 | 1.74 | 0.914 | 0.938 | 0.975 | 1.16 | 1.02 | 0.434 | 0.551 | 0.788 |
| 0.38 | 1.66 | 0.905 | 0.931 | 0.972 | 1.18 | 1.02 | 0.423 | 0.541 | 0.782 |
| 0.40 | 1.59 | 0.896 | 0.924 | 0.969 | 1.20 | 1.03 | 0.412 | 0.531 | 0.776 |
| 0.42 | 1.53 | 0.886 | 0.917 | 0.966 | 1.22 | 1.04 | 0.402 | 0.521 | 0.771 |
| 0.44 | 1.47 | 0.876 | 0.909 | 0.963 | 1.24 | 1.04 | 0.391 | 0.512 | 0.765 |
| 0.46 | 1.42 | 0.865 | 0.902 | 0.959 | 1.26 | 1.05 | 0.381 | 0.502 | 0.759 |
| 0.48 | 1.38 | 0.854 | 0.893 | 0.956 | 1.28 | 1.06 | 0.371 | 0.492 | 0.753 |
| 0.50 | 1.34 | 0.843 | 0.885 | 0.952 | 1.30 | 1.07 | 0.361 | 0.483 | 0.747 |
| 0.52 | 1.30 | 0.832 | 0.877 | 0.949 | 1.32 | 1.08 | 0.351 | 0.474 | 0.742 |
| 0.54 | 1.27 | 0.820 | 0.868 | 0.945 | 1.34 | 1.08 | 0.342 | 0.464 | 0.736 |
| 0.56 | 1.24 | 0.808 | 0.859 | 0.941 | 1.36 | 1.09 | 0.332 | 0.455 | 0.730 |
| 0.58 | 1.21 | 0.796 | 0.850 | 0.937 | 1.38 | 1.10 | 0.323 | 0.446 | 0.724 |
| 0.60 | 1.19 | 0.784 | 0.840 | 0.933 | 1.40 | 1.11 | 0.314 | 0.437 | 0.718 |
| 0.62 | 1.17 | 0.772 | 0.831 | 0.929 | 1.42 | 1.13 | 0.305 | 0.429 | 0.713 |
| 0.64 | 1.16 | 0.759 | 0.821 | 0.924 | 1.44 | 1.14 | 0.297 | 0.420 | 0.707 |
| 0.66 | 1.13 | 0.747 | 0.812 | 0.920 | 1.46 | 1.15 | 0.289 | 0.412 | 0.701 |
| 0.68 | 1.12 | 0.734 | 0.802 | 0.915 | 1.48 | 1.16 | 0.280 | 0.403 | 0.695 |
| 0.70 | 1.09 | 0.721 | 0.792 | 0.911 | 1.50 | 1.18 | 0.272 | 0.395 | 0.690 |
| 0.72 | 1.08 | 0.708 | 0.781 | 0.906 | 1.52 | 1.19 | 0.265 | 0.387 | 0.684 |
| 0.74 | 1.07 | 0.695 | 0.771 | 0.901 | 1.54 | 1.20 | 0.257 | 0.379 | 0.678 |
| 0.76 | 1.06 | 0.682 | 0.761 | 0.896 | 1.56 | 1.22 | 0.250 | 0.371 | 0.672 |

[†] From *Mechanics of Fluids* by Irving Shames.  Copyright © 1962 by McGraw-Hill, Inc.  Used with permission of McGraw-Hill Book Company.

**Table C.3 One-dimensional isentropic relations** (*Continued*)

| M | $A/A^*$ | $p/p_0$ | $\rho/\rho_0$ | $T/T_0$ | M | $A/A^*$ | $p/p_0$ | $\rho/\rho_0$ | $T/T_0$ |
|---|---------|---------|---------------|---------|---|---------|---------|---------------|---------|
| 1.58 | 1.23 | 0.242 | 0.363 | 0.667 | 2.30 | 2.19 | 0.080 | 0.165 | 0.486 |
| 1.60 | 1.25 | 0.235 | 0.356 | 0.661 | 2.32 | 2.23 | 0.078 | 0.161 | 0.482 |
| 1.62 | 1.27 | 0.228 | 0.348 | 0.656 | 2.34 | 2.27 | 0.075 | 0.157 | 0.477 |
| 1.64 | 1.28 | 0.222 | 0.341 | 0.650 | 2.36 | 2.32 | 0.073 | 0.154 | 0.473 |
| 1.66 | 1.30 | 0.215 | 0.334 | 0.645 | 2.38 | 2.36 | 0.071 | 0.150 | 0.469 |
| 1.68 | 1.32 | 0.209 | 0.327 | 0.639 | 2.40 | 2.40 | 0.068 | 0.147 | 0.465 |
| 1.70 | 1.34 | 0.203 | 0.320 | 0.634 | 2.42 | 2.45 | 0.066 | 0.144 | 0.461 |
| 1.72 | 1.36 | 0.197 | 0.313 | 0.628 | 2.44 | 2.49 | 0.064 | 0.141 | 0.456 |
| 1.74 | 1.38 | 0.191 | 0.306 | 0.623 | 2.46 | 2.54 | 0.062 | 0.138 | 0.452 |
| 1.76 | 1.40 | 0.185 | 0.300 | 0.617 | 2.48 | 2.59 | 0.060 | 0.135 | 0.448 |
| 1.78 | 1.42 | 0.179 | 0.293 | 0.612 | 2.50 | 2.64 | 0.059 | 0.132 | 0.444 |
| 1.80 | 1.44 | 0.174 | 0.287 | 0.607 | 2.52 | 2.69 | 0.057 | 0.129 | 0.441 |
| 1.82 | 1.46 | 0.169 | 0.281 | 0.602 | 2.54 | 2.74 | 0.055 | 0.126 | 0.437 |
| 1.84 | 1.48 | 0.164 | 0.275 | 0.596 | 2.56 | 2.79 | 0.053 | 0.123 | 0.433 |
| 1.86 | 1.51 | 0.159 | 0.269 | 0.591 | 2.58 | 2.84 | 0.052 | 0.121 | 0.429 |
| 1.88 | 1.53 | 0.154 | 0.263 | 0.586 | 2.60 | 2.90 | 0.050 | 0.118 | 0.425 |
| 1.90 | 1.56 | 0.149 | 0.257 | 0.581 | 2.62 | 2.95 | 0.049 | 0.115 | 0.421 |
| 1.92 | 1.58 | 0.145 | 0.251 | 0.576 | 2.64 | 3.01 | 0.047 | 0.113 | 0.418 |
| 1.94 | 1.61 | 0.140 | 0.246 | 0.571 | 2.66 | 3.06 | 0.046 | 0.110 | 0.414 |
| 1.96 | 1.63 | 0.136 | 0.240 | 0.566 | 2.68 | 3.12 | 0.044 | 0.108 | 0.410 |
| 1.98 | 1.66 | 0.132 | 0.235 | 0.561 | 2.70 | 3.18 | 0.043 | 0.106 | 0.407 |
| 2.00 | 1.69 | 0.128 | 0.230 | 0.556 | 2.72 | 3.24 | 0.042 | 0.103 | 0.403 |
| 2.02 | 1.72 | 0.124 | 0.225 | 0.551 | 2.74 | 3.31 | 0.040 | 0.101 | 0.400 |
| 2.04 | 1.75 | 0.120 | 0.220 | 0.546 | 2.76 | 3.37 | 0.039 | 0.099 | 0.396 |
| 2.06 | 1.78 | 0.116 | 0.215 | 0.541 | 2.78 | 3.43 | 0.038 | 0.097 | 0.393 |
| 2.08 | 1.81 | 0.113 | 0.210 | 0.536 | 2.80 | 3.50 | 0.037 | 0.095 | 0.389 |
| 2.10 | 1.84 | 0.109 | 0.206 | 0.531 | 2.82 | 3.57 | 0.036 | 0.093 | 0.386 |
| 2.12 | 1.87 | 0.106 | 0.201 | 0.526 | 2.84 | 3.64 | 0.035 | 0.091 | 0.383 |
| 2.14 | 1.90 | 0.103 | 0.197 | 0.522 | 2.86 | 3.71 | 0.034 | 0.089 | 0.379 |
| 2.16 | 1.94 | 0.100 | 0.192 | 0.517 | 2.88 | 3.78 | 0.033 | 0.087 | 0.376 |
| 2.18 | 1.97 | 0.097 | 0.188 | 0.513 | 2.90 | 3.85 | 0.032 | 0.085 | 0.373 |
| 2.20 | 2.01 | 0.094 | 0.184 | 0.508 | 2.92 | 3.92 | 0.031 | 0.083 | 0.370 |
| 2.22 | 2.04 | 0.091 | 0.180 | 0.504 | 2.94 | 4.00 | 0.030 | 0.081 | 0.366 |
| 2.24 | 2.08 | 0.088 | 0.176 | 0.499 | 2.96 | 4.08 | 0.029 | 0.080 | 0.363 |
| 2.26 | 2.12 | 0.085 | 0.172 | 0.495 | 2.98 | 4.15 | 0.028 | 0.078 | 0.360 |
| 2.28 | 2.15 | 0.083 | 0.168 | 0.490 | 3.00 | 4.23 | 0.027 | 0.076 | 0.357 |

**Table C.4  One-dimensional normal-shock relations (For a perfect gas with $k = 1.4$.)** †

| $M_1$ | $M_2$ | $\dfrac{p_2}{p_1}$ | $\dfrac{T_2}{T_1}$ | $\dfrac{(p_0)_2}{(p_0)_1}$ | $M_1$ | $M_2$ | $\dfrac{p_2}{p_1}$ | $\dfrac{T_2}{T_1}$ | $\dfrac{(p_0)_2}{(p_0)_1}$ |
|---|---|---|---|---|---|---|---|---|---|
| 1.00 | 1.000 | 1.000 | 1.000 | 1.000 | 1.72 | 0.635 | 3.285 | 1.473 | 0.847 |
| 1.02 | 0.980 | 1.047 | 1.013 | 1.000 | 1.74 | 0.631 | 3.366 | 1.487 | 0.839 |
| 1.04 | 0.962 | 1.095 | 1.026 | 1.000 | 1.76 | 0.626 | 3.447 | 1.502 | 0.830 |
| 1.06 | 0.944 | 1.144 | 1.039 | 1.000 | 1.78 | 0.621 | 3.530 | 1.517 | 0.821 |
| 1.08 | 0.928 | 1.194 | 1.052 | 0.999 | 1.80 | 0.617 | 3.613 | 1.532 | 0.813 |
| 1.10 | 0.912 | 1.245 | 1.065 | 0.999 | 1.82 | 0.612 | 3.698 | 1.547 | 0.804 |
| 1.12 | 0.896 | 1.297 | 1.078 | 0.998 | 1.84 | 0.608 | 3.783 | 1.562 | 0.795 |
| 1.14 | 0.882 | 1.350 | 1.090 | 0.997 | 1.86 | 0.604 | 3.869 | 1.577 | 0.786 |
| 1.16 | 0.868 | 1.403 | 1.103 | 0.996 | 1.88 | 0.600 | 3.957 | 1.592 | 0.777 |
| 1.18 | 0.855 | 1.458 | 1.115 | 0.995 | 1.90 | 0.596 | 4.045 | 1.608 | 0.767 |
| 1.20 | 0.842 | 1.513 | 1.128 | 0.993 | 1.92 | 0.592 | 4.134 | 1.624 | 0.758 |
| 1.22 | 0.830 | 1.570 | 1.140 | 0.991 | 1.94 | 0.588 | 4.224 | 1.639 | 0.749 |
| 1.24 | 0.818 | 1.627 | 1.153 | 0.988 | 1.96 | 0.584 | 4.315 | 1.655 | 0.740 |
| 1.26 | 0.807 | 1.686 | 1.166 | 0.986 | 1.98 | 0.581 | 4.407 | 1.671 | 0.730 |
| 1.28 | 0.796 | 1.745 | 1.178 | 0.983 | 2.00 | 0.577 | 4.500 | 1.688 | 0.721 |
| 1.30 | 0.786 | 1.805 | 1.191 | 0.979 | 2.02 | 0.574 | 4.594 | 1.704 | 0.711 |
| 1.32 | 0.776 | 1.866 | 1.204 | 0.976 | 2.04 | 0.571 | 4.689 | 1.720 | 0.702 |
| 1.34 | 0.766 | 1.928 | 1.216 | 0.972 | 2.06 | 0.567 | 4.784 | 1.737 | 0.693 |
| 1.36 | 0.757 | 1.991 | 1.229 | 0.968 | 2.08 | 0.564 | 4.881 | 1.754 | 0.683 |
| 1.38 | 0.748 | 2.055 | 1.242 | 0.963 | 2.10 | 0.561 | 4.978 | 1.770 | 0.674 |
| 1.40 | 0.740 | 2.120 | 1.255 | 0.958 | 2.12 | 0.558 | 5.077 | 1.787 | 0.665 |
| 1.42 | 0.731 | 2.186 | 1.268 | 0.953 | 2.14 | 0.555 | 5.176 | 1.805 | 0.656 |
| 1.44 | 0.723 | 2.253 | 1.281 | 0.948 | 2.16 | 0.553 | 5.277 | 1.822 | 0.646 |
| 1.46 | 0.716 | 2.320 | 1.294 | 0.942 | 2.18 | 0.550 | 5.378 | 1.839 | 0.637 |
| 1.48 | 0.708 | 2.389 | 1.307 | 0.936 | 2.20 | 0.547 | 5.480 | 1.857 | 0.628 |
| 1.50 | 0.701 | 2.458 | 1.320 | 0.930 | 2.22 | 0.544 | 5.583 | 1.875 | 0.619 |
| 1.52 | 0.694 | 2.529 | 1.334 | 0.923 | 2.24 | 0.542 | 5.687 | 1.892 | 0.610 |
| 1.54 | 0.687 | 2.600 | 1.347 | 0.917 | 2.26 | 0.539 | 5.792 | 1.910 | 0.601 |
| 1.56 | 0.681 | 2.673 | 1.361 | 0.910 | 2.28 | 0.537 | 5.898 | 1.929 | 0.592 |
| 1.58 | 0.675 | 2.746 | 1.374 | 0.903 | 2.30 | 0.534 | 6.005 | 1.947 | 0.583 |
| 1.60 | 0.668 | 2.820 | 1.388 | 0.895 | 2.32 | 0.532 | 6.113 | 1.965 | 0.575 |
| 1.62 | 0.663 | 2.895 | 1.402 | 0.888 | 2.34 | 0.530 | 6.222 | 1.984 | 0.566 |
| 1.64 | 0.657 | 2.971 | 1.416 | 0.880 | 2.36 | 0.527 | 6.331 | 2.003 | 0.557 |
| 1.66 | 0.651 | 3.048 | 1.430 | 0.872 | 2.38 | 0.525 | 6.442 | 2.021 | 0.549 |
| 1.68 | 0.646 | 3.126 | 1.444 | 0.864 | 2.40 | 0.523 | 6.553 | 2.040 | 0.540 |
| 1.70 | 0.641 | 3.205 | 1.458 | 0.856 | 2.42 | 0.521 | 6.666 | 2.060 | 0.532 |

† From *Mechanics of Fluids* by Irving Shames.  Copyright © 1962 by McGraw-Hill, Inc.  Used with permission of McGraw-Hill Book Company.

**Table C.4  One-dimensional normal-shock relations** (*Continued*)

| $M_1$ | $M_2$ | $\dfrac{p_2}{p_1}$ | $\dfrac{T_2}{T_1}$ | $\dfrac{(p_0)_2}{(p_0)_1}$ | $M_1$ | $M_2$ | $\dfrac{p_2}{p_1}$ | $\dfrac{T_2}{T_1}$ | $\dfrac{(p_0)_2}{(p_0)_1}$ |
|---|---|---|---|---|---|---|---|---|---|
| 2.44 | 0.519 | 6.779 | 2.079 | 0.523 | 2.76 | 0.491 | 8.721 | 2.407 | 0.403 |
| 2.46 | 0.517 | 6.894 | 2.098 | 0.515 | 2.78 | 0.490 | 8.850 | 2.429 | 0.396 |
| 2.48 | 0.515 | 7.009 | 2.118 | 0.507 | 2.80 | 0.488 | 8.980 | 2.451 | 0.389 |
| 2.50 | 0.513 | 7.125 | 2.138 | 0.499 | 2.82 | 0.487 | 9.111 | 2.473 | 0.383 |
| 2.52 | 0.511 | 7.242 | 2.157 | 0.491 | 2.84 | 0.485 | 9.243 | 2.496 | 0.376 |
| 2.54 | 0.509 | 7.360 | 2.177 | 0.483 | 2.86 | 0.484 | 9.376 | 2.518 | 0.370 |
| 2.56 | 0.507 | 7.479 | 2.198 | 0.475 | 2.88 | 0.483 | 9.510 | 2.541 | 0.364 |
| 2.58 | 0.506 | 7.599 | 2.218 | 0.468 | 2.90 | 0.481 | 9.645 | 2.563 | 0.358 |
| 2.60 | 0.504 | 7.720 | 2.238 | 0.460 | 2.92 | 0.480 | 9.781 | 2.586 | 0.352 |
| 2.62 | 0.502 | 7.842 | 2.260 | 0.453 | 2.94 | 0.479 | 9.918 | 2.609 | 0.346 |
| 2.64 | 0.500 | 7.965 | 2.280 | 0.445 | 2.96 | 0.478 | 10.055 | 2.632 | 0.340 |
| 2.66 | 0.499 | 8.088 | 2.301 | 0.438 | 2.98 | 0.476 | 10.194 | 2.656 | 0.334 |
| 2.68 | 0.497 | 8.213 | 2.322 | 0.431 | 3.00 | 0.475 | 10.333 | 2.679 | 0.328 |
| 2.70 | 0.496 | 8.338 | 2.343 | 0.424 | | | | | |
| 2.72 | 0.494 | 8.465 | 2.364 | 0.417 | | | | | |
| 2.74 | 0.493 | 8.592 | 2.396 | 0.410 | | | | | |

# D
## notation

| Symbol | Quantity | Units (ft-lb-sec) | Dimensions (M.L.T) |
|--------|----------|-------------------|---------------------|
| $u$ | Constant, pulse wave-speed | ft/sec | $LT^{-1}$ |
| $a$ | Acceleration | ft/sec² | $LT^{-2}$ |
| $\mathbf{a}$ | Acceleration vector | ft/sec² | $LT^{-2}$ |
| $a^*$ | Velocity | ft/sec | $LT^{-1}$ |
| $A$ | Area | ft² | $L^2$ |
| $\mathbf{A}$ | Adverse slope | none | |
| $b$ | Distance | ft | $L$ |
| $b$ | Constant | | |
| $c$ | Speed of surge wave | ft/sec | $LT^{-1}$ |
| $c$ | Speed of sound | ft/sec | $LT^{-1}$ |
| $c_p$ | Specific heat, constant pressure | ft-lb/slug °R | |
| $c_v$ | Specific heat, constant volume | ft-lb/slug °R | |
| $C$ | Concentration | No./ft³ | $L^{-3}$ |
| $C$ | Coefficient | none | |
| $C$ | Stress | lb/ft² | $ML^{-1}T^{-2}$ |
| $\mathbf{C}$ | Critical slope | none | |
| $D'$ | Volumetric displacement | ft³ | $L^3$ |
| $D$ | Diameter | ft | $L$ |
| $e$ | Efficiency | none | |
| $e$ | Internal energy per unit mass | ft-lb/slug | $L^2T^{-2}$ |

| Symbol | Quantity | Units (ft-lb-sec) | Dimensions (M.L.T) |
|---|---|---|---|
| $E$ | Internal energy | ft-lb | $ML^2T^{-2}$ |
| $E$ | Specific energy | ft-lb/lb | $L$ |
| $E$ | Losses per unit weight | ft-lb/lb | $L$ |
| $E$ | Modulus of elasticity | lb/ft$^2$ | $ML^{-1}T^{-2}$ |
| $f$ | Friction factor | none | |
| $F$ | Force | lb | $MLT^{-2}$ |
| **F** | Force vector | lb | $MLT^{-2}$ |
| **F** | Froude number | none | |
| $F_B$ | Buoyant force | lb | $MLT^{-2}$ |
| $g$ | Acceleration of gravity | ft/sec$^2$ | $LT^{-2}$ |
| $g_0$ | Gravitational constant | lb$_m$-ft/lb-sec$^2$ | |
| $G$ | Mass flow rate per unit area | slug/sec-ft$^2$ | $ML^{-2}T^{-1}$ |
| $h$ | Head, vertical distance | ft | $L$ |
| $h$ | Enthalpy per unit mass | ft-lb/slug | $L^2T^{-2}$ |
| $H$ | Head, elevation of hydraulic grade line | ft | $L$ |
| **H** | Horizontal slope | none | |
| $I$ | Moment of inertia | ft$^4$ | $L^4$ |
| $J$ | Junction point | none | |
| $k$ | Specific-heat ratio | none | |
| $K$ | Bulk modulus of elasticity | lb/ft$^2$ | $ML^{-1}T^{-2}$ |
| $K$ | Minor loss coefficient | none | |
| $L$ | Length | ft | $L$ |
| $L$ | Lift | lb | $MLT^{-2}$ |
| $l$ | Length, mixing length | ft | $L$ |
| ln | Natural logarithm | none | |
| $m$ | Mass | slug | $M$ |
| $m$ | Form factor, constant | none | |
| $m$ | Strength of source | ft$^3$/sec | $L^3T^{-1}$ |
| $m$ | Mass per unit time | slug/sec | $MT^{-1}$ |
| $M$ | Molecular weight | | |
| $M$ | Momentum per unit time | lb | $MLT^{-2}$ |
| **M** | Mild slope | none | |
| **M** | Mach number | none | |
| $\overline{MG}$ | Metacentric height | ft | $L$ |
| $n$ | Exponent, constant | none | |
| $n$ | Normal direction | ft | $L$ |
| $n$ | Manning roughness factor | | |
| $n$ | Number of moles | | |

| Sym-bol | Quantity | Units (ft-lb-sec) | Dimen-sions (M.L.T) |
|---|---|---|---|
| $\mathbf{n}_1$ | Normal unit vector | | |
| $N$ | Rotation speed | 1/sec | $T^{-1}$ |
| $NPSH$ | Net positive suction head | ft | $L$ |
| $p$ | Pressure | lb/ft$^2$ | $ML^{-1}T^{-2}$ |
| $p$ | Force | lb | $MLT^{-2}$ |
| $p$ | Height of weir | ft | $L$ |
| $p$ | Wetted perimeter | ft | $L$ |
| $q$ | Discharge per unit width | ft$^2$/sec | $L^2T^{-1}$ |
| $q$ | Velocity | ft/sec | $LT^{-1}$ |
| $\mathbf{q}$ | Velocity vector | ft/sec | $LT^{-1}$ |
| $q_H$ | Heat transfer per unit mass | ft-lb/slug | $L^2T^{-2}$ |
| $Q$ | Discharge | ft$^3$/sec | $L^3T^{-1}$ |
| $Q_H$ | Heat transfer per unit time | ft-lb/sec | $ML^2T^{-3}$ |
| $r$ | Coefficient | | |
| $r$ | Radial distance | ft | $L$ |
| $\mathbf{r}$ | Position vector | ft | $L$ |
| $R$ | Hydraulic radius | ft | $L$ |
| $R$ | Gas constant | ft-lb/slug °R | |
| $R, R'$ | Gage difference | ft | $L$ |
| $\mathbf{R}$ | Reynolds number | none | |
| $s$ | Distance | ft | $L$ |
| $s$ | Entropy per unit mass | ft-lb/slug °R | |
| $s$ | Slip | none | |
| $S$ | Entropy | ft-lb/°R | |
| $S$ | Specific gravity, slope | none | |
| $S$ | Stroke ratio | none | |
| $\mathbf{S}$ | Steep slope | none | |
| $t$ | Time | sec | $T$ |
| $t, t'$ | Distance, thickness | ft | $L$ |
| $T$ | Temperature | °R | |
| $T$ | Torque | lb-ft | $ML^2T^{-2}$ |
| $T$ | Tensile force/ft | lb/ft | $MT^{-2}$ |
| $T$ | Top width | ft | $L$ |
| $u$ | Velocity, velocity component | ft/sec | $LT^{-1}$ |
| $u$ | Peripheral speed | ft/sec | $LT^{-1}$ |
| $u$ | Intrinsic energy | ft-lb/slug | $L^2T^{-2}$ |
| $u_*$ | Shear stress velocity | ft/sec | $LT^{-1}$ |
| $U$ | Velocity | ft/sec | $LT^{-1}$ |

| Symbol | Quantity | Units (ft-lb-sec) | Dimensions (M.L.T) |
|---|---|---|---|
| $v$ | Velocity, velocity component | ft/sec | $LT^{-1}$ |
| $v_s$ | Specific volume | ft³/slug | $M^{-1}L^3$ |
| $\upsilon$ | Volume | ft³ | $L^3$ |
| **V** | Velocity vector | ft/sec | $LT^{-1}$ |
| $V$ | Velocity | ft/sec | $LT^{-1}$ |
| $w$ | Velocity component | ft/sec | $LT^{-1}$ |
| $w$ | Work per unit mass | ft-lb/slug | $L^2T^{-2}$ |
| $W$ | Work per unit time | ft-lb/sec | $ML^2T^{-3}$ |
| $W$ | Work of expansion | ft-lb | $ML^2T^{-2}$ |
| $W_s$ | Shaft work | ft-lb | $ML^{-2}T^{-2}$ |
| $W$ | Weight | lb | $MLT^{-2}$ |
| **W** | Weber number | none | |
| $x$ | Distance | ft | $L$ |
| $x_p$ | Distance to pressure center | ft | $L$ |
| $X$ | Body-force component per unit mass | lb/slug | $LT^{-2}$ |
| $y$ | Distance, depth | ft | $L$ |
| $y_p$ | Distance to pressure center | ft | $L$ |
| $Y$ | Expansion factor | none | |
| $Y$ | Body-force component per unit mass | lb/slug | $LT^{-2}$ |
| $z$ | Vertical distance | ft | $L$ |
| $Z$ | Vertical distance | ft | $L$ |
| $Z$ | Body-force component per unit mass | lb/slug | $LT^{-2}$ |
| $\alpha$ | Kinetic-energy correction factor | none | |
| $\alpha$ | Angle, coefficient | none | |
| $\beta$ | Momentum correction factor | none | |
| $\beta$ | Blade angle | none | |
| $\Gamma$ | Circulation | ft²/sec | $L^2T^{-1}$ |
| $\nabla$ | Vector operator | 1/ft | $L^{-1}$ |
| $\gamma$ | Specific weight | lb/ft³ | $ML^{-2}T^{-2}$ |
| $\delta$ | Boundary-layer thickness | ft | $L$ |
| $\epsilon$ | Kinematic eddy viscosity | ft²/sec | $L^2T^{-1}$ |
| $\epsilon$ | Roughness height | ft | $L$ |
| $\eta$ | Eddy viscosity | lb-sec/ft² | $ML^{-1}T^{-1}$ |
| $\eta$ | Head ratio | none | |
| $\eta$ | Efficiency | | |
| $\theta$ | Angle | none | |
| $\kappa$ | Universal constant | none | |
| $\lambda$ | Scale ratio, undetermined multiplier | none | |

| *Sym-bol* | *Quantity* | *Units* ($ft$-$lb$-$sec$) | *Dimen-sions* ($M.L.T$) |
|---|---|---|---|
| $\mu$ | Viscosity | lb-sec/ft² | $ML^{-1}T^{-1}$ |
| $\mu$ | Constant | | |
| $\nu$ | Kinematic viscosity | ft²/sec | $L^2T^{-1}$ |
| $\phi$ | Velocity potential | ft²/sec | $L^2T^{-1}$ |
| $\phi$ | Function | | |
| $\pi$ | Constant | none | |
| $\Pi$ | Dimensionless parameter | none | |
| $\rho$ | Density | slug/ft³ | $ML^{-3}$ |
| $\sigma$ | Surface tension | lb/ft | $MT^{-2}$ |
| $\sigma$ | Cavitation index | none | |
| $\tau$ | Shear stress | lb/ft² | $ML^{-1}T^{-2}$ |
| $\psi$ | Stream function, two dimensions | ft/sec | $L^2T^{-1}$ |
| $\psi$ | Stokes stream function | ft³/sec | $L^3T^{-1}$ |
| $\omega$ | Angular velocity | rad/sec | $T^{-1}$ |

# E

# computer programming aids

## FORTRAN IV compiler

The programs listed in the text are in FORTRAN IV compiler language (G level). They have been executed on an IBM 360-67 system, using the NAMELIST as a convenient means of data input. The NAMELIST is described in the Organick[1] Primer. It is assumed that the reader is acquainted with FORTRAN IV. Several useful programming techniques for engineering calculations are not given in first computing courses. These include quadratures, numerical integration using Simpson's rule, parabolic interpolation, solution of algebraic equations by the bisection method, and the Runge-Kutta methods of solving systems of ordinary simultaneous differential equations. These techniques are discussed in this appendix.

### E.1 quadratures, numerical integration by Simpson's rule

The integral

$$V = \int_{y_0}^{y_1} F(y) \, dy$$

is to be evaluated between the known limits $y_0$ and $y_1$ for the known, finite, continuous function $F(y)$. By dividing the interval between $y_0$ and

---

[1] E. I. Organick, "A FORTRAN IV Primer," Addison-Wesley Publishing Company, Inc., Reading, Mass.

**Fig. E.1** Determination of area under a curve by Simpson's rule.

$y_1$ into $N$ equal reaches ($N$ even) (Fig. E.1), Simpson's rule may be applied to find the area under the curve.   A statement sequence to find $V$ is as follows: (let G(Y)= F(Y))

```
    H = (Y1 − Y0)/N
    V = G(YD) + G(Y1)
    DO 2   I = 1,N,2
2   V = V + 4.*G(YD + I*H)
    N1 = N − 1
    DO 3   I = 2,N1,2
3   V = V + 2.*G(Y0 + I*H)
    V = V*H/3.
    WRITE (6,1) V
1   FORMAT ('0 V = ', F 20.4)
    IF intermediate values are desired:
    V = .0
    N2 = N − 2
    DO 4   I = 0, N2, 2
    V = V + H*(G(YO + I*H) + G(YO + (I + 2)*H)
  1 + 4.*G(Y0 + (I + 1)*H))/3.
    Y = Y0 + (I + 2)*H
4   WRITE (6,5) Y,V
5   FORMAT ('0 Y = ', F 20.4, 5X , 'V = ', F20.4)
```

## E.2   parabolic interpolation

It is frequently desirable to use experimental data in computer programs. For example, consider that $A$, the area of a reservoir, is known for 10-ft intervals of elevation $z$, starting with $z_0$.   Then for any elevation within the range of the data, the area of reservoir is desired.   More generally (Fig.

**Fig. E.2**   Parabolic interpolation.

E.2), values of $y$ are known for equal increments in $x$.   If the value of $y$ is desired for the $x$ shown, a parabola through the three points, with axis vertical, is first found by transferring the origin to $x'$, $y'$.

$$y' = ax'^2 + bx'$$

Let $x_{n+1} - x_n = x_n - x_{n-1} = h$; then

$$y_{n+1} - y_n = ah^2 + bh$$
$$y_{n-1} - y_n = ah^2 - bh$$

from which

$$a = \frac{1}{2h^2}(y_{n+1} + y_{n-1} - 2y_n)$$

$$b = \frac{1}{2h}(y_{n+1} - y_{n-1})$$

and

$$y = y_n + \frac{\theta^2}{2}(y_{n+1} + y_{n-1} - 2y_n) + \frac{\theta}{2}(y_{n+1} - y_{n-1})$$

in which $\theta h$ has been substituted for $x'$.

**example E.1**   The area of reservoir given for each 10 ft of elevation above $z_0 = 6320$ is

| $A$ | 348 | 692 | 1217 | etc. |
|---|---|---|---|---|
| $z$ | 6320 | 6330 | 6340 | |

The program is, for $dz = 10$:

```
I = (Z − Z0)/DZ + 2
TH = (Z − Z0 − (I − 1)*DZ)/DZ
Area = A(I) + .5*TH*(A(I + 1) − A(I − 1) + TH*(A(I + 1)
2 + A(I − 1) − 2.   *A(I)))
WRITE (6,1) Z, AREA
1   FORMAT('0 Z = ', F10.2, 5X, 'AREA = ',F10.2)
```

In this program TH takes the place of $\theta$, and the interpolation is taken so that TH is always negative.

### E.3   solution of algebraic equations by the bisection method

In the algebraic expression $F(x) = 0$, when a range of values of $x$ is known that contains only one root, the *bisection* method is a practical way to obtain it.   It is best shown by an example: The critical depth in a trapezoidal channel is wanted for given flow $Q$ and channel dimensions (Fig. E.3). The formula

$$GG = 1 - \frac{Q^2 T}{g A^3} = 0$$

must be satisfied by some positive depth $YCR$ greater than 0 and less than, say, 100 ft. $T$ is the top width $(B + 2.*M*YCR)$.   The interval is bisected and this value of $YCR$ tried.   If the value of $GG$ is positive, as with the solid line in Fig. E.3$b$, then the root is less than the mid-point and the upper limit is moved to the mid-point and the remaining half bisected, etc.

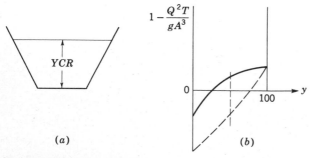

$(a)$                                  $(b)$

**Fig. E.3**  Bisection method.

In program form

```
REAL M
F(YY) = 1.   −Q**2*(B + 2.*M*YY)/((YY*(B + M*YY))**3*G)
YMAX = 100.
YMIN = .0
YCR = .5*(YMAX + YMIN)
DO  2  J = 0,13
X = F(YCR)
IF (X.GT..0) YMAX = YCR
IF (X.LE..0) YMIN = YCR
2   YCR = .5*(YMAX + YMIN)
WRITE (6,1) YCR
```

The 14 iterations reduce the interval within which the root must be to about 0.01 ft.

## E.4  Runge-Kutta solution of differential equations

The family of Runge-Kutta solutions is for various orders of accuracy, but they all have the same characteristic that the differential equation has its solution extended forward from known conditions by an increment of the independent variable without using information outside of this increment.

*first order*

In the equation

$$\frac{dy}{dz} = F(y,t)$$

**Fig. E.4** First-order Runge-Kutta method.

$y = y_n$ when $t = t_n$ and $y_{n+1}$ is desired when $t = t_n + h$.   In Fig. E.4,

$$u_1 = hF(y_n,t_n)$$
$$y_{n+1} = y_n + u_1$$
$$t_{n+1} = t_n + h$$

the equation is evaluated at the initial known conditions, and the extension is taken as the tangent to the curve at this point.

### second order

The equation is evaluated at the end points of the interval $h$, as shown in Fig. E.5:

$$u_1 = hF(y_n,t_n)$$
$$u_2 = hF(y_n + u_1,\, t_n + h)$$
$$y_{n+1} = y_n + \tfrac{1}{2}(u_1 + u_2)$$
$$t_{n+1} = t_n + h$$

$u_2$ is evaluated for the point found by the first-order method.

**Fig. E.5** Second-order Runge-Kutta method.

**Fig. E.6**  Third-order Runge-Kutta method.

*third order*

The slope of the curve is evaluated at the initial point, the $\frac{1}{3}$ point, and the $\frac{2}{3}$ point, as follows (Fig. E.6):

$$u_1 = hF(y_n, t_n)$$

$$u_2 = hF\left(y_n + \frac{u_1}{3}, t_n + \frac{h}{3}\right)$$

$$u_3 = hF\left(y_n + \frac{2u_2}{3}, t_n + \frac{2h}{3}\right)$$

$$y_{n+1} = y_n + \frac{u_1}{4} + \frac{3u_3}{4}$$

$$t_{n+1} = t_n + h$$

Differential equations of higher order and degree may be simplified by expressing them as simultaneous first-order differential equations.

**example E.2**   Put Eq. (12.1.17) into suitable form for solution by the third-order Runge-Kutta method.

In Eq. (12.1.17)

$$\frac{d^2z}{dt^2} + \frac{f}{2D}\frac{dz}{dt}\left|\frac{dz}{dt}\right| + \frac{2g}{L}z = 0$$

Let $y = dz/dt$, then $dy/dt = d^2z/dt^2$, and

$$\frac{dy}{dt} = -\frac{f}{2D} y|y| - \frac{2g}{L} z = F_1(y,z,t)$$

$$\frac{dz}{dt} = y \qquad\qquad\quad = F_2(y,z,t)$$

The two equations are solved simultaneously, from known initial conditions $y_n$, $z_n$, $t_n$:

$$u_{11} = hF_1(y_n,z_n,t_n) = h\left(-\frac{f}{2D} y_n|y_n| - \frac{2g}{L} z_n\right)$$

$$u_{12} = hF_2(y_n,z_n,t_n) = hy_n$$

$$u_{21} = hF_1\left(y_n + \frac{u_{11}}{3}, z_n + \frac{u_{12}}{3}, t_n + \frac{h}{3}\right) = h\left[-\frac{f}{2D}\left(y_n + \frac{u_{11}}{3}\right)\right.$$
$$\left. \times\left|y_n + \frac{u_{11}}{3}\right| - \frac{2g}{L}\left(z_n + \frac{u_{12}}{3}\right)\right]$$

$$u_{22} = hF_2\left(y_n + \frac{u_{11}}{3}, z_n + \frac{u_{12}}{3}, t_n + \frac{h}{3}\right) = h\left(y_n + \frac{u_{11}}{3}\right)$$

$$u_{31} = hF_1(y_n + \tfrac{2}{3}u_{21}, z_n + \tfrac{2}{3}u_{22}, t_n + \tfrac{2}{3}h)$$
$$= h\left[-\frac{f}{2D}(y_n + \tfrac{2}{3}u_{21})|y_n + \tfrac{2}{3}u_{21}| - \frac{2g}{L}(z_n + \tfrac{2}{3}u_{22})\right]$$

$$u_{32} = hF_2(y_n + \tfrac{2}{3}u_{21}, z_n + \tfrac{2}{3}u_{22}, t_n + \tfrac{2}{3}h) = h(y_n + \tfrac{2}{3}u_{21})$$

$$y_{n+1} = y_n + \frac{u_{11}}{4} + \frac{3}{4} u_{31}$$

$$z_{n+1} = z_n + \frac{u_{12}}{4} + \frac{3}{4} u_{32}$$

$$t_{n+1} = t_n + h$$

The equations for simultaneous solution have been written for a general case as well as for the specific case of solution of Eq. (12.1.17).

# answers to
# even-numbered problems

chapter one

**1.6**  $W = 95.1$ lb.

**1.8**  $g_0 = 1000$ slug-ft/kip-sec$^2$.

**1.10**  $g = 10.7$ ft/sec$^2$.

**1.14**  $\mu = 6.67$ $(10^{-5})$ lb-sec/ft$^2$.

**1.16**  $\mu = 0.011397$ lb-sec/ft$^2$.

**1.18**  88.5 per cent.

**1.20**  $\nu = 5.38$ $(10^{-5})$ ft$^2$/sec, 4.99 $(10^{-2})$ stoke.

**1.22**  $l = 0.00335$ in.

**1.24**  7.62 $(10^{-3})$ stoke.

**1.26**  $\nu_s = 0.687$ ft$^3$/slug.

**1.28**  2.94, 0.34 cm$^3$/gm, 288 $(10^3)$ dynes/cm$^3$.

**1.30**  0.00539 slug/ft$^3$, 21.55 $(10^{-3})$ slug.

**1.32**  0.000616 slug/ft$^3$.

**1.34**  3.37 $(10^3)$ psia.

**1.36**  Exponentially.

**1.38**  1500 psi.

**1.40**  10,080 lb/ft$^2$.

**1.42**  15.53 psia.

**1.44**  0.14 in.

**1.46**  0.045 in.

chapter two

**2.2**  $p_A = 249.6$ lb/ft$^2$; $p_B = p_C = -62.4$ lb/ft$^2$; $p_D = -374.4$ lb/ft$^2$.

**2.4**  $p_A = -0.866$ psi; $p_B = p_C = +0.866$ psi; $p_D = 3.206$ psi.

**2.8**  10.15 psia; $\rho = 0.00178$ slug/ft$^3$.

**2.10**  (a) 16.33 in.; (b) 18.50 ft; (c) 6.29 ft.

**2.12**  68.9 ft H$_2$O.

**2.14**  20.4 ft; 24.6 ft; 69.4 ft.

**2.16**  8.34 ft.

**2.18**  0.725 in.; 34.26 ft.

| 2.20 | $-12.60$ in. | 2.22 | $(a)$ 13.8 psi; $(b)$ 4.58 ft. |

**2.20**    $-12.60$ in.      **2.22**    $(a)$ 13.8 psi; $(b)$ 4.58 ft.

**2.24**    1.187 ft.      **2.26**    3458 lb/ft$^2$.

**2.28**    16.8 in.      **2.30**    3600 lb.

**2.32**    $-352.9$ lb.      **2.34**    222,600 lb; 67,860 lb.

**2.36**    $\dfrac{\gamma b h^2}{3}$.      **2.38**    $\frac{1}{8}\gamma b^2 h^2$.

**2.40**    0.775 ft below AB.      **2.42**    2352 lb.

**2.44**    5990 lb. 3 ft below A.      **2.46**    20,860 lb.

**2.48**    0.42 ft.      **2.50**    $\frac{3}{4}h$, $\frac{3}{8}b$.

**2.52**    7.43 ft.      **2.54**    $\sqrt{\frac{3}{4}}b$.

**2.56**    $\frac{10}{7}$ ft.      **2.60**    0.836 ft.

**2.62**    1 ft.

**2.66**    $(a)$ $\bar{x} = 34.57$ ft; $(b)$ $C_{\max} = 12{,}870$ lb/ft$^2$; $C_{\min} = 1110$ lb/ft$^2$.

**2.68**    3990 lb.      **2.70**    1083 lb (in air).

**2.72**    1.44 in.      **2.74**    0.60 in.

**2.76**    1770 lb.

**2.78**    $(a)$ 29,200 lb, 13.23 ft down; $(b)$ 33,050 lb, 2.86 ft left of hinge; $(c)$ 0; $(d)$ 0.

**2.80**    150 lb.      **2.82**    1600 lb, $\bar{x} = 1.20$ ft.

**2.84**    $20 - (4\rho/3)$ lb/ft.      **2.86**    5120 lb-ft.

**2.88**    196 lb.

**2.90**    $(a)$ 225 lb inward, 2 ft above center; $(b)$ 450 lb inward, 1.27 ft left of center.

**2.92**    0.641 in.      **2.94**    7.16 ft.

**2.96**    $1\frac{1}{3}$ ft.      **2.98**    0.3 ft, 168 lb.

**2.100**    150 lb.      **2.102**    $6 < l < 15.9$.

**2.104**    No.      **2.106**    Unstable.

**1.108**    86.5 ft/sec$^2$.

**2.110**    $\theta = 14.03°$, $p_B = 0$; $p_C = 0.0866$ psi; $p_D = 0.952$ psi; $p_E = 0.693$ psi.

**2.112**    $\theta = 9°28'$, $p_B = 0$; $p_C = -0.26$ psi; $p_D = 1.30$ psi; $p_E = 1.04$ psi.

**2.114**    $p_A = 0$; $p_B = 2.38$ psi; $p_C = 1.52$ psi.

**2.116**    $p = p_0 \exp\left(-a_x x \rho/p_0\right)$.

**2.118**    $a_x = 6.68$ ft/sec$^2$; $a_y = -3.86$ ft/sec$^2$; $\theta = 13.28°$.

**2.122**    3.28 rad/sec.      **2.124**    5.67 rad/sec.

**2.126**    $2(gh_0/r_0)^{1/2}$.      **2.128**    $r^2\left(\dfrac{\omega^2}{2g}\right) - r\sin\theta = \dfrac{p - p_0}{\rho g}$.

**2.132**    $p = \left[ p_0^{(n-1)/n} + \dfrac{n-1}{n}\dfrac{\rho_0 \omega^2 r^2}{2p_0^{1/n}} \right]^{n/(n-1)}$

**2.134**    22.1 rpm.      **2.136**    15.2 lb.

**2.138**    $F_H = 471$ lb; $F_V = 943$ lb.

## chapter three

| | | | |
|---|---|---|---|
| **3.2** | 68 per cent, 88 ft-lb/lb$_m$. | **3.4** | $(5 - z)/x = 2 = x\sqrt{y}$. |
| **3.6** | 13.33 ft-lb/lb$_m$, 30.0 ft-lb/lb$_m$. | **3.8** | 1.85 power. |
| **3.10** | 3.5 slugs/sec. | **3.12** | $13.66 \Big/ \left(1 - \dfrac{5}{8}\dfrac{x}{L}\right)^2$. |
| **3.14** | Yes. | **3.22** | 34,300,000 ft-lb. |
| **3.24** | 144 ft-lb/sec. | **3.26** | 12.43 ft; 28.28 ft/sec. |
| **3.28** | 71.5°; 85.08 ft/sec. | **3.30** | 1.035. |
| **3.32** | 250$\rho$ ft-lb/sec. | **3.34** | 1.45 ft, 8.90 ft. |
| **3.36** | 1.54 ft, 8.09 ft. | **3.38** | 1.14 ft, 7.96 ft. |
| **3.40** | 53.2 cfs, 50.4 cfs. | **3.42** | 1.75 cfs. |
| **3.44** | 3.52 cfs. | **3.46** | 6.13. |
| **3.48** | 0.513 cfs; 9.45 ft. | **3.50** | $r = R/4\sqrt{1 + y/H}$. |
| **3.52** | $-5.2$ psi. | **3.54** | 2.39 cfs; $-4.35$ psi, 0.554 psi. |
| **3.56** | $H_p = 65.8$ ft. | **3.58** | 32.6 cfs; 21,900 lb-ft. |
| **3.62** | 3.58 ft/sec. | **3.64** | Zero |
| **3.66** | 0.04. | **3.68** | 0.168 ft-lb/slug °R. |
| **3.70** | 4/3. | **3.74** | Zero. |
| **3.76** | Surface force $= -\rho g$. | **3.78** | 56 lb. |
| **3.84** | 2973 lb, 2973 lb. | **3.86** | 5546 lb, 9335 lb. |
| **3.88** | $-680$ lb, $-836$ lb. | **3.90** | 2717 lb (upward). |
| **3.92** | 9220 lb; 945,000 ft-lb/sec; 6800 hp; 75 per cent; 182 lb/ft$^2$. | | |
| **3.94** | 4132 hp. | **3.96** | 2543 ft/sec. |
| **3.98** | 84.7 cfs; 39.5 per cent. | **3.100** | 0.354 ft$^2$. |
| **3.102** | 53,000 lb, 53,000 lb. | **3.104** | 92.3 per cent. |
| **3.106** | 4567 ft/sec. | **3.108** | 137 miles. |
| **3.112** | $84\frac{1}{4}°$. | **3.114** | $V_0/3$. |
| **3.116** | $-281$ lb, $+54.1$ lb. | **3.122** | 1494 hp. |
| **3.124** | $152\frac{3}{4}°$. | **3.126** | 0.5. |
| **3.128** | 80.6, 1.04. | **3.134** | 8.3 ft-lb/ lb$_m$. |
| **3.136** | 31.3 cfs/ft. | **3.138** | 0.354 ft/sec$^2$. |
| **3.140** | 161.5 lb. | | |
| **3.142** | 17.24 lb-ft; 3.94 hp; 38.95 ft-lb/lb$_m$. | | |
| **3.144** | 453 rpm | **3.146** | 285.5 rpm. |

## chapter four

| | | | |
|---|---|---|---|
| **4.2** | (a) $\dfrac{\rho V^2}{\Delta p}$; (b) $\dfrac{Fg^2}{\rho V^6}$; (c) $\dfrac{t\,\Delta p}{\mu}$. | **4.4** | 86,400,000 slugs. |

**4.6** Dimensionless; $T^{-1}$; $FLT^{-1}$; $FL$; $FL$; $LT$.

**4.8** $f\left(\dfrac{\Delta h}{l},\dfrac{\mu D}{Q\rho},\dfrac{Q^3\rho^5 g}{\mu^5}\right)=0.$     **4.10** $p=f(\gamma\,\Delta z).$

**4.12** $F_B=f(\rho\mathcal{V}g).$     **4.16** $\mathbf{M}=f\left(\dfrac{V}{\sqrt{p/\rho}},k\right).$

**4.18** 10.43 ft/sec.     **4.20** $\gamma H^4 f\left(\dfrac{\omega H^3}{Q},e\right).$

**4.22** $\rho V^2 D^2 f\ (\mathbf{R},\mathbf{M}).$     **4.24** 0.522.

**4.26** Choose model size $\frac{1}{70}$ or less of prototype size;

$$\text{loss}_p=\text{loss}_m\left(\dfrac{D_m\nu_p}{D_p\nu_m}\right)^2.$$

**4.28** $c=\sqrt{gd},\ c=\text{speed},\ d=\text{depth}.$

**4.30** $\dfrac{\omega D^{3/2}\rho^{1/2}}{\sigma^{1/2}}.$

**4.32** 111.0 ft/sec, 1108 ft³/sec, same when expressed In velocity heads.

## chapter five

**5.2** $\dfrac{dp}{dl}(p+\gamma h)=\dfrac{2\mu U}{a^2};\ Q=\dfrac{Ua}{3}.$

**5.4** 0.189 lb; 1.88 × 10⁻⁶ ft³/sec.

**5.6** $Q=-\dfrac{1}{\mu}\dfrac{dp}{dl}\dfrac{a^3}{12}+\dfrac{a}{2}(U-V).$

**5.8** $\frac{54}{35},\ \frac{6}{5}.$

**5.12** 0.695 lb/ft² to right.     **5.14** Efficiency $=\frac{1}{3}.$

**5.16** $\dfrac{1}{270}\rho\left[\dfrac{1}{\mu}\dfrac{d}{dl}(p+\gamma h)\right]^2 a^5;\ \dfrac{1}{3780}\rho\left[\dfrac{1}{\mu}\dfrac{d}{dl}(p+\gamma h)\right]^3 a^7;$ both per unit width.

**5.18** $\frac{4}{3}.$     **5.20** $\dfrac{\sqrt{2}}{2}\,a.$

**5.24** 0.0269 lb/ft².     **5.26** 0.00168 ft³/sec; 20.1.

**5.28** 0.00152 ft³/sec.     **5.30** 620 ft.

**5.32** 25,120.     **5.34** 33.7 ft/sec.

**5.38** 400 particles/ft³.     **5.40** 0.223.

**5.42** 1430 lb.     **5.44** $\delta=\dfrac{4.80}{\sqrt{\mathbf{R}_x}};\ \tau_0=0.327\sqrt{\dfrac{\mu U^3\rho}{x}}.$

**5.46**  $\delta = \dfrac{0.254x}{\mathbf{R}_x^{1/6}}.$

**5.48**  $1.05°.$

**5.50**  4 ft/sec.

**5.52**  1.

**5.54**  1160 lb.

**5.56**  214 lb.

**5.62**  0.00988 ft/sec.

**5.64**  0.0024 in.; 0.86 ft/sec.

**5.66**  1.84 ft/sec.

**5.68**  0.00245 ft/ft.

**5.70**  1050 ft³/sec.

**5.72**  0.000481 ft/ft.

**5.74**  310 ft³/sec.

**5.76**  9.22 ft/sec.

**5.78**  $Q = f(y^{8/3}).$

**5.80**  1.76 ft.

**5.82**  $y = 0.458B.$

**5.84**  1.60 hp.

**5.86**  2.91 gpm.

**5.88**  Approx. $1.6 \times 10^6.$

**5.90**  0.588 ft.

**5.94**  2.43 hp.

**5.96**  1300 hp.

**5.98**  12.9 miles.

**5.100**  236 gpm.

**5.102**  1.19 gpm.

**5.104**  388,000 gpm.

**5.106**  185 hp.

**5.108**  6.16 lb/sec.

**5.110**  2.13 ft.

**5.112**  $12,000.

**5.114**  0.78 ft.

**5.116**  3.94 ft.

**5.118**  0.00134 cfs.

**5.120**  9.06; 495 ft.

**5.122**  23.4 cfs.

**5.124**  $(a)$ 7.58 ft; $(b)$ 4.26 ft; $(c)$ 89.4 ft.

**5.126**  146 ft.

**5.132**  120,000 lb/ft².

## chapter six

**6.2**  0.331 Btu/lb$_m$°R.

**6.4**  19.86.

**6.6**  0.206 Btu/°R.

**6.8**  4020 Btu/slug.

**6.10**  $\rho_1/\rho_2 = (T_1/T_2)^{1/(n-1)}.$

**6.12**  2.33.

**6.14**  16 per cent.

**6.16**  $V = \sqrt{gy}.$

**6.18**  114°F; 46.4 psia.

**6.20**  Same.

**6.22**  57.37 lb$_m$/sec; $\mathbf{M} = 0.583$; 79.5 psia; 26.9°F.

**6.24**  185 psia; 0.799 lb$_m$/ft³; 165°F.

**6.26**  0.265 lb$_m$/sec.

**6.28**  0.31 in.

**6.30**  4.21 in.; 5.05 in.; 6.31 in.

**6.32**  0.134 slug/sec.

**6.34**  0.955; 0.0938.

**6.36**  $\mathbf{M} = 0.578$; 13.5 psia; 418°F; 839 ft/sec.

**6.38**  $\mathbf{M}_1 = 1.55$; $\mathbf{M}_2 = 0.755$; 0.00175 slug/ft³; 300°F.

**6.50**  68 per cent.

**6.52**  0.98 ft.

**6.54**  0.505 lb$_m$/sec.

**6.56**  7350 Btu/lb$_m$.

**6.58**  0.168 slug/sec.

**6.60**  18.2 Btu/lb$_m$.

**6.62**  $q_H = \dfrac{V_2{}^2 - V_1{}^2}{2}.$

**6.64**  60.1 ft.

**6.66**  5.08$D$; 0.366 psia.

**6.68**  0.108 ft.

## chapter seven

**7.2** $(a)$ 0; $(b)$ 0; $(c)$ 0.  **7.4** $\omega_x = \frac{3}{2}$; $\omega_y = -2$; $\omega_z = -\frac{1}{2}$.

**7.6** $w = -2(x + y)z$.

**7.8** $\phi = -4x - 6y + \frac{7}{2}(x^2 - y^2) + c$.

**7.12** $\psi = \theta + c$.  **7.14** $\phi = 18x + c$.

**7.16** $\left.\dfrac{\partial \phi}{\partial r}\right|_{r=a} = 0$; $q_\infty =$ free-stream velocity.

**7.18** $u = -2.785$ ft/sec, $v = w = 0$; $u = 0.459$ ft/sec, $v = w = 1.021$ ft/sec.

**7.20** $\phi = \dfrac{15}{r} + 15\, r \cos \theta$; $\psi = 15 \cos \theta + \dfrac{15}{2} r^2 \sin^2 \theta$.

**7.22** $\phi = 12x + 3.64 \left[ \dfrac{1}{\sqrt{(x - 1.456)^2 - \hat{\omega}^2}} - \dfrac{1}{\sqrt{(x - 1.456)^2 + \hat{\omega}^2}} \right]$;
$\psi = 6r^2 \sin^2 \theta + 3.64(\cos \theta_1 - \cos \theta_2)$.

**7.24** $p = (139 - 871 \sin^2 \theta)$ lb/ft².

**7.32** $u = 0$; $v = \dfrac{2\mu y}{1 + y^2}$; $p = -2\rho\mu^2 \left(\dfrac{y}{1 + y^2}\right)^2$; $F = -\rho\mu^2\pi$.

**7.36** $q(0,1) = \dfrac{\sqrt{170}}{\pi}$ ft/sec, $q(1,1) = \dfrac{\sqrt{260}}{\pi}$ ft/sec, $p(0,1) = 121.0$ lb/ft²,
$p(1,1) = 112.8$ lb/ft².

## chapter eight

**8.2** 4.27 psi.  **8.4** 18.1 ft/sec.

**8.6** 68.1 ft/sec  **8.8** 1.204.

**8.10** 39.8 cfs.  **8.12** 40.5°F; 858 ft/sec.

**8.14** 0.648 gpm.  **8.16** 28.4 gpm.

**8.18** $y = 0.0181x^2$.  **8.20** $Y = H \cos^2 \alpha$.

**8.24** $C_d = 0.751$; $C_v = 0.953$; $C_c = 0.788$.

**8.26** 0.707 ft-lb/lb; 35.8 ft-lb/sec.  **8.28** 455-lb/sec.

**8.30** 1.44 in.  **8.32** 0.853 ft.

**8.34** $D = 3.63y^{1/4}$, units: ft.  **8.36** $D = 0.303y^{3/4}$, units: ft.

**8.38** 89.4 sec.  **8.40** 200 cfs.

**8.42** 0.872 psi.  **8.44** 0.00569 slug/sec; 531 ft/sec.

**8.46** 5.74 in.  **8.48** 0.00754 slug/sec.

**8.50** 592 gpm.  **8.52** 24.7 cfs.

**8.54** 1.77 ft.  **8.56** $(a)$ 3.06 ft; $(b)$ 2.09 ft.

**8.58** 2.72 lb-ft.  **8.60** $0.963(10^{-2})$ poise.

## chapter nine

**9.2**  $Q_c = \left(\dfrac{Q}{N}\right) n;\; H_c = \left(\dfrac{H}{N^2}\right) n^2;\; c = \text{corrected},\; n = \text{const.}$

**9.4**  Synchronization is not exact.  **9.6**  $Q = 0.125Q_1;\; H = 4H_1.$
**9.8**  319 rpm.  **9.10**  89 in.; 303 rpm.
**9.12**  9.37 ft.
**9.14**  (*a*) 1.78 ft; (*b*) 1200 rpm; (*c*) 200 hp; (*d*) 0.967 hp.
**9.16**  14°47′.  **9.18**  60.3 ft/sec; 181 ft/sec.
**9.20**  117.5 ft.  **9.22**  93.24 per cent.
**9.24**  $H = 54.3\text{--}17.2Q.$
**9.26**  (*a*) 505 rpm; (*b*) 13.1 ft; (*c*) 30.7 lb-ft; (*d*) 2.96 hp; (*e*) 595 lb/ft².
**9.30**  45.03 ft.  **9.32**  6.8 in.
**9.36**  272 lb/ft, 96.7 per cent.  **9.38**  11.6 ft.

## chapter ten

**10.2**  164.8  **10.4**  44.8 ft.
**10.6**  3.975 cfs; 9.94 psia.  **10.10**  31.9 ft.
**10.12**  2.90 cfs.  **10.14**  0.25 ft.
**10.16**  2.72 in.  **10.18**  38.7 ft.
**10.20**  4.46 cfs.  **10.24**  2.82 cfs.
**10.26**  8.48 cfs.
**10.28**  $Q_1 = 0.0734$ cfs; $Q_2 = 0.165$ cfs; $Q_{\text{total}} = 0.238$ cfs.
**10.30**  9225 ft.
**10.32**  $Q_{AJ} = 1.27$ cfs; $Q_{BJ} = 1.25$ cfs; $Q_{JC} = 2.52$ cfs.
**10.34**  $Q_A = 0.42$ cfs; $Q_B = 2.02$ cfs.
**10.36**  1.86 cfs; 106.0 ft.
**10.38**  $Q_{BJ_1} = 9.43;\; Q_{J_1A} = 16.63;\; Q_{J_2J_1} = 7.20;\; Q_{CJ_2} = 5.68;$
  $Q_{DJ_2} = 1.52$ cfs.
**10.40**  58.5, 41.5; 31; 44; 2.5.  **10.42**  61.5, 38.5; 31, 44; 5.5.
**10.44**  0.391.  **10.46**  0.165 cfs.
**10.48**  4.43 ft.

## chapter eleven

**11.2**  0.00219 ft.  **11.4**  562 ft² per 100 ft.
**11.6**  $m = \sqrt{3}/3;\; 7.11$ ft.
**11.8**  $m = \sqrt{3}/3;\; b = 13.45$ ft; $y = 11.65$ ft.

| | | | |
|---|---|---|---|
| **11.10** | 0.000165. | **11.16** | 1.825 ft; 5.54 ft. |
| **11.18** | 1.803 ft. | **11.20** | 7.4 ft. |
| **11.22** | 1.72 ft; 56.6 cfs/ft. | **11.26** | 385 ft. |
| **11.34** | 2.10 ft rise. | **11.36** | 1.24 ft. |
| **11.40** | 9.62 ft/sec; 9.61 cfs/ft. | **11.44** | $y = 0.00345(x/2 + 644)^2$. |

## chapter twelve

| | | | |
|---|---|---|---|
| **12.2** | 6.33 ft/sec, 4.96 sec. | **12.4** | $z = V_0 t \exp(-mt)$. |
| **12.6** | $z_1 = -14.6$ ft, $z_2 = -14.2$ ft. | **12.8** | 40.2 sec. |
| **12.10** | 3371 ft/sec | **12.12** | 1.779 sec. |
| **12.14** | 1500 ft. | **12.18** | 148.1 psi. |
| **12.28** | $c = -24.1$ ft/sec; $y_1 - y_2 = 0.83$ ft. | | |
| **12.30** | 8.56 ft; $c = 11.68$ ft/sec. | | |

# index

# index

# VISCOSITY - RESISTANCE OF FLUID TO FLOW

$$\tau = \mu \frac{du}{dy} \qquad \frac{du}{dy} = \text{SLOPE OF LINE}$$

$$\tau = \text{SHEAR STRESS}$$

WHEN VELOCITY DISTRIBUTION IS LINEAR, $du/dy$ IS CONSTANT

# FLUID STATICS

$P = \gamma h \qquad h = -y$ FROM FREE SURFACE

MANOMETER PROBLEMS, PAGE 38

# FORCES ON PLANE AREAS

|  | HORIZONTAL | INCLINED SURFACE |
|---|---|---|
| FORCE: | $F = PA$ | $F = \gamma \sin\theta \, \bar{y} \, A = \gamma \bar{h} A$ |
| DIRECTION: | VERTICAL | $\perp$ to plane |
| POSITION: | $\bar{x}, \bar{y}$ | CENTER OF PRESSURE |

$$X_P \cdot F = \gamma \int x^2 dA$$
$$Y_P \cdot F = \gamma \int y^2 dA$$

HORIZONTAL COMPONET OF FORCE ON CURVED SURFACE = FORCE EXERTED ON PROJECTION

VERTICAL COMPONET =
(AREA ABOVE CURVED SURFACE)(WIDTH) $\gamma$

# RELATIVE EQUILIBRIUM

$$\frac{dP}{dx} = -\rho a_x \qquad \frac{dP}{dy} = -\gamma - \rho a_y$$

# RADIAL ACCELERATION

$$P = \frac{\gamma}{2g} w^2 r^2$$

AT DISTANCE h BELOW
$$P = \frac{\gamma}{2g} w^2 r^2 + \gamma h$$

# BERNOULLI'S EQUATION

steady state Flow
Along stream Line
Deal only with Pressure and Gravity

$$\frac{V_1^2}{2g} + \frac{P_1}{\gamma} + Z_1 = \frac{V_2^2}{2g} + \frac{P_2}{\gamma} + Z_2 + \text{Losses}$$

1-2

# MOMENTUM

$$F = \rho Q (\quad_2 - \quad)$$
$$F_x = \rho Q (V_{2x} - V_{1x})$$
$$F_y = \rho Q (V_{2y} - \quad)$$

Forces that medium exerts on fluid

# SIMILITUDE

$$E \text{ (EULER)} = \frac{\sqrt{\quad}}{\sqrt{\quad \Delta P/\rho}}$$

CLOSED BOUNDARY FLOW
GRAVITY HAS NO EFFECT
G USUALLY CANCELS

$$F \text{ (FROUDE)} = \frac{\quad}{\sqrt{Lg}} \quad \text{GRAVITY HAS EFFECT BUT USUALLY ONLY}$$

$$R \text{ (REYNOLDS)} = \frac{\quad}{\quad} \quad \nu \text{ (DYNAMIC VISCOSITY)}$$

G CANCELS

$$R = \frac{D}{\nu} \quad \text{LAMINAR FLOW}$$

$$P_1 - P_2 = \frac{12 \mu u L}{B^2} \quad \parallel \text{ PLATES}$$

$$\quad = \frac{32 \mu V L}{D^2}$$

$$h_f = f \frac{L}{D} \frac{V^2}{2g} \qquad f = \frac{64}{R} \text{ for laminar}$$

$$Q = \frac{\Delta P}{L} \times \frac{\pi D^4}{128 \mu}$$

$$\frac{\Delta P}{L} = f \frac{1}{D} \rho V^2 \qquad h_f = \frac{8 L Q^2}{\pi g \pi^2 D} f$$

$$DRAG = C_D A \rho \frac{V^2}{2}$$

$\rho = \dfrac{r}{g}$